PUBS
& INNS

The Best in Food & Accommodation

Over 1350 establishments in Great Britain

Egon Ronay's Guides
73 Uverdale Road
London SW10 0SW

Consultant **Egon Ronay**
Editorial Director **Bernard Branco**
Managing Editor **Andrew Eliel**
Chief Inspector **Mario Wyn-Jones**
Publishing Director **Angela Nicholson**

Commercial and Advertising Sales **071-351 7441**

**First published 1992 by Pan Books Ltd
a division of Pan Macmillan Publishers Ltd
Cavaye Place, London SW10 9PG**

9 8 7 6 5 4 3 2 1

Cover Design © **Elizabeth Ayer**

Cover Concept and Illustration
© **Chris Ackerman-Eveleigh**

ISBN 0 330 329 42 1

Typeset in Great Britain by Spottiswoode Ballantyne,
Colchester, Essex

Printed in Great Britain by BPCC Hazell Books Ltd

**All inspections are anonymous and carried out by
Egon Ronay's Guides' team of professional inspectors.
Inspectors may reveal their identities in order to check
all facilities. The Guide is independent in its
editorial selection and does not accept advertising,
payment or hospitality from listed establishments.**

Contents

How to Use This Guide

Order of Listings

London appears first and is in alphabetical order by **establishment name**. Listings outside London are in alphabetical order by **location** within divisions of England, Scotland, Wales, Channel Islands and the Isle of Man. See contents page for specific page numbers.

Map References

Entries contain references to the map section before the listings.

Good Food

We include establishments where our team of professional inspectors found good-quality bar food. Such pubs are indicated by the word **FOOD** printed in the margin alongside the entry. Reference may also be made to the pub's restaurant, but our chief concern has been with bar food.

Typical dishes are usually listed, with prices valid at the time of our visit. Prices may, however, have risen a little since then. If vegetarian dishes and a children's menu are available, the statistics at the end of each entry will say so.

We indicate when bar food is served and also any times when food is not available.

Times of restaurant meals may differ and are then listed separately.

Pubs serving outstanding food are indicated by a ★ alongside their name (see starred list).

Good Accommodation

We also inspected the accommodation, and those pubs recommended for an overnight stay are indicated by the letters **B&B** in the margin alongside the entry.

We list the number of bedrooms, the price for an en-suite bedroom and a full cooked breakfast for two, and whether children are welcome overnight.

If residents can check in at any time, we print *all day*; if check-in is confined to certain hours we print the time; if it's advisable to arrange a time when booking, we print *by arrangement*.

Pubs with Atmosphere

Pubs recommended as pleasant or interesting places for a drink rather than for their bar food or accommodation are indicated by the letter **A** alongside their entry.

Short Listings

Pubs accorded a short entry are worthwhile entries, but not necessarily recommended for any specific features.

Beer

We indicate whether an establishment is a free house, and list the names of a number of beers.

Children Welcome

Entries indicate whether the pub is suitable for families; those that welcome children in a bar to eat, or have a family room, or outdoor play area are usually marked by the ☺ symbol.

Outdoors

We indicate pubs with outdoor eating areas.

Symbols

FOOD	Recommended bar food
B&B	Recommended for accommodation
A	Recommended for atmosphere
★	Outstanding bar food
	Best of British meat
	Best of British cheese
☺	Suitable for families

BRITISH MEAT
CATERING
FOREWORD

It seems fitting that British Meat Catering should once again sponsor Egon Ronay's Pub Guide, as more and more people choose British meat when eating out of the home - recent independent research shows that 97% of the population eat beef, lamb and pork.

Today's consumers are increasingly looking for quality and variety on pub menus. To meet this demand from a more discerning customer, publicans are insisting on British meat as their guarantee of consistent quality.

British Meat Catering advises large breweries and independent public houses alike on all aspects of meat catering, from training and hygiene to menu and recipe development, ensuring you, the customer, enjoy a variety of British meat dishes of excellent eating quality.

Derek Andrews.
Catering Development and
Promotions Manager,
Meat and Livestock Commission

THE 1992 BRITISH MEAT PUB OF THE YEAR COMPETITION

British Meat Catering set the Guide's inspectors the difficult task of selecting finalists from nearly 2,000 pubs recommended in the Guide. After reviewing and cross referring the information received from inspectors, seven pubs were selected:

▶ The Bell Inn, Stilton

▶ The White Horse, Parsons Green, London

▶ The Kilberry Inn, Kilberry

▶ The Roebuck, Brimfield, Nr Ludlow (1992 Pub of the Year)

▶ The Rose and Crown, Romaldkirk

▶ The Royal Oak, Over Stratton

▶ The Sun Inn, Winforton

Chefs from the seven pubs were invited to a live cook-off final, where they were asked to prepare an original and tempting main course featuring either British beef, pork or lamb.

Christopher Davy of the Rose and Crown Hotel met stiff competition from

the six other pubs but the decision of the judges was final with his Duet of British Pork: a delightful combination of roasted faggot from the belly and a pan fried collop from the fillet.

The next few pages will feature the winning recipes from six of the finalists.

Why not encourage your local to try them and savour the great taste of quality British meat.

BRITISH BEEF

Traditional British beef is still the number one in British pubs whether it is the "steak and kidney pie", "a juicy steak", or nowadays "chilli con carne". Increasingly, pub chefs are selecting more adventurous cuts from their butcher and adding marinades, spices and sauces to attract customers, while not forgetting mince, the most versatile of meats.

THE ROYAL OAK,
OVER STRATTON, SOMERSET
Chef: Robert Beeson

FILLET OF BRITISH BEEF
with Somerset Royal Oak Sauce

INGREDIENTS:

1¹/₂lb British beef fillet; 1 large onion, finely chopped; 1 large Granny Smith, peeled and chopped; 1tsp parsley; 2fl oz Somerset Royal Ale; 1tsp tomato purée; 10fl oz strong beef stock; 1oz butter; 1oz brown breadcrumbs; 1oz pine nuts; 2oz sliced mushrooms; 8oz prepared puff pastry.

Method

Sauté the apple, onion, parsley and mushrooms together in the butter, add the Somerset Royal Ale, tomato purée and beef stock, bring to boil, strain and cool. Mix the breadcrumbs into the apple mixture. Split the fillet and beat out until flat. Spread with the stuffing. Sprinkle on the pine nuts and roll up. Wrap in puff pastry and brush with beaten egg. Bake in moderate oven for about 20 minutes. Bring sauce to boil, reduce until thickened, season with salt and coarse black pepper.

Serve the fillet cut into medallions on hot sauced plates with sprigs of fresh watercress and apple slices.

BOILED FILLET OF BRITISH BEEF
with Mustard, Caper and Savory

INGREDIENTS:

1¹/₂lb British beef fillet, trimmed;

2pts good beef stock;

2tbsp Hereford cider;

1tbsp capers;

2tbsp mustard;

6oz single cream;

1oz butter;

1 bunch of savory.

Method

Marinate fillet in stock overnight. Remove fillet from stock.
Make insertions along the fillet and insert approximately half a dozen capers
and savory leaves. In a pan in which the fillet fits snugly, bring stock to boil.
Turn down the heat and add the beef. Gently simmer for approximately 12-15
minutes for rare beef, or up to 20 minutes for medium beef. Remove from
stock, cover and keep warm.

Sauce

Reduce stock, add cider, remaining capers and savory together with the
mustard. Stir well. Add cream to thicken and finally a knob of butter to shine,
if necessary. Carve meat into slices and arrange on four plates, surround with
sauce, decorate with sprigs of savory.

*Serve with Jersey potatoes and a selection of seasonal vegetables including
carrots which have been cooked in the beef stock.*

BRITISH PORK

Chefs and the dining public alike are becoming more aware of the versatility and superb eating quality of lean British pork. Boneless roasting joints are as popular as ever, but more and more caterers are being more creative.

THE ROSE AND CROWN HOTEL,
ROMALDKIRK, BARNARD CASTLE, CO DURHAM

Chef: Christopher Davy

DUET OF BRITISH PORK
A roasted faggot from the belly and a pan fried collop from the fillet

INGREDIENTS:

12oz minced British belly pork; 4oz pigs liver; 2 rashers smoked back British bacon; 1 yolk of egg; 2fl oz cream; 1oz breadcrumbs soaked in the cream; salt and pepper to taste; pinch of nutmeg and ginger; 24 fresh spinach leaves, or Chinese leaves or lettuce leaves; pigs caul; 1 cooking apple; sugar to taste; fresh sage; 1oz breadcrumbs.

Pan Fried Collop: 18oz trimmed British pork fillet; chilled butter; clarified butter for pan frying; 2 tbsp boullion; 10fl oz elderflower wine; 1tsp redcurrant jelly; salt and pepper to taste.

◆ ——— *Method* ——— ◆

Mince the British pork belly and bacon twice through a fine blade into a bowl; mince pigs liver, add; egg, the bread squeezed dry, cream and seasonings and mix well. Chill. Peel and core apples, cook with the sugar and a little water; add the sage and breadcrumbs. Soak the caul and stretch out; cover with four spinach leaves and place some forcemeat on top; make an indentation, pipe on the apple purée, seal and enrobe the faggot in the spinach and caul. Glaze with butter and roast gas mark 7 for 15 minutes.

Pan Fried Collop: Cut the fillet into collops, season and dust with flour; pan fry in the butter until cooked; remove from the pan and deglaze with the wine; add the redcurrant jelly and reduce; whisk in the boullion and butter to thicken, season to taste. *Serve with fresh noodles and spiced red cabbage.*

THE ROEBUCK,
BRIMFIELD, NR LUDLOW, SHROPSHIRE

C h e f :   J a n e   M a l c o l m

BRITISH PORK TENDERLOINS
Stuffed with Lovage Mousse on a Grain Mustard and King Offa Cider Brandy Sauce

INGREDIENTS:

2 British pork tenderloins, trimmed; pigs caul.

For the mousse:

6oz pork trimmings from the tenderloin; 2 egg whites; 2tsp salt; small handful of lovage leaves, blanched in salted water and cooled; 6fl oz double cream.

For the sauce:

6fl oz strong chicken stock; 1tbsp whole grain mustard; 4fl oz double cream; 1tbsp apple cider vinegar; King Offa cider brandy; salt and pepper; lovage leaf to garnish.

◆ ─── *Method* ─── ◆

Trim pork tenderloins, cut into two portions. Mix pork trimmings with egg whites and salt in a food processor until fine, keep chilled. Push through a mouli. Add the cream with blanched, finely chopped lovage leaves, chill. Seal pork tenderloins in clarified butter, cool. Push a wooden spoon handle through the tenderloins and fill with mousse. Wrap the tenderloins in caul. Brush with clarified butter, season. Roast for 15-18 minutes.

For the sauce: Reduce apple cider vinegar to about 1 teaspoon, add chicken stock and cream, reduce a little. Add a dash of King Offa cider brandy and season, reduce again until sauce thickens to consistency of single cream.

To serve: Slice the British pork tenderloin and arrange on the sauce with a potato cake and garnish with a fresh lovage leaf.

BRITISH LAMB

The range of cuts of British lamb has increased greatly over recent years with leg, shoulder, rump, loin and valentine steaks, cubed, diced and stirfry strips and not forgetting mince, for that traditional touch.

Nothing is better suited to a good pub on a Sunday than traditional roast lamb with crisp seasonal vegetables and minted potatoes. British lamb, however, is increasingly finding its way into a huge variety of dishes; lamb and haricot bean pie, spring navarin of lamb, lamb korma, lamb and celery milanese and lamb kebabs.

THE WHITE HORSE,
PARSONS GREEN, LONDON SW6
C h e f :   K a t i e   J e n k i n s o n

BRITISH LAMB CUTLETS
Marinated in a Highgate Dark Mild, pan fried with lamb kidneys and served in their juices

INGREDIENTS:

2pts Highgate Dark Mild;

16 British lamb cutlets;

4 British lambs kidneys, fat removed and split into two;

salt and pepper;

$1/2$pt olive oil.

Method

Marinate the cutlets and the kidneys in the Highgate Dark Mild for 24 hours. Heat a little olive oil in a frying pan and place cutlets in it. Cook until the outsides of the cutlets are brown and sealed, then turn down heat and cook for a further 5 minutes. Remove the cutlets from the pan and add about 1 pint of Highgate Dark Mild - reduce liquid until required thickness. Meanwhile skewer the kidneys and cook for 5 minutes. Serve with juices poured over and add a sprig of fresh rosemary for garnish, (optional).

Serve with seasonal fresh vegetables or salad and new potatoes.

THE BELL INN,
GREAT NORTH ROAD, STILTON, CAMBRIDGESHIRE
Chef: James McCallum

CASSEROLED BRITISH LAMB
with Stilton Dumplings

INGREDIENTS:

3lb British lamb, diced;
1tbsp sunflower oil; 1lb onions,
diced; 1lb shallots, peeled;
1tbsp English mustard;
2oz plain flour; 2pts lamb stock
(from cube); 1pt medium sweet
cider; 1 bouquet garni; salt and black
pepper; 5 large carrots, sliced;
2 old potatoes, diced; 10 baby
sweetcorn, halved (optional);
5 courgettes, sliced (optional).

Stilton Dumplings: 1/2 loaf white
bread, small dice; 5oz self raising
flour; 1 packet chives, chopped;
4oz suet; 8oz grated Stilton cheese;
1/2pt milk; 2 size 3 eggs.

Method

Heat the oil in a large ovenproof casserole. Add the diced onions and
whole shallots, sweat without colour. Add the diced lamb, cook until browned
then add the mustard. Stir in flour to make a roux. Cook out for 2-3 minutes.
Gradually stir in the stock and cider. Season well and add the bouquet garni.
Cover and cook in a preheated oven for 1 hour. Add the carrots and potatoes to
the casserole and cook for a further 15 minutes. Meanwhile, prepare the
dumplings: In a bowl mix together the diced bread, flour, chives, suet and
Stilton. Then add the milk and eggs. Divide the dumpling mixture into
approximately 18. Remove casserole from the oven. Stir in the sweetcorn and
courgettes. Drop the dumplings into the liquid, cover the casserole and return
to the oven for a further 20 minutes. Cook until the dumplings are firm but
light, ensuring vegetables are cooked and meat is tender.

m

Meat and Livestock Commission.

eat

to

live

1993 Pubs of the Year

British Meat Pub of the Year

Rose & Crown, Romaldkirk, Co Durham (see page 19)

British Cheese Pub of the Year

The Down Inn, Bridgnorth, Shropshire

The Down Inn's impressive cheese selection came about as the result of a unique association between chef/landlord Paul Millington and Janet Grant, proprietor of the Indoor Market Delicatessen in town, who has produced a printed menu of her specialist cheeses for use throughout the pub. Paul now features a "Cheese of the week" on a blackboard display, and sales have soared with customers taking especially to the Somerset "Masterpiece", a novel blend of Cheddar and fruit cake which makes for an interesting dual-purpose pudding.

On a recent visit whole Stilton and Shropshire Blue cheeses were on display in tip-top condition, Cheese of the week was a chive-studded Coverdale and among a fine selection on the cheeseboard were Cotherstone, Curworthy and Cornish Yarg, Sage Derby, Red Windsor and a Somerset Brie. The Welsh Teifi and Llanboidy, Scottish Dunsyre and Lanark Blue, and flavoured Cheddars such as Rutland (with beer and garlic) and Cotswold (with chives) have all found favour with an increasingly enthusiastic clientele.

Wine Pub of the Year

George & Dragon, Rowde, Wiltshire

Tim and Helen Withers have a commendable policy regarding the sale of wine, by offering over 40 quality bottles (those priced under £16 on the wine list), any of which may be drunk by the glass. There are no half bottles on the list, instead they are prepared to open a bottle, sell it by the glass, and if any remains it is sold (in good condition) as a bargain at the bar. The house white is a Chateau Pierrail from Bordeaux (£1.40 a glass), the red, a Bergerac at £1.25, and other examples include a Cotes-du-Rhone at £1.25 and a sparkling Blanquette de Limoux priced at £2.50. The red Jacob's Creek continues to be a best-seller at £1.35

Family Pub of the Year

Star Inn, Harome, North Yorkshire

A box of Lego down on the floor by the fire of this delightful 14th-century thatched pub tells you every thing you need to know about their attitude to families and children. At lunchtime families can also use the loft room, a coffee lounge for restaurant customers in the evenings, where board games and playing cards can be found. The cottage garden to the rear is reached only through the pub, so it makes a safe haven for the tots in summer and is sufficiently unkempt for parents not to have to worry too much about the little darlings running all over the flower beds. The bar menu includes a special section for children.

Bed and Breakfast Pub of the Year

Falcon Hotel, Castle Ashby, Northamptonshire

Situated minutes away from the Marquess of Northampton's Castle Ashby House and its magnificent grounds, The Falcon is a charming and peaceful inn, privately owned and managed by Jo and Neville Watson. Bedrooms are divided between the historic inn and the nearby cottage, and the hearty country breakfast includes home-made jams and jellies, croissants and pastries, freshly brewed coffee, a selection of loose-leaf teas, orange juice squeezed that morning, in addition to cooked fare such as porridge, kippers and haddock.

Newcomers of the Year

Fox & Hounds, Starbotton, North Yorkshire

Though neither the pub, nor the proprietors are new to the Guide, their association is. James and Hilary McFadyen (previously at the Cuilfail Hotel, Kimelford, Strathclyde) took over here in November last year, and set about improving the quality of the cooking, which now offers not only typical local dishes – large Yorkshire puddings with a choice of fillings – but an ever-changing blackboard menu featuring spicy lentil and peanut paté and home-made beefburgers, as well as Hilary's own home-baked granary bread.

Woodbridge Inn, North Newnton, Nr Pewsey, Wiltshire

One of our readers, Charles Bartholomew from London SW1, says this of the Woodbridge Inn: "akin to a modern day staging post for relaxing the weary traveller. A warm reception and atmosphere, with an excellent selection of food, wine and beers. It really does make a pleasant change to find somewhere with opening hours to suit the customer". That's our view, too: Wadworth Brewery and tenants Lou and Terry Vertessy can be justly proud of what they have achieved in less than three years, when it was near-derelict and not trading.

Introduction

Though recent times have been no less hard for pubs than for other sectors of the hospitality industry, we've certainly found some signs of improvement among the pubs which we consider for inclusion in our annual Guide. For a pub to survive these days, food is an essential ingredient; in refreshing numbers this year fresh food competently cooked and served at a fair price is increasingly emerging as the key to successful growth. Just a few are doing it *very well*, and more pubs-with-restaurants than ever before have been researched and approved this year for inclusion in our recently published 1993 *Hotel & Restaurant Guide*.

But the news isn't all good. An ever-increasing number of pubs seem to be following an opposite course by looking to the combination of frozen ready-meals and microwave productions as a way to foist second-rate food upon their customers, often at highly inflated prices. "Who needs a Chef these days?" goes the argument; but the day has already dawned when the home cook can also microwave his own ready meal, and the public at large will refuse to accept such standards on its limited eating-out budget. Of the many pubs we list several (although still an unrepresentative minority) are now being run successfully by licensees, many with specialist chefs or cooks, who are well able to provide their own brand of ethnic pub food with universal appeal. Some others have joined the bandwagon and "gone ethnic"; our inspectors, though, are as easily put off by the smells of raw curry powder and burnt garlic emanating from pub kitchens as they are by that "chips-and-vinegar with everything" odour which so often offends both them and our readers alike.

Nationally, there yet remain vast differences in pub-goers' expectations of what constitutes "good eating out" which still appear to divide very much upon regional lines. A degree of sophistication seems well accepted, in, say, Berkshire and Wiltshire that perhaps remains a foreign concept in the North West. A rack of lamb heaped with chips, vegetables, roast potatoes and gravy may be thought of as over-facing by the people of Winchester; served with pineapple chutney and port wine glaze it might be called effete in Warrington. Salmon and salad freshly served to tourists in Hay-on-Wye will probably be considered incomplete without chips by the trenchermen of Hull.

True value for money remains nonetheless more the exception than the rule. Nowhere is this more clearly illustrated than in the case of draught beer, whose price has risen twice as fast as inflation in each of the last three years. Following the MMC rulings on pubs, it is only fair that independent brewers should compete with the "majors" to supply their products as guest beers to the trade at competitive prices. At the pump, however, it still appears fair game for avaricious publicans not to pass on these savings to the paying customer. Yet even this doesn't fully explain how a pint of the now national-owned Boddington Bitter purchased for £1.15 in an East Wales pub cost the same inspector £1.65 at a comparable outlet in East Anglia.

Pub wines provide another case in point: while the variety and value for money of everyday supermarket wines have improved beyond measure over recent years, the captive pub customer is constantly being fobbed off at the bar with a limited choice of over-priced, poor quality wines. These wines, often nationally distributed to the licensed trade through the major brewers, are sometimes greedily marked up; we have found many a glass of "house wine" priced at £1.50 or over for a stated 125 ml measure, while the identical product can be bought in a High Street off-licence for little over £3 per bottle.

However, we have discovered one small Cotswold brewer who appears to be bucking the trend. The Wadworth brewery of Devizes owns around 140 tenanted and leasehold properties in the counties of Wiltshire, Avon and Gloucestershire, many of which are old favourites in our Guide, with several more featured here for the first time. Wadworth's operation of a laudable hands-off policy combined with a steadfast refusal to standardise their many highly individual outlets produces a double dividend: the brewery both attracts new licensees with entrepreneurial flair and clearly supports them in their endeavours to mutual advantage. The benefits are clear for all to see – from which many others could learn.

We would not necessarily deny a place in the market (but we don't include them in our Guide) for themed pubs, steakhouses, carveries and their like, since quite obviously the majority of the public who eat out support them in huge numbers – witness some of the operators' profits. There *is* no doubt a place for them in a society which has not traditionally been brought up to appreciate the real benefits of fresh, well-cooked food that can readily be found in many of the pubs that this Guide chooses to support. Our name has been synonymous with quality for over 35 years, and we make no apology for discriminating in favour of pubs who provide quality at affordable prices. Call it elitism if you like, but it can only help to improve and set overall standards that we hope other pubs not already listed in this Guide will strive to emulate.

Take Seven Pubs

by Andrew Eliel

On the evening when England were eliminated from the European football championships, landlords and chefs from seven very different pubs gathered for dinner at a Swedish hotel in central London, prior to taking part in a cook-off to find this year's best British Meat Pub. Egon Ronay himself sat engrossed listening to tales from publicans and probably wondered, as I did, what's happened to the 'Great British Pub', a topic this Guide has highlighted almost every year since it was first published. If all pubs were run in similar style to those that reached the cook-off, there would be no concern; indeed most of the pubs listed in this Guide represent all that is good, but there are over 65,000 nationwide and most of them leave a lot to be desired.

Christopher and Alison Davey at the Rose & Crown, Romaldkirk, Co Durham

Visiting our winners, the 1993 British Meat Pub of the Year, at the end of August, the bar was full of satisfied Germans and Italians, no doubt celebrating a successful day's shooting on the grouse moors. Teesdale, untouched and unspoilt, must be every foreigner's view of the real England and the Rose & Crown epitomises the country inn. At its heart is the kitchen, and at the the stoves you'll find Christopher. For someone trained in hotel management, it may seem strange that he's ended up in whites. While his course at Westminster College did include basic kitchen training, he pursued a management career, first as a post-graduate trainee with Trusthouse Forte, then taking a salary cut to move into the private sector, before spending five happy years at The Chester Grosvenor. There, he met Alison – a bilingual secretary in French and German – and in 1983 turned down a position at London's Savoy Hotel, instead taking over a run-down pub, the Black Swan at Ravenstonedale in Cumbria, and thus fulfilling his ambition to have his own business by the age of 30. It was at this time that he returned to the kitchen, enjoying the creativity of cooking and putting to good use his interest in food, while Alison grew into her hands-on, front-of-house role. After five years' success,

they felt it the right time to move on, still in the north, "sold well", and viewed over 50 properties. Gazumped several times, they finally settled on The Rose & Crown, after just one visit. At the time the inn was in receivership, so they were able to complete the purchase quickly, and by dint of a lot of hard work over the last five years, have built it up into the fine establishment it is today. Now, with young children, Christopher and Ali are staying put, very much the proud hosts of a quintessentially English inn, at the heart of the village community.

Katy Jenkinson at the White Horse, London SW6

That it's difficult to believe the White Horse to be a brewery owned and managed house is a tribute to licensee Sally Cruickshank who has not only managed to build-up an enviable reputation for good food (incidentally, it's just as good at night as it is at lunchtime, which is when everybody seems to want to eat here) but also to preserve a genuine pub atmosphere. This is very much a pub with food rather than a winebar (although there is a good wine list) or restaurant with bar. Katy Jenkinson is currently in charge of the food here and she regards the quality of the raw ingredients as a top priority. She has even been known to accompany her local butcher on an early morning trip to Smithfield Market to check out the meat, something she knows about having spent her first seven years on the Yorkshire farm where her grandfather raised and slaughtered the beef and lamb and pork needed to supply his own county-wide chain of butchers shops, and where grandmother experimented with new dishes for her bakery which sold the likes of haslet, meat pies, and pressed duck. Later Katy took a B.Tech National Diploma at Birmingham College of Food only to become a 'debt consultant' for the Midland Bank before returning to her first love, food, and arriving at the White Horse.

Carole Evans at the Roebuck, Brimfield, Hereford & Worcester

By her own admission Carole had a privileged childhood: the family were in the motor trade, and indeed her grandfather's racing car "Red Flash", a 1926 Morris Oxford, raced at Brooklands, can still be seen in the Heritage Motor Museum, Syon Park. She remembers being taken out to eat in London in the 60s at all the fine restaurants of the day (Simpson's, Quaglino's, Coq d'Or, the Caprice etc). Convent-educated, she married a South Wales farmer at 19, had four children, enjoyed life and cooking, learnt to handle food, game especially, often preparing dinners after local shoots. Carole and the family moved from Abergavenny to Bromyard, where she met John, a free trade rep with Ansell's Brewery. Sadly, John died earlier this year, but the growth of the Roebuck is their joint success (incidentally, it was our 1992 Pub of the Year). He captained the village cricket team for 24 years, and Carole's first experience of 'outside' catering were the cricket teas, graduating to Ansell's private box at Ludlow racecourse, where she often provided meals for 25. She and John had lots of dinner parties and was often asked "why not cook professionally"? This happened quite soon, when John's job disappeared and Ansell's offered them the tenancy of the Brimfield village pub in 1982/83.

Modest cooking – chili, lasagne, cottage pie, home-baked ham – was the order of the day then. There were six wines on the list, the weekly order for lemons was six. Now, she orders a case and a half of lemons, and there are 120 bins. Keen wine enthusiast Robert King, the local chemist, dictated their wine policy, selling them bottles from his own cellar. Today, he sells fine wines from his chemist shop in Tenbury Wells.

After three years they managed to purchase the freehold and sold their house, which enabled them to refurbish and improve the pub annually, and as Carole says "by working seven days a week I learnt to cook properly and John fell into organisation". Gradually the pub went upmarket, there were the usual disagreements, mostly over expenditure, but none when the three bedrooms were added in 1989. With typical modesty Carole describes herself as "just a grafter", but since John's death, she seems to be grafting even harder, and it's more than likely that the Roebuck will continue to progress rather than rest on its laurels.

Lyn Holland at the Royal Oak, Over Stratton, Somerset

Lyn's first encounter with catering occurred in the late 70s at the Ilchester 393 Club, a private members' club. She got the job, literally through the back door, as she was dating the owner's son. There, she developed her interest in cooking, spending many hours in the kitchen. The club was sold suddenly, so she and her boyfriend applied to Gibbs Mew and became trainee managerss at the Pig's Nose, Melksham. They lasted six months, perhaps expecting too much – in Lyn's words "it was a disaster". For the next nine years she left the pub business, went into commerce, married, became a housewife and continued cooking. The Royal Oak (then a free house) became her local. Lyn joined as a part-time barmaid, and after six months was promoted to manageress. The pub was sold in 1990 to a small brewery, Hall & Woodhouse (Badger beers) so that its character was retained, even though larger breweries and other parties expressed an interest. Unknown to Lyn, she herself was part of the sale, the owner having negotiated acceptable terms. Naturally concerned that she should be allowed a free hand, she's been impressed by the subtle changes that the brewery has instituted, mostly introducing their own beers and nominated suppliers. It is one of the brewer's busiest and classiest pubs in a portfolio of about 100, a food rather than an alcohol pub with a turnover of more than £½m. All the staff are female ("women work harder"), with six full-time and around 20 part-time. The one exception is head chef Bob Beeson, who's bought flair and personality to the job according to Lyn. There are winter and summer menus, barbecues, and healthy King Charles booty food boxes for children, so that they can play with Lyn's dogs (a black Labrador and Great Dane) or make use of the extensive outdoor play area, and return to their lunch packs when they are hungry. It is a pub as much for wine buffs (there are over 90 bins) as locals, Tuesday night especially, and a location where as Lyn says you are not served "bog-standard pub grub, but good food that's different".

James MacCallum at the Bell Inn, Stilton, Cambridgeshire

The Bell Inn at Stilton can fairly claim to be the home of the cheese that takes its name from the village. It was from the Bell that it was first sold to travellers on the Great North Road by the then landlord, Cooper Thornhill, whose sister-in-law, Mrs Paulet, was the first to produce the cheese in the 1720s. Not surprisingly, Stilton appears on the menu in various guises and in many dishes so it was only natural for James to use it in his dish that reached the final 'cook-off' for the Meat Pub of the Year. James is an ambitious young man with more than one string to his bow. At the tender age of 20 he has not only managed to progress from YTS trainee to second chef at the Bell, squeezing in a 'sandwich' course at the local hotel school along the way, but also plays semi-professional football as centre-forward for Warboys Town FC who play in the Jewson League. James's career in the kitchen very nearly did not get started as the catering option he favoured during his final years at school did not meet with parental approval – he ended up doing woodwork instead – but three weeks work experience, under the Project Trident Scheme, in an industrial catering unit along with various 'after school' jobs in local hotels and restaurants reinforced his determination to become a chef. A career on which he has made a flying start.

Brian and Wendy Hibberd at the Sun Inn, Winforton, Hereford & Worcester

Brian and Wendy have taken an interesting route from South Wales to Winforton. Brian had a painting and decorating company, Wendy in her time ran boarding kennels, a hairdressing shop and a shoe shop. In 1976 they sold up and bought the Red Lion at Llangorse, a free house pub they knew from their holiday caravan in the village. At the time it had no letting bedrooms, so they converted upstairs into ten, refurbished downstairs, and cooked well, gaining an entry into this Guide in 1981. Not wishing to risk becoming complacent, they sold it in 1983 and took a year off, before purchasing (from Marstons Brewery) the Sun Inn, a spit-and-sawdust pub serving chips and burgers, in a village with a population of only about 120, but with an excellent roadside location. The first thing they did was to close for six weeks, so that Brian could put his talents to good use, strip out the interior, refurbish and paint. Later they sold off two building plots, effectively paying for the pub. They have four children between the ages of 30 and 12 and two of them help out in the pub: Nick and Amanda, the eldest girl, who "cooks better than I did at her age" says Wendy, whose mum makes the pickles and chutneys. In winter Wendy practises new dishes on the family (in fact the pub is very different in winter, more of a local, with two quiz teams and a darts team). "It would be fair to say the busy summer trade subsidises the quieter winter months" says Brian, introducing Dr Charles Greatorex (ex Guys Hospital) who has his own bar stool and always wears out the right hand knee of his trousers, by facing customers as they enter, and explaining every dish on the blackboard. He should know, as he's tried them all, including 'Aunty Blodwyn's tipsy bread pudding' which didn't sell when it was just plain bread pudding. In their spare time Brian plays golf, Wendy is learning Welsh, and because they believe in serving fresh, home-made food, their pub was deservedly British Meat Pub of the Year in 1992.

John and Kath Leadbeater at the Kilberry Inn, Kilberry, Strathclyde

The Kilberry Inn has many unusual features, notably its location, sixteen miles down a scenic single-track road from Tarbert, seventy miles from the nearest traffic lights (those regulating the traffic flow on Inveraray bridge don't count!). It's also the village post office; in fact it's not really an inn at all, having evolved in 1984 from a general store and petrol pump. Owners John and Kath Leadbeater originally hail from Bradford. Childhood sweethearts (Kath's father referred to John as a 'vacant lot'), he was a travelling rep selling toys and fancy goods, she a housewife. In 1980, with three small children, and fed up with their lifestyle, they invested £2.50 in the *Oban Times*, saw an ad. for a general store and small post office, beat off 64 other interested parties and bought the property. Living at first in a caravan, then graduating to a rented cottage, they found Kilberry and with the assistance of the Highlands and Islands Development Board (80% loan, 20% grant) they applied for a change of usage, submitted planning applications and opened as an inn in 1984. With local support (Mrs. Coats provided the unusual stag's head – unusual because it faces sideways – and Miss Campbell of Kilberry gave them the cook's chair and four meat platters that still adorn the bar today). The inn serves probably the best bar food in Scotland. Self-taught Kath's baking is without equal – her fresh malted granary loaves appear on the bar counter at lunchtime and are soon snapped up to be taken home, alongside jams, chutneys and marmalades. Teetotal John jovially looks after front of inn – he's famous for his Daffy (or is it Donald?) Duck impressions, has been known to move table vases every twenty minutes so that diners don't get bored with the colours of their flowers, and takes a strong stand if smokers irritate non-smokers (there is a non-smoking family dining area). The inn is open from Easter to mid-October, 10 days around Christmas/New Year, but closed on Sundays. Out of season the Leadbeaters' meagre post office salary just about pays the mortgage. There's no outdoor eating (because of the midges), but the long drive, with breathtaking scenery, is certainly worth the journey.

Maps

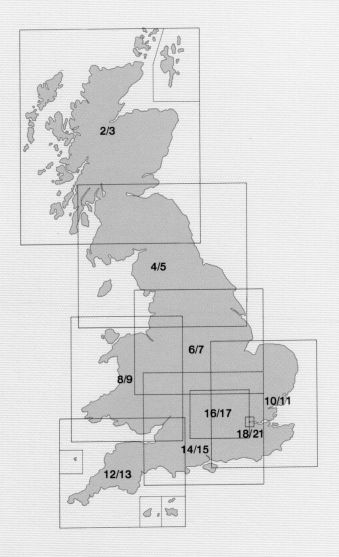

2/3

4/5

6/7

8/9

10/11

16/17

18/21

14/15

12/13

Motorways	●	Food	
Primary Routes	□	Accommodation	
Other Roads	▣	Accommodation and Food	
County Boundaries	○	Listed Pub	

Designed and Produced by
Euromap Ltd, Pangbourne, Berkshire.

1

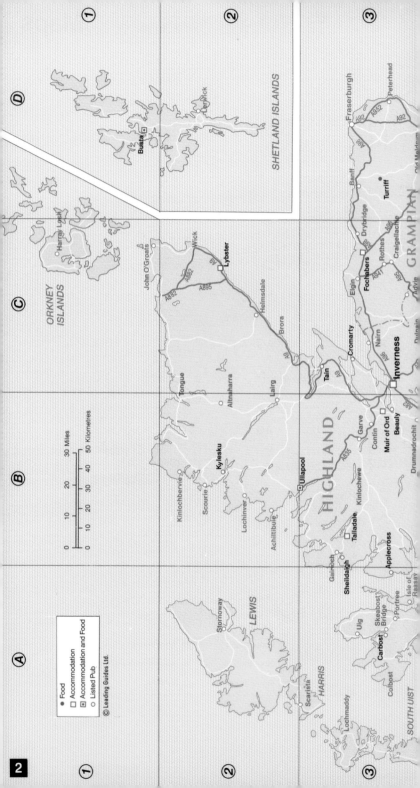

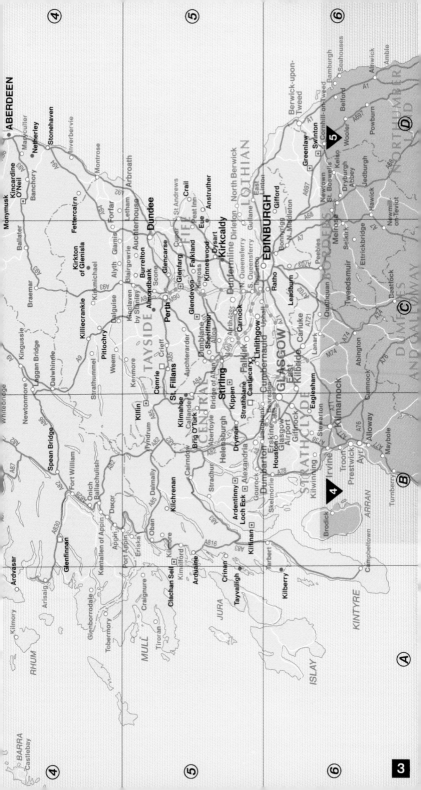

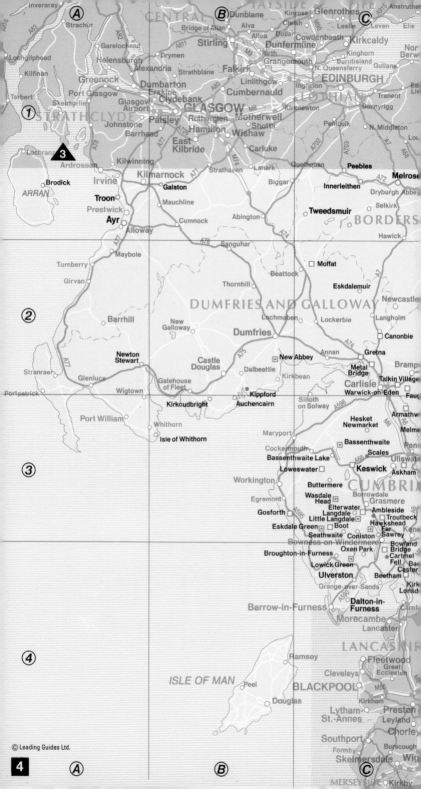

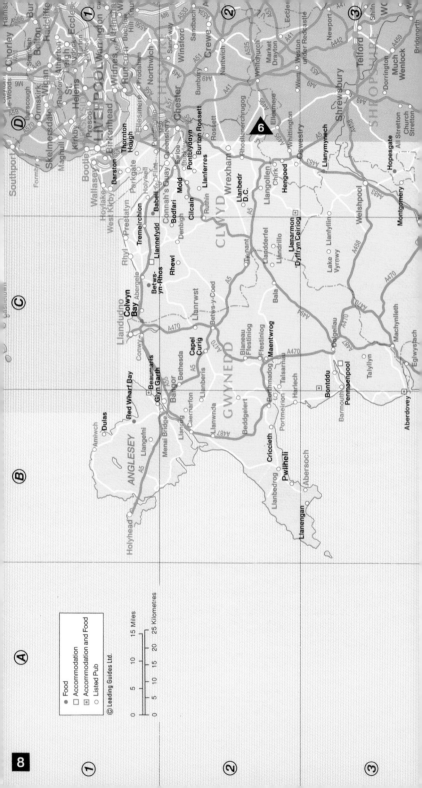

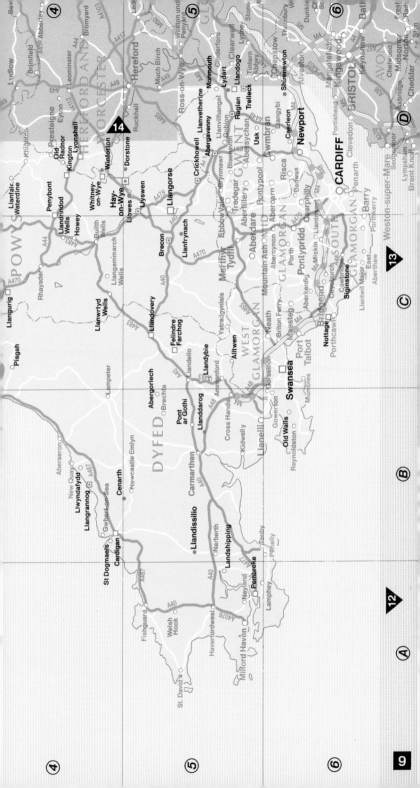

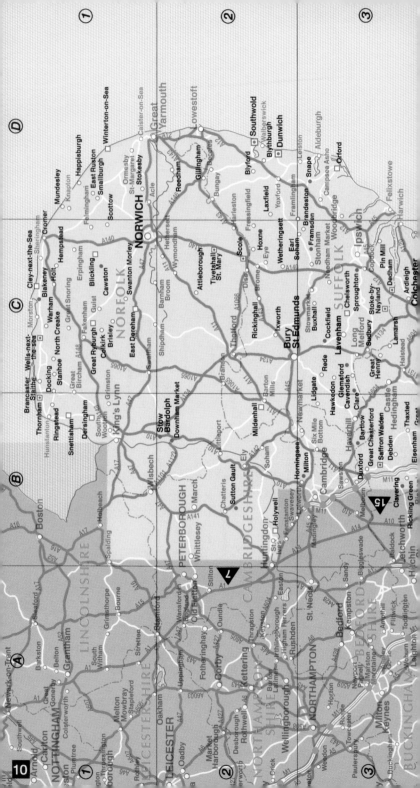

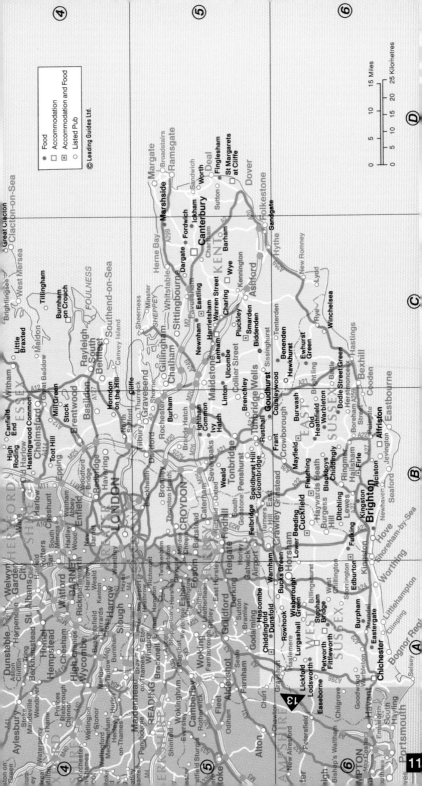

11

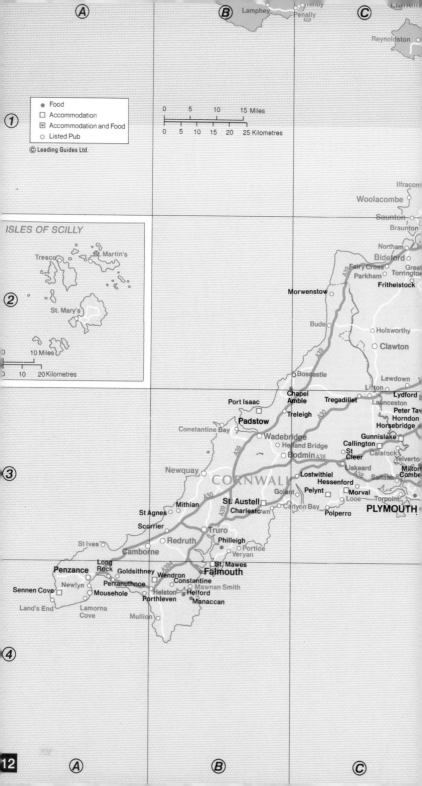

Legend

- ● Food
- □ Accommodation
- ▣ Accommodation and Food
- ○ Listed Pub

© Leading Guides Ltd.

0 5 10 15 Miles
0 5 10 15 20 25 Kilometres

ISLES OF SCILLY

Tresco
St. Martin's
St. Mary's

0 10 Miles
0 10 20 Kilometres

Lamphey
Tenby
Penally
Llanelli
Reynoldston

Ilfracombe
Woolacombe
Saunton
Braunton
Northam
Bideford
Fairy Cross
Parkham
Great Torrington
Frithelstock
Morwenstow
Bude
Holsworthy
Clawton
Boscastle
Lewdown
Litton
Chapel Amble
Port Isaac
Tregadillet
Lydford
Launceston
Peter Tavy
Treleigh
Padstow
Horndon
Horsebridge
Constantine Bay
Wadebridge
Gunnislake
Callington
Calstock
Helland Bridge
St Cleer
Bodmin
Yelverton
Newquay
CORNWALL
Liskeard
Milton Combe
St. Austell
Lostwithiel
Hessenford
Saltash
St Agnes
Mithian
Golant
Pelynt
Morval
Plymouth
Scorrier
Charlestown
Carlyon Bay
Looe
Torpoint
St Ives
Redruth
Truro
Philleigh
Polperro
Camborne
Portloe
Veryan
Penzance
Long Rock
Goldsithney
Wendron
St. Mawes
Newlyn
Perranuthnoe
Constantine
Falmouth
Sennen Cove
Mousehole
Helston
Mawnan Smith
Helford
Land's End
Lamorna Cove
Porthleven
Manaccan
Mullion

12

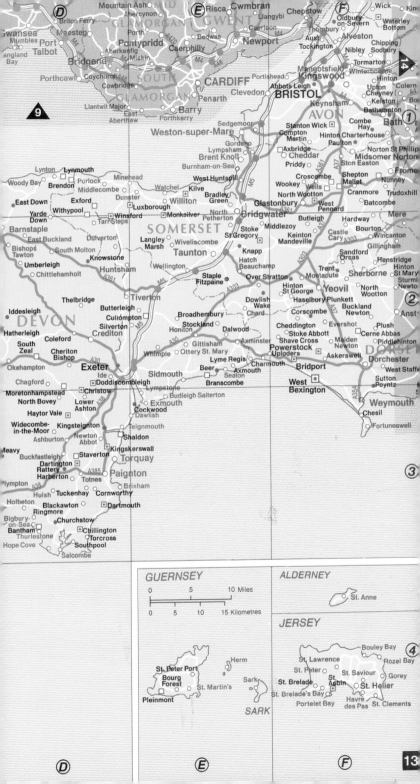

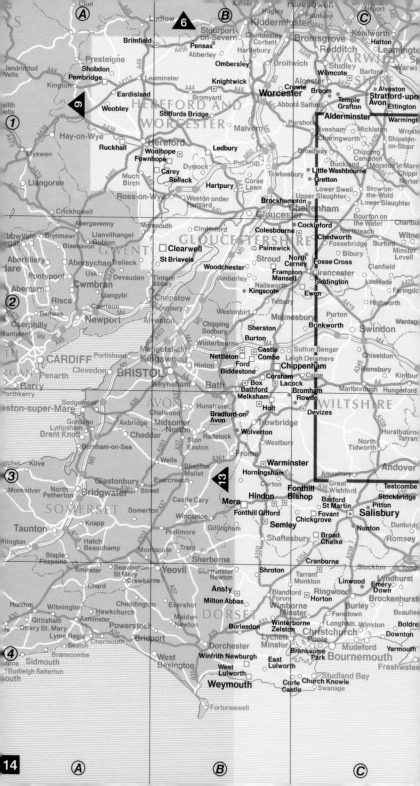

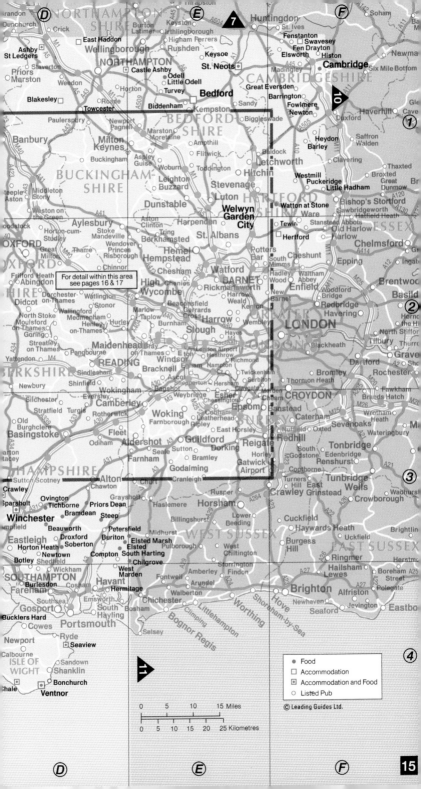

19

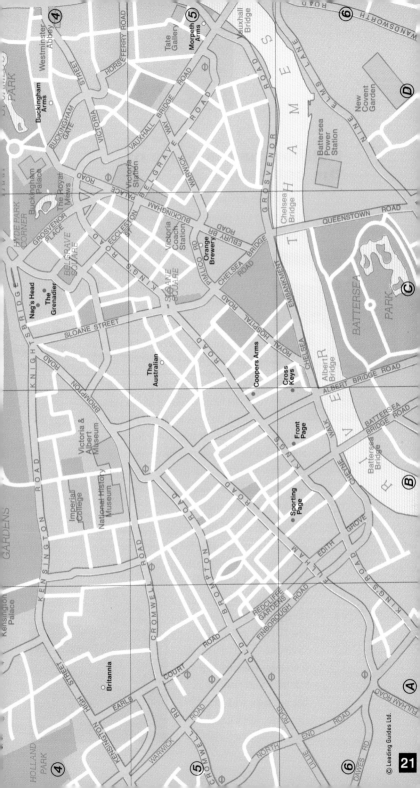

Cellnet makes more of the cellphone.

With the technological expertise and financial support of our parent companies – BT & Securicor – Cellnet has played a key role in developing the UK mobile telecommunications market ever since the launch of cellular systems in the mid-1980s.

Today, we are acknowledged industry leaders with an unrivalled record of innovation.

Having first developed the most comprehensive range of relevant and proven services for the business user, Cellnet has now made it possible for anyone and everyone to use a mobile phone with Lifetime, an exciting new service designed to bring all the benefits of the mobile phone to the less frequent user.

Offering considerable savings over the standard business rate for people who make the majority of calls in the early morning, evenings and weekends, it's perfect for the occasional call – when you just have to get hold of someone – and, of course, it enables your friends, relatives and customers to get in touch with you. Anytime. Anywhere.

The siting of our transceivers and aerials is critical, if we're to ensure the best possible radio reception for Cellnet users.

The higher, the better – is the rule for cellular equipment. To this end we sometimes take advantage of the most unlikely sites – Ely Cathedral, for example, and even Manchester City's football stadium.

Altogether there are over 800 cellular stations nationwide all regularly tuned by a dedicated team of over 400 Cellnet engineers.

Better coverage – nationwide.

The locations of Cellnet radio antennae ensure better coverage and uninterrupted service as cellphone users travel from one part of the country to another.

Cellnet's quality and reliability standards are assured by the size of our national network which includes exclusive coverage of the Channel Islands and the Isle of Man and enables our mobile service to embrace over 98% of the UK population.

Cellnet gives you more choice.

Making mobile communications more accessible and affordable for everyone, and recognising that different users have very different needs, Cellnet offers two very different tariffs. Now you can choose the service which best suits your lifestyle.

Lifetime – A new low cost tariff package for people who tend to use a mobile phone outside the peak period: before 8am, evenings after 7pm, and at weekends. It offers savings of up to 50% on our standard business rate for callers making less than 25 minutes of calls a month. Calls can be made at anytime but will be charged at a higher rate during the peak period.

This exciting new package gives you access to messaging services, such as Callback* and MessageLine*. No ordinary answering services, these take messages when your cellphone is engaged or switched off and play them back when your phone is free.

Primetime – A tariff for the business user and people who use a mobile phone frequently during the day. The fixed costs are higher than Lifetime but calls are cheaper during peak hours: 8am to 7pm. Primetime also includes important services like Callback and MessageLine, International calls, Premium Rate and Star Services.

Now, when you come to consider mobile communications, you'll have two decisions to make. Your choice of phone. And the network it will run on.

Choose Cellnet and you'll be connected to the network that is really geared to your needs.

*Callback is a value added service provided by Cellnet Solutions Limited, a wholly owned subsidiary of Cellnet Group Limited. MessageLine is a value added service provided by Cellcom Limited. Both services use the Cellnet Callback advanced network feature. Using these services will incur extra charges.

Star-Rated Pubs 1993

Here is a complete list of the cream of the crop, those pubs which have most impressed our inspectors this year:

London

EC1, Farringdon: **The Eagle**
NW1, Primrose Hill: **The Lansdowne**
SW6, Parsons Green: **The White Horse**
W11, Notting Hill Gate: **The Ladbroke Arms**

England

Berkshire, West Ilsley: **Harrow**
Berkshire, Yattendon: **Royal Oak**
Cambridgeshire, Keyston: **Pheasant Inn**
Cheshire, Higher Burwardsley: **Pheasant Inn**
Cornwall, Chapel Amble: **Maltsters Arms**
Cumbria, Cartmel Fell: **Masons Arms**
Devon, Kingsteignton: **Old Rydon**
Devon, Meavy: **Royal Oak**
Durham, Romaldkirk: **Rose & Crown**
Gloucestershire, Cockleford: **Green Dragon Inn**
Gloucestershire, Great Rissington: **Lamb**
Hampshire, Winchester: **Wykeham Arms**
Hereford & Worcester, Brimfield: **Roebuck**
Hereford & Worcester, Winforton: **Sun Inn**
Kent, Ightham Common: **Harrow Inn**
Kent, Ivy Hatch: **Plough**
Norfolk, Stow Bardolph: **Hare Arms**
North Yorkshire, Starbotton: **Fox & Hounds**
North Yorkshire, Wass: **Wombwell Arms**
Northamptonshire, Ashby St Ledgers: **Olde Coach House Inn**
Northumberland, Warenford: **Warenford Lodge**
Somerset, Monksilver: **Notley Arms**
Somerset, Over Stratton: **Royal Oak**
Suffolk, Southwold: **Crown**
West Yorkshire, Shelley: **Three Acres Inn**
Wiltshire, North Newnton: **Woodbridge Inn**
Wiltshire, Rowde: **George & Dragon**

Scotland

Fife, Kirkcaldy: **Hoffmans**
Strathclyde, Kilberry: **Kilberry Inn**

Wales

Anglesey, Beaumaris: **Ye Olde Bull's Head**
South Glamorgan, East Aberthaw: **Blue Anchor**
Powys, Llyswen: **Griffin Inn**

London

N1   The Albion

Tel 071-607 7450	**FOOD**
10 Thornhill Road Islington N1	**Map 18 C3**

A Georgian pub which was once a coaching inn. In the middle of a quiet residential part of Islington, the front is welcoming with creeping ivy, tables and benches outside and an old-fashioned illustrated sign of a coach. The front room has plenty of tables, settles and chairs around a large wooden bar. The top part of the bar and the walls are decorated with coaching and horse-related bric-a-brac. At the back, there is a dark-panelled bar and a homely pinkish non-smoking and non-dining lounge. The lovely paved garden (unusual for London) has a weeping willow, a trellis covered with creepers and plenty of tables and chairs. Food is served during meal hours and, weather permitting in the summer, there is a barbecue as an alternative menu. Excellent quality cooking covers a simple menu of old favourites like Welsh rarebit (£3.20), steak and kidney pie with creamed potatoes, lamb chops and mint sauce and beer-battered fried fish (from £4.95). *Bar Food & Restaurant Meals 12-2.30, 7.30-9.30 (restaurant closed Sun). Vegetarian dishes. Children allowed in beer garden to eat. Beer Ruddles Best Bitter, Websters Yorkshire Bitter. Garden. Access, Amex, Diners, Visa.*

SW18   The Alma

Tel 081-870 2537	**FOOD**
499 Old York Road Wandsworth SW18	**Map 19 B5**

Conveniently located across from Wandsworth station and close to Young's brewery, the Alma is distinctive with its bright green-tiled facade and hanging flower baskets. In the dark wood atmosphere of the airy central room, cast-iron tables and pinball and slot-machines range around an island bar counter. At the back, the dining room has yellow-painted walls, framed cartoons, illustrations and beautiful pieces of antique kitchen and restaurant equipment. Daylight coming through the ceiling gives a soft and comfortable feel. Although we highly recommended the food last year, a recent visit was disappointing and we advise sticking to basic dishes like Toulouse sausage and frites (£4.30), bagels d'Alma (£4) or the bar menu offering soup (soupe de poisson £3.75) and sandwiches. Besides the Youngs on handpump, you'll find a selection of international wines including Portuguese and Californian. Espresso and regular coffee are also available. *Bar Food All day. Restaurant Meals 12-2.45, 7-10.45 (not Sun eve). Vegetarian meals. Children's portions. Beer Youngs Special, Porter. Access, Amex, Visa.*

SE1   Anchor

Tel 071-407 1577	**A**
34 Park Street Bankside SE1	**Map 19 D4**

Listed for atmosphere and position rather than food; there was a pub on this site during the Great Fire of London, though the present building is mid-18th century, refurbished in the 1960s. Lots of panelling, beams, four little rooms, leather seating and a waterside patio. *Beer Courage Best, Directors, Anchor Best. Family room, riverside garden.*

W1   Argyll Arms

Tel 071-734 6117

18 Argyll Street W1   **Map 20 D2**

Still lots of traditional city tavern atmosphere at this large, rambling
oasis opposite the side underground station exit at Oxford Circus.
Quieter upstairs.

SW3   The Australian

Tel 071-589 3114   **FOOD**

29 Milner Street Chelsea SW3 2QD   **Map 21 C5**

A short walk from Harrods and Peter Jones is a haven for cricket fans
with walls covered with pictures of famous British and Australian
players; the name and theme of this Nicholson's pub celebrate a very
early game played by the first Australian touring team in nearby
Lennox Gardens. Outside tables under the ivy-covered facade face
south, taking in the sun. The bar snack menu is straightforward,
ranging from ploughman's lunches (£3.45) to deep-fried cod (£4.25)
or hot, hot chili con carne (£3.95), plus daily specials (fettucine with
tomato, smoked ham and mushroom sauce plus garlic bread £3.95)
and tip-top, freshly cut sandwiches made from a local baker's loaves
(rare roast beef with horseradish sauce £2.25, crispy fried bacon
£1.95). Everything is home-cooked and prepared with care.
Vegetarians will doubtless be satisfied with crunchy crumbed
courgettes and mushrooms served with a mayonnaise dip (£3.75). No
desserts are offered in summertime, but home-made spotted dick and
Christmas pudding appear on the menu in winter. The Australian is a
good example of a pub where the long-established tenants (Mr & Mrs
Childs) have created a market and nurtured it; the quality and
consistency of the food is obviously of paramount importance to
them. *Bar Food* 12-2.30, 6-9 (*not Sat eve or all day Sun*). *Vegetarian
meals. Children's portions. Beer Burton Ale, Greene King IPA, Tetley.
Outdoor eating. Access, Visa.*

W4   Bell & Crown

Tel 081-994 4164   **FOOD**

Strand on the Green Chiswick W4 3PF   **Map 19 A5**

With a cane furniture-filled conservatory and two levels of tables and
benches outside overlooking the river, this Thameside pub is useful to
know about in good weather. Fullers' tenants Mary and Gwynne Jones
have been here for almost ten years and take delight in running this
friendly watering hole. Apart from the ever-popular local brew,
there's a small choice of home-made hot dishes (all £2.95) like
rigatoni bolognese or tomato lamb stew (Welsh lamb, of course, is
preferred by the Gallic landlords) served with boiled new potatoes and
a macedoine of vegetables), plus other favourites like cauliflower
cheese and chili; chef Tina's Italian influence is shown in the regular
daily vegetarian dish that might be pasta, or courgette bake. Salad
plates made with either smoked mackerel, home-made paté, sardines
or ham are carefully prepared (£2.50) and even Gorgonzola is
available for ploughman's lunches (£1.95) made with good bread.
There is an extensive choice of up to 24 different, ready-prepared
sandwiches at lunchtime. *Bar Food* 12-2.30 (*sandwiches only Sat &
Sun*). *Vegetarian dishes. Children's portions and prices. Beer Fullers.
Outdoor eating. No credit cards.*

EC4   Black Friar

Tel 071-236 5650

174 Queen Victoria Street EC4

A

Map 19 D4

Probably the most extraordinary public house in London; a Victorian wedge-shaped pub occupying the site of a medieval friary, and pre-occupied with these historic themes: friars disport themselves in various stages of drunkenness on the outside walls, and in the inner back room, Edwardian art nouveau includes gaudy marble walls and fireplace, a mosaic ceiling, ornate seating and mirrors, bas-relief friezes of friars at play, and stern monastic mottoes. *Beer Tetley. Patio/terrace.*

W8   Britannia

Tel 071-937 1864

1 Allen Street Kensington W8

A

Map 21 A4

Cheering and often surprisingly peaceful old pub just a few yards off Kensington High Street. At the front, public and saloon bars are divided by a partition, and share a horseshoe bar; wood panelling, settles and other seats, some in the bow windows. At the back, beyond the saloon, a spacious room has its own bar and food servery. *Beer Youngs. Garden.*

SW1   Buckingham Arms

Tel 071-222 3386

62 Petty France St James's SW1

Map 21 D4

Busy Westminster pub close to Wellington barracks and the Passport Office. *Beer Youngs.*

W4   Bull's Head

Tel 081-994 1204

Strand on the Green Chiswick W4

A

Map 19 A5

The Bull's Head's story starts during the Civil War when Cromwell escaped the Royalist troops, reaching the island through a tunnel under the Thames. Today, it is an attractive shelter overlooking the river with an unusual warren of rooms. Several cottages were joined together to create different levels and atmospheres: dark intimate corners, quiet salons overlooking the river, a modern sheltered terrace, and a small garden. It's just a pity that the earth moves every time a train crosses the nearby Chiswick railway bridge. *Free House.*

W8   The Churchill Arms

Tel 071-727 4242

119 Kensington Church Street W8 4LN

FOOD

Map 20 A3

Talk about atmosphere, charm and originality and the Churchill Arms qualifies for all of them. Its cheerful owner, Gerry O'Brien, is a collector *par excellence*; the walls of the attractive conservatory restaurant exhibit his impressive collection of 1600 butterflies and the ceiling of the bar is covered with chamber pots, brasses and copper ornaments. A typical menu mixes steak and kidney pie, moussaka and plaice and chips (all £3.75) with Thai dishes such as beef in green curry paste and coconut milk (£4.25) or fried rice with chicken, spring onions and Thai spices (£3.95); both chef and staff are Thai, but Oriental dishes are generally not as successful as the traditional pub favourites. Sandwiches and ploughman's lunches (£2.95) are also offered. Honest cooking made with fresh ingredients and served with enthusiasm. *Bar Food* 12-3, 6-9.30. *Beer Fullers Chiswick, London Pride, ESB. No credit cards.*

WC1   Cittie of York

Tel 071-242 7670   **A**

22 High Holborn WC1   Map 18 C3

High Victorian architecture on a medieval pub and 17th-century coffee house site. The vast gothic-style drinking hall has a vaulted ceiling and the longest bar counter in Britain, the gantry above it stacked with thousand-gallon wine vats, and a catwalk (for filling the now redundant vats) above that; lamps suspended from the rafters, and a coal-burning stove. Be early for a seat in one of the little booths; it gets extremely busy. Or head for the little wood-panelled room leading off, adorned with old York prints (patriotic references to Sam Smiths brewery ownership). *Beer Sam Smiths. Access, Visa.*

W4   City Barge

Tel 081-994 2148   **A**

27 Strand on the Green Chiswick W4   Map 19 A5

Riverside pub dating back to the 15th century; charming original, intimate bar at river level, plus a modern extension and warm, bright conservatory upstairs. *Beer Courage.*

EC14   The Cock Tavern

Tel 071-248 2918   **FOOD**

East Poultry Avenue Smithfield EC14 9LF   Map 18 D3

A large basement restaurant hidden away in a pub at the very heart of Smithfield market. Not a place known for its decor (which hasn't changed since the 60s), but certainly popular among food-hovering meat traders, City folk and medics from Bart's. The animation and cheerful atmosphere start at 5.30am with a generous breakfast – choose from black pudding, kidneys, smoked haddock with poached egg, hash browns, bubble & squeak, eggs any way and so on... The choice is extensive: seven set breakfasts, omelettes, rolls or sandwiches, all at competitive prices (£2.45-£4.85). The lunch menu concentrates on meat and on a recent visit the special offer was a 40oz T-bone steak with trimmings for £16.50! A fun place with gloomy decor enlivened by the banter of serious trenchermen! *Bar Food Breakfast 5.30-10.30am. Lunch 12-2.45. Vegetarian meals (on request). Children's portions. Free House. Beer Courage Best Bitter, John Smiths Yorkshire, Pedigree, Whitbread IPA. Access, Amex, Visa.*

N1   Compton Arms

Tel 071-359 2645   **A**

4 Compton Avenue off Canonbury Lane N1   Map 18 D3

Cosy, old-fashioned alehouse in a cobbled mews, with a little rear terrace. *Beer Greene King.*

SW3   Coopers Arms

Tel 071-376 3120   **FOOD**

Flood Street Chelsea SW3 5TB   Map 21 B5

Under the same tenancy as *The Ship* and *The Alma* in Wandsworth (see entries) and equally busy at times. A small, lively Youngs pub on two floors; the ground floor is a recently refurbished room with a large, solid table on which newspapers are laid for perusal; upstairs is a rather lifeless room with tired decor but useful if you want to get away from the hustle and bustle downstairs. To the rear, a small room is quieter and has a feature fireplace. The short blackboard menu offers a mix of traditional (fish pie, chicken liver salad £4, lamb andasparagus casserole £4.50) and more modern pub fare (almond and vegetable curry served with raita and small poppadums £4.25); most dishes are well executed and you can help yourself to bread and butter. Vegetarians might enjoy leek and butter bean dijonnaise £4.25. Desserts might include crème caramel and trifle (£1.50). Service can be slow when the pub is full, but it maintains a cheerful edge. Open all day except Sunday from 3 to 6pm. *Bar Food 12.30-2.30, 6.30-9.30. Beer Youngs. Access, Amex, Visa.*

NW8   Crockers

Tel 071-268 6608   **A**

24 Aberdeen Place NW8   **Map 20 B1**

Extraordinary lavish, spacious and high-ceilinged folly, built in the belief that Marylebone Station was to be located on the site next door. It wasn't. *Beer Arkells, Brakspear, Marston. Family room. Patio/terrace.*

SW3   Cross Keys

Tel 071-352 1893   **FOOD**

Lawrence Street Chelsea SW3   **Map 21 B6**

Behind the brown facade is a lovely old-fashioned pub. Three small rooms with high ceilings revolve around the central bar. One of them has a wood fire in the winter. There is an additional back room, which leads out on to a lovely flowery courtyard. No music or fruit machines here but a warm and friendly welcome. The food is prepared with care by the licensee's wife. Daily specials might include marrow with savoury stuffing (£3.50), rack of lamb and crispy pork with two vegetables (£3.50). Salads, sandwiches and a home-made sweet are also available. *Bar Food 11-2.30. Vegetarian dishes. Children's portions. Children allowed in back room and patio. Beer Courage Best Bitter, Directors, 6X, guest beer. Patio/terrace, outdoor eating. Access, Visa.*

W6   Dove

Tel 081-748 5405   **A**

19 Upper Mall Hammersmith W6   **Map 19 A4**

Well-known, well-loved riverside pub. The tiny front snug is in the Guinness Book of Records; the main bar has leatherette seating and copper-top tables, and there's a quieter upper level with nicer furnishings and food servery, plus a very popular (but small) outdoor drinking area by the river. No children indoors. *Beer Fullers London Pride, ESB. Riverside patio/terrace.*

EC1   The Eagle   ★

Tel 071-837 1353   **FOOD**

159 Farringdon Road EC1R 3AL   **Map 18 C3**

Converted bare-boards pub transformed lunchtime and evening into an excellent restaurant serving new-wave Italian food. It remains a pub even during meal times, so the fairly cramped seating area is shared between drinkers and eaters at a hotch-potch of old tables and chairs – one old leather sofa looks as if it was reclaimed from a skip! No booking, but a wait with a pint is well worth while for the voguish New Mediterranean cooking on offer; the daily-changing blackboard menu offers the likes of ribollita soup (£3.50) – beans, vegetables and chunks of lovely Italian bread, all in a fresh chicken stock; grilled scallops with a salad of roast peppers, bacon, watercress and frisée lettuce (£7.50), aubergine stew with couscous and yoghurt (5.50), seafood risotto (6.50). Other dishes might include Portuguese soup of spring cabbage, potatoes and chorizo sausage, linguine with scallops, parsley, chili andgarlic; grilled mackerel with coriander and lime salsa, and marinated roast loin of pork with roast potatoes and braised sweet red onions. Ten wines are offered by the glass. The first floor, reached from the bar, is given over to an art gallery. *Meals L 12.30-2.30 D 6.30-10.30. Pub closed Sat & Sun, Bank Holidays, 3 weeks Xmas. No credit cards.*

N1   The Eagle Tavern

Tel 071-253 4715 | **A**
2 Shepherdess Walk off City Road N1 | Map 18 D3

Immortalised in the old nursery rhyme 'Pop Goes the Weasel', this is the Eagle where the money went after its customers had pawned their possessions – or popped the weasel. The Royal Grecian Theatre once stood next door, and among the many famous performers who appeared on stage there was the much-loved vaudeville star Marie Lloyd. Today, posters and a model of the theatre serve as reminders in the convivial bar. *Beer Charrington. Garden. Pub closed Sat & Sun.*

NW3   Flask

Tel 071-435 4580 | **A**
14 Flask Walk Hampstead NW3 1HE | Map 18 B2

Atmospheric old Hampstead village pub, bursting to the gunnels most weekends and summer evenings; attractively simple and down at heel inside. Reputedly the local actors' hangout. Conservatory/wine bar. *Beer Youngs.*

SE1   Founders Arms

Tel 071-928 1899 | **A**
52 Hopton Street Bankside SE1 | Map 19 D4

Successfully designed modern Young's pub, near Blackfriars Bridge. Its almost entirely glass walls at the rear make the most of the river frontage; eat on the large brick-floored terrace in fine weather, with its view of the City and St Paul's. *Beer Youngs. Patio/terrace. Access, Amex, Diners, Visa.*

EC1   Fox & Anchor

Tel 071-253 4838 | **FOOD**
115 Charterhouse Street EC1 | Map 18 D3

The meat is undeniably fresh at this highly traditional old Smithfield pub, where the market men gather for generous plates of English breakfast (£6.50). The steak and kidney pie (£7.25) is recommended. Non-carnivories may like to try plaice or smoked mackerel. There's a minimum £3 charge. Note it closes for staff holidays in late August. *Bar Food 7-10.15 (breakfast), 12-2.30, 5.30-9. Vegetarian meals. Beer Ind Coope Burton Ale, Tetley Bitter, Youngs Bitter. Children allowed in bar to eat. Access, Visa.*

SW19   Fox & Grapes

Tel 081-946 5599 | **A**

Camp Road Wimbledon SW19 | **Map 19 A6**

Once a gin shop, converted with the next door stables into a pub in
1956, fronting Wimbledon Common. Lots of theme nights. Tapas
bar. No children indoors. **Beer** *Courage Best, Directors, John Smith's
Bitter, Magnet. Access, Visa.*

SW3   Front Page

Tel 071-352 2908 | **FOOD**

35 Old Church Street Chelsea SW3 | **Map 21 B6**

In a quiet residential area of Chelsea, just off the hustle and bustle of
Kings Road, stands the Front Page, on a prime corner site, its white-
painted exterior decked with colourful hanging baskets and large
attractive gas lamps. Inside is spacious, extremely light and airy, thanks
to high ceilings and large windows which let in plenty of natural
daylight. Rich navy blue curtains are matched by painted ceiling
borders, and whirling ceiling fans help keep the room fresh. Part-
panelled, it's furnished in informal rustic style with solid stripped
wood tables, round-back chairs and long benches on well-worn
floorboards; walls have minimal covering, save some Victorian-style
nudes. At either end of the bar, two large blackboards display the day's
food choice, which is interesting and light in a bistro style: regular
favourites include snacks like chickenand brandy paté (£3.70) or
sautéed chicken liver and garlic butter (£3.20); as main courses,
perhaps smoked salmon and scrambled eggs (£5.30), salmon fishcakes
(£5.70) or Indonesian beef rendang and rice (£5.80). Those
traditionalists who crave a more solid English lunch are catered for
with dishes like sausage and mash (£4.25). The cooking here will
never win awards, but is reliable enough, and fresh produce is well
handled. Young, friendly and keen staff provide good service, with a
smile. This is a pub worth knowing about, just moments from the
crush of the Kings Road and its array of noisier, busier, less
welcoming places. **Bar Food** *12-2.15, 7-10.15. Vegetarian meals.* **Beer**
*Ruddles County, Websters Yorkshire Bitter, Whitbread Boddingtons Bitter.
No credit cards.*

SE1   George Inn

Tel 071-407 2056 | **A**

77 Borough High Street Southwark SE1 1NH | **Map 19 D4**

London's only surviving original coaching inn dating back to when
London Bridge was the only way into the City. After almost 400
years of history it was rescued by the National Trust in the 1930s and
is now run by Whitbread. A large cobbled courtyard terrace
overlooks the beautiful black and white frontage with its galleried
section and hanging flower baskets. A series of bars is interlinked: the
wine bar contains a disappointing food counter, the George Bar has
low ceilings, dark beams, latticed windows and lantern lamps and the
Old Bar has a dark, quiet atmosphere and an open fireplace. A popular
pub with tourists. **Beer** *Boddingtons, Flowers, Fullers London Pride,
Wadworth 6X.*

E14   Grapes

Tel 071-987 4396

A

76 Narrow Street Wapping E14

Map 19 D4

Over 300 years old, the Grapes probably hasn't changed much since Dickens, a frequent visitor, used it as the model for the Six Jolly Fellowship Porters in '*Our Mutual Friend*'. A narrow riverside pub, squeezed in between buildings that used to house ships' chandlers, block and tackle makers, barge builders and the like, it's easy to imagine Thames watermen drinking in the downstairs bar, with its bare floorboards and boarded, nicotine-stained ceiling. Prime position for watching the passing traffic is from the two tables on a (now glassed-in) verandah overlooking the river, whose murky water laps at the back wall of the building. *Beer Ind Coope Burton Ale, Tetley Bitter.*

SW1   The Grenadier

Tel 071-235 3074

FOOD

18 Wilton Row Belgravia SW1

Map 21 C4

Not far from Hyde Park Corner, but well hidden in the curve of cobbled Wilton Row, the bright red and blue frontage of this intimate Chef & Brewer pub can't be missed. The small dark bar and restaurant were once used as a mess for the Duke of Wellington's Grenadiers. The place is full of historical atmosphere with a few sabres, daggers and bugles hanging from the ceiling. The dark panelled bar is small and customers spread outside on to the quiet cul-de-sac. Two intimate dining rooms at the back are intimate with have seats for just 22; prices reflect the quality of the cooking and ingredients: smoked Scottish salmon (£8), venison terrine (£4.50), carpet bag steak (fillet stuffed with oysters £16.95). Traditional English food is presented at its best with perfectly executed classics like fish and chips served with mushy peas, jugged hare stewed with barley (£11.50), grilled or poached wild Scotch salmon (£14.25) and even a vegetarian dish. A selection of ports, dessert wines and cognacs is offered on the dessert menu. A set menu (£17.95) offers the likes of prawn cocktail or soup to start, followed by fish and chips, pudding and coffee. Good snacks in the bar – from soup of the day (£2.30) or ploughman's lunch (£3.95) to sausage, beans and chips (£4.40) or scampi and chips (£4.90). Sunday roast (£11.25). *Bar Food & Restaurant Meals 12-2.30, 6-10. Vegetarian dishes. Beer Websters, Ruddles, Courage Directors. Access, Amex, Diners, Visa.*

W1   The Guinea

Tel 071-409 1728 (Rest 071-499 1210)

FOOD

30 Bruton Place off Berkeley Square W1

Map 20 D3

Tucked away in a mews between Bruton Street and Berkeley Square, this Mayfair institution gained its reputation by serving charcoal-grilled Prime Scotch Highland steaks along with Rossmore oysters and Scottish smoked salmon in its rear restaurant. The bar menu offers a cheaper alternative to eating in the restaurant with classics like their superior steak and kidney pie, shepherd's pie or chili. An interesting selection of hot ciabatta bread sandwiches is also out of the ordinary: try the Siciliano (£4.25) made with free-range chicken, bacon, sun-dried tomatoes, mascarpone and chopped olives; or the Mirabeau (£3.95) with Aberdeen sirloin steak, tarragon, anchovies, tomatoes and mayonnaise; sandwiches are made to order (often at least a ten minute wait) and well worth the struggle through the Mayfair regulars who pack the small bar at lunchtime, when getting a seat is nigh on impossible. **Beer** *Youngs.*

NW3   Holly Bush

Tel 071-435 2892	**A**
Holly Mount off Heath Street NW3	Map 18 B2

Be early for a seat in the original front bar, converted from stables in the 18th century: unpretentiously stylish, with its real gas lighting and old wooden settles; a more modern lounge leads off at the rear. **Beer** *Benskins, Ind Coope, Tetley, Youngs. Patio/terrace.*

EC1   The Hope & Sirloin

Tel 071-253 8525	**FOOD**
94 Cowcross Street Smithfield EC1	Map 18 D3

Giant breakfasts served in the first- and second-floor rooms from early morning. Start the day with the full works (English Breakfast including black pudding, £7.50) or any combination from eggs-any way to kippers (£3.50). Open from 7-10am on Saturday, but not for food. Reservations essential. **Meals** *7am-10.15am, 12-2.15 (no food in evenings).* **Beer** *Courage, Websters, Youngs, Ruddles. Pub closed from 3.30pm Mon-Fri, from 10am Sat, all day Sun. Credit cards.*

SE1   Horniman's

Tel 071-407 3611	**FOOD**
Hay's Galleria Tooley Street London Bridge SE1 2HD	Map 19 D4

Right at the entrance of the newly developed Hay's Galleria on the south bank overlooking the Thames by London Bridge, Horniman's is a modern interpretation of Victorian style in the premises of the family's tea-packing company. The tribute to Frederick John Horniman's travels is discreetly paid through a painted mural on top of the bar. It's part pub, part café and the tables on the gallerias have views of the river and the city in the background. The restaurant offers good hot and cold dishes (turkey pie, liver and bacon, lamb chasseur casserole, broccoli and leek pie – all served with chips and vegetables £4.75) throughout the day; there's also a hot salt beef bar (platter with salad £4.75). A popular pub with both tourists and businessmen. Families are welcome in a special area in the Pantry restaurant and children are offered special portions at special prices. **Bar Food** *11-5.30, evenings booking required.* **Restaurant Meals** *12-3, evenings booking required. Vegetarian dishes. Children's portions.* **Beer** *Burton, Nicholson's Best, 6X. Pub closed weekend evenings. Access, Amex, Visa.*

W11   Ladbroke Arms   ★

Tel 071-727 6648	**FOOD**
54 Ladbroke Arms Notting Hill Gate W11 3NN	Map20 A3

On the corner of Ladbroke Road and the charming Willby Mews, the Ladbroke Arms recently changed hands and is now a shining light, hopefully leading other pubs where many fear to tread. Care is taken over the preparation of all the food – from the skinning of black pudding slices for grilling to the nice finishing touch of a drizzle of olive oil in gazpacho soup – and results are considerably above average. The front terrace welcomes you with open arms: built a few steps above street level, it is well stocked with tables, benches and parasols. Inside is a traditional mixture of mahogany panelling, yellow velvet-covered banquettes, large etched mirrors, a semi-circular bar with pillars and a split-level area at the back. There's a very civilised atmosphere with smiling faces and classical music softly playing in the background. To choose from the tempting and varied menu can be a dilemma. Examples of the satisfying, well-balanced dishes include yoghurt and cucumber soup, grilled black pudding with a complementary creamy grain-mustard sauce, grilled sausage with Cumberland sauce (£4.50), honey-baked ham salad with potato and mayonnaise, baked aubergine with savoury mincemeat or the light, home-made salmon fishcakes with a zesty hollandaise (£7.25). Desserts, however, seem a poor relation. A good selection of beer is offered with Royal Oak, Webster and Courage on handpump and a reasonable selection of wines. Parking is difficult. **Bar Food & Restaurant Meals** 12-2.30, 7-9.30. Vegetarian dishes. Children's portions. **Beer** Courage Directors, Eldridge Pope Royal Oak, Ruddles Best, Websters Yorkshire. Outdoor eating. Family room. Access, Visa.

WC1   Lamb

Tel 071-405 0713	**A**
94 Lambs Conduit Street WC1	Map 18 C3

A lovely old Victorian local, popular with Bloomsbury office and lecturer types for an excellent after-work pint of Youngs. The cosy, usually rather cramped bar winds around the splendid counter, complete with its original gantry and snob screens, from a quiet little anteroom down some steps at the top left, via leather wall benches, little wooden tables and stools, to a locals' public end at the right hand side. **Beer** Youngs. Patio/terrace.

WC2   Lamb & Flag

Tel 071-237 4088	**FOOD**
33 Rose Street (off Garrick Street) Covent Garden WC2	Map 20 D3

A busy Georgian pub which retains its atmosphere from Dickens' time with low ceilings, dark-wood panelling and built-in benches on the ground floor. The two small, separate bars downstairs have limited seating areas and customers tend to spread out on to the paved area in front of the pub or in the quieter dining room upstairs. The bar serves excellent ploughman's lunches (£2.50) made with French bread and Cheddar, Double Gloucester, Blue Shropshire or Stilton – all farmhouse cheeses. In complete contrast, the food offered upstairs, although healthy in its intentions, is considerably less exciting. **Bar Food** 12-9.30 (not Sun). **Beer** Courage. No credit cards.

EC3   Lamb Tavern

Tel 071-626 2454	**FOOD**
10-12 Leadenhall Market EC3	Map 19 D4

Right next to Richard Rodgers' ultra-modern Lloyds building is Leadenhall market, which is known for its Victorian cast iron and glass-covered cobbled lanes, as well as being home to the Lamb Tavern. A characterful place, with engraved glass windows, cast iron pillars, a tiled picture panel depicting Dick Whittington and a spiral staircase leading up to a mezzanine floor. The pub was used as a location for the filming of Branigan with John Wayne (as a photo of the 'Duke' together with landlady Linda Morris testifies) as well as a scene from the Winds of War with Robert Mitchum. Foodwise the thing to go for is the succulent hot roast beef sandwich (£3.50): the wing-rib is carved to order and served in lengths of real French bread. There are other things available: various sandwiches (from £1.25) in the tiled basement bar where the dart players congregate; some hot dishes of the day, like cottage pie (£3.50) and seafood mornay (£3.50) in the first floor bar, where there are also proper tables to sit at; but the beef is the best and by far the most popular choice. A delicious spin-off from all this beef-roasting is the dripping it generates, which can be had with a piece of French Bread – a real treat. About a dozen wines are listed on a blackboard with house wine and a Liebfraumilch available by the glass. Pub closed Saturday and Sunday. **Bar Food** *11-2.30.* **Beer** *Youngs Bitter, Special. Access, Amex, Visa.*

NW1   The Lansdowne   ★

Tel 071-483 0409	**FOOD**
90 Gloucester Avenue Primrose Hill NW1	Map 18 C3

A low-cost conversion job at this old Victorian Charrington pub has completely changed its character, giving it something of a café feel; it is still a pub, though, with Everards Tiger for real ale buffs. Opened up and reduced to bare boards there is a motley collection of tables and chairs (including some folding chairs stacked up against the wall), vases of fresh flowers and a few magazines piled up on an old chest. Amanda Pritchett, late of *The Eagle* in Farringdon Road (*qv*), can be seen at work in the small, spick and span, kitchen where she cooks up the likes of roast mackerel on a bed of white beans with salsa verde (£7), carrot and tarragon soup with lots of fresh herbs and the tang of orange zest (£3), Caesar salad (£5), and spiced lamb and aubergine stew with Basmati rice (£7.50). The shortness of the menu – just five or six dishes written up on the blackboard daily – goes a long way to explain the excellence of the results. **Bar Food** *12-2.30, 7-10.15 (except D Sun, all day Mon).* **Beer** *Bass Everards Tiger. Pub closed Sun 3-7pm.*

N1   Marquess Tavern

Tel 071-354 2975	**A**
32 Canonbury Street N1	Map 18 D2

Splendid, spick and span 1850 corner pub, handsome outside and in, rather prettily set in a sleepy affluent Islington mews, by the canal walk. Comfortable and plush inside, with distinguished features, elegant fireplaces, a fine bar counter and swags and tails. Picnic tables on the pavement. **Beer** *Youngs. Patio.*

W2   Monkey Puzzle

Tel 071-723 0143	**FOOD**
30 Southwick Street off Sussex Gardens W2 1JQ	Map 20 B2

Set on the ground floor of a modern building, the Monkey Puzzle benefits from a flowery outdoor terrace. The main attraction is the good selection of draught bitters, although there is also an extensive menu with fair cooking showing some attention to detail (coconut, mango chutney and salad served with lamb curry). Home-made, peppery vegetable soup (£1.50), ploughman's (£3.25), seafood salad (£3.25), chicken carbonara and salad (£4.95), Lancashire hot pot (£4.50). Only ice cream for dessert. Tables are set for both lunch and dinner. Three-course Sunday lunch £6.95. **Bar Food & Restaurant Meals** *12-2, 7-9.30. Vegetarian dishes. Children's portions. Free House.* **Beer** *Brakspear, Bass, Monkey Puzzle Bitter, Pedigree, Tetley, Wadworth 6X. Terrace, outdoor eating. Access, Visa.*

SW1   Morpeth Arms

Tel 071-834 6442

58 Millbank SW1   Map 21 D5

Purpose-built for the warders of the old Millbank prison, now very
handy for visits to the Tate Gallery. *Beer Youngs. Patio.*

SW1   Nag's Head

Tel 071-235 1135   **FOOD**

53 Kinnerton Street Belgravia SW1   Map 21 C4

Probably the smallest pub in London but certainly not the least
interesting. The front was built in 1780, when horses running around
on Grosvenor Estate provided the inspiration for the name. The low-
ceilinged, panelled bar and dining room communicate through a
narrow stairway. A 1930s' what-the-butler-saw machine and a
fortune-telling machine taking old pennies are popular features, with
takings going to Queen Charlotte's Hospital. Personal bric-a-brac and
photographs give a homely and intimate feel. The home-made
cooking brings shepherd's pie, chili con carne (£3.95) and real ale
sausage, mash and beans (£3.65) back to life. Vegetarians are offered
the likes of tomato and onion quiche plus macaroni and cheese. No
puddings in the summer; spotted dick and sponge puddings in the
winter. A cover charge of £1 is charged for meals served between 7
and 10pm. *Bar Food All day. Vegetarian meals. Children's portions.
Children allowed in bar to eat (minimum age 12 after 7pm). Free House.
Beer Benskins, Youngs. No credit cards.*

WC2   Opera Tavern

Tel 071-836 7321

23 Catherine Street WC2   Map 19 C4

Directly opposite the Theatre Royal, Drury Lane. *Beer Ind Coope
Burton Ale, Tetley Bitter, Youngs Bitter. Patio.*

SW1   Orange Brewery

Tel 071-730 5984

37 Pimlico Road SW1   Map 21 C5

Good fruity home-brewed beers are a major attraction at this
characterful old-fashioned pub, with woody alehouse style, tall stools
around high tables, sofas and nice pieces of Victoriana. *Beer Own
range. Patio.*

SE5   Phoenix & Firkin

Tel 071-701 8282   **FOOD**

5 Windsor Walk Denmark Hill SE5 8BB   Map 19 D5

Denmark Hill station was destroyed by a fire in 1980; the Phoenix &
Firkin rose from its ashes thanks to Bruce's Brewery and public
support. The interior structure of the station remains, with an
extremely high ceiling allowing enough room for a comfortable
mezzanine level. An enormous double-faced clock stands near the
door. The decor is of brick, green paint and bare wood and there is
live rock and blues music Sunday and Monday night. The large food
counter offers an appetising selection of varied salads, cold cuts, pies,
samosas and onion bhajis (£1); two daily hot dishes (mushroom and

ham quiche with three salads £3.25, chicken with rice, diced peppers and lemon sauce, beef & ale £3.50) and a Sunday roast. **Beers** *Rail Ale, Phoenix, Dogbolter. No credit cards.*

WC1   Princess Louise

Tel 071-405 8816	**A**
208 High Holborn WC1V 7BW	**Map 18 C3**

Wonderfully lively pub which rarely empties. The decor still retains its original late-Victorian features with gold-embossed mirrors, enamelled tiles, wallpapered ceiling and painted cornices; even the gents toilets are a listed building. The place is popular for its real ales like the Princess Louise, exclusively brewed for them in Yorkshire. An impressive U-shaped bar threads through the room. Service is managed efficiently by staff in red bow ties. The restaurant upstairs is quieter; unfortunately we cannot recommend the Thai cooking. *Free house.* **Beer** *Sheffield Best Bitter, Thorne Best (Princess Louise), Vaux Samson, Wards York.*

WC2   Salisbury

Tel 071-836 5863	**A**
90 St Martins Lane WC2N 4AP	**Map 20 D3**

The oldest theatre pub in London. Beautiful cut glass, carved mahogany fittings, brass lamps, velvet curtains, and a theatrical atmosphere. Welcoming and cheery. **Beer** *Ind Coope, Websters. Family room.*

SW18   The Ship

Tel 081-870 9667	**FOOD**
41 Jews Row Wandsworth SW18	**Map 19 B5**

Directions to find the Ship don't sound promising: drive past Wandsworth bus garage and you'll see the pub beside a ready-mix concrete plant. Once there, though, things immediately begin to look up. A delightful terrace, complete with rose-covered rustic trellis, stretches all the way to the riverside. The pub gets very busy in fine weather, when barbecues (lunch and evening) offer steaks, kebabs, burgers and fish alongside the likes of half lobsters, pastry-wrapped salmon stuffed with herby cream cheese (£6.50), and well-kept cheeses from a cold cabinet. In less clement weather, the cold dishes are displayed on an old butcher's block in the centre of the conservatory bar, where hot dishes can also be chosen from a blackboard menu (costa kebab with sour cream dip and deep-fried new potatoes – £4.50, creamy curried vegetable risotto – £4). The setting is informal and the food very good. Individual dishes change often, according to what's seasonal: a half lobster grilled with lemon butter and served with composite salads is a summer treat. Salads are fresh and chunky, the cheeses usually look ripe and appealing, and there's good French bread served with the cheese platter (£4.50). The conservatory bar makes a pleasant venue, with its motley collection of old wooden tables, benches, chairs and pews; there's also a public bar, very much a locals' haunt, where simple filled rolls are also on offer. The Ship is a Young's pub, under a joint tenancy with the nearby *Alma* (see entry), and now also *The Coopers Arms* in Chelsea (qv) – if this kind of quality can keep being duplicated in other parts of London, this is empire-building of the very best kind. The beer is good and there's a wine list of two dozen decent labels, with a choice of around eight by the glass, in addition. Note that when weather permits, the barbecue (king prawns £6.50, pork or beef hamburger £5.50, fillet steak stuffed with Stilton £6.50) is very much the focal point of the pub, more or less replacing the indoor hot menu, apart from dishes that lend themselves to barbecuing. **Bar Food** *12-10 (lunch and evening Sunday). Vegetarian meals.* **Beer** *Youngs. Riverside garden, outdoor eating, summer barbecue. Access, Amex, Visa.*

N1   Slug & Lettuce

| Tel 071-226 3864 | **FOOD** |

Islington Green N1 — Map 18 D3

An airy and bright pub at the corner of Islington Green. All the Slug & Lettuces have different lay-outs but similar decor and green-painted front. They all offer the same versatile menu where hamburger is served with salad and no chips, deep-fried Brie with cranberry sauce and Cumberland sausage presented in a skillet with a creamy grain-mustard sauce and a warm crunchy baguette. Unfortunately, not all Slug & Lettuce pubs are as reliable as this one. Tea, coffee and biscuits are available between 3 and 6. **Bar Food** *12-3, 6-9 (Mon-Fri), 12-4 (Sat), 12-2.30, 7-9 (Sun).* **Beer** *Courage Directors, Ruddles Best, Websters Yorkshire Bitter.*

NW3   Spaniards

| Tel 081-455 3276 | **A** |

Spaniards Road Hampstead NW3 — Map 18 B2

Atmospheric whitewashed pub, once the home of the Spanish ambassador to James I. Dick Turpin, the Gordon rioters, Charles Dickens and John Keats were later visitors; the garden and aviary are said to have prompted *Ode to a Nightingale*. Lovely old settles, open fires and intimate corners in the downstairs bar (very busy); quieter upstairs in the evenings. **Beer** *Draught Bass, Fullers London Pride, Highgate Mild. Family room, garden.*

SW3   Sporting Page

| Tel 071-352 6465 | **FOOD** |

6 Camera Place Chelsea SW10 OBH — Map 21 B6

The former Red Lion was remodelled and renamed a couple of years ago, and now has the atmosphere of a wine bar, with a predominantly young clientele. There are dark blue walls above pale wood dado panelling, with decorative tiled panels depicting famous sporting events, the Boat Race among them, and sporting figures like W G Grace, while the seating is largely made up of upholstered benches around solid lightwood tables. The blackboard menu makes a nod towards traditional bar room stodge, listing dishes like bangers, mash and beans (£4.50), contrasted wittily with more upwardly mobile delicacies like scrambled eggs with smoked salmon (nice soft egg over a generous helping of fish, and a salad garnish – £5); chicken liver paté (£3.50), salmon fishcakes with a hollandaise sauce (£5.50), a vegetable and nut stir-fry (£4), or tomato and bacon soup (£2.50). **Bar Food** *12-2.30, 7-10. Vegetarian dishes.* **Beer** *Ruddles, Websters, Whitbread Boddingtons Bitter. Children allowed in bar to eat (usually). Patio, outdoor eating. No credit cards.*

EC1   **Thomas Wethered**

Tel 071-278 9983	**FOOD**
33 Rosoman Street Farringdon EC1 0OH	Map 18 D3

A Whitbread pub, renovated with a country theme four years ago, and the first pub in London to serve Wethered Bitter. The U shape is laid out into different bars and lounges and comfortable Directors Lounge at the back is used as a family room. The real ale bar offers live jazz on Tuesday evenings and piano music on Sunday mornings. They serve delicious salt beef sandwiches (£2.50) – except on Saturdays – with mustard and gherkins, and the salad counter is varied; hot dishes (steak & kidney pie, beef curry £3.95) are less successful. Closed Sun evenings. *Bar Food 12-3(12-4 Sun), 5.30-9 Mon-Fri. Vegetarian dishes. Children's portions.* **Beer** *London Pride, Pedigree, Wethered. Family room. Access, Amex, Diners, Visa.*

SW6   **White Horse**   ★

Tel 071-736 2115	**FOOD**
1-3 Parsons Green SW6	Map 19 A6

A substantial part-red sandstone Victorian pub standing at the northern end of Parsons Green with a large triangular low redbrick walled patio at the front which in fine weather makes the most of the midday and afternoon sunshine. The interior can only be described as hugely spacious – emphasising the decidedly pubby character of the place. On the periphery of the U-shaped room, the bar occupying the centre of the U, is a selection of leather chesterfields and a few round tables with bentwood chairs. The food counter along one side of the bar has a series of booths each seating about six comfortably. Whether you're eating or just drinking, seating can at peak times be at a premium. This can rather detract from full and proper enjoyment of what is quite remarkable food produced freshly in a tiny, spotless kitchen with stainless steel fittings. The food selection changes twice daily with lunchtimes presently being the busier period though with last year's full evening opening of the food counter, trade is also picking up then. Oddly, the choice of food is greater in the evening. A blackboard lists the foods on offer and includes snacky patés, terrines and wonderfully crisp fresh salads – grated carrot with poppy seeds, baby leaf spinach with toasted sesame seeds. The dressings too are wonderful – particularly a mustardy vinaigrette with balsamic vinegar. Hot dishes, about three a lunchtime, a few more for the evening session make excellent use of the pub's other fine asset – its splendid selection of well-maintained beers. Dishes like beef marinated in Mackeson and casseroled with dumplings (£5.50); pan-fried lamb cutlets marinated in Highgate mild and Bass sausages with farmhouse bread and home-made chutney (£5.50) are typical. Even the traditional bar foods (when offered) such as steak and kidney pie (£4.75), are pepped up with pickled walnuts – a sure sign of a creative and enthusiastic hand in the kitchen. Here you'll find an exciting, truly eclectic menu of influences from around the world, so salmon fish cakes (£5.25) will be offered alongside the likes of chicken jambalaya (£4.75), tagliatelle with squid, tomato, garlic and wine (£4); goat's cheese parcels with yoghurt, honey and mint sauce (£3.95) and a dish of tender, lean cubes of pork with diced red and green peppers in an authentic sweet and sour sauce (£4.75) accompanied by not quite sticky enough rice (though brown or white is available). One or two puddings tend to be around when Sally

Cruickshank is there to prepare them and are very much of the hot, sticky nursery variety (all £1.70). The White Horse under Sally's direction is an establishment other publicans, particularly in London, would do well to take account of and emulate. *Bar Food 12-2.45 (1-2.30 winter Sun), 6-10; bar snacks both sessions. Vegetarian meals. Beer Adnams, Draught Bass, Highgate Mild. Children allowed in bar to eat. Outdoor play area, patio/terrace, outdoor eating. No credit cards.*

W8   Windsor Castle

Tel 071-727 8491	**A**
114 Campden Hill Road Kensington W8 7AR	Map 21 A4

A charming Georgian pub built in 1826 by two brewer brothers from Chiswick. The original panelling and built-in benches still remain and the three small bars have separate entrances. Originally, one could see Windsor Castle 20 miles away, the entrance on Campden Hill Road being at the same height as the top of St Paul's Cathedral. Recently under a new licensee, a new chef has changed the menu and offers traditional English cooking throughout the day; initial offerings have, however, been disappointing. A shaded beer garden at the rear is the main attraction in summer (and gets packed to the gills), while a cosy country inn atmosphere prevails inside in winter. Not suitable for children. *Beer Bass, Charrington IPA, Young's & guest beers. Garden.*

EC4   Witness Box

Tel 071-353 6427	**FOOD**
36 Tudor Street Temple EC4 YOBH	Map 19 D4

Between the Embankment and Fleet Street, tucked away in the long basement of a modern office building. The decor is a mixture of traditional wood features, modern brick walls and painted murals of the Thames bank. Framed newspaper clippings of famous criminal events hang on the walls; there is even a special award for the best crime story of the year. Plenty of seating accommodates the busy crowd of regulars. The home-made cooking is only available at lunchtime and vanishes quite fast. The blackboard menu offers sandwiches (chicken tikka £2.25, beef, turkey or ham £1.80), salads (£3.70) and a few daily specials, possibly lamb curry (£3.75), a cheese, bacon, onion and potato pie (£2.55) or savoury meatballs (£2.55). Good selection of desserts, but not home-made: lemon meringue pie, cherry pie, lime sorbet, chocolate fudge cake. A more extensive blackboard menu (calf's liver, goujons of plaice, grilled trout, fillet steak) is available (lunchtime only) in the wine bar/restaurant at street level. *Bar Food & Restaurant Meals 12-2.30 (no bar food Sat & Sun eves). Vegetarian dishes. Beer Courage Best, Websters. Access, Amex, Diners, Visa.*

Great British Cheeses

Delicious, versatile and good value.

England

Abbots Leigh   George Inn

`Tel 0275 372467`

Pill Road Abbots Leigh Bristol Avon BS8 3RP

FOOD
Map 13 F1

There's a quaintly old-fashioned air to this flower-adorned old pub by
the busy A369, a two and a half mile climb from junction 19 of the
M5. Hung with horse brasses and antique saddlery, it's a good deal
cleaner than its walls of nicotine might initially suggest. "Good food
takes time" proclaims Mrs Meredith's blackboard menu, but diners
don't seem to mind waiting over a drink in the colourful rear garden.
Eagerly anticipated are her home-made soups (£2.55) and paté
(£2.95), the famed "Dragon Pie" (£6.95 – also known as "Landlady's"
and made from organic beef), Catalan garlic chicken (£7.35) and
boozy puddings – bread-and-butter with Calvados, and plum and port
crumble (£2.65). Fresh fish daily, in the form of green-lip mussels
(£4.25), Floyd's fish pie (£6.95), and salmon and broccoli gratin
(£7.55) occupy a separate menu board. Beers are from Courage, with
a weekly guest ale. House wines are equally ordinary: by the bottle
there's a marginally better selection. *Bar Food & Restaurant Meals
12-2.15, 6.30-9 (except Sun eve). Vegetarian dishes. Beer Courage, guest
beer changes every two weeks. Garden, outdoor eating. No credit cards.*

Acomb   Miners Arms

`Tel 0434 603909`

Main Street Acomb Northumberland NE46 4PW

Map 5 D2

So enthusiastic are they about their reputation for good real ales at the
Miners Arms that the bar is to be altered to accommodate a staggering
14 beers and ciders. This is a charming, traditional village pub, built in
1745, with exposed stone walls, original beams and open fire. *Beer
Federation Best, Laurells Varsity, Big Lamp Prince Bishop Ale. Garden.
Children's play area.*

Acresford   Cricketts Inn

`Tel 0524 760359`

Acresford Derbyshire

Map 6 C3

Old coaching inn on the Leicestershire border. *Beer Bass.*

Albury Heath   King William IV

`Tel 048 641 2685`

Little London Albury Heath Surrey GU5 9DB

Map 17 E4

A surprisingly old-fashioned pub; cottagey little rooms, rustic
furnishings, and attractive odd bits of bric-a-brac. *Free House. Beer
Benskins, Courage Best, Greene King Abbot, Sam Smiths OB. Garden.*

Alciston   Rose Cottage

`Tel 0323 870377`

Alciston nr Polegate East Sussex BN22 6UW

Map 11 B6

Cosy, rambling cottage pub with old pews, interesting bric-a-brac,
cased stuffed birds and real fires. *Free House. Beer Harveys, Ruddles
Best.*

Aldbourne   Crown

Tel 0672 40214	**B&B**
Aldbourne nr Marlborough Wiltshire SN8 2DU	**Map 16 A3**

Overlooking the duck pond, the Crown is a spick-and-span 18th-century inn with very friendly staff. Beams and brasses give a traditional feel to the bar, and the courtyard is a pleasant spot for summer sipping. All bedrooms are en suite, with TVs. The best room boasts a stylish four-poster. New landlords. *Courtyard, children's play area.* **Beer** *Usher Best Bitter, Ruddles County, Websters, Wadworth 6X, Yorkshire Bitter.* **Accommodation** *3 bedrooms, all en suite, £40. Children welcome overnight, additional beds available. Check-in all day. Access, Visa.*

Aldbury   Valiant Trooper

Tel 044 285 203	
Trooper Road Aldbury Hertfordshire HP23 5RW	**Map 17 E2**

Handy pub in a popular walking area. *Free House.* **Beer** *Eldridge Pope Hardy, Fullers ESB & London Pride, Marston Pedigree, Greene King Abbot. Garden.*

Alderminster   Bell

Tel 0789 450414	**FOOD**
Alderminster nr Stratford-upon-Avon Warwickshire CV37 8NX	**Map 14 C1**

Food is very much the thing at the Bell, an old coaching inn standing alongside the A34 a few miles south of Stratford. It advertises itself as a Bistro and Bar, and the description is an apt one: the interior of this much-refurbished pub is now mainly given over to dining. The small bar area, with its exposed brickwork, wood and flagstone floors, sets the tone, and the main room features splendid polished flagstones, original wall and ceiling timbers, and farmhouse-style tables, each bearing a small vase of flowers and surrounded by rustic chairs, while a brick inglenook fireplace complete with stove features a number of polished brasses. Half the dining area has been designated non-smoking. The bar food is certainly above average, and so are the prices, though not excessively so. Only fresh produce, as much of it locally grown as possible, is used on a regularly changing blackboard menu, on which shrimps Phoebe (£4.75), carrot and parsnip soup (£2.25) and artichoke vinaigrette (£3.75) are typical starters, followed perhaps by crispy top lamb in cider (£7.25), wild Scotch salmon with hollandaise (£7.95) or faggots in rich gravy (£5.75). Vegetables are good and fresh, and there's always a decent vegetarian alternative, like a hazelnut roast with spicy tomato sauce (£5.95). Puddings (£2.95), which are listed on a separate blackboard brought to your table, are also an appealing bunch, featuring perhaps banoffi pie or baked chocolate cheesecake, both guaranteed to be oozing with calories. *Bar Food 12-2 (12-1.45 Sun), 7-9.45 (7-9 Sun). Vegetarian meals. Children's portions.* **Beer** *Flowers OB, Marston Pedigree. Garden, outdoor eating. Family room. Access, Visa.*

Aldworth   Four Oaks

Tel 0635 578367	**FOOD**
Haw Lane Aldworth Berkshire RG8 9DL	**Map 16 C3**

Low, thatched cream-painted building resembling three cottages knocked into one. The flower-covered front of the pub detracts from the fact that it faces a three road junction on the B4009 between

Streatley and Newbury. There's a long, narrow, low-ceilinged bar decorated with antique wooden carpentry planes and horse brasses. Seating for 50-60 and eating in all areas. Large portions are served on hot plates, ensuring that you will not leave here hungry: vegetable soup (£1.10), sprats (£3.50), half a roast chicken (£8.95), T-bone steak (£9.95), apple crumble (£1.50), trifle (£1.50). Two large car parks. *Bar Food 11-3, (12-2.30 Sun), 5.30-11 (7-10.30 Sun). Children's menu (£1.50 per dish). Free House. Beer Morland Original, London Pride. Children's play area. No credit cards.*

Alford   White Horse Hotel

Tel 0507 462218

29 West Street Alford Lincolnshire LN13 9DG   Map 7 F2

Successfully restored and refurbished 16th-century town pub. *Beer Bass, Bateman XB.*

Alfriston   George Inn

Tel 0323 870319   **B&B**

High Street Alfriston East Sussex BN26 5SY   Map 11 B6

Tourists love this friendly, well-run little place, so overnight guests are advised to book well ahead. Outwardly appealing, flint and timber-built, it's also charming inside, with heavy dark timbers aplenty and an enormous inglenook fireplace. The best bedroom has a splendid four-poster bed and some carefully preserved original plaster; some of the others are more ordinary. *Free House. Beer Ruddles County, King & Barnes Festive. Accommodation 8 bedrooms, 6 en suite, £60 plus 10% service. Children welcome overnight, additional beds available. Check-in after midday. Access, Amex, Diners, Visa.*

Allenheads   Allenheads Inn

Tel 0434 685200

Allenheads nr Hexham Northumberland NE47 9HJ   Map 5 D3

Pretty, remote village high in the North Pennines, a good walking area. The former home of Sir Thomas Wentworth, the inn now offers an Antiques Bar and Royal Room. *Beer Tetley Bitter.*

Alrewas   George & Dragon

Tel 0283 791476

Main Street Alrewas Staffordshire DE13 7AE   Map 6 C3

A very popular old inn with three characterful bars opening off a central servery. *Beer Marston Pedigree. Outdoor play area, garden. Family room.*

Alstonefield   Watts-Russell Arms

Tel 033 527 271

Alstonefield nr Hopedale Staffordshire DE6 2GD   Map 6 C3

Stone-built estate pub in the Peak District National Park, in good walking country. *Free House. Beer Mansfield, Old Bailey, Riding Mild, Marston Pedigree. Garden. Children's play area.*

Altrincham   The Old Packet House

FOOD
B&B

Tel 061 9291331

Navigation Road Broadheath Altrincham Greater Manchester

Map 6 B2

Hard by a canal bridge on the main A56, the distinctive Packet House stands dwarfed by newer development, its former purpose in life scarcely recalled by the old wharf behind it. Black and white outside, with its heavy leaded-light windows protected by ornamental wrought-iron, it's unexpectedly spacious within and lent a cottagey feel by open brick fireplaces, patterned curtains and button-back banquettes in the lounge and raised dining sections. The single chalk-board menu serves all comers: for lunchtime snacks choose Scotch broth, Welsh rarebit with bacon, tuna and prawn pancakes with cheesy sauce, or a daily roast dish with fresh vegetables. Tuesday to Saturday, full evening meals extend the range with typically substantial portions for hearty eaters. Mushrooms in beer batter and smoked salmon paté; rabbit casserole with mustard and herbs and rack of lamb with mint gravy; treacle tart and chocolate fudge cake exemplify the range. Service is informal, verging on the jovial, diners replenishing their real ales and (draught) house wines direct from the bar. Of five recently completed bedrooms, one double has bath/WC en suite, the 3 singles and remaining twin sharing two spacious bathrooms. The TVs, trouser presses, fitted mahogany furniture and bright brass taps are smart and modern, though the counter-sink wash hand-basins are mostly plastic. *Bar Food & Restaurant Meals 12-2, 6.30-9.30 (closed Sun/Mon eves). Vegetarian dishes. Children's portions. Free House. Beer Boddington Best Bitter, Websters Yorkshire Bitter, Wilsons. Garden, Outdoor eating. Accommodation 5 bedrooms, 1 en suite, 4 sharing 2 bathrooms, £60 (single £30). No credit cards.*

Alveston   Ferry Inn

FOOD

Tel 0789 269883

Alveston Warwickshire CV37 7QX

Map 14 C1

Off the B4089, overlooking a small green at the centre of a quiet village only three miles from Stratford-upon-Avon, the well-run Ferry Inn is cream-painted and hung with large, hugely colourful baskets; the peaceful countrified atmosphere of both village and pub – a welcome contrast to the commercially-orientated "plastic" pubs that predominate in Shakespeare's town. David and Sarah Russon's highly accomplished bar meals are attracting a growing number of customers and on Friday and Saturday evenings, the pub is frequently packed to the gunnels. A large blackboard at the end of the lounge bar lists a menu strong on the fresh and local. While not exhaustive, the choice is interesting and well handled, from the simplest York ham and Cheddar ploughman's to starters like avocado with smoked salmon and prawns (£3.75), home-made chicken liver paté (£3.25) or whitebait (£2.95). More substantial meals might include a large Yorkshire pudding with a filling of steak and kidney (£5.50), chicken tikka masala (£5.95) or seafood au gratin (£5.95). The Ferry's interior is neat and uncluttered, one large room broken up by large columns, with false-beamed ceilings and plain painted walls hung with fishy pictures. Upholstered benches and round-back chairs – some arranged in one of the bay windows – redbrick fireplaces and dried flower displays complete the picture. Besides a selection of well-kept beers, some nine quality wines are served by the glass. A patio, complete with white garden furniture, comes into its own in fine weather. *Bar*

Food 11.45-2 (12-2 Sun), 6.30-9 (except Sun). *Vegetarian dishes. Children allowed in bar to eat (minimum age 5).* **Beer** *Theakston OP and Best Bitter, Wadworth 6X. Flowers Original, Bass. Patio/terrace, outdoor eating. Access, Diners, Visa.*

Amberley   Black Horse

Tel 0453 872556

Amberley Gloucestershire GL5 5AD

Map 14 B2

200-year-old country pub with lovely views over a neighbouring hillside, a pleasantly modernised, carpeted bar. Walk any excesses off with a stroll on nearby Minchinhampton Common. *Free House.* **Beer** *Mitchells, Tetley, Fullers London Pride, Greene King Abbot, Burton Ale. Garden. Children's play area. Family room.*

Ambleside   Gables Inn

Tel 05394 36696

FOOD

Tarn Hows Hotel Hawkshead Ambleside Cumbria LA22 0PR

Map 4 C3

A rustic, stone-flagged bar attached to the rear of the newly opened Tarn Hows hotel (use the upper car park). Sensibly priced lunches are listed on blackboards: soups (£2.20), vegetable samosas (£4.50), lamb curry (£5.75), lemon sole with prawns (£7.50), three British cheeses with biscuits (£2.80). Picnic tables in front, fabulous views. **Bar Food** *12-2. Vegetarian dishes.* **Beer** *Jennings Bitter, Cumberland Ale. Garden, outdoor eating. Amex, Diners.*

Amersham   King's Arms

Tel 0494 726333

30 High Street Old Amersham Buckinghamshire HP7 0DJ

Map 17 E2

Dating back to the 15th century, the King's Arms has plenty of character, with beams, settles and an inglenook fireplace. Further seating in a courtyard and lawn to the rear. **Beer** *Greene King, Benskins, Ind Coope. Garden, children's play area.*

Ampney Crucis   Crown of Crucis

Tel 0285 85806

Ampney Crucis Gloucestershire GL7 5RS

Map 16 A2

The original roadside inn, charmingly built of local stone, has a modern, gabled bedroom extension, grouped around an open courtyard. *Free House.* **Beer** *Tetley Bitter, Marston Pedigree, Archers Village. Garden, children's play area.*

Ansty   Fox Inn

Tel 0258 880328   Fax 0258 881097

FOOD

B&B

Ansty Dorset DT2 7PN

Map 14 B4

Deep in Thomas Hardy territory, lost in narrow country lanes, this well-known pub has managed to keep something of a farming pub atmosphere, despite the dizzying scale of the food operation in its five bars. There are original nooks and crannies, simple furnishings, lots of beams, and flattering deep reds and blues, as well as vast plate collections in the Platter Bar, and Toby jugs (almost 800 of them) in the Toby Bar. A modern extension housing the family room is less inspiring. The Platter Bar is home to the carvery, with 14 cold meats and perhaps as many as 30 salads; there are also jacket potatoes in the Spud Bar (£1.35 to £3.85), and a barbecue char-grill indoors and out.

Other bar food could include turkey curry Madras (£3.95) or grilled swordfish steak (£5.75). The restaurant offers a variety of dishes including barbecued sirloin steak (£7.95), fillet steak filled with Stilton in a red wine sauce (£9.95) and chicken Wessex County (£7.45). Bedrooms are clean and comfortable; those in the extension are lighter and airier. *Bar Food & Restaurant Meals 12-2, 7-9.30 (10.30 Sat). Vegetarian dishes. Children's menu/portions. Free House. Beer Ansty Ale, Hall & Woodhouse Badger Best Bitter, Tetley Bitter, Wadworth 6X, guest beer. Cider Addlestones. Garden, outdoor eating, summer barbecue, children's play area. Family room. Accommodation 14 bedrooms, all en suite, £48 (single £35). Children welcome overnight, additional beds, cots supplied. Check-in all day. Access, Amex, Visa.*

Appleby · Royal Oak

FOOD
B&B

Tel 076 83 51463   Fax 076 83 52300
Bongate Appleby Cumbria CA16 6UN

Map 5 D3

Ancient black and white coaching inn, dating back in parts to the year 1100. Outside, leaded windows, flowers in tubs and hanging baskets; inside, a comfortable and popular meeting and eating place. A cosy tap room features oak panelling and an open fire; there's a relaxing, beamed lounge, and a little snug encloses the bar counter. The separate dining room, candlelit at night, has the same menu as the bar; in both, the evening menu is slightly different from the lunchtime list, and a nice wine list offers lots of half bottles. Some typical dishes may include Tudor pork (£4.95), pie of the day (£4.95) or leek and cheese sausages (£3.75). The homely little beamed and unevenly floored bedrooms have been refurbished. A pleasant residents' lounge looks out towards Appleby Castle. *Bar Food & Restaurant Meals 12-2, 6.30-9. Vegetarian dishes. Children's menu/portions. Free House. Beer Caledonian 80/-, Draught Bass, Yates Bitter, Youngers Scotch. Cider Westons. Children allowed in bar to eat. Accommodation 9 bedrooms, 7 en suite, £55 (£24 single). Children welcome overnight, cots supplied. Check-in all day. Access, Amex, Diners, Visa.*

Appletreewick · Craven Arms

A o

Tel 0756 720270
Appletreewick nr Burnsall North Yorkshire BD23 6DA

Map 6 C1

A delightful 300-year-old stone-built National Park pub, with good views over Wharfedale from the garden. Log fires and a Yorkshire range, oak beams and bridle bits. *Free House. Beer Tetley, Theakston Best and XB, Old Peculier. Garden. Family room. No credit cards.*

Ardleigh · Wooden Fender

Tel 0206 230466
Harwich Road Ardleigh Essex CO7 7PA

Map 10 C3

Surprisingly ancient inn, now a busy, modernised but pleasant roadside inn, named after a fence built to stop cattle falling into a nearby pond. *Beer Adnams Courage, Greene King Abbot.*

Armathwaite · Duke's Head Hotel

B&B

Tel 069 92 226
Font Street Armathwaite nr Carlisle Cumbria CA4 9PB

Map 4 C3

A modest, but welcoming pebbledash pub overlooking the river Eden. Overnight accommodation is offered by six pleasant bedrooms, three with en-suite facilities. The main bar is a warm and cosy spot with its

open fire and wheelback chairs; the public bar offers darts and pool.
Beer Whitbread Castle Eden, Trophy. Garden. **Accommodation**
*6 bedrooms, 3 en suite, £40 (single £22.50). Children welcome overnight,
additional beds (£10). Check-in all day. No credit cards.*

Arnold   Burnt Stump

`Tel 0602 631508`

Burnt Stump Hill Arnold Nottinghamshire NG5 8PA   Map 7 D3

Surrounded by some thirty acres of parkland, a popular pub. The
garden is lovely in summer; no children indoors. *Beer Mansfield
Riding Bitter. Garden.*

Ashby St Ledgers   Olde Coach House Inn   ★

`Tel 0788 890349`

Ashby St Ledgers 3 miles from J18 M1 Northants CV23 8UN

FOOD
B&B
Map 15 D1

The traditional role of the local pub at the hub of community life is
much the case here. A tiny, protected, village, Ashby St Ledgers is full
of thatched houses and cottages clustered around the manor and 12th-
century church, and has a population of just one hundred. 98% of them
we're told, drink here; the remaining two are doubtless just under age.
An imposing rather than handsome ivy-clad exterior is today mostly
reminiscent of the estate farmhouse it once was. Peering through the
bow windows, you'll see a rather austere snug bar to one side and a
sparsely furnished pool room to the other. But this frontage is very
deceptive. Behind these is a cavernous structure incorporating small
alcoves, huge log fires and oak beams, which progress past the main
interior bar and food buffet to an elevated, beamed restaurant beyond
and, to the rear, a flat-roofed function and meeting room. Part of the
adjoining old stables once housed the village post office, and today the
stable yard makes a safe, enclosed area for bored youngsters to explore
– as often as not with the McCabe children as resident playmates. The
food operation is both thematic and diverse. Cold roast meats, salads,
whole Stilton and Brie cheeses are displayed on the buffet, while daily
kitchen specials like lemon sole (£8.75) and sirloin of venison
(£7.50). Diverse fishes and cuts of meat are laid out by the nearby
patio barbecue, cooked to order and brought out to diners at tables in
the garden – quite the most popular of the Coach House's summer
attractions. When the cooking and eating are confined to indoors, the
kitchen steps in with a menu which runs, daily, through "all day
breakfast", bangers and mash, vegetarian "Chinese meatballs", steak,
fillets stuffed with stilton, or salmon poached with dill and white
wine. Puddings, too, are all home-made and include chocolate mousse,
bread-and-butter pudding, sherry trifle and lemon meringue pie. But
the Olde Coach House Inn is equally a classic ale drinkers' pub; the
four usual beers supplemented on any given day by three further guest
beers fromanywhere in Britain. Twice-yearly beer festivals add
considerably to this number, and few British real ales are left untried.
A sense of fun is imbued by the resident landlords, Brian and Philippa
McCabe, and their staff, who go out of their way to make visitors
welcome. *Bar Food & Restaurant Meals 12-2, 6-9.30 (not Sun eve).
Vegetarian dishes. Children's menu/portions. Free House.* **Beer** *Beacon,
Boddingtons, Everards Old Original, Flowers Original, IPA, Jennings
Cumberland, Morels Bitter, Thwaites. Garden, outdoor eating, summer
barbecue. Family room.* **Accommodation** *6 bedrooms, all en suite, from
£45 (single £38). Children welcome overnight; cots available. Check-in all
day. Access, Amex, Visa.*

Ashford-in-the-Water — Ashford House

Tel 0629 812725

Ashford-in-the-Water nr Bakewell Derbyshire DE4 1QB

Map 6 C2

Pleasant, well-kept roadside hotel with local stone exterior. Red patterned carpets, lots of brass nick-nacks, chintzy curtains and mint green plush-topped stools. **Beer** Draught Bass. Garden. Children's play area. Family room.

Ashton — Old Crown

Tel 0604 862268

1 Stoke Road Ashton Northamptonshire NN7 2JN

Map 7 E4

15th-century pub with lots of brass, weaponry and other bric-a-brac, an inglenook fireplace and an old piano for singalongs. Children in dining room only. **Beer** Charles Wells Eagle Bitter, Bombardier. Garden. Children's play area.

Ashwell — Bushel & Strike

Tel 046 274 2394

Mill Street Ashwell Hertfordshire SG7 5LY

FOOD

Map 17 F1

It's in summer that the Bushel and Strike's pretty garden and patio really come into their own: a peaceful retreat from the madness of the A1(M), just four miles away through pretty countryside. It's an unassuming white-painted building, standing opposite the village church, but behind this typical local pub facade lies a frequently hectic, thriving business well-versed in the rapid provision of bar meals. The interior, comprising three adjoining rooms, is uncluttered, kitted out in Laura Ashley style wallcoverings and rustic wooden furniture. Two of the rooms are always laid with place mats and cutlery at mealtimes and the third remains free as a bar for drinkers. A pine table in one corner holds a couple of cold joints, ham on the bone and beef (both £6.75) perhaps, alongside which are about ten large pots of different salads. The menu is displayed on a large wall-mounted board. The choice is varied, even cosmopolitan: oriental parcels of prawn and sweetcorn in filo pastry with tomato, chili sauce (£3.50), herring roes (£3.50) or mushroom and bacon salad (£2.75) to begin with perhaps, followed by rabbit casserole (£5.75), Indonesian beef (£5.95) or Jakarta fish – white fish in peanut sauce (£6.50). It's a long list, running to around 40 items. To follow, perhaps fruit crumble, bread and butter pudding (both £2) or chocolate banana cake (£2.50). The cheeseboard of several farmhouse cheeses makes up a delicious ploughman's (£3.50). Sunday lunchtime sees a self-service (£9.95) hot and cold buffet in the former restaurant dining area. **Bar Food** 12-2.30, 7-10. Vegetarian dishes. Children's portions. **Beer** Adnams, Charles Wells Bombardier and Eagle. Garden, outdoor eating. Access, Amex, Visa.

Ashwell — Three Tuns Hotel

Tel 046 274 2107

High Street Ashwell nr Baldock Hertforshire SG7 5NL

B&B

Map 17 F1

Dating back to 1806, this welcoming inn stands in the heart of a pretty village some four miles from the end of the A1(M) and near the Ashwell Springs. There are four neatly kept bedrooms attractively decorated and furnished in solid, traditional style. All offer TVs, tea-

makers and radio-alarms and there are two gleaming public
bathrooms. The new landlords have plans to give en-suite facilities to
all bedrooms. Enjoy a pint in the inviting bars or large garden. *Free
House.* **Beer** *IPA, Raynemans, Abbott.* **Accommodation** *4 bedrooms, not
en suite, £40 (single £25). Children welcome overnight, additional beds
and cots available. Check-in all day. Access, Visa.*

Askerswell   Spyway Inn

`Tel 0308 85250`

Askerswell Dorset DT2 9EP   Map 13 F2

Charming pub in popular tourist area; be early in summer. Various
cosy little rooms have old-fashioned furniture, some window seats, and
pretty oddments of countryware. The garden is delightful. *Free House.*
Beer *Ruddles County, Ushers Best, Websters Yorkshire. Garden.
Children's play area. Family room.*

Askham   Punch Bowl

`Tel 093 12 443`

Askham nr Penrith Cumbria CA10 2PF   Map 4 C3

Traditionally furnished village pub, prettily situated by the green, on
the edge of the Lowther estate. **Beer** *Whitbread, Boddington, Castle Eden
Ale. Garden. Children's play area. Family room.*

Askham   Queen's Head Inn

`Tel 093 12 225`   **B&B**

Askham nr Penrith Cumbria CA10 2PF   Map 4 C3

You can enjoy the landscaped grounds of this 17th-century coaching   ☺
inn, or just relax with a drink in the mellow lounge bar or
atmospheric beamed public bar with its brassware and oak furniture.
Books, pot-pourri and ornaments lend a homely air to the charming
bedrooms, which share two thickly carpeted bathrooms. Residents also
have the use of a comfortably furnished TV lounge. New landlords.
Family room. **Beer** *Wards, Vaux Samson.* **Accommodation** *5 bedrooms,
not en suite, £35 (single £17.50). Children welcome overnight, additional
beds and cots available. No dogs. Check-in all day. No credit cards.*

Askrigg   Kings Arms Hotel

`Tel 0969 50258`   **B&B**

Market Place Askrigg North Yorkshire DL8 3HQ   Map 5 D4

A listed former manor house and an inn since 1800, it was once used   ☺
as a base by Turner when painting the Dales, and more recently for
filming bits of *All Creatures Great and Small*. High-ceilinged parlour
bar, cosy low-beamed front bar, and juke box public bar. Country
house-style bedrooms with draped beds. *Free House.* **Beer** *Tetley,
McEwan 80/-, Burton Ale.* **Cider** *Scrumpy Jack. Patio. Family room.*
Accommodation *9 bedrooms, all en suite, £60 (single £40). Children
welcome overnight, cots supplied. Check-in all day. Access, Visa.*

Aston   The Flower Pot

`Tel 0491 574721`   **FOOD**
                                                    B&B

Ferry Lane Aston nr Henley-on-Thames Oxfordshire RG9 3DG   Map 16 B2

Situated off the A423 down a narrow lane in Aston. The 1890s
building is solid brick with plants attempting to climb the outside.
Two small rooms provide a bar with banquette seating and rowing

gear decorating the walls, and tables for 20 people. A large garden
seats for about 50. The pub is situated by a bridle path, and as it is half
a mile from the river towpath (where a sign advertises the pubs
presence), walkers make up a large part of its trade. The food is simple
but served in ample portions: home-made soup (£2), chicken pie
(£4.50), ploughman's (£4), date and apple crumble (£2). A
traditional 3-course roast Sunday lunch is served in winter (£8.50).
Bar Food 12-2, 6.30-9. *Vegetarian dishes. Children's portions. Free
House.* **Beer** *Brakspears Special and Best. Garden, outdoor eating.*
Accommodation *4 bedrooms, 2 en suite, £49 (single £39). Children
welcome overnight, additional beds. Check-in all day. Access, Visa.*

Aston Clinton   The Oak

Tel 0296 630466

FOOD

119 Green End Street Aston Clinton Buckinghamshire HP22 5EU

Map 17 E2

Recently re-opened, The Oak is self styled as an 'ale house' catering for
the middle age group – there is no draught lager, cigarette machines
(but they can be purchased from the bar), piped music or juke boxes.
The building is part-thatched, painted black and white and there has
been an ale house on this site since the 13th century. It has a stone
floor, dark wood furniture and a large inglenook fireplace. There's a
choice of 20 wines, plus special offers, and ale comes in 4 pint jugs at
£6. All the food is home made and is well presented. 'Old Favourites'
on the light meals menu include freshly made soup (£1.65),
'Oakmans' home-cooked ham (£3.60), or the farmer's platter (£5 –
ham, beef, cheddar, hot sausage, salad, bread and butter). Six pies are
available at any one time (£4.95), locally made sausages are a
speciality (£2.95-3.95) as is 'The Oak Sirloin' (£10.95) served with
asparagus, mushrooms and Stilton or a whole oak-smoked pink trout
(£4.85). A traditional roast is served on Sundays (£6.95). If time is
precious, you may telephone ahead to place your food order. **Bar
Food** 12-2.30, 5.30-10. *Vegetarian dishes. Children's portions.* **Beer**
Fullers London Pride, Chiswick, ESB. **Cider** *Scrumpy Jack. Garden,
outdoor eating. Access, Visa.*

Aswarby   Tally Ho

Tel 05295 205

B&B

Aswarby nr Sleaford Lincolnshire NG34 8SA

Map 7 E3

A mellow 18th-century country inn, its two rooms featuring exposed
stone and brickwork aplenty, country prints, log fire and
woodburning stove. Bedrooms in the adjoining stable block are
comfortable, soothingly decorated and provide plenty of hanging and
writing space. *Free House.* **Beer** *Batemans Bitter, Flowers, Greene King
IPA. Outdoor play area, garden.* **Accommodation** *6 bedrooms, all en suite,
£42 (single £28). Children welcome overnight, cot available. Check-in all
day. Access, Visa.*

Attleborough   Griffin

Tel 0953 452149

Church Street Attleborough Norfolk NR17 2AH

Map 10 C2

Charming 16th century coaching inn with a wealth of period details,
in town centre. Sensitively refurbished. Open fires, lots of bric-a-brac,
welcoming atmosphere. **Beer** *Greene King, Marston, Whitbread. Patio.*

Aust   Boar's Head

Tel 045 45 2278

Main Road Aust Avon BS12 3AX   Map 13 F1

Characterful village pub with lots of small rooms, exposed stone walls,
old winged settles, big country tables and rugs. 18 guest beers are
rotated. **Beer** *Courage Best, Directors, guest beers. Garden. Children's play
area. Family room.*

Axbridge   Lamb Inn

Tel 0934 732253

The Square Axbridge Somerset   Map 13 F1

Rambling, ancient town pub, romantically set opposite King John's
hunting lodge. Real fire, bric-a-brac, beams and settles, as well as more
modern intrusions. **Beer** *Butcombe Bitter, Wadworth 6X. Garden.*

Axbridge   Oak House

Tel 0934 732444   Fax 0934 733112   **B&B**

The Square Axbridge Somerset BS26 2AP   Map 13 F1

In the centre of a medieval town 1½ miles from Cheddar, the Oak
House has a long tradition of hospitality. Inside, there's a cosy,
welcoming feel, particularly in the bar-lounge with its stone walls,
beams and open fire, and in the bedrooms, some of which are in an
annexe 50 yards from the main building. **Accommodation** *12 bedrooms,
£51. Children welcome overnight, cots and extra beds available. Check-in
all day. Access, Amex, Diners, Visa.*

Axmouth   Ship

Tel 0297 21838

Axmouth Devon EX12 4AF   Map 13 E2

Comfortable village pub with a large collection of dolls, a real fire and
a large interesting garden with birds from Newbury Wildlife Hospital
recuperating. **Beer** *Cornish Original, Royal Wessex. Garden. Children's
play area. Family room.*

Ayot St Lawrence   Brocket Arms

Tel 0438 820250

Ayot St Lawrence nr Welwyn Hertfordshire AL6 9BT   Map 17 F1

Splendid medieval pub in an equally splendid village, in unlikely
proximity to the commuter belt, but even closer to Shaw's Corner,
where GBS lived and now National Trust-owned. The unspoilt
interior has oak beams, an inglenook fireplace and usually tasteful
piped music. Children in restaurant only. *Free House.* **Beer** *Adnams,
Greene King Abbot & IPA, Marston Pedigree, Wadworth 6X. Garden.
Children's play area.*

Baginton   Old Mill Inn

Tel 0203 303588   Fax 0203 307070   **B&B**

Mill Hill Baginton nr Coventry West Midlands CV8 2BS Map 6 C4

A super place to stay, handy for the A45 and A46 yet tucked away
peacefully in pine-studded grounds running down to the river Sowe.
Public areas still retain many features of the 19th-century working
mill, and outside a riverside patio is linked by a bridge to the garden.
A well-designed modern block houses the bedrooms, where you will

find pine furniture and Laura Ashley designs, remote-control TVs, tea-makers, direct-dial phones, trouser presses and en-suite bathrooms. New landlords. *Large garden, children's play area.* **Beer** *Websters, Ruddles Best County, John Smith, Directors, Courage Best.* **Accommodation** *20 bedrooms, all en suite, £74 (single £61). Children welcome overnight, additional beds and cots available, no charge for under 3s. No Dogs. Check-in all day. Access, Amex, Diners, Visa.*

Bainbridge   Rose & Crown

| Tel 0969 50225   Fax 0969 50735 | **B&B** |

Bainbridge nr Wensleydale North Yorkshire DL8 3EE   Map 5 D4

Overlooking the green in an attractive Wensleydale village, the inn has a history going back to the 15th century. The famous Forest Horn, once used to guide lost travellers and still blown on winter evenings, hangs in the panelled hall. Elsewhere, old-world character is most notable in the low-beamed bar. Floral fabrics give the bedrooms a cottagey look; three rooms have four-poster beds. All are equipped with TVs, clock radios, tea/coffee making facilities and hairdryers. Trouser presses and irons are also available. *Free House.* **Beer** *John Smith Magnet. Patio, children's play area.* **Accommodation** *13 bedrooms, all en suite, £68 (single £43). Children welcome overnight, cot available. Check-in all day. Access, Visa.*

Bamber Bridge   Olde Hob Inn

| Tel 0772 36863 |

8 Church Road Bamber Bridge Lancashire PR5 6EP   Map 6 B1

Family-run 17th-century thatched coaching inn near junction 29 of the M6, and as such a useful stop-off. **Beer** *Theakston Best, Old Peculier. Garden. Family room.*

Bamburgh   Lord Crewe Arms

| Tel 066 84 243 |

Front Street Bamburgh Northumberland NE69 7BL   Map 5 D1

Large old inn/hotel, with a choice of bars; the 'cocktail bar' is the pubbiest. **Beer** *Theakston Best.*

Bamburgh   Victoria Hotel

| Tel 066 84 431 |

Front Street Bamburgh Northumberland NE69 7BP   Map 5 D1

Pleasant old inn at the centre of a beautiful coastal village; a good port of call after a bracing beach walk or a closer look at the enormous clifftop castle. **Beer** *Longstone Bitter, Tetley, Mitchells Best. Family room.*

Bantham   Sloop Inn

| Tel 0548 560489 | **B&B** |

Bantham nr Kingsbridge Devon TQ7 3AJ   Map 13 D3

16th-century landlord John Widdon was a notorious smuggler, and the atmospheric flagstoned interior of the Sloop still has a strongly nautical atmosphere and lots of old seagoing memorabilia. Good-sized bedrooms have modern furnishings. There are also self-catering flats available. Just 300 yards from the sea. *Free House.* **Beer** *Bass, Ushers.* **Cider** *Churchwards. Family room.* **Accommodation** *5 bedrooms, all en suite, £49 (single £28), self-catering flat from £195 per week (accommodation closed Dec-Feb). Children welcome overnight, additional beds (charge), cots supplied (£2). Check-in all day. No credit cards.*

Barbon   Barbon Inn

Tel 05242 76233	**FOOD**
Barbon via Carnforth Cumbria LA6 2LJ	Map 4 C4

In a peaceful spot just off the A683 Sedburgh-Kirkby Lonsdale road
(signposted), this is a long and rangy, cream-painted coaching inn with
a Georgian feel. Enter through the creaking iron gate into a pretty
garden with outdoor furniture, and into the inn itself, which is
immediately striking for its genteel and civilised air. An extremely
pleasant bar with comfortable little rooms leading off is friendly and
relaxing, with a nice crowd of regulars. Bar meals are very popular.
But the dining room is the star here: it has real coaching inn
character, is spaciously laid out, with good glass and silver, fresh
flowers, and windows overlooking the garden. A small adjoining
drinking area serves as a diners' bar. The set five-course dinners
(£15.45) are a popular feature. Home-made celery and Stilton soup
and a slice of melon in elderflower champagne is beautifully presented.
Hot seafood Mediterranean-style, roast supreme of duck and fillet of
pork in pastry could feature as main courses. Puddings are a varied
bunch including crème caramel in brandy and blackcurrant
cheesecake. Sunday lunch is £9.50, including coffee. Bar food is good
and reliable, and features dishes like steak and kidney pie (£5.50),
lasagne (£4.75) and Cumberland sausage (£4.25). Service is hospitable
and hard-working. This is a handsome and atmospheric place to visit
for a meal, in a romantic rural area of great beauty. *Bar Food 12-2,
7-9.* **Restaurant Meals** *12.30-1.30, 7.30-9 (not Sun). Vegetarian dishes.
Children's portions. Free House.* **Beer** *Theakston Old Peculier. Children
allowed in bar to eat. Garden, outdoor eating. Access, Visa.*

Barford St Martin   Barford Inn

Tel 0722 742242	
Barford St Martin Wiltshire SP3 4AB	Map 14 C3

An old inn with beams, natural brick, a log fire and a music, machine
and pool table-free environment; all maintained with justifiable pride.
Beer Hall & Woodhouse Badger Best.

Barham   Dolls House

Tel 0227 831241	
Elham Valley Road Barham Kent CT4 6LN	Map 11 C5

A refurbished 16th-century building with a pretty old-fashioned
garden featuring doves and life-like dolls. Inglenook fireplace in
restaurant, plus piano: "musicians welcome". *Beer King & Barnes
Sussex Bitter, Shepherd Neame Master Brew, Wadworth 6X. Garden.
Children's play area.*

Barley   Fox & Hounds

Tel 0763 848459	**FOOD**
High Street Barley nr Royston Hertfordshire SG8 8HU	Map 15 F1

Pleasingly traditional white-painted 15th-century village local, with
rambling, low-ceilinged rooms, splendid open fires, plus a separate
dining area and conservatory. A beer drinker's favourite – The Fox &
Hounds have served 280 different real ales to date and four
handpumps are constantly in use. A small bar menu offers lunchtime
snack meals such as filled jacket potatoes (from £1.20) or large

granary baps (from £1.20), ploughman's (£2.75), breaded plaice (£3.35), omelette with chips and salad (£2.35). The longer main menu operates throughout the pub in the evenings (bar and restaurant): Chinese dim sum (£3.35), whitebait (£2.85), various steaks (from £6.75), home-made curries (from £3.45) and pies (from £4.45, try the seafood pie £4.95), scallops, prawns and mushrooms in white wine (£6.55). Vegetarians are well catered for with their own menu of at least seven choices. Children also have their own menu (£1.65 per dish). No home-made puddings but a large choice of ice creams and sorbets. Traditional pub games are very popular with indoor and outdoor skittles, bar-billiards, shove-ha'penny, darts and dominoes. *Bar Food and Restaurant Meals 12-2, 6.30-10. Vegetarian dishes. Children's menu (£1.65 per dish). Free House. Beer Theakston Best, XB and Old Peculier, Recession ale: McEwans 70/-. Cider Thatchers, Biddenden. Garden, outdoor eating, children's play area. No credit cards.*

Barnard's Gate   Boot Inn

FOOD

`Tel 0865 881231`

Map 16 B2

Barnard's Gate Witney Oxfordshire OX8 6AE

Formerly the Britannia just off the Oxford-Cheltenham A40, about 5 miles from Oxford, the Boot Inn was opened by George Dailey (who used to own the successful Harcourt Arms at Stanton Harcourt) in partnership with his brother-in-law Steve Chick in 1991 and has quickly established itself as one of the most popular pubs near Oxford. The secret of its success is happy, young staff offering good food at extremely competitive prices. The result is an extremely busy pub at almost all times, so you would be well advised to book a table, although the staff will do their utmost to fit you in providing you are prepared to wait. Owing to the large turnover of customers a well-built extension was added in 1992, doubling the number of tables on offer. This extension, complementing the bar with apricot walls covered with prints and stone-flagged floors, has enabled the Boot to offer a larger menu with special dishes of the day on a blackboard next to the large open log fire. A terrace complete with fountain has also been built, offering more tables outside; it's illuminated at night, creating the festive feeling of being abroad. Recommended from the menu are the grilled king prawns (£3.95) or the home-made soup (£2.50), followed by a variety of pasta dishes (around £5.75), or for the very hungry a roast half-shoulder of lamb with honey and rosemary (£8.95 including vegetables). Steaks are good, too, and there is a selection of puddings (treacle tart, toffee pudding or lemon tart). *Free House. Bar Food 12-2, 7-10. Vegetarian dishes. Beer Hook Norton, Boddingtons. Patio, outdoor eating. Access, Visa.*

Barnoldby-le-Beck   Ship Inn

`Tel 0472 822308`

Map 7 D2

Main Road Barnoldby-le-Beck Humberside DN37 0BG

18th-century village pub with a warming, real fire and a separate restaurant. *Beer Whitbread.*

Barnsley   Village Pub
Tel 0285 740421

Barnsley Gloucestershire GL7 5EF

Map 14 C2

On the Cirencester to Burford road. Commmunicating rooms are pleasantly modernised. Low-ceilinged still, with some settles and stripped stone walls, and tasteful agricultural memorabilia; log fires in winter. *Free House.* **Beer** *Flowers IPA, Wadworth 6X. Children's play area. Family room.*

Barnston   Fox & Hounds
Tel 051-648 1323

Barnston Road Barnston Greater Manchester L61 1BW

Map 6 A2

Three rooms, two bars, lots of bric-a-brac. **Beer** *Websters, Ruddles Best and County. Children's play area. Family room.*

Barnwell   Montagu Arms
Tel 0832 273725

Barnwell nr Oundle Northamptonshire PE8 5PH

Map 7 E4

Named after Henry VIII's Chief Justice to the Court of the King's Bench, who lived in Barnwell Castle; the inn also dates from about 1540. There's also a tea room open on Sundays in summer. *Free House.* **Beer** *Batemans XB, Hook Morton, Greene King Abbot. Garden. Children's play area. Family room.*

Barrington   Royal Oak
Tel 0223 870791

31 West Green Barrington Cambridgeshire CB2 5RZ

Map 15 F1

Timbered and thatched country favourite on the large village green, seemingly always busy. Inside, rambling traditionally furnished rooms. *Free House.* **Beer** *Adnams Bitter, Greene King IPA & Abbot, Flowers IPA. Garden. Children's play area. Family room.*

Bartlow   Three Hills
Tel 0223 891259

Bartlow nr Linton Cambridgeshire CB1 6PW

FOOD

Map 10 B3

The Dixons have created a welcoming atmosphere here, aided by fresh flowers, polished brasses and an inglenook fireplace. There's reliably good food on the twice-daily changing blackboard menu which serves both bar and restaurant – avocado filled with fresh crab(£3.20), whitebait (£2.70), rump steak Café de Paris (£8.55), medley of seafood (salmon, halibut and swordfish £8.95). Home-made puddings (all £1.95) include raspberry Romanoff, fruit crumble and upside-down pudding. A wide choice on the cheeseboard. *Bar Food 12-1.45, 7-9.30 (except Sun; 7-9 Mon). Vegetarian dishes. Children's portions* **Beer** *Greene King IPA. Garden, outdoor eating. Access, Visa.*

Bassenthwaite   Sun
Tel 059 681 439

Bassenthwaite Cumbria

Map 4 C3

Popular country inn at the top of a little village two miles from the lake. Two traditional bars with plenty of nooks and crannies, beyond the monumental bar counter. Nice views from the front terrace. **Beer** *Jennings Bitter, Tetley. Family room.*

Bassenthwaite Lake   Pheasant Inn

FOOD
B&B

Tel 07687 76234   Fax 07687 76002

Bassenthwaite Lake Cumbria CA13 9YE

Map 4 C3

Originally a farm, the Pheasant has been a hotel since 1826, and has a genuinely unspoilt atmosphere still wonderfully suggestive of the Victorian country inn. Its inimitable style occupies the place at which country house hotel and farmers' pub meet and converge. The bar has a smoky patina of age, in enfolding tones of terracotta, and simple country furniture; the lounge is more country house, with prettily patterned easy chairs gathered round a roaring log fire, and there are also two residents' lounges. Afternoon tea or bar snacks may be taken in the garden. The restaurant menu offers grilled salmon steak with dill and cucumber butter (£6.90) and breast of chicken with asparagus in cheese and tomato sauce (£5.60) in a non-smoking environment. Bedrooms are all prettily furnished and well-equipped, though true escapists may find some of them more modern in style than they might expect in so nostalgic a place. They will not be disappointed in the surrounding countryside, though. There is also a bungalow available to accommodate five people. No TVs. *Bar Food 11-2 (12-1.30 Sun). Restaurant Meals 12.30-1.15, 7-8.30. Vegetarian dishes. Children's portions. Free House. Beer Draught Bass, Theakston Best, Youngs Scotch. Garden, outdoor eating, children's play area. Accommodation 20 bedrooms, all en suite, £88 (single £49). Children welcome overnight, cots supplied (£12). Check-in all day. No dogs. No credit cards.*

Batcombe   Three Horseshoes

Tel 074 985 359

Batcombe nr Shepton Mallet Somerset BW4 6HE

Map 13 F1

Very old coaching inn not far from the A359, in a quiet pretty village. Much renovated: newest facilities include a reception area, new toilets and cellar; log fires and old beams remain, however. *Beer Whitbread, Marston Pedigree, Oakhill Bitter. Garden. Children's play area. Family room.*

Bathampton   George Inn

Tel 0225 425079

Mill Lane Bathampton Avon BA2 6TR

FOOD

Map 13 F1

Creeper-clad 15th-century pub by the Kennet and Avon canal. Several wood-beamed and recently redecorated cosy lounge areas to choose from. From the terrace in front one can watch the activities on the canal and consequently many barge visitors stop here for refreshment. The three chefs offer a daily-changing blackboard menu which serves the whole pub with dishes such as garlic mushrooms (£2), salmon and asparagus crepe (£2), stuffed peppers (£4.95) and mousseline of smoked haddock and coley in onion and dill sauce (£5.50) as well as a choice of home-made puddings (all £2): bakewell tart, treacle and walnut tart, and Somerset tart (apple, sponge and marmalade). *Bar Food 12-2, 6.30-9.45 (7-9.30 Sun). Vegetarian dishes. Beer Courage Best, Bass, Webster Yorkshire Bitter. Garden, outdoor eating, children's play area. Family Room. No credit cards.*

Bathford   Crown

Tel 0225 852297

2 Bathford Hill Bathford Avon BA1 7SL   Map 14 B2

Eminently civilised old pub with a pleasingly informal, relaxing feel.
Various rooms are decorated in various ways, from conservatory
simplicity to country house style. Polished wood floors with rugs,
nicely decorated walls, newspapers and magazines to read, cafetière
coffee and a nice wine list. **Beer** *Ushers Best, Ruddles Best, Bass. Garden.*
Children's play area. Family room.

Beaconsfield   Old Hare

Tel 0494 673380

41 Aylesbury End Beaconsfield Buckinghamshire HP9 1LU   Map 17 E3

Rambling, nicely chaotic multi-roomed dining pub, busy but well-
organised, and with a large back garden. **Beer** *Benskins, Tetley Bitter,*
Burton Ale.

Beauworth   Milbury's

Tel 0962 771248   **FOOD**

Beauworth nr Cheriton Alresford Hampshire SO24 0PB   Map 15 D3

The South Down Way passes by the front door of this old tile-hung   ☺
pub. It's set on a hill just to the south of the village, the site of some
bronze age burial mounds or barrows, the pub's name is actually a
corruption of Mill-Barrow, the name of the last remaining mound just
150 yards away. The main bar boasts old brickwork, a flagstone floor
and rough hewn three-legged tables, but the most fascinating feature is
an enormous treadmill, within which a poor donkey once walked to
raise water from a 300-foot well. For the price of a donation to the
Guide Dogs for the Blind, you are invited to drop an ice-cube down
the well and count the nearly eight seconds it takes to splash in the
water far below. The bar menu runs the gamut from home-made soup
and ploughman's served with great wedges of granary bread to beef
chasseur (£4.20) and open steak sandwiches with salad (£3.50). For
more formal eating, there's a pretty, pink, dado-panelled restaurant
where the 3-course menu is priced according to the main dish chosen
(from £13.80). One can order stuffed mushrooms with Stilton cheese
and garlic butter and duck breast with walnut and honey sauce with

cream. Home-made puddings include Bavarian cheesecake (£1.75) and apple and raspberry crumble (£1.30). Children are made positively welcome, with their own small section on the menu (from £2.50 per dish) and swings out in a large garden carved from one corner of a field. There is also a new skittle alley which must be booked. *Bar Food 12-2.30, 6.30-10. Restaurant Meals 12-2.30, 7.30-9.30. Vegetarian dishes. Children's menu. Free House. Beer Courage Directors and Best, John Smith, Gales HSB, King Alfred, Ruddles County. Garden, outdoor eating, children's play area. Family room. Access, Amex, Visa.*

Beckley   Abingdon Arms

Tel 086735 311	**FOOD**
High Street Beckley Oxfordshire OX3 9UU	Map 16 C2

Beautifully positioned village pub with inspiring views from the pretty garden. The interior is plainly furnished with cloth-covered wall seats in the lounge and a separate public bar. People come here for the excellent food, which mirrors the seasons, with lots of delicious picnicky things in summer, cold poached salmon and smoked chicken (£6.75) amongst them, and warming bakes (£6.75), curries with Basmati rice (£6.75) and other hot dishes in winter (game pie with port sauce – £6.95). Puddings include home-made ice cream (£2 – flavours change every two weeks) and apple and almond tart (£2). The food is very much Mary Greatbatch's side of things and there is a possibility of a change in ownership, so telephone prior to making a special journey. *Bar Food (except Sun) 12.15-1.45, 7.15-9.15. Vegetarian dishes. Beer Adnams Bitter, Wadworth 6X, John Bull. Garden, outdoor eating. Family room. No credit cards.*

Bedford   The Embankment Hotel

Tel 0234 261332 Fax 0234 325085	**B&B**
Bedford Bedfordshire MK40 3PD	Map 15 E1

A small town-centre hotel which overlooks the river Ouse and provides excellent accommodation. An informal sitting area at reception is attractive and comfortable, and the Raj bar is well designed and full of character with its artefacts and prints. Twenty spacious upstairs bedrooms feature radios, TVs, trouser presses and tea-makers. All rooms are en suite with shower facilities. *Beer Worthington Best Bitter, Toby Bitter. Garden. Family room. Accommodation 20 bedrooms, all en suite, £49.95 (single £29.95). Children welcome overnight, additional beds, cots available. Check-in all day. Access, Amex, Diners, Visa.*

Beenham Village   Six Bells

Tel 0734 713368	**FOOD**
	B&B
Beenham Village nr Reading Berkshire RG7 5NX	Map 16 C4

This pub is a mixture of old and new, dating back some 200 years, with additions approximately 100 years ago to the present day. The bar is old, dimly lit, with mahogany counter and characteristic of an old village pub. To the rear they have added an extension which has a large room suitable for parties and wedding receptions. All food is home-made: a large variety of omelettes (£2.80), spare ribs (£5.50), loin of pork (£5.50), and a roast meal is served on Sundays. Upstairs there are four letting rooms, with tea/coffee-making facilities, radios and televisions. The bathrooms are adequate, the beds comfortable and all the rooms have lovely views over the neighbouring farmlands. *Bar food & Restaurant Meals 12-2.30, 6-9.30. Vegetarian dishes. Children's portions. Free House. Beer Wethered, Flowers IPA, Craftsman. Garden, Outdoor eating, children's play area. Accommodation 4 bedrooms, all en suite, £49 (single £36). Children welcome overnight. Additional beds (£6). Check-in by arrangement. Access, Visa.*

Beer   Anchor Inn

| Tel 0297 20386 | **FOOD** |

Fore Street Beer Exeter Devon EX12 3ET   Map 13 E2

A sturdy pub in a fishing village, with a clifftop garden overlooking Beer beach and the sea. Fish dominates the menu: dishes not only include local haddock, cod and sole, but also brill, monkfish, home-smoked salmon (£7.95) and a pleasing variety of seafood in season, including lobsters. They also cater for meat-eaters and vegetarians. *Bar Food & Restaurant Meals 12-2, 7-9.30. Vegetarian dishes. Children's menu (from £1.10). Free House. Beer Dartmoor Best, Strong, Murphys Stout, Wadworth 6X. Cider Luscombes. Garden, outdoor eating. Access, Visa.*

Beeston   Beeston Castle Hotel

| Tel 0829 260234 |

Beeston Bunbury Heath Cheshire CW6 9NJ   Map 6 B2

Close to the Shropshire Union Canal, and next door to Beeston Smithfield market (market days Wednesday and Friday). *Beer Stone's Bitter, Bass, Robinson Old Tom. Children's play area. Family room.*

Beetham   Wheatsheaf Hotel

| Tel 05395 62123 | **B&B** |

Beetham nr Milnthorpe Cumbria LA7 7AL   Map 4 C4

At this fine old coaching inn just off the A6 black and white gables and leaded windows distinguish the facade; inside, the three beamed bars are full of character and there is a comfortable upstairs TV lounge and dining room for residents' use. Attractively appointed bedrooms with TVs and tea-makers all have private bathrooms. The inn faces the River Dela and there is an interesting walk to the Fairy Steps with views of Morecambe Bay. *Free House. Beer Thwaites Bitter, Boddingtons, Youngers. Accommodation 6 bedrooms, all en suite, £40 (single £30). Children welcome overnight, additional beds (£10), cots available. Check-in all day. Access, Visa.*

Belbroughton   Queen's Hotel

| Tel 0562 730276 |

Belbroughton nr Stourbridge Hereford & Worcester DY9 0DU   Map 6 B4

Popular pub in pretty village with a stream and old millstones by the car park. *Beer Marston Best & Pedigree. Family room.*

Belford   Blue Bell

| Tel 0668 213543   Fax 0668 213787 | **B&B** |

Market Place Belford Northumberland NE70 7NE   Map 5 D1

Handsome, creeper-clad old inn dominating a hamlet close by the A1. Stylishly refurbished lounge with matching carpets and upholstery; newish public/family room in former stables, and nice old-fashioned dining room overlooking the garden. Bedrooms are pretty and homely, with period-style furnishings, a couple or armchairs and lots

of decorative ornaments; two are in the annexe. *Free House.* **Beer**
Theakston, guest ales. Garden. Family room. **Accommodation**
*17 bedrooms, all en suite, £66 (single £33). Children welcome overnight,
cot available. Check-in all day. Access, Amex, Visa.*

Bellingdon   Bull

Tel 024 029 8163   ·

Bellingdon Road Bellingdon Buckinghamshire   Map 17 E2

Delightful little redbrick cottage on the north side of the village.
Attractive furnishings, beams, bric-a-brac displays and an inglenook
fireplace. **Beer** *Benskins, Greene King IPA, Burton Ale. Garden.*

Belton   George Hotel

Tel 0530 222426

Market Place Belton Leicestershire LE12 9UH   Map 7 D3

Modernised roadside hotel with a comfortable rather than attractive
interior. Red plush banquettes line the bar walls, waiting-room style,
the centre of the room taken up by a free-standing brazier fireplace.
Beer *Mathew Brown Home Mild & Bitter, Younger's Scotch. Garden.
Family room.*

Benenden   King William IV

Tel 0580 240636   **FOOD**

The Street Benenden Kent TN17 5DJ   Map 11 C6

16th-century tile-hung pub, upmarket rustic in style, reflecting its
well-heeled location. Fresh flowers on plain wooden tables, a log fire
in the inglenook, exposed beams, and a relaxing, lived-in air.
Vigorously traditional home cooking recommended, particularly the
duck liver paté (£2.95), ham and leek gratin (£4.50) and salmon and
broccoli bake (£5.25). Home-made pies (from £4.50) and sweet and
sour pork (£4.95) are also popular. **Bar Food** *12-2 (except Sun), 7-9
Wed-Sat. Vegetarian dishes. Children's portions.* **Beer** *Shepherd Neame.
Children allowed in bar to eat. Garden, outdoor eating. No credit cards.*

Bentworth   Sun

Tel 0420 62338

Sun Hill Alton Road Bentworth Hampshire   Map 17 D4

Lovely, unspoilt old country pub, with two linked low-beamed bars,
one brick-floored, one board; nice furnishings, prints and decor and
twin woodburning stoves. *Free House.* **Beer** *Bunces Best, Gales HSB,
Bass, Marston Pedigree. Garden.*

Bewdley   Black Boy

Tel 0299 402199   **FOOD**
                                               B&B

Kidderminster Road Bewdley Hereford & Worcester DY12 1AG   Map 6 B4

Solidly built 17th-century inn with two pleasantly traditional beamed
bars, one devoted to displays of regimental insignia of the British
army. Lunchtime bar meals from a small menu include assorted
sandwiches (£1.40), home-made soup (£1.30) and cottage pie (£2.90)
with daily changing additions, carefully and enjoyably prepared, like
salmon mayonnaise with sautéed potatoes (£4.25), oxtail casserole
(£3.95) and cauliflower cheese with bacon (£2.75). From the 3-
course table d'hote dinner menu (£12.75), choices include Stilton and
walnut paté, fillet of plaice mornay and a home-made pudding to

finish. The best bedrooms are in the Georgian annexe, bright, homely and comfortable; residents have the use of the three lounge areas, including a delightfully chintzy Georgian one. *Bar Food and Restaurant Meals* 11.30-2, 7-9. *Children's portions.* **Beer** *Mitchells & Butlers. Family room.* **Accommodation** *20 bedrooms, 8 en suite, £60 (single £44). Children welcome overnight, additional beds and cots available. Check-in all day. Access, Amex, Visa.*

Bewdley   Little Packhorse

Tel 0299 403762

31 High Street Bewdley Hereford & Worcester DY12 2DH   Map 6 B4

Atmospheric old-fashioned pub, early 17th-century. Lots of bric-a-brac. Cheap, cheerful and friendly. *Free House.* **Beer** *Home-brewed Lumphammer, Burton Ale. Family room.*

Bibury   Catherine Wheel   FOOD / B&B

Tel 0285 740250

Bibury Gloucestershire GL7 6DJ   Map 16 A2

Pear trees grow against the wall at each side of the entrance to this 500-year-old stone pub. Inside the three small rooms have the mellow atmosphere of an unpretentious, unspoilt local. Open from 11am to 11pm (except Sunday), most of the drinking is done in the first bar, which has a log fire in winter and ceiling beams taken from old wooden ships, when they were broken up in Gloucester docks – an example of 15th-century recycling. Most of the eating takes place in the other two rooms, both with woodburning stoves and one with redplush upholstery. A blackboard menu covers the regular dishes like sandwiches (the home cooked ham is first rate), ploughman's, steaks and salads, as well as the specials of the day, perhaps moules marinière (£3.75), jellied eels (£2.95), chicken curry (£4), fresh halibut with prawn, wine and mushrooms (£5.95) or steak and kidney pie (£5.25). There are usually several excellent home-made soups on offer (£1.75). Walk off lunch, or build an appetite for dinner, with a stroll around this pretty village; the trout farm welcomes visitors and there's a rustic museum in Arlington Mill. For overnight guests, there are two modest bedrooms, furnished with cheap modern white melamine furniture, although both have remote-control television and tea and coffee kit. The larger room has three beds to accommodate families. A shared bathroom has a separate shower cubicle in addition to the tub. Massive cooked breakfasts challenge the healthiest of appetites. *Bar Food* 11-11 (12-3, 7-10.30 Sun). *Vegetarian dishes. Children's menu (£1.50-£2.50 per dish). Children allowed in the bar to eat. Free House.* **Beer** *Courage Best and Directors, Marston's Pedigree, Whitbread West Country Pale Ale. Garden, outdoor eating.* **Accommodation** *2 bedrooms, shared bathroom, £32.50 (single £20). Children welcome overnight, additional beds, cots and highchairs supplied. Check-in all day. No credit cards.*

Bicester   Plough Inn

Tel 0869 249083

63 North Street Bicester Oxfordshire OX6 7NB   Map 16 C1

16th-century town pub with beamed ceilings, open fires and a horseshoe-shaped bar. **Beer** *Morrells Varsity.*

Bickley Moss   Cholmondeley Arms

FOOD

Tel 0829 720300

B&B

Cholmondeley Bickley Moss Cheshire SY14 8BT

Map 6 B3

Standing beside the A49 trunk road hard by the entrance to
Cholmondeley Castle and Gardens, the Harrisons' unique roadhouse
exists primarily to provide upmarket pub food in surroundings more
than a little unusual. This they achieve in staggering quantity (up to
200 diners on some Saturday nights), so book if you're able to. It's a
Victorian brick building, with steep, white-painted gables and an
octagonal bell tower, originally the village school. Enter a T-shaped
hall, and the pine-built bar, which has desks and blackboards mounted
on a gallery over it, is flanked on each side by high-roofed halls of
salmon pink hue, with well-spaced tables in stripped pine, assorted
pews and former chapel chairs with hymnbook racks. Someone's
interest in serious French food is indicated by a gallery of framed
Parisian menus. The old blackboards are put to good use, listing the
daily specials – pick of the food on offer – and an impressive house
wine selection which includes a good Sauvignon, house claret and
Cotes du Rhone. Soups (£1.95) and pies (£5.75) change daily;
courgette and tomato perhaps, then steak and kidney, or chicken and
parsley. Look a little further, and typically, there's lamb kidneys with
sherry and parsley sauce (£6.95), vegetable-stuffed aubergine and a
generously sauced portion of salmon and spinach lasagne (£5.90)
served with salad. Puddings (£2.65) on the board might well include
school traditions. The unchanging printed menu offers an even wider,
if plainer, choice. "The School Lunch" is a hot spicy sausage in a
baguette, "The Cholmondeley Open" an open prawn sandwich with
egg, tomato, cucumber and mayonnaise. Across the car park are four
bright, cottagey bedrooms (three double and one family) in the old
schoolhouse building. All have showers, television, telephone, clock
radio, tea tray and hairdryer. Report back to the classroom next
morning for a slap-up breakfast. *Bar Food* 12-2.15 (12-2 Sun), 6.30-10
(6-10 Sat/7-9.30 Sun). *Vegetarian dishes. Children's menu (£3.30 per
dish). Free House.* **Beer** *Marston Pedigree, Ruddles County, Boddingtons,
Flowers IPA, weekly guest beer. Garden, outdoor eating, children's play
area.* **Accommodation** *4 bedrooms, all en suite, £40 (single £30).
Children welcome overnight, cots available. Check-in by arrangement.
Access, Visa.*

Biddenden   Three Chimneys

Tel 0580 291472

FOOD

Ashford Biddenden Kent TN27 8HA

Map 11 C5

The Three Chimneys has every natural advantage of being a classic
country pub, its original, small-roomed layout and old-fashioned
furnishings intact. Old settles, low beams, nice decor, warming open
fires: glorious. Then there's the range of more than decent bar food
including mussel soup (£2.45), Highland venison casserole (£5.95)
and chicken breast in tomato and tarragon (£5.95). There's a daily
choice of four home-made puds. You can book tables in the family
Garden Room, and the garden is lovely for summer eating. Don't,
incidentally, look for the three chimneys on the roof: the name comes
from the pub's location at the meeting of three lanes, or Trois
Chemins, as it was called by French prisoners of war kept near here in
another century. *Bar Food* 11.30-2, (12.15-2 Sun) 6.30-10 (7-11 Sun);
bar snacks both sessions. Vegetarian dishes. Children's portions. Free House.

Beer Adnams, Fremlins, Goachers, Harveys, Marstons Pedigree, Wadworth 6X. Cider Biddenden. Family room. Garden, outdoor eating. No credit cards.

Biddenham   Three Tuns
Tel 0234 54847
57 Main Road Biddenham Bedfordshire   **Map 15 E1**

Stone-built village pub, modernised but attractive, with a comfortable low-beamed lounge and noisy public bar. *Beer Greene King IPA and Abbot. Garden. Children's play area.*

Biddestone   White Horse
Tel 0249 713305
The Green Biddestone Wiltshire SN14 7DG   **Map 14 B2**

Unassuming village local in delightfully quaint village, overlooking duck pond. Traditional multi-room layout retained; friendly atmosphere. *Beer Courage, Wadworth 6X. Garden. Children's play area.*

Bilsborrow   Owd Nells
Tel 0995 40010
Canalside St Michael's Road Bilsborrow Lancashire PR3 0RS   **Map 6 A1**

Part of an unusual mini leisure complex called Guy's Thatched Hamlet. This is a nicely furnished, traditionally styled modern pub by the canal. *Free House. Beer Boddington, Flowers IPA, Whitbread, Castle Eden and guest beers. Garden. Children's play area. Family room.*

Binfield   Stag & Hounds
Tel 0344 48553   **A**
Forest Road Binfield Berkshire RG12 5HA   **Map 17 D3**

Built as a royal hunting lodge in the heart of Windsor Great Forest some 600 years ago; blackened beams, low ceiling, open fires and five cosy little bars with nice old furnishings, as well as a pleasant lounge adorned with a thimble collection. The remains of an ancient elm (which once marked the very centre of the forest) are in the garden. *Beer Courage. Garden. Family room.*

Birch Vale   Sycamore
Tel 0663 42715
Sycamore Road Birch Vale Derbyshire   **Map 6 C2**

Downstairs drinking bar with indoor fountain, and upstairs dining bar. *Beer Ward's Sheffield Best, Bass. Garden. Children's play area. Family room.*

Birchover   Druid Inn
Tel 0629 650302   **FOOD**
Main Street Birchover Derbyshire DE4 2BL   **Map 6 C2**

Climb the long hill from the B506 signposted Stanton Moor Stone Circle, and be sure not to miss a glimpse of Row Tor, high above the pub, where extraordinary fissures and passageways through the rock suggest (rather than prove) very early occupation by man; hence the Druid's unusual name. The Druid is an egalitarian sort of place, frequented in about equal numbers by both county types and country walkers; Range Rovers and Transits rub tyre tracks in the car park. From portal to chimney pot it's entirely ivy-covered, with a terrace in front and, to one side, a restaurant area on two floors, connected by a tiled umbilical passageway. There's no bar at which to stand, except when ordering food. The menu fills four blackboards, including a complete vegetarian selection with Kashmiri pilau and garlic and peanut sauce with salad (£4.90). Starters may include tarka dhal, a lentil purée served with a poppadom (£3.80), or prawns with apple and celery in hot garlic butter (£3.85). The main-course menu may feature honey roast saddle of lamb with gooseberry and redcurrant sauce (£9.10) or steamed trout with ground walnuts and coriander sauce (£8.40), perhaps followed by apple and marzipan torte (£2.30) for dessert, all partnered by an above average range of good value wines by glass or bottle. *Bar Food & Restaurant Meals 12-2, 7-9.30 (9 winter). Vegetarian dishes. Free House. Beer Marston Pedigree, Ruddles Best. Children allowed in bar to eat. Patio/terrace. Access, Amex, Visa.*

Bishop Wilton   Fleece Inn

| Tel 07596 251 | **B&B** |

Bishop Wilton Humberside YO4 1RU   Map 7 D1

Lovely village setting overlooking the green, the Norman church and the Wolds beyond. A central bar divides lounge and public areas, with a breakfast/dining room to the rear. Four bedrooms are in the original building, and three en suite rooms in a separate pantiled block. Baby listening devices have been installed. Live country and western music on Friday evenings. *Free House. Beer John Smith's Bitter, Tetley Bitter. Accommodation 7 bedrooms, 4 en suite, £40 (single £20). Children welcome overnight, cot available. Check-in all day. No dogs. No credit cards.*

Blackawton   Normandy Arms

| Tel 080 421 316 |

Chapel Street Blackawton Devon TQ9 7BN   Map 13 D3

15th-century modernised and well-run village pub of great popularity. The Normandy Landings theme is much in evidence. *Beer Blackhawton Bitter and Devon Gold, Bass. Garden. Children's play area. Family room.*

Blackboys   Blackboys Inn

| Tel 0825 890283 |

Blackboys East Sussex   Map 11 B6

Lots of interesting bric-a-brac, and a ramble of delightfully old-fashioned little rooms in this partly medieval old inn. Seats at the front of the building overlook the pond; seats at the rear in the orchard. *Beer Harveys BB, Armada. Garden. Children's play area.*

Blackbrook   Plough

| Tel 0306 886603 |

Blackbrook Road Blackbrook Surrey   Map 17 F4

Nice views through large windows in the spacious, no-smoking saloon bar; traditional public bar with sewing machine tables and a vast collection of ties; the large garden is popular for barbecues in summer. *Beer King & Barnes Sussex, Broadwood, Festive and Old Ale (in winter). Garden.*

Blacko   Moorcock Inn

Tel 0282 614186

Gisburn Road Blacko Lancashire BB9 6NF

FOOD

Map 6 B1

Standing on its own, alongside the A682 north of Blacko, the whitewashed Moorcock Inn is situated in wonderful rolling countryside near Pendle Hill and the Forest of Bowland. Inside is unassuming and unpretentious. Two adjoining rooms have plain painted walls, simple prints, brass plates and a collection of china plates; stone fireplaces are topped with ornaments and brassware. All the tables are laid for dining, surrounded by upholstered bench seating and simple wooden chairs, a style continued in the large adjoining dining room. Large picture windows in both rooms offer lovely views over the surrounding landscape. Licensees Elizabeth and Peter Holt have built up an enviable reputation for good fresh food, and custom comes from far and wide. The printed menu is backed up by a daily changing specials board, where dishes, could include a home-made game pie (£4.95), seafood pasta, medallions of fillet steak with red wine sauce (£6.50) or halibut mornay (£5.95). Beside these, the menu covers tried and trusted pub favourites like ham shank with light mustard sauce (£5.50) and a good selection of vegetarian dishes. Cooking is perfectly competent, without ever being spectacular; prices realistic, portions generous, service friendly and quick. Popular Sunday lunch (£4.95). The Moorcock's a useful resting place after a bracing morning on the moors, the Pendle Walk almost passes the door, and in sunny weather the garden is lovely. *Bar Food 12-2, 7-10. Vegetarian dishes. Children's menu/portions. Beers Thwaites. Children allowed in bar to eat. Garden. No credit cards.*

Blackstone Edge   White House

Tel 0706 78456

Blackstone Edge Greater Manchester

Map 6 B1

Moorland pub of local stone; walkers bar; sofa-strewn Pennine Room; plain third bar with picture window. *Free House. Beer John Smiths, guest beers (Marston Pedigree, Exmoor Gold).*

Blakeney   King's Arms

Tel 0263 740341

Westgate Street Blakeney Norfolk NR25 7NQ

Map 10 C1

Three pleasant knocked-through rooms in a pretty Grade II listed cottage pub not far from the harbour. *Free House. Beer Websters Yorkshire, Marston Pedigree, Ruddles County. Garden. Children's play area. Family room.*

Blakesley   Bartholomew Arms

Tel 0327 860292

High Street Blakesley Northants NN12 8RE

B&B

Map 15 D1

Charming, welcoming 17th-century inn with a collection of model ships and nautical artefacts in the public bar, plus guns and cricket memorabilia in the lounge. Simple, well-kept bedrooms at very reasonable prices. *Beer Marston Pedigree, Ruddles County. Outdoor play area, garden. Family room. Accommodation 5 bedrooms, 1 en suite, from £35 (single £18). Children welcome overnight (extra bed £6), cots available. Check-in all day. No credit cards.*

Blanchland   Lord Crewe Arms

Tel 0434 675251

Blanchland nr Consett Co Durham DH8 9SP   Map 5 D2

The original building dates from 1235, when the inn was built as a
monastic guest house: you can still see the remains of the old
monastery in the garden. The Derwent Bar has settles and beams; the
Crypt Bar is exactly what it says it is is, its stone walls curving into a
remarkable barrel-vaulted ceiling. *Free House.* **Beer** *Vaux Sampson.*

Bledington   Kings Head Inn

Tel 0608 658365   **B&B**

The Green Bledington nr Kingham Oxfordshire OX7 6HD   Map 16 B1

Cotswold village pub on the Oxfordshire border, in a gloriously
unspoilt spot by the green and brook, complete with ducks (all known
by name to regulars). The original low-ceilinged bar is charming,
with a smoky patina of age, ancient settles, simple wooden furnishings
and an open fire, as well as tapestry-topped stools and other modern
touches. A lounge overlooking the garden and dining room are less
quaint, but attractive enough; there's also a locals' public bar.
Bedrooms are white-painted with co-ordinated floral fabrics and
antique pine furniture; TVs and direct-dial telephones are standard.
Free House. **Beer** *Wadworth 6X, Hook Norton Best Bitter, Tetley Bitter,
monthly guest beers.* **Cider** *Scrumpy throughout the summer. Garden,
children's play area. Family room.* **Accommodation** *7 bedrooms, all en
suite, £49 (single £28). Children welcome, additional beds, cots available
(£5). Check-in by arrangement. No credit cards.*

Bledlow   Lions of Bledlow

Tel 08444 3345   **FOOD**

Church End Bledlow Buckinghamshire HP27 9PE   Map 17 D2

Two miles north of Chinnor on the B4009, turn right into West Lane
and, after a mile, this 16th-century former coach staging post is on the
right at the top of a small hill. The white painted building is covered
in plants and an eating area is provided on the Green in front of it.
The bar is long and quite narrow with very low dark beams, dried
flowers, horse brasses and copper pots covering the walls. The 3-sided
bar serves the four rooms. Bar food ranges from garlic mushrooms
(£3.50) or smoked salmon coronets (£4.50), to lasagne verde (£5)
and steak and Guinness pie (£6). Home-made puddings could be the
Lions pavlova (£2.20) or treacle sponge (£1.80). From Wednesday to
Saturday the 30-seater restaurant is open, offering a more elaborate
menu: duck liver paté (£4.50) or oceanautic cocktail (£5.50),
followed by venison with sour cherries (£11) or chicken Wellington
(£9). Children are allowed in the bar or restaurant to eat. **Bar Food**
12-2, 6.30-9.30. **Restaurant Meals** *(Wed, Thur, Fri, Sat only) 12-2,
6.30-9.30. Vegetarian dishes. Children's portions. Free House.* **Beer**
*Courage Directors, Eagle IPA, Wadworth 6X. Garden, outdoor eating.
Access, Visa.*

Blickling — Buckinghamshire Arms

Tel 0263 732133

B&B

Blickling off B1354 nr Aylesham Norfolk NR11 6NF

Map 10 C1

Splendid 17th-century inn which stands deferentially at the gates of the even more splendid Blickling Hall; both are now National Trust properties. It's an excellent place to stay, two of the three bedrooms have dramatic evening views across to the floodlit hall; original features and four-posters in each room make this a characterful bed and breakfast stop. *Free House.* **Beer** *Adnams, Woodfords. Garden, outside play area, outdoor eating. Family room.* **Accommodation** *3 bedrooms, all en suite, £50 (single £40). Children welcome overnight, cots available. Check-in all day. No dogs. Access, Visa.*

Blidworth — Bird in Hand

Tel 0623 792356 .

Main Street Blidworth Nottinghamshire

Map 7 D3

Genuinely friendly, cosy one-bar village local with an island bar and lovely views over Sherwood Forest; real fire; no music. **Beer** *Mansfield Riding, Old Baily. Garden.*

Blockley — Crown Inn and Hotel

Tel 0386 700245   Fax 0386 700247

FOOD

B&B

High Street Blockley Gloucestershire GL56 9EX

Map 16 A1

Smartened up, well-heeled Cotswold village inn of mellow golden stone. Original bar fittings, comfortable traditional chairs, pretty carpeting, flashes of exposed stone, attractive light fittings, and the general air of a market town hotel lounge all characterise the public drinking and bar meal areas. The excellent Coach House Restaurant is pink and piney and the Brasserie has recently been redecorated. Choices on the bar menu include home-made soup (£2.50), seafood lasagne (£5.25) or Spanish-style tapas (£5.95). The Brasserie's menu is more substantial with moules marinière (£4.95), half a crispy local duckling (£10.95) or monkfish in mustard cream sauce (£12.95) as some examples. Every evening and Sunday lunchtime the restaurant offers a 4-course set menu for £16.95. A traditional Sunday roast is available in both Brasserie (main dish £6.95) and Restaurant (3 courses £10.95). There's a varied cheeseboard and home-made puddings. Comfortable, carpeted bedrooms feature co-ordinating modern fabrics as well as the odd original beam and some nice pine furniture. **Bar Food** *12-2 (12-2.30 Sat/Sun).* **Brasserie** *12-2, 7-10.* **Restaurant Meals** *12-2 (Sun only), 7-9.30. Vegetarian dishes. Children's portions. Children allowed in bar to eat. Free House.* **Beer** *Bass, Marstons Pedigree & Border Bitter, Thwaites. Patio/terrace, outdoor eating.* **Accommodation** *21 bedrooms, all en suite, £72 (single £49.50). Children welcome overnight, additional beds (£10), cots supplied. Check-in after midday. Dogs permitted (£10). Access, Amex, Visa.*

Blyford — Queen's Head

Tel 050 270 404

Southwold Road Blyford Suffolk IP19 9JY

Map 10 D2

Traditional features at the family-run Queen's Head include a huge log fire, low-beamed ceiling, secret passage, and a charming ghost. It's the smallest pub in the area, with the largest menu. Vintage cars meet outside. No juke box, no music, no gaming machines. **Beer** *Adnams Bitter, Mild and Broadside. Garden. Children's play area. Family room.*

Blythburgh   White Hart

Tel 0502 70217

Blythburgh nr Halesworth Suffolk IP19 9LQ   Map 10 D2

16th-century inn on a much older site; splendid Elizabethan and
Stuart features, and lots of people, as it's on the A12; despite the
roadside location, there are lovely views across the river and marshes.
Volleyball and pétanque are played on the lawn. *Beer Adnams Bitter &*
Broadside. Garden. Children's play area. Family room.

Bodle Street Green   White Horse Inn

Tel 0323 833243   **FOOD**

Bodle Street Green Herstmonceux East Sussex BN27 4RE   Map 11 B6

Bright, cheerful pub run by a bright, cheerful couple. They pride
themselves on producing properly pubby, informal but honest fare
("quality not quantity, and value for money"): seafood platter £8.95,
Tahitian melon with prawns, smoked salmon and salad £5.50,
chicken curry £3.75, 14oz T-bone steak £9.95, rather than
developing into a licensed restaurant business. The good choice of
vegetarian dishes (perhaps up to 6 or 8) might include wheat and
walnut casserole (£4.50). *Bar Food 12-2, 7-9. Vegetarian dishes. Free*
House. Beer Harveys Best Bitter. Patio, outdoor eating. Pub closed
Mondays. No credit cards.

Boldre   Red Lion

Tel 0590 673177

Boldre nr Lymington Hampshire SO41 8NE   Map 14 C4

Delightful old pub, dating from around 1650 and mentioned as an
alehouse in the Domesday Book. Outside, an old cart is strewn with
flowers, and hanging baskets and troughs are a riot of colour in
summer. Inside, four charming, black-beamed rooms each have their
own country style, with real fires, a mix of old furnishings, hunting
prints, a chamber pot collection, tapestries and man-traps. *Beer Eldridge*
Pope, Dorchester and Royal Oak. Garden.

Bollington   Church House Inn

Tel 0625 574014

Church Street Bollington Cheshire SK10 5PY   Map 6 B2

Friendly, typical village local with two open fires and agricultural
bric-a-brac. *Beer Boddington, Marston Pedigree, Tetley, Theakston XB.*
Children's play area. Family room.

Bolter End   Peacock

Tel 0494 881417   **FOOD**

Lane End Bolter End Buckinghamshire HP14 3LU   Map 17 D3

At the time of going to press, the Peacock was being repainted
externally with 'country cream' paint and carpets being replaced.
Bolter End is a crossroads with a few houses and the pub is located
opposite the Common. The only bar is divided into three sections and
one menu applies throughout. Examples of menu dishes include
Jamaican chicken (£5.50), stincotto (whole gammon hock cooked in
herbs – £8.50), or kidney bean and mushroom provençale (£4.25).
Home-made puddings (all £2.15) are the traditional kind – fruit

crumbles, jam roly-poly, honey oat and lemon tart or home-made passion cake. *Bar Food 12-2, 7-10 (except Sun). Vegetarian dishes. Beer ABC, Bass, Tetley, Ansells Mild. Garden, outdoor eating. Access, Amex, Visa.*

Bolton-by-Bowland   Coach & Horses

Tel 020 07 202

20 Main Street Bolton-by-Bowland Lancashire BB7 4NW   Map 6 B1

Pretty, well-run pub in glorious spot, with coal fires. Very busy at weekends in summer. *Beer Whitbread Castle Eden, Boddington Mild and Bitter. Family room.*

Bonchurch   Bonchurch Inn

Tel 0983 852611

The Shute Bonchurch Isle of Wight   Map 15 D4

Bonchurch's only pub has an invigorating Italian flavour and a good nautical atmosphere, too: the public bar is cut into the rocks of the Shute. Solid fuel stove. *Beer Burts VPA, Bass, Flowers Original. Children's play area. Family room.*

Boot   Burnmoor Inn

Tel 094 67 23224

Boot Eskdale Cumbria CA19 1TG   Map 4 C3

In the same family for close on 40 years, the Burnmoor is an attractive gabled and white-painted hotel in glorious hill scenery at the foot of Scafell. The bar is basic rahter than quaint, and the beamed ex-stable dining room rather starkly white, but softened by evening lighting: it has a similar menu to the bar, at slightly higher prices. They grow their own vegetables and fruit, and keep pigs and hens, so produce is assured of freshness. Mrs Foster brings an Austrian influence to the menu and wine list. There are eight lettign rooms (no children under 6). *Free House. Beer Jennings Bitter & Cumberland. Garden, children's play area.*

Boot   Woolpack Inn

Tel 09 467 23230   B&B

Boot Eskdale Cumbria CA19 1TH   Map 4 C3

A 17th-century inn at the head of Eskdale valley in good walking country. Convivial public bar and attractive exposed-stone-walled lounge. Bright, traditional bedrooms come equipped with teamakers, electric blankets and cosy candlewick bedspreads. Four have their own shower cabinets; all share a neat public bathroom. Chintzy residents' lounge. *Free House. Beer Theakston Best, XB. Garden, outdoor eating, children's play area. Family room. Accommodation 8 bedrooms, 4 with showers, £40 (single £20). Children welcome overnight, additional beds (no charge under 5 years), cots supplied. Check-in all day. No dogs. Accommodation closed 17-25 Dec. Access, Visa.*

Boscastle   Napoleon

Tel 0840 250204

Top of the Village Boscastle Cornwall   Map 12 C2

One of three pubs in a quaintly steep old fishing village with glorious miniature harbour owned by the National Trust. A pretty little inn with polished slate floors and various cosy rooms. *Beer St Austell Tinners, Bass. Garden. Family room.*

Boston   Burton House Hotel

Tel 0205 362307

Wainfleet Road Boston Lincolnshire   Map 7 F3

Hotel proper with pubby stable bar, spacious lounge overlooking garden. **Beer** *Batemans XB, Bass.*

Botley   Bugle Inn

Tel 0489 783773

The Square Botley Hampshire SO3 2EA   Map 15 D4

Pleasant dining pub, with a smart beamed bar and separate restaurant. **Beer** *Whitbread, Marston Pedigree.*

Bottom of the Oven   Stanley Arms

Tel 026 05 2414

Bottom of the Oven nr Wildboarclough Macclesfield Forest Cheshire SK11 0AR   Map 6 C2

Remote moorland pub of unspoilt charm. Two drinking rooms with black woodwork, discreetly floral fabrics, wall seating and copper-topped tables, plus attractive dining room. Open fires, good rural views and very popular. **Beer** *Marston Pedigree, Burton Ale. Garden. Family room.*

Bourton   White Lion

Tel 0747 840866

High Street Bourton Dorset SP8 5AT   Map 13 F2

Popular, friendly, genuinely unspoilt old pub run by the same licensee for ten years. All the traditional features: beams, flagstones, nice old furnishings, real fires. Pretty garden. **Beer** *Ushers Best, Ruddles Best & County, Ash Vine, Tanker & Challenger. Garden. Children's play area. Family room.*

Bourton-on-the-Hill   Horse & Groom Inn

Tel 0386 700413   **B&B**

Bourton-on-the-Hill nr Moreton-in-Marsh Gloucestershire GL56 9AQ   Map 16 A1

Standing on the hill at the top end of the village is a solid inn from which there are fine views over the Cotswold countryside. The rustic stone-walled bars are hung with equestrian prints. Upstairs, three neat bedrooms with primarily modern decor all have shower cubicles and washbasins, and share a bathroom. *Free House.* **Beer** *Beamish, Toby, Bass, Worthington Best Bitter. Garden.* **Accommodation** *3 bedrooms, £32. No children under 10. Check-in all day.*

Bowland Bridge   Hare & Hounds

Tel 04488 333   **B&B**

Grange-over-Sands Bowland Bridge Cumbria LA11 6NN   Map 4 C4

Truly rural, good-looking old inn owned by ex-international soccer player Peter Thompson. The bar successfully blends ancient and modern, with its rough stone walls, discreet farming bric-a-brac and simple wooden furniture; open fires spread warmth in winter weather. The dramatically high-ceilinged dining room is for residents only; the residents' lounge is rather more chintzy. Bedrooms are immaculately kept, beamy and floral, on the small side. Delightful

garden. *Free House.* **Beer** *Tetley Bitter. Garden, outdoor play area.*
Accommodation *16 bedrooms, 13 en suite, £42 (single £31). Children*
welcome overnight, cots available. Check-in all day. Access, Visa.

Box   Bayly's   FOOD
Tel 0225 743662   B&B
High Street Box nr Corsham Wiltshire SN14 9NA   Map 14 B2

For a while known as the Bear, the solid-looking Bath stone inn,
standing four-square on the A4 Bath to Chippenham road, reverted to
its original name after its acquisition by present owners Jan and
George Gynn. The pub's first landlord in the early 1600s was one
Jacob Bayly, whose last will and testament hangs to this day behind
the bar. Most noteworthy of its many period features is a magnificent
open stone fireplace, and amongst recent additions the circular pool
table is quite a talking point. The greater part of the premises,
however, is given over to eating, with speedy, informal service to its
neatly laid tables. From a daily changing blackboard, lunch dishes may
well include Wiltshire ham with egg and chips (£2.95), chili con
carne (£3.95) or a toasted club sandwich (£1.50). The comprehensive
fixed menu offers a wider selection of garlic mushrooms (£2.75),
salmon mornay (£7.50), liver and bacon (£4.50) or beef stew and
dumplings (£4.95) with, to follow, the vicars tart (almond and fruit
flan – £2.50) and Wiltshire whitepot (creamed bread-and-butter
pudding £2.50). Jan's cooking is highly popular, and at peak times it
is a busy, lively place. For peace and quiet, and for weary travellers,
Bayly's offers half a dozen bedrooms, of which three on the ground
floor have neat en suite WC's and showers: all have colour TV and
tea/coffee making machines. **Bar food & Restaurant Meals** *12-2.30,*
7-10. Vegetarian dishes. Children's menu (£1.50-£2.75 per dish). Free
House. **Beer** *Wadworths 6X, Bass, guest beers.* **Accommodation**
6 bedrooms, 3 en-suite, £45 (single £27.50). Children welcome overnight,
additional beds, cots available. Check-in by arrangement. Access, Visa.

Boxford   Bell   FOOD
Tel 048838 721   Fax 048838 749   B&B
Lambourn Road Boxford Nr Newbury Berkshire RG16 8DD   Map 16 B3

Mock-Tudor pub at a country crossroads not far from Newbury. A
recently created patio complete with tubs, climbing plants and pond
provides a pleasant outdoor eating area. Food can be eaten anywhere
in The Bell's one bar and restaurant. The blackboard menu advertises
the regularly-changing specials: New Zealand green-lip mussels
(£4.95), oysters mornay (£4.95), rack of lamb in garlic honey
(£8.95), chicken New Orleans (£8.25), while the restaurant offers a
2-course (£15) or 3-course menu (£18.95) with dishes such as
devilled whitebait, black pearl mushrooms, lamb Madeira, NJ sea bass
(after chef Nick Jones) and brandy snap basket. The light and airy
bedrooms are all equipped with duvets, hairdryers, tea/coffee making
facilities, TVs, telephones and trouser presses. **Bar Food** *12-2, 7-10.*
Vegetarian dishes. Free House. **Beer** *Wadworth 6X, Boddingtons, Flowers*
Original. **Cider** *Scrumpy Jack. Patio/terrace, outdoor eating, children's play*
area. **Accommodation** *11 bedrooms, all en suite, £40 (single £32.50).*
Children welcome overnight, additional beds and cots available. Check-in all
day. Access, Amex, Diners, Visa.

Bradford   Shoulder of Mutton

| Tel 0274 726038 |
28 Kirkgate Bradford West Yorkshire BD1 1QL   Map 6 C1

Unprepossessing city-centre Sam Smith's pub with a real oasis of a
garden, which can take 200 people if pressed (and it often is). Children
welcome in the garden. *Beer Sam Smith's Old Brewery Bitter.*

Bradford-on-Avon   Bunch of Grapes

| Tel 02216 3877 | **FOOD**
14 Silver Street Bradford-on-Avon Wiltshire BA15 1JY   Map 14 B2

Appropriately, given its name, but somewhat incongruously for a
town-centre pub, there is a grapevine clinging to the outside of the
Bunch of Grapes. The pub was once a shop, and has a little bow
window which now houses a copy of the blackboard menu and also,
more often than not, the pub cat having a doze in the sunshine. Old
enough that its true age is shrouded in mystery, an old indenture
records that the Grapes changed hands in 1846 for £300. It's long and
narrow with red hessian walls above dark brown dado panelling, and
the decor is unpretentiously old rather than of the style known as olde
worlde. Convivial landlord Clive Crocker strives to keep the balance
firmly that of a pub, which also serves food rather than becoming a
dining pub, and stocks recherché beers with wonderful names like
Summer Lightning, Lifeboat and Ash Vine, drawn up from the cellar
by a genuine 1890s brass and porcelain beer engine. Just four beers are
on the go at any one time, but are rotated from a repertoire of over
30 brands. A short list of about half a dozen wines changes almost as
frequently, depending upon Clive's fancy, but might include the likes
of Chateau Musar from the Lebanon, Marques de Caqueres and
Ricasoli Chianti, all available by the glass. The blackboard food menu
lists whatever wife Chris has decided to cook that day. Fresh salmon
and broccoli quiche (£3.30), venison casserole (£3.95), pork in cider
(£3.75) and, if your luck is in, one of her pies made from fruits from
the garden – greengage and apple or gooseberry and elderflower at
£1.20. *Bar Food (except Sun) 12-2, 6-8.45. Vegetarian dishes.
Children's portions. Free House. Beer Burton Bridge Festival, Bateman
XXXB, Cotleigh Tawny, Smiles. Cider Thatchers. No credit cards.*

Bradley Green   Malt Shovel

| Tel 0278 653432 |
Blackmoor Lane Bradley Green nr Cannington Somerset TA5 2NE   Map 13 E1

Rangy white-painted roadside inn with a traditional interior: wooden
settles and other furniture in the main bar, and there's also a tiny red-
walled snug. *Free House. Beer Butcourse, Wadworth 6X, Guest beers.
Garden. Children's play area. Family room.*

Bramdean   Fox Inn

| Tel 0962 771363 | **FOOD**
Bramdean Hampshire SO24 0LP   Map 15 D3

Attractive 400-year-old white weatherboard pub set back from the
main road (A272). Inside is extensively modernised, and very much
dining orientated, but well-kept and comfy. Good lunchtime bar food
is simple with dishes such as home-made lasagne (£5.95), beef
stroganoff (£7.95) and fresh cod (£5.95). The evening menu is more
restauranty with fillet steaks (£10.95) and fresh fish from Portsmouth

(sea bass £12.95); for dessert, home-made puddings like pavlova, crème brulée and treacle tart (all £2.50) are offered. The choice from the cheeseboard is wide with eleven cheeses available at any one time – Torvill, Wensleydale with apricots, white Stilton with pear and peaches, Jersey blue. *Bar Food 12-2, 7-9. Vegetarian dishes. Children's menu in summer (£2 per dish). Beer Marston Pedigree, Burton Best. Garden, outdoor eating, children's play area. Access, Visa.*

Bramley   Jolly Farmer

FOOD
B&B

Tel 0483 893355

High Street Bramley Surrey GU5 0HB

Map 17 E4

A riot of flowers in window boxes and tubs and colourful umbrellas over the terrace tables certainly make for a jolly first impression here. Inside is a cheerful hotch-potch of stuffed birds in a glass case, a fish tank, ancient mechanical fruit machine, beer-mat covered ceiling and much else besides. Brothers Steve and Chris Hardstone have taken over the running of the pub from their father, who spent twenty years 'on Smithfield' and Steve knows just where to get the best meat on his regular early morning trips to the London market (he takes in Billingsgate too) but prime Aberdeen Angus steaks (from £10) and fish like swordfish steaks (£6.50), sardines in garlic butter (£3) and whole grilled Dover sole (£8.50), are just a small part of a very extensive menu: whole spring chicken with mustard sauce (£7), cottage pie (£5), tacos with chili and cheese (£4.75), home-made burgers (from £5) with various sauces, omelettes (from £2.50), jacket potatoes, sandwiches. The same menu operates both in the bar and in the bistro, which is a splendid medieval barn rebuilt here by Chris and Steve's own hands. Three modestly comfortable bedrooms have TVs and tea/coffee making kits and share a single shower room. Be ready for the substantial breakfast in which they take particular pride. *Bar Food & Restaurant Meals 12-2, 7-10. Vegetarian dishes. Children's portions. Free House. Beer Theakstons Old Peculier and Best, Badger Best, Tanglefoot. Cider Westons Old Rosie. Garden, Outdoor eating. Accommodation 3 bedrooms, sharing facilities, £40 (single £25). Children welcome overnight. Additional beds and cots available. Check-in by arrangement. Access, Visa.*

Brancaster Staithe   Jolly Sailors

Tel 0485 210314

Brancaster Staithe nr Kings Lynn Norfolk PE31 8BJ

Map 10 C1

Very popular country pub on the edge of a huge dune and salt flat area. Three rooms blend traditional and modern. *Beer Greene King IPA & Abbot. Garden. Children's play area. Family room.*

Brandeston   Queen's Head

Tel 072 882 307

The Street Brandeston Suffolk IP13 7AD

Map 10 C3

Splendid country pub with lovely summer garden and a good family room; open fire; no music, and a drinks-only rear bar. *Beer Adnams Southwold, Bitter & Broadside. Garden. Children's play area.*

Branksome Park   Inn In The Park
Tel 0202 761318

Pinewood Road Branksome Park Dorset BH13 6JS   Map 14 C4

On the road to Branksome Chine and the sea, this pub looks from the outside like a substantial Victorian guest house, but the bar is pubbier than first impressions might suggest. *Free House. Beer Adnams Southwold Bitter, Bass, Wadworth 6X. Family room.*

Branscombe   Masons Arms   **FOOD**
B&B
Tel 029780 300

Branscombe nr Seaton Devon EX12 3DJ   Map 13 E2

15 minutes from the sea, tucked into a hillside, with a pretty front terrace and colourful gardens, a delightful 14th-century, creeper-clad inn stands in the heart of an unspoilt Devon village. Inside, an enormous open fire not only warms the beamed and flagstoned main bar but, throughout the winter, also cooks the spit-roasts offered on Thursday lunchtimes as well as the suckling pig suppers (3-course meal £10.50) served once a month in the restaurant. Alternatives from the bar include home-made steak and kidney pudding (£5.25), salmon fishcakes (£5.50) or a ploughman's offered with a choice of Devonshire cheese and locally baked crusty bread (£3-4). Fresh local fish regularly appears on the restaurant menu (3-course meal with lobster £24). Vegetarian meals are available and Sunday lunch is a feature. The inn, having until recently been leased out, has now reverted into the hands of the management. Exposed beams add to the charms of attractive bedrooms in the inn and nearby ancient cottages. All but three have en-suite bathroom facilities, while TVs, telephones and tea-makers are standard throughout. The inviting residents' lounge commands lovely rural views. *Bar Food 12-2, 7-9.30 **Restaurant Meals** 7-9.30 and lunch on Sunday 12-2. Vegetarian dishes. Children's portions. Free House. **Beer** Bass, Wadworth 6X, Dartmoor Best. **Cider** Luscombe. Terrace, outdoor eating. **Accommodation** 20 bedrooms (17 en suite), from £54 (single from £27). Children welcome overnight, additional beds (£10), cots supplied. Check-in all day. Access, Visa.*

Brassington   Olde Gate
Tel 062 985 448

Well Street Brassington Derbyshire DE4 4HJ   Map 6 C3

17th-century pub built of local stone and oak timbers salvaged from the Armada. No music, no fruit machines or space games. Very traditional and attractive inside, with open log fires in winter; simple wooden furnishings and oak-panelled dining room. *Beer Marston Pedigree, Merrie Monk, Owd Rodger (in winter). Garden.*

Braunston   Old Plough
Tel 0572 722714

Church Street Braunston Leicestershire LE15 8QY   Map 7 E4

Rejuvenated, stone-built old coaching inn just two minutes outside Oakham on the Leicester road. *Beer Courage Best & Directors, Theakston Best. Garden. Children's play area.*

Brearton   Malt Shovel

Tel 0423 862929	**FOOD**
Brearton nr Harrogate North Yorkshire HG3 3BX	Map 6 C1

The quiet country village of Brearton, just a short drive from the
B6165, has a splendid pub in the Malt Shovel. Standing on the
village's main street (it only has one!), it is a 16th-century cream-
painted building with colourful hanging baskets. The interior, reached
through a recently added porch, has a relaxed and civilised air, and is
pleasingly unpretentious in its decor and fittings. The bar counter has
some fine old woodwork, and oak half-panelling lines the rough
white-painted and stripped stone walls. Red cushioned seating graces
the benches and simple spindleback chairs which surround the solid
wood tables; hunting prints, old bottles, highly polished brass plates
and other ornaments also feature. The smaller room has a dartboard,
although this isn't really a local's pub. It's a real family business:
Marilyn Parsons owns the pub and does the cooking, along with
daughter Joanne, while son Leigh is in charge of the cellar and front of
house. Mother's and daughter's cooking has won many admirers, some
coming surprisingly far to eat here. The lunchtime trade tends to be
dominated by the retired age group, while evenings bring a more
varied crowd. The day's dishes, all freshly prepared, are written up on
the blackboard; the choice isn't exhaustive but should suit most tastes.
Fresh produce is well handled in dishes like roast ham with parsley
sauce (£4.25), Trinidad prawn curry (always popular) (£5.10) and
lamb steak with fresh mint sauce (£6.50). Beautifully fresh haddock
comes in a light crisp batter (£5.50) and with proper home-made
chips; the size of the fillet will take your breath away. Vegetarians
aren't forgotten either: perhaps a nut roast (£4.25), spinach and
mushroom lasagne (£4.10) or vegetable samosas (£3.75). And you
shouldn't leave without trying the desserts (£1.75): lemon flan,
banana fudge flan or a gooseberry and apple crumble, all home-
produced. Service is informal, friendly and helpful. To the rear, a
paved terrace has white tables and garden chairs, while at the end of
the car park there's a small lawned area and discreet little caravan site.
A real country village pub this, run by charming people. *Bar Food*
12-2, 7-9 (except Sun eve). Vegetarian dishes. Children's portions.
Children allowed to eat in the bar. Free House. Beer Theakston Best and
Mild, Tetley, Old Mill, Daleside, guest beer. Patio. No credit cards.

Brenchley   Rose & Crown

Tel 089 272 2107	
High Street Brenchley Kent TN12 7NQ	Map 11 B5

Pretty, typically Kentish, 15th-century inn, originally the stables and
staff rooms for the old Palace of Brenchley opposite. Lots of exposed
timber, a pretty little carpeted bar. *Beer Adnams Southwold Bitter,*
Harvey's Best, Marston Pedigree, Wadworth 6X. Children's play area.

Brendon   Stag Hunters Hotel

Tel 059 87 222	**B&B**
Brendon nr Lynton Devon EX35 1PS	Map 13 D1

The Stag Hunters stands in a wonderful position by the East Lyn
river, and makes a good base for guests wishing to explore Exmoor
and the Doone Valley. The new owners have recently renovated the
exterior and refurbished the interior bars. Neat bedrooms in the main
house and stone-built annexe all have TVs and tea-makers and 18 offer

en-suite facilities; there's a residents' lounge. *Free House.* **Beer** *Country Hardy, Tetley, Stag Hunters. Garden.* **Accommodation** *20 bedrooms, 13 en suite, £56 (single £34). Children welcome overnight, additional beds and cots available. Check-in all day. Access, Amex, Diners, Visa.*

Brereton Green   Bears Head Hotel

FOOD

B&B

Tel 0477 35251   Fax 0477 35888

Brereton Green nr Sandbach Cheshire CW11 9RS

Map 6 B2

A celebrated roadhouse alongside the A50, the Bear has expanded into a collection of buildings, fronted by the original half-timbered inn which dates from 1615, if not earlier. Panels of wattle and daub, carefully preserved and displayed in the bar, are evidence of the building's longevity and, despite the many more recent extensions, its inglenook fireplaces and oak beams hung with horse brasses still have lots of old-fashioned charm. Today's pub, run by the Tarquini family for some 30 years, is divided into cosy alcoves by means of cleverly placed original timbers and panels, and is full of fragrance of ubiquitous fresh flowers. Burtonwood Bitter and Bass are the bonuses for beer drinkers. Lunchtime and evening bar food is both stylish and substantial, ranging from open sandwiches (£3.75-£5.50) with salad to satisfying hot dishes like garlic buttered lamb chops (£5.55) with seasonal vegetables, or a Scotch salmon salad (£5.95); daily specialities typically feature seafood and mushroom pancake (£4.50), Cumberland sausage (£4.50), baked haddock mornay (£5.50) or the house speciality, black pudding with whisky and mushroom sauce (£5.95). By night the restaurant evokes the stuff of dinner dates and anniversaries tinged with more than a hint of déjà-vu: spumantes and pink champagnes are popped in discreetly hidden corners, while steak Diane or veal Marsala sizzles lovingly at your table. The 3-course à la carte menu is £16.95. Mammoth desserts (all £2.25) arrive by trolley. And so to bed where practical considerations for the business traveller generally take precedence over romance, with formica-topped, dual-purpose dressing tables and work spaces, television, radio, dial-out phones and trouser presses. **Bar Food and Restaurant Meals** *12-2, 7-10 (except Suns). Vegetarian dishes. Children's portions. Free House.* **Beer** *Bass, Burtonwood Best. Patio/terrace, outdoor eating.* **Accommodation** *24 bedrooms, all en suite, from £49.50 (single £25). Children welcome overnight, additional beds (£10). No dogs. Access, Amex, Visa (in restaurant and hotel only).*

Bretforton   Fleece Inn

A

Tel 0386 831173

The Cross Bretforton Hereford & Worcester WR11 5JE

Map 16 A1

National Trust-owned timewarp of a pub with 19th-century and older atmosphere and a museum-like array of beautiful things, many of them extremely valuable and rare – note especially the priceless collection of Stuart pewter. 60-70 guest ales are on offer during the course of the year. *Free house.* **Beer** *Burton Bridge, Hook Norton Best, Jolly Roger Shipwrecked, Uley Pigs Ear.* **Cider** *Weston. Garden, children's play area. Family room.*

Bridgnorth   Down Inn

Tel 074635 624	**FOOD**
Ludlow Road Bridgnorth Shropshire WV16 6HA	Map 6 B4

This is an atmospheric pub where food is taken fairly seriously but, according to licensees Paul and Beverley Millington, ably assisted by Beverley's father Bill Watson, nothing else need be. Previously known for 250 years as the Unicorn, the pub is on the B4364, some two and a half miles from Bridgnorth on the Ludlow road and, despite some development in the rather ponderous style of the 1960s, still aims to remain as traditional a pub as possible. Some modern innovations are more welcome, like fresh machine-squeezed-to-order orange juice. Most people would opt for one of the beers though, with national brands like Websters, Ruddles and Ansells appearing alongside the likes of Fullers ESB or Royal Oak in the five guest slots. The new list of wines, 25% of which are New World wines, offers five house wines and a choice of locally produced English varieties. Unsurprisingly, the food retains a similarly traditional feel: the ploughman's (£2.75) is available with up to thirty British cheeses (Berkswell, Llanboidy – Welsh cheese from a rare Red Poll milking herd). There are plenty of steaks, and a traditional Sunday lunch is served throughout the bar and restaurant. Both menus have a seasonal bias, so that pheasant, venison and guinea fowl come into their own in autumn as the Down's celebrated fresh fish and garden produce become more scarce. Nonetheless a late summer specials board spoils for choice: home-potted shrimps (£2.95), baked scallops with herbs and garlic (£4.50), sauté of chicken livers with lemon and pomegranate juice (£3.30), pepper-crusted monkfish with red pepper relish (£8.30), trout (£6.85) and fresh salmon (£8.50) represented in various guises. Equally traditional, the bar menu lists shish kebab (£3.10), casserole of wild boar with Calvados and cream (£8.30) and Brixham crab salad (£8.50), served with three fresh vegetables and a daily potato dish. Children's portions of any of these can be provided should young palates have risen beyond the (very fairly priced) fishfingers, baked beans and toasties. "Choccy rum pots", treacle and nut tart, apple Bakewell or fresh fruit vacherin (£2.50) weigh in at the end alongside cafetière or espresso coffee and half a dozen teas, while light opera and classical overtures play softly in the background. *Bar Food and Restaurant Meals* 12-2, 7-9.30 *(except Sun)*. *Vegetarian dishes. Children's menu (£1.60 per dish). Free House.* **Beer** *Constantly changing – five at any one time, plus guest beers. Patio, outdoor eating. Family room. Access, Visa.*

Bridgnorth   Falcon Hotel

Tel 0746 763134 Fax 0746 765401	**B&B**
St John Street Lowtown nr Bridgnorth Shropshire WV15 6AS	Map 6 B4

This white-painted 16th-century inn 10 yards from the river Severn has recently had all public areas decorated and refurbished. All bedrooms offer en-suite facilities, practical modern furnishings, TVs and direct-dial telephones. *Free House.* **Beer** *Draught Bass, Worthington, Tennants. Family Room.* **Accommodation** *15 bedrooms, all en suite, £40 (single £30). Children welcome overnight, additional beds, cots available. Check-in all day. Access, Amex, Visa.*

Bridport   Bull Hotel

Tel & Fax 0308 22878

B&B

34 East Street Bridport Dorset DT6 3LF

Map 13 F2

This white-painted 16th-century coaching inn stands in the historic town centre. There is a pleasant reception area and first-floor lounge and an additional bar with live music at weekends has recently been added by the new owners. There are 23 bedrooms, 18 with full en-suite facilities. Fabrics and wallcoverings are in attractive soft shades with cream-coloured units. *Free House.* **Beer** *Bass, Boddingtons, Castleden, Flowers Original, Royal Wessex.* **Cider** *Scrumpy Jack.* **Accommodation** *23 bedrooms, 18 en-suite, £49 (single £36). Children welcome overnight, additional beds (children 5-14 years old £14), cots available. Check-in all day. Access, Amex, Diners, Visa.*

Bridport   George Hotel

FOOD

Tel 0308 23187

B&B

4 South Street Bridport Dorset DT6 3NQ

Map 13 F2

Delightfully eccentric pub in a handsome Georgian building. Consistently reliable food from a daily-changing menu including excellent snacks such as field mushrooms on toast (£2.50), Welsh rarebit with bacon (£3.20) or cauliflower and Stilton soup (£1.75); fresh fish direct from the quay such as grilled plaice (£4.75) or mussels marinière (£5) and home-made pies (game pie £3.75). There is also a variety of omelettes (from £3.50) and sandwiches, as well as home-made desserts with French apple tart and blackberry and apple pie both at £1.75. An old-fashioned local in style, with young staff and perhaps loud jazz in the bar; the dining room is quieter. Non-residents can get a Continental breakfast from 8.30am. Bedrooms are modest. **Bar Food** *12-2.30 (not Sun), 6.30 (Sun 7)-9.30. Vegetarian dishes. Children's portions.* **Beer** *Palmers Bitter, IPA, Tally Ho. Family room.* **Accommodation** *4 bedrooms, sharing a bathroom, £37 (single £18.50). Children welcome overnight, additional bed (£12.50 over 7 years), cots supplied. Check-in all day. Access, Visa.*

Brighton   Greys

FOOD

Tel 0273 680734

105 Southover Street Brighton East Sussex BN2 2UA

Map 11 B6

Jackie Fitzgerald's splendid cooking draws the lunchtime crowds to this lively, popular little pub. The handwritten menu changes constantly but usually includes four starters and six main courses like pastry horn filled with seafood in a Pernod cream and saffron sauce (£3.50), warm chicken liver salad with raspberry vinaigrette (£3), poussin with wild rice and kumquat sauce (£6) and fillet of salmon with lime butter (£6). Mainly fish, poultry and game are used. Live music Sunday lunchtimes and Monday evenings. **Bar Food** *12.30-2 (not Sun). Vegetarian dishes. Children's portions.* **Beer** *Flowers Original, Castle Eden Bitter, Charles Wells Eagle, guest bitter every 3-4 months. Patio/terrace, outdoor eating. No credit cards.*

Brightwell Baldwin   Lord Nelson

FOOD

Tel 0491 612497

Brightwell Baldwin Nr Watlington Oxon OX9 5NP

Map 16 C2

Already a couple of hundred years old when it was named after
Admiral Nelson – the pub's name was changed to Lord Nelson when
England's most famous sailor was elevated to the peerage – some later
additions to the original stone buildings include 18th-century gable
ends and a quaint verandah at the front, where it faces the village
church of a sleepy hamlet. Inside it is immediately clear that this is a
'foodie' pub; half is set up as a restaurant and raffia place mats on the
remaining tables are ready to receive the bar snacks. Peter Meal is the
man behind the bar while partner Richard Britcliffe is in the kitchen
preparing the food. The restaurant menu (also available in the bar)
ranges from smoked salmon (£6.95) and steak and kidney pie (£6.95)
to melon and strawberries with white port (£4.25) and guinea fowl
with a creamy cider and onion sauce (£9.45). The more snacky bar
menu might include Welsh rarebit (£4.55), pasta dishes and
ploughman's lunch (£4.25). There's a patio with tables for summer
eating and a pretty garden overhung by a large weeping willow. The
pub reopened in 1974 after having been closed for nearly 70 years
because the local squire disapproved of strong drink. *Bar Food* 12-2,
7-10. *Restaurant Meals* 12-2, 7-10 (*except Sunday eve*). *Children's
portions. Free House.* **Beer** *Brakspear's Ordinary. Garden, outdoor eating.
Access, Diners, Visa.*

Brimfield   The Roebuck   ★

FOOD

B&B

Tel 058 472 230   Fax 058 472 654

Brimfield Hereford & Worcester SY8 4NE

Map 14 A1

There's no more individual a pub in these parts than the Roebuck, and
no finer pub restaurant than this one, Poppies. Whether it's a pub with
a restaurant, or a restaurant with rooms doesn't really matter because it
remains the village local. Indeed, the public bar retains just that
atmosphere, whereas the lounge bar, a characterful room with a 15th-
century beamed ceiling and dark oak panels, could be the restaurant. It
isn't – there's a separate dining room which has recently been
refurbished from a bright and cheery room with parquet floor and
cane-back chairs into a more chintzy style, in keeping with the rest of
the building. You can now book tables in the lounge bar, where
Carole's food can also be enjoyed at a fraction of the restaurant price.
Her command of composition and subtle blends of colour and flavour
are frankly bewildering for one who is, it also turns out, self-taught:
the savoury bread and butter pudding with pine kernels and tomato
custard (£5.20) is unique. Warm salad of smoked chicken breast with
sun-dried tomato, crispy bacon and garlic croutons (£6.50), old
fashioned steak and kidney pie (£6.20) and baked queen scallops
stuffed with mushrooms and garlic butter (£7) have all featured
recently in the bar menu. Meanwhile, in the restaurant, diners can
enjoy ham terrine with parsley and white wine jelly (£5.50), and
Cornish brill with two sauces (£15). Either way, there's a
comprehensive list of hot and cold desserts to follow – try the fresh
lemon tart (£4.70) – and some sixteen cheeses from local St Anne's
goat's cheese to faraway Cashel Blue, listed on a separate cheese menu.
And then, if you're wise enough to choose to stay, there are three
lovely cottage bedrooms (two doubles with showers and a twin with
full bathroom) to choose from. Here, you'll find homemade biscuits,

cake, cafetière coffee and quality teas, an example of the care you're likely to receive. A wonderful country breakfast, including Herefordshire apple juice, honey from the garden, and Carole's home-made sausages, will set you up for the day and set the seal on a memorable stay. The Roebuck was our Pub of the Year last year, but sadly in the intervening time Carole's husband John died. His memory, of course, lives on and the excellent wine list (with five pages of half bottles) remains as a tribute to just one of his many ideas that have led to this pub being one of the best around. **Bar Food and Restaurant Meals** (except Sun/Mon) 12-2, 7-10. Vegetarian dishes. Free House. **Beer** Woods, Tetley. Patio/terrace, outdoor eating. **Accommodation** 3 bedrooms, all en suite, £60 (single £35). Children welcome overnight (minimum age 8). Check-in all day. Pub and accommodation closed one week in Oct, fortnight in Feb. Access, Amex, Visa.

Brinkworth   Three Crowns

Tel 066 641 366

Brinkworth nr Chippenham Wiltshire SN15 5AF   Map 14 C2

The rambling, cosy interior offers quiet corners for tete-à-tetes; two of the tables are 18th-century former bellows. Nice setting on village green by church. **Beer** Archers Village, Bass, Wadworth 6X. Garden. Children's play area.

Brisley   Bell

Tel 0362 668108

The Green Brisley Norfolk NR20 5DW   Map 10 C1

16th-century pub with original beams and winter log fires in its three inglenooks. In the small cottage to the rear, Richard Taverner translated the Bible from Latin into English in 1575. The Bell overlooks the largest common land in Norfolk, at some 200 acres; just 200 yards from the village centre. **Beer** Whitbread, Tetley Bitter, Burton Ale, Woodfordes. Children's play area.

Bristol   Highbury Vaults

Tel 0272 733203   **A**

164 St Michael's Hill Ringsdown Bristol Avon B52 8DE   Map 13 F1

A serious contender for Bristol's smallest pub, close to the University and Infirmary, thus popular with students and nurses. Six bar stools, the tiny bar and rear patio are all often crowded with young imbibers who seem to enjoy the odd libation. **Beer** Smiles, Brains. Garden.

Broad Campden   Bakers Arms

Tel 0386 840515

Broad Campden nr Chipping Campden Gloucestershire GL55 6UR   Map 16 A1

This old village granary makes a delightful country pub, with its Cotswold stone walls and oak beams, splendid old bar counter and good mix of furnishings, a framed hand-woven rug outside of the inn, and large open fire where logs crackle in winter. A good base for a walk and light lunch; it gets very busy. Let them know if you are intending to leave your car in the car park while off on an extended ramble. **Beer** Eugene Rail Ale, Butcombe, Donnington, Theakston Best & XB. Garden. Children's play area.

Broad Chalke   Queens Head

Tel 0722 780344   **B&B**

Broad Chalke nr Salisbury Wiltshire SP5 5EN   Map 14 C3

100 yards from the River Ebble and once the village bakehouse, the
Queens Head has cleverly switched its monopoly from cakes to ale
having outlasted the three other inns in the parish. The main Village
bar has stone walls, a beamed ceiling and an inglenook. There is a
sheltered courtyard for outdoor drinking, across which lies the new
accommodation block housing four light and airy bedrooms with
floral fabrics, some period furniture, remote- control TVs and direct-
dial telephones. *Free House.* **Beer** *Bass, Wadworth 6X, Ringwood Best,
Hook Norton.* **Accommodation** *4 bedrooms, all en suite, £45 (single
£30). No children under 10. No dogs. Check-in all day. Access, Amex,
Visa.*

Broadhembury   Drewe Arms

Tel 040 484 267

Broadhembury Devon EX14 0NF   Map 13 E2

Quaint little thatched pub, in a similar Tudor village unique in its
preservation. The pub was built in 1298 to house masons working on
the local church; the delightful interior, with its romantic mullion
windows, features some 15th-century linenfold panelling. *Free House.*
Beer *Cotley Tawny, Otter Bitter, Bass. Garden.*

Broadway   Crown & Trumpet

Tel 0386 850202

Church Street Broadway Hereford & Worcester WR12 7EE   Map 16 A1

Picturesque village inn just off the green. **Beer** *Boddington, Flowers IPA
& Original.*

Brockhampton   Craven Arms

Tel 0242 820410   **FOOD**

Brockhampton Gloucestershire GL54 5XH   Map 16 A1

A deservedly popular pub hidden down winding lanes deep in the
rolling Gloucestershire countryside: Brockhampton is 2 miles north of
the A436 Cheltenham to Gloucester road. Approached under a
stone lych gate, the garden extends to an enclosed paddock with a children's
play area which includes a small summer house containing games for
soggier days. Revealed within the Craven Arms are stone-flagged
floors and a warren of rooms given over primarily to eating. Real ales
are well represented the bar, where the less adventurous may order
smoked salmon quiche (£6.50) and steak sandwiches with chips
(£4.50). The daily blackboard menu, though, is the thing to go for,
chicken in Stilton sauce (£6.50), poached salmon with lime and
pistachios (£8.95) or Dundee lamb (£7.50) representing both quality
and value. Dining tables are predominantly pine, their evening
adornment of fresh carnations and candles quite in keeping with the
pub's relaxed environment: the girls who serve are friendly and
informal too. **Bar Food** *12-2, 7-9.30 (except Sun).* **Restaurant Meals**
7-9.30 (except Sun). Vegetarian dishes. Children's portions. Free House.
Beer *Butcombe, Hook Norton, Wadworth 6X. Garden, outdoor eating,
children's play area. No credit cards.*

Brockton   Feathers

Tel 074 636 202	**FOOD**
Brockton nr Much Wenlock Shropshire TF13 6JR	Map 6 B4

The historic Feathers stands at a crossroads on the B4378 Much
Wenlock to Craven Arms road, signed left to Bridgnorth and right to
Church Stretton. Deceptively small outside, it's half-timbered at one
end and stone-clad to the rear, where the entrance leads via a
picturesque patio through the conservatory. Inside, it divides into an
intimate public bar where one corner table is formed by a huge
bellows on legs, and three interconnecting rooms, on two levels,
devoted largely to eating. Martin and Andrea Hayward's first two
years here, after long experience in the wine bar and bistro trade, have
signalled the arrival of some serious pub food, commendable for both
its quality and diversity. A two-page handwritten menu is
supplemented by an extensive range of blackboard specials: home-
made soup (£1.95), garlic mushrooms (£2.95) with granary bread,
salami and tomato salad (£3.45). Of more substantial stuff are main
courses, including rack of pork (£7.95) or salmon Wellington
(£8.25) and chicken tournedos (£8.95). Traditional puddings (£2.45)
are guaranteed to fill up every remaining corner; raspberry and
nectarine crumble and crème caramel with fresh blackberries are
typical. Beer drinkers will enjoy a good pint of hand-pulled Banks
bitter, house wine comes by the bottle, glass or goblet, there are half a
dozen each of named reds and whites by the bottle, and coffee arrives
in a cafetière. Andrea's kitchen hand-bell announces when each
cooked-to-order dish is ready, ensuring prompt delivery to tables;
salad and garnishes are generous and Martin arrives equally promptly
with the two-pint jug of home-made dressing. *Bar Food 12-2.30,
6.30-9.30 (7-9 Sun). Vegetarian dishes. Children's menu (£1.75 per dish).
Free House. Beer Banks's Bitter, Bass. Patio, outdoor eating. No credit
cards.*

Bromham   Greyhound Inn

Tel 0380 850241	**FOOD**
Bromham nr Chippenham Wiltshire SN15 2HA	Map 14 B2

Just three miles from Devizes Locks (longest set of locks in Europe),
this lively pub is run with enterprise and verve. Parts of it go back
300 years – in the more recent bar extension, an old well still remains
in the middle of the room. The menu is often ingenious, featuring fine
Malaysian dishes, e.g. sambal udang (£6.40). There are two dining-
rooms seating 18 and 50 respectively but everyone eats everywhere in
the Greyhound – pork devils (£5.90), crab and mushroom bake
(£3.10), chicken thingies (£5.90), whole fresh crab (£6.10), and on
Sunday the roast lunch main course is £4.50. Tons of atmosphere,
thanks largey to bric-a-brac festooned walls and ceilings in both bars –
over 500 advertising jugs in one! Intriguingly-named puddings
(£2.30): Mars Bar cheesecake, toffee nutty banana pudding and tiddly
nickers. Parents can get extra plates for informal children's portions.
*Bar Food 12-2, 7-10.30. Vegetarian dishes. Free House. Beer Wadworth
IPA and 6X. Garden, outdoor eating, children's play area. No credit cards.*

Brompton-on-Swale   Crown

Tel 0748 811666

Richmond Road Brompton-on-Swale North Yorkshire DL10 7UE   Map 5 D3

The Italian landlord brings a touch of the Med to North Yorkshire.
Very close to Catterick racecourse. *Garden. Children's play area.*

Broom   Cock Inn

Tel 0767 314411   **FOOD**

23 High Street Broom Bedfordshire SG18 9NA   Map 17 F1

Stretching back from the only street of a village with no middle, no
shops and a postage stamp-sized post office in the postmistress's front
room, the Cock is a conversion of three interlinked Victorian cottages,
its three panelled sitting areas furnished with bench seats and varnished
tables, and a games room complete with the locally popular chair-
skittles table. Look inside the two front rooms and find a novel
collection of metallised tobacco adverts and shelves of aged beer and
medicine bottles. The bar, central to everything here, is unchanged for
over a century, its cellar down four wooden steps, where the Greene
King IPA and Abbot ales are drawn direct from the cask. A new
dining-room has been created in the next cottage which seats 22. The
emphasis is on Jackie Little's country-style dishes – home-made soup
(£1.75), lamb and apricot pie (£4.50), mushroom stroganoff (£4.50),
or the dependable steak, mushroom and Guinness pie (£4.50). Also
particularly popular – and meals in themselves – are the Vienna rolls
filled with hot beef (£2.95), gammon (£2.50) or sausage (£2.25).
Children are now made equally welcome and offered smaller portions
of almost anything. *Bar Food 12-2, 7-9.30. Vegetarian dishes. Children's
menu (£2.50). Beer Greene King IPA, Rayment Special, Abbot Ale.
Garden, outdoor eating. Family room. No credit cards.*

Broom   Broom Tavern

Tel 0789 773656   **FOOD**

High Street Broom Warwickshire B50 4HL   Map 14 C1

Timbered 16th-century village pub, still very much a local despite its
popularity for food, which is good and reliable. Bar food suggestions:
French onion soup (£2), Cumberland cottage pie (£6), seafood
mornay (£6) and puddings such as fresh fruit pavlova or chocolate
rum crunch (both £2.50). A novel dish for two in the restaurant is
appropriately called Can't Decide (£6.50) since it is a selection of all
the starters. The decision is hopefully easier with the main courses –
halibut with asparagus (£11.30), surf and turf (£13) or duck
Montmorency (£12.90) are some choices. *Bar Food 12-2, 6.30-10.
Restaurant Meals 12-2, 7-10. Vegetarian dishes. Children's menu. Beer
Bass, Marston, Whitbread. Garden, outdoor eating, children's play area.
Family room. Access, Visa.*

Broseley   Cumberland Hotel

Tel 0952 882301

Jackson Avenue Broseley Shropshire TF12 5NB   Map 6 B4

Handsome, family-run Victorian hotel in its own grounds, two miles
from the famous Iron Bridge. *Beer Webster's Yorkshire, Ruddles Best,
Bass. Garden. Children's play area. Family room.*

Broughton   Red Lion

Tel 0652 652560	**FOOD**

High Street Broughton Humberside DN20 0HY

Map 7 D2

In an area distinctly lacking in good pubs, it's refreshing to find one as fine as the Red Lion, a part redbrick, part pebbledash building dominating the main village street. There are two bars, one either side of a main entrance, the first a high-ceilinged locals' public, its well-trodden black and red tiling topped with modest furniture, and a masculine simplicity rather compromised by tasteful patterned wallcoverings in subtle tones of pink. The smaller, carpeted lounge is quieter and more intimate, its walls almost wholly panelled and decorated with assorted china and prints, the large window hung with pretty chintzy curtains. Food is the domain of landlord Melvyn Beniston. Fresh produce is used and a good choice of butcher means meat is notably good: tender, pink-cooked lamb chops come with real chips, crisp and perfectly fried. Vegetables, too, are done with excellent care: al dente carrots, fresh celery provençale and broccoli with a bite. Daily-changing specials (a larger choice at weekends when the pub's at its busiest) typically include brunch, poached smoked haddock, and liver and onions, while the standard printed menu begins with freshly made sandwiches, salads and omelette and moves on to house specialities like kidneys Portuguese (£2.15), chicken Hussar (£5.95), prepared and served with no little care and attention. Desserts are good too, perhaps a treacle sponge (£1.45) or a delicious strawberry shortcake (£1.75). Set Sunday lunch offers a choice of roasts at highly competitive prices. It gets very busy. *Bar Food 12-2, 7.30-10 (except Sun eve). No food Mon. Vegetarian dishes. Children's portions.* **Beer** *Mansfield beers. Children allowed in bar to eat. Garden, outdoor eating, summer barbecue. No credit cards.*

Broughton-in-Furness   Black Cock Inn

Tel 0229 716529	

Princes Street Broughton-in-Furness Cumbria L20 6WQ

Map 4 C4

16th-century street-side coaching inn. The renovated lounge bar has beams, a real fire and piney country furniture. **Beer** *Ruddles Best & County. Garden. Family room.*

Buckden   Buck Inn

Tel 0756 760228 Fax 0756 760227	**FOOD**
	B&B

Buckden North Yorkshire BD23 5JA

Map 5 D4

Both the creeper-clad Georgian coaching inn and the village take their names from the fact that this was once the meeting place for local stag hunts; today it is tourists and walkers who are attracted to this fine old inn. The small bar with flagstone floor and old stone fireplace is in great contrast to the smart staff in wing collars and fancy bow ties who offer swift, efficient service both in the extensive, carpeted bar-meal areas with their tapestry banquette seating wheelback chairs, and in the pretty restaurant formed out of what was once the courtyard where local sheep auctions were held. The menu offers something for everybody from snacks like ploughman's (£4.40), jacket potatoes (£2.80) and French stick sandwiches (from £2.75) to full meals with the likes of avocado and mussel salad (£3.25), chicken liver parfait with Cumberland sauce (£3), lasagne al forno (£4.95), poached salmon (£6.75), steaks and specials from the blackboard such as steak and smoked oyster pie (£5.50) and grilled haddock with lemon butter. There are also vegetarian and children's sections, and a long list of home-made puddings at £1.95. Anything from the menu can be eaten in the bar except for the daily changing table d'hote menu (£16.50). Pretty bedrooms with matching floral duvets and curtains are furnished in pine and all have TV, direct dial telephone and tea and coffeemaking kit (although there is also room service available throughout the day and evening). Bathrooms, like the bedrooms, are smart and well-kept, mostly just with showers but four have bathtubs. *Bar Food & Restaurant Meals* 12-2, 6.30-9 (9.30 Fri & Sat, from 7 Sun). *Vegetarian dishes. Children's portions. Free House. Beer Theakstons Old Peculier, Best Bitter, XB. Patio, outdoor eating. Family room. Accommodation 15 bedrooms, all en suite, £60 (single £30). Children welcome overnight, additional beds, cot available. Check-in all day. Access, Visa.*

Buckland Newton   Gaggle of Geese

Tel 030 05 249

Buckland Newton Dorset DT2 7BS   Map 13 F2

Civilised and attractive main bar in tranquil village pub with pretty garden complete with pond. *Free House. Beer Hall and Woodhouse Badger Best. Marston Pedigree, Wadworth 6X, Bass. Garden. Children's play area. Family room.*

Buckler's Hard   Master Builder's House

Tel 0590 616253   Fax 0590 616297   **B&B**

Buckler's Hard nr Beaulieu Hampshire SO42 7XB   Map 15 D4

An 18th-century hotel in a village where many famous ships were built for Nelson's fleet. Heavy beams and rustic furnishings make the Yachtsman's Bar popular with sailors and tourists alike, and residents have their own homely lounge with easy chairs, period furniture and a large inglenook fireplace. Creaky floorboards and old-world charm make the six bedrooms in the main house appealing; rooms in a purpose-built block are plainer but well equipped. The best rooms have four-posters. Children under 14 stay free in parents' room. *Accommodation 23 bedrooms (21 en suite), £80, single (adjacent bathroom) £45. Children welcome overnight, additional beds and cots supplied. Garden. Access, Amex, Diners, Visa.*

Bucks Green   Queen's Head

Tel 0403 822202

Guildford Road Bucks Green nr Rudgwick West Sussex RH12 3JF   Map 11 A6

Well-kept, well-loved 17th-century pub with log fires (some of them cheating ones) and non-smoking areas. *Beer Courage Best & Directors. Children's play area. Family room.*

Burcot   Chequers

Tel 086730 7771   **FOOD**

Abingdon Road Burcot Oxfordshire OX14 3DP   Map 16 C2

Originally a staging post for River Thames barges and their crews, until what is now the A415 was built outside. Charming, part-16th century beamed and thatched building with unspoilt quarry-tiled bars, open fires and a choice of books for customers to read. A daily-changing blackboard menu is the same for the bar and dining room. It offers simple home-made fare – deep-fried Cambazola (£3.25), chicken liver paté (£2.75), Desperate Dan pie (£5.50), breast of duck

(£8.75), broccoli and hazelnut pasta (£4.95) followed by layered
pudding (£1.95) or brown bread ice cream (£1.95) made from the
daily home-baked bread. Piano music on Friday and Saturday nights.
Bar Food and Restaurant Meals (except Sun) 12-2, 6.30-9.30.
*Vegetarian dishes. Children allowed in bar to eat. Beer Ruddles County,
Ushers Best, Websters Keg. Garden, outdoor eating. Access, Visa.*

Burford   The Angel

FOOD

B&B

Tel 0993 822438

Witney Street Burford Oxfordshire OX18 4SN

Map 16 A2

The Angel is situated in a quaint narrow side street at the bottom of
the hill in Burford. Parking is difficult, but worthwhile as this is the
only pub in the area offering this type of menu. The building is
typical Cotswold stone both inside and outside, the bar has two rooms
with open log fires, raffia-seated chairs and mahogany tables. The
restaurant to the rear seats 20 and is more like a cottage dining room.
The floor is covered with an oriental carpet, a Welsh dresser full of
China plates and coffee pots hang from the walls. Candles, flowers and
individual pepper mills are on the tables. No background music. The
food is well served, very hot on hot plates. The melon with Marsala
(£3.95) was ripe, good flavour, the chicken breast was rolled in bacon
and grilled with an excellent home-made stuffing (£7.25). Vegetables
were well cooked, and in plentiful supply. The puddings appeared to be
rather special, the apricot sorbet with home-made wafers was excellent
and a glass of Monbazillac 1988 at £1.75 could accompany it. A 3-course
meal, half bottle of wine, coffee and pudding and service will cost around
£28. There are two letting bedrooms. *Bar Food* 12-2. *Restaurant Meals*
7-9.30. *Vegetarian dishes. Children's portions. Free House. Beer Flowers
IPA, Marston Pedigree. Garden, outdoor eating. Accommodation 2 bedrooms, both en suite, £40 (single £20). Children welcome overnight,
additional beds available. Check-in by arrangement. Access, Visa.*

Burford   Bull Hotel

B&B

Tel 0993 822220

High Street Burford Oxfordshire OX8 4RH

Map 16 A2

Reputed to be the oldest hotel in Burford, the Bull is situated on the
town's main thoroughfare. Downstairs is taken up with two bars on
different levels, and on the first floor is the reception area, which also
serves as a lounge. Two rooms have four-posters and all the furniture
is modern and free-standing. All rooms have en-suite bath or shower
rooms. The others share two neat public bathrooms. New owners.
*Free House. Beer Ruddles Best, John Smith, Webster's. Family room.
Accommodation 14 bedrooms, 10 en suite, £55 (single £27.50).
Children welcome overnight, additional beds and cots available. Check-in all
day. Access, Amex, Diners, Visa.*

Burford   Inn For All Seasons

B&B

Tel 04514 324   Fax 04518 44375

The Barringtons Burford Oxfordshire OX8 4RH

Map 16 A2

If you are thinking of touring the Cotswolds, here is the ideal base, a
solid stone inn beside the A40 about 3 miles west of Burford. It has
been sympathetically preserved to retain its original 17th-century
charm and delightfully furnished from the bar and the residents'
lounge to the neat bedrooms. Front-facing rooms are double-glazed

and all have TVs, tea-makers, trouser presses and simple en-suite bathrooms. *Free House. Beer Hall & Woodhouse Badger Best, Wadworth 6X. Garden. Accommodation 10 bedrooms, all en suite, £70 (single £45). Children over 10 welcomed. No dogs. Check-in all day. Access, Visa.*

Burford   Lamb Inn

Tel 0993 823155

Sheep Street Burford Oxfordshire OX18 4LR   Map 16 A2

Well-loved bed and breakfast inn of great charm and unspoilt character, which contrives to be both upmarket and informal. Lovely public rooms with superior furnishings, rugs in the lounge, bare stone floors in the public bar. Log fires. The garden is a little suntrap. *Free House. Beer Wadworth IPA & 6X. Old Timer (in winter). Family room.*

Burford   Mermaid

Tel 0993 822193   **FOOD**

High Street Burford Oxfordshire OX18 4QF   Map 16 A2

Reliably good food, with a separate lunchtime menu serving the bar and new conservatory. Hot meals start at about £4.50 – scampi (£5.95), Cumberland sausage (£4.75), medium-sized cod (£4.50). Meanwhile the à la carte menu is being served in the two restaurants and takes over in all areas in the evening – chef's soup (£2), moules marinière (£4.95), fillet of beef Wedgwood (£14.95), salmon Wellington (£9.95). Flagstoned, romantically gloomy bar of unspoilt charm; on sunny days the wide pavement's tables are the place to be. *Bar Food and Restaurant Meals 12-11. Vegetarian dishes. Beer Morlands. Patio/terrace, outdoor eating. Access, Visa.*

Burghclere   Carpenters Arms

Tel 0635 27251   **FOOD**

Harts Lane Burghclere Berkshire RG14 9JY   Map 16 C4

From the outside it is one of those square, white-painted, undistinguished pubs that date from the early 1880s, inside it is delightfully homely with the odd sofa and armchair mixed up with the more usual pub furniture, fresh flowers, sepia-tinted photos, gleaming brass ornaments and a friendly smile of welcome. Most of the eating is done in a little conservatory to the rear. The varied, imaginative menu – half daily specials written up on blackboards above the bar – includes Staffordshire oatcakes filled with cheese and smoky bacon, goat's cheese on mixed leaves with toasted peanuts (£4.50), grilled lemon sole on the bone (£7.50), bahmi goreng – an Indonesian dish (£6.25), pork tenderloin with Stilton and cream sauce (£7.95) and moules marinière (£5.95). There is also a variety of sandwiches from £1.80 and ploughman's from £3. Three or four desserts come daily from a good local patisserie. *Bar Food & Restaurant Meals 12-2.30, 7-9.30 (except Mon eve). Vegetarian dishes. Children's portions. Free House. Beer Archers Golden, Fullers London Pride. Garden, Outdoor eating. Access, Visa.*

Burham   Golden Eagle

Tel 0634 668975

80 Church Street Burham Kent ME1 3SD   Map 11 B5

Original beams, mugs, jugs, views of the North Downs and some Malaysian dishes on the menu. *Beer Marston Pedigree, Flowers Original, Wadworth 6X.*

Buriton   Five Bells

Tel 0730 63584

High Street Buriton nr Petersfield Hampshire GU31 5RX

Map 15 D3

Nicely refurbished 16th-century pub 400 yards from the start of the South Downs Way walk; four large open fires are cheering to cold-numbed ramblers. *Free House.* **Beer** *Ballards Best, Badger Tanglefoot, Friary House Best, Fullers London Pride. Garden.*

Burnham-on-Crouch   Olde White Harte Hotel

B&B

Tel 0621 782106   Fax 0621 782106

The Quay Burnham-on-Crouch Essex CM0 8AS

Map 11 C4

Scenically located town-centre pub overlooking the yachting marina; the waterside terrace is lovely in summer. Two characterful wood-panelled bars have polished oak furnishings and a nautical atmosphere; there's also a small residents' lounge. Ask for one of the bedrooms with a window seat overlooking the estuary. *Free House.* **Beer** *Adnams Bitter, Tolly Cobbold Bitter. Family room.* **Accommodation** *19 bedrooms, 11 en suite, from £59.40 (single £37.40). Children welcome overnight, cots available. Check-in all day. No credit cards.*

Burnham-on-Sea   Royal Clarence Hotel

Tel 0278 783138

The Esplanade Burnham-on-Sea Somerset TA8 1BQ

Map 13 E1

Overlooking the Estuary, the Royal Clarence (once a coaching inn) is now much modernised with rather downmarket looking bars. Beers include two of their own; Clarence Pride and Repent. *Other Beers Butcombe Bitter, Wadworth 6X. Family room.*

Burpham   George & Dragon

FOOD

Tel 0903 883131

Burpham Nr Arundel West Sussex BN18 9RR

Map 11 A6

Signposted off the A27 near Arundel, Burpham is at the end of two miles of a winding, climbing lane. At the end one is rewarded with some fine views of the Arun valley, with Arundel Castle in the distance, and the pretty George & Dragon with its good food and real ales. Once the haunt of smugglers, the mid-18th-century inn is now divided into two very different halves; the bar with its exposed timbers, rustic tables and country chairs, and the smart dining room with crisp white napery and elegant Regency-style chairs. The printed bar food menu covers the standard items – home-made soup (£2.50), deep-fried mushrooms with garlic (£2.85), steaks, jacket potatoes, ploughman's and sandwiches – while a daily-changing blackboard menu lists the likes of beef stew with dumplings (£5.75) whole lobster salad (£15) vegetable moussaka (£4.95) and sweet and sour chicken (£5.55). Another blackboard lists a particularly good range of home-made puds (all at £2.50) from apple strudel and gateau Pithiviers to boozy caramel slice and bread-and-butter pudding. **Bar Food** *12-2, 7-9.45.* **Restaurant Meals** *12-2.30 (Sunday only), 7-9.30 (except Sunday). Vegetarian dishes. Children's portions. Free House.* **Beer** *Harveys, guest beers. Terrace, outdoor eating. Access, Visa.*

Burrough-on-the-Hill   Stag & Hounds

Tel 066 477 375

Burrough-on-the-Hill nr Melton Mowbray Leicestershire LE14 2JQ   Map 7 D3

Village local with some unique beers, Lloyds of Ingleby brew, a Stag
Bitter and a Hounds Premium brewed to the landlord's recipe. *Other
beers Bateman XB, Marston Pedigree. Garden. Children's play area.
Family room.*

Bursledon   Jolly Sailor

Tel 0703 40555

Lands End Road Old Bursledon Bursledon Hampshire SO3 8DN   Map 15 D4

Harbourside pub, a retreat for yachtsmen ever since the days of Lord
Nelson and used as a set for BBC TV's *Howard's Way*. Lovely
position, with outdoor drinking overlooking the river and its many
boats. Nautical front bar with good views, and flagstoned back bar,
both notably well-kept and managed. *Beer Badger Best and Tanglefoot,
Gales HSB, Everards Old Original, Wadworth 6X. Riverside garden.*

Burston   Greyhound

Tel 088 97 263

Burston nr Stafford Staffordshire ST18 0PR   Map 6 C3

Simple country pub with a plainly furnished, carpeted interior and
'playland' for children. *Beer Burtonwood Bitter, Tetley, Burton Ale.
Garden. Children's play area. Family room.*

Burton   Old House at Home

Tel 0454 218227   **FOOD**

Burton nr Chippenham Wiltshire SN14 7LT   Map 14 B2

Somewhat up-market for a village local, the Old House at Home
produces considerably more than the home cooking its name suggests.
Full-time chefs produce such daily fare as steak Dijon (£10.90),
tarragon salmon (£9.30) alongside 'Sally's steak and mushroom pie'
(£6.20) and the 'Chef's vegetable and mushroom stir-fry' (£6.20).
Expect also to pay rather more than standard pub prices as the extras
can mount up a bit: granary bread is 45p. A soft-stone building with a
warm and welcoming timbered interior and log fires in winter, its
real ales include Butcombe, Smiles, Wadworth 6X and regular guest
beers. *Bar Food 12-2 (except Tue), 7-10 (7-9.30 Sun). Vegetarian dishes.
Children's portions. Children allowed in bar to eat at lunchtime only. Free
House. Beer Butcombe, Smiles, Bass, Wadworth 6X, Tanglefoot. Garden,
outdoor eating, children's play area. No credit cards.*

Burton   Plume of Feathers

Tel 0454 218251   **FOOD**

        B&B

Burton nr Chippenham Wiltshire SN14 7LP   Map 14 B2

Antipodean licensees bring a little Eastern magic to their mixed menus
of 'Orientalities' such as Balinese fried chicken (£6.35), Sunday
'Rijsttafel' buffet lunch of Asian dishes and daily curries (£6.35)
graduated in strength from biryani to paralita. Plume smokies (£3.25)
– three types of smoked fish cooked in white sauce and served under
grilled cheese, game casserole (£6.45) and Wiltshire roast ham and
eggs (£5.45) for the less adventurous: home-made sweets and ice
cream specialities. Overnight accommodation in twin rooms with

duvets and matching curtains with radio alarms and tea-makers:
bathrooms are rather spartan. **Bar Food** *12-2, 7-9.30 (7-9 Sun).
Vegetarian dishes. Children's portions. Free House.* **Beer** *Tetley, Marston
Pedigree. Garden, outdoor eating. Family room.* **Accommodation**
*2 bedrooms, both en suite, £42 (single £35). No children overnight.
Check-in by arrangement. Access, Visa.*

Burwash   Bell Inn

Tel 0435 882304	**B&B**
High Street Burwash East Sussex TN19 7EH	Map 11 B6

Heavy carved wooden pews set off rich red walls in the bar, where a
log fire, beams and yellowing plasterwork all add to the superb
traditional character of this early 17th-century inn; it's also friendly,
well-run and clean. Recommended for bed and breakfast; a couple of
the rooms have ancient beams and sloping floors; all have old-
fashioned furniture, and share a neat, functional bathroom. Rooms are
equipped with tea/coffee making facilities and some have TVs (but no
telephones). **Beer** *Harveys, Burwash. Garden.* **Accommodation**
*3 bedrooms, sharing a bathroom, £35 (single £25). Children welcome
overnight. Check-in all day. No dogs. Access, Visa.*

Bury   Church Inn

Tel 061-764 2857	
Castle Hill Road Birtle Bury Greater Manchester BL9 6UH	Map 6 B2

Behind Birtle church, the original 17th-century building is charming
and much extended. **Beer** *Theakston Best and Old Peculier. Garden.*

Bury St Edmunds   Masons Arms

Tel 0284 753955	
Whiting Street Bury St Edmunds Suffolk IP33 1NX	Map 10 C2

Popular town-centre pub serving the famous local brew. **Beer** *Greene
King IPA & Abbot Ale. Children's play area.*

Butleigh   Rose & Portcullis

Tel 0458 50287	
Butleigh nr Glastonbury Somerset BA6 8TQ	Map 13 F2

Solid stone-built roadside pub, stylishly refurbished, with a good mix
of furnishings and a large, attractive dining conservatory.
Beer *Courage, Wadworth 6X. Garden.*

Butterleigh   Butterleigh Inn

Tel 0884 855407	
Tiverton-Cullompton Road Butterleigh Devon	Map 13 E2

Unspoilt farming pub in glorious countryside, just three miles from
junction 5 of the M5 motorway. The two-part main bar is half
lounge, half public end with simple wooden furnishings; a tiny snug
takes just four intimate tables. Inglenook fireplace and old fashioned
pub games. No children indoors. *Free House.* **Beer** *Cotleigh Tawny,
Harrier and Old Buzzard, Mitchells Best. Garden. Children's play area.*

Buttermere   Bridge Hotel

Tel 059 685 252

Buttermere Cumbria CA13 9UZ   Map 4 C3

Handsome roadside stone-built hotel, with a quietly civilised country hotel interior – the bar is distinctly unpubby, but certainly relaxing. The sitting room offers a successful clash of florals, with good squashy sofas and an open fire. **Beer** *Theakston Best, XB & Old Peculier, Youngers Scotch.*

Butterton   Black Lion

Tel 053 88 232

Butterton Staffordshire ST13 7ST   Map 6 C3

Interesting old pub built of Derbyshire stone, with horse brasses, music and games machines in its four small, characterful rooms. Opposite the church. *Free House.* **Beer** *Theakston Best & XB, Youngers Scotch. Garden. Family room.*

Buxhall   Crown

Tel 0449 736521

Mill Road Buxhall Suffolk IP14 3BW   Map 10 C3

A tucked-away 15th-century cottage pub with original beams throughout. *Free House.* **Beer** *Adnams, Greene King IPA, Felinfoel. Garden. Children's play area.*

Byland Abbey   Abbey Inn

Tel 034 76 204

Byland Abbey nr Coxwold North Yorkshire YO6 4BL   Map 5 E4

In an isolated spot, but signposted as a tourist attraction from the A170, this is a rambling, old-fashioned pub sited opposite the popular abbey ruins. Handsome furnishings, flag and board floors and attractive decorative pieces. *Free House.* **Beer** *Tetley Bitter, Theakston Best. Garden. Children's play area. Family room.*

Cadeby   Cadeby Inn

Tel 0709 864009

Main Street Cadeby nr Doncaster South Yorkshire DN5 7SW   Map 7 D2

Stone-built ex-farmhouse pub with a cricket-mad main lounge, comfortable with one or two old pieces and a good open fire. Another little room, to the front, is usually quieter, and there's a separate darts room/public bar. No music. They sell 184 whiskies. *Free House.* **Beer** *Sam Smith, Tetley Bitter, John Smiths Magnet, Courage Directors. Garden. Children's play area. Family room.*

Callington   Coachmakers Arms

Tel 057 98 2567   B&B

Newport Square Callington Cornwall PL17 7AS   Map 12 C3

New owners have recently taken over this bright 300-year-old inn close to the centre of town alongside the A388. Wooden settles and exposed beams characterise the bar areas and it's a popular place for the locals to meet. The bedrooms are furnished in neat modern style. Prints hang on the plain-painted walls and all rooms have duvets, TVs and tea-makers. The largest room has its own patio, and there is double-glazing throughout. Private facilities are standard, three with

showers and one with a bath. *Free House. **Beer** Bass, guest bitters.*
Accommodation 4 bedrooms, all en suite, £37 (single £24). Children
welcome overnight. Check-in all day. Access, Diners, Visa.

Cambridge   Cambridge Blue
Tel 0223 61382

85/87 Gwydir Street Cambridge Cambridgeshire CB1 2LG   Map 15 F1

Rowing-mad, cosy little pub in a row of terraced houses. Quiet and
traditional in feel apart from a nasty modern quiz machine, with open
fires and solid old furniture. Three rooms include a tiny snug and
another reserved for non-smokers. A nicer garden than you might
expect in the backstreets of a city features a boules pitch. No children
indoors. ***Beer** Banks's & Taylor. Garden.*

Cambridge   Free Press
Tel 0223 68337   **FOOD**

Prospect Row Cambridge Cambridgeshire CB1 1QU   Map 15 F1

Tiny, highly atmospheric rowing-mad pub tucked away behind the
police station, close to the city centre. Simply furnished, unspoilt
interior, the snug also used as the dining area, and rowing photographs
everywhere. It gets extremely busy; be early. Simple, hearty home
cooking is of the sort to defrost a cold-numbed oarsman – try the
home-made soup (£1.75), followed by a raised pie (£4.50) and finish
with carrot cake (£1.65). ***Bar Food** 12-2, 6.30-8.30. Vegetarian dishes.
Children's portions. **Beer** Greene King IPA, Abbot. Patio/terrace, outdoor
eating. No credit cards.*

Cambridge   Tram Depot
Tel 0223 324553

Dover Street Cambridge Cambridgeshire   Map 15 F1

Sister-pub of the celebrated Victoria at Earl Soham (*qv*), brilliantly
converted from the old Cambridge Street Tramway Company stables,
in classic alehouse style. No music. ***Beer** Earl Soham Victorian Bitter,
Gannet Ale.*

Canfield End   Lion & Lamb
Tel 0279 870257

Canfield End Essex CM6 1SR   Map 11 B4

Popular family dining pub, with cold buffet, salad table, and large car
park. ***Beer** Adnams Southwold Bitter, Ridleys IPA. Garden. Children's
play area.*

Canterbury   Falstaff Inn
Tel 0227 462138   Fax 0227 463525   **B&B**

8 St Dunstan's Street Canterbury Kent CT2 8AF   Map 11 C5

A centuries-old coaching inn by the outer walls of the city. Day
rooms get character from original beams, leaded windows and
polished oak tables. Bedrooms are neat and pretty and the majority use
solid modern furniture that suits the feel of the place perfectly.
Children under 16 are accommodated free – with a full traditional
English breakfast – when sharing with an adult. Within easy walking
distance of the town centre, near the Westgate Tower. Lansbury
(Whitbread) Hotels. ***Accommodation** 24 bedrooms, £87.50. Children
welcome overnight, additional beds and cots available. No dogs. Access,
Amex, Diners, Visa.*

Cardington   Royal Oak

Tel 069 43 266

Cardington nr Church Stretton Shropshire SY6 7JZ   Map 6 A4

Old country free house in a pretty spot. Pleasing, relaxing bar mixes
traditional and modern, with a good log fire and nice decorative bits
and pieces. There's also a noisy games machine bar upstairs. *Free House.*
Beer *Springfield Bitter, Bass, Ruddles County, Wadworth 6X.*

Carey   Cottage of Content

Tel 0432 840242   **B&B**

Carey Hereford & Worcester HR2 6NG   Map 14 B1

Signposted from Hoarwithy, and enjoying a tranquil rural setting
beside a hump-backed bridge over a tributary of the river Wye is this
delightful 500-year-old pub which is indeed aptly named. Staff are
friendly and welcoming in the tiny beamed bars, where open fires and
ancient settles add to the old-world charm. Upstairs, thick walls,
beams and sloping floors are complemented by sturdy oak furnishings
in the four cottage bedrooms. All have simple carpeted bathrooms,
tea-makers and TVs. *Free House.* **Beer** *Hook Norton Best Bitter & Old
Hookey.* **Ciders** *Old Rosey. Garden.* **Accommodation** *4 bedrooms, 3 en
suite, £45 (single £30). Children welcome overnight. Check-in by
arrangement. Access, Amex, Visa.*

Carthorpe   Fox & Hounds

Tel 0845 567433   **FOOD**

Carthorpe Bedale North Yorkshire DL8 2LG   Map 5 E4

Very popular dining pub in a delightful village ex-blacksmith's, with
an attractively modernised L-shaped bar and high-ceilinged dining
room with exposed rafters. The same menu, fairly restauranty in style
and price, applies in both – duck and asparagus terrine(£3.95), white
Stilton and onion soup (£1.95), fresh crab (£4.95), chicken breast
filled with Coverdale cheese (£6.95), rolled lemon sole fillet filled
with salmon and prawns (£7.95), rack of English lamb (£7.95). **Bar
Food and Restaurant Meals** *(except Monday) 12-2, 7-10. Children's
portions. Free House.* **Beer** *John Smith, Tetley, Younger. Pub is closed on
Mondays. No credit cards.*

Cartmel Fell   Masons Arms   ★

Tel 04488 486   **FOOD**

Strawberry Bank Cartmel Fell Grange-over-Sands Cumbria LA11 6NW   Map 4 C4

The only problem with the perfect pub is that too many people know
about it, and so it is with the justifiably famous, well-loved Masons
Arms, a classic if ever there was one. The setting is glorious – perched
on the hillside at Strawberry Bank with Lakeland views in all
directions, and the interior is equally inspiring, a series of quaint,
unspoilt little farmhouse rooms. In the main bar are polished old
flagstones, a big open fire, sagging ceiling beams, simple country
furniture and well-chosen pictures. Several cottagey anterooms offer
old pews, odd bits of furniture, a sideboard, an old stove, and a curious
little cupboard set into the wall. Tiny thickset windows frame pretty
valley views; rough stone walls are freshly whitewashed. Aside from
excellent bar food, there's the widest choice of drinks to be found

anywhere – including their own three home brews, and, in edition II of their comprehensive bottled beer list, well over 200 interesting international names, including Kriek and Weizenthaler. The blackboard menu offers a pleasing variety of home-made dishes including half a dozen or so vegetarian choices. Simple country casseroles, like coachman's (£7.50) and damson and pork hotpots are the star of the list; pies are good too. Also on offer are spare ribs (£6.95), spinach and pepper lasagne (£5.50), cashew chicken (£6.95) or fennel and cashew nut bake (£5.25). Puddings, mostly of the good old-fashioned sort, are also not to be missed. Simple, well-cooked food tastes outstandingly fine in such splendid surroundings; be early for a seat on the terrace in summer. *Bar Food 12-2, 6-8.45. Vegetarian dishes. Children's portions. Free House. Beer Lakeland beers (brewed here). Cider Westons. Garden, outdoor eating. Family room. No credit cards.*

Casterton   Pheasant Inn

| Tel 05242 71230 | **B&B** |

Casterton Kirkby Lonsdale Cumbria LA6 2RX   Map 4 C2

This well-maintained, white pebbledash building at the heart of the village enjoys some fine rear views over open country to the hills beyond. At the front, next to the A683, a colourful paved patio is furnished with rustic tables and bench seating. The Garden Room, a small summery lounge full of parlour plants, leads to the main bar which is sectioned around a central servery; burgundy banquette seating, polished wood tables with fresh flowers, aerial photos of the pub and country pictures on the walls make for a pleasant, restful spot. While by no means luxurious, the bedrooms are both comfortable and well kept, with colour television, direct-dial phones, beverage trays and neat, if rather small, bathrooms. There's one four-poster bed for the romantically inclined, and a twin-bedded ground floor room suitable for the disabled; most bedrooms have lovely countryside views. New proprietors Melvyn and May Mackie took over in April 1991 and are keen to enhance the Pheasant's already enviable reputation; further refurbishment is planned during a brief winter closure early in 1993. *Free House. Beer Jennings, Burton, Tetley. Garden. Family room. Accommodation 10 rooms, all en suite, £52.50, single £37.50. Children welcome overnight, additional beds and cots supplied. Check-in all day. Closed 2 weeks Jan. Access, Visa.*

Castle Ashby   Falcon Hotel

| | **FOOD** |
| Tel 0604 696200   Fax 0604 696673 | **B&B** |

Castle Ashby Northamptonshire NN7 1LF   Map 15 D1

Just six miles from Northampton and easily found off the A428 Bedford road, the Falcon strikes a happy balance between historic country inn and well-appointed modern cottage hotel. Its founding in 1594 is commemorated in the atmospheric cellar bar approached by way of an original flagstone stairway. Bar meals are served here on mahogany-topped beer barrel tables. Daily offerings of carrot and coriander soup (£1.50), soused herrings with potato salad (£1.75), steak and mushroom pie (£4.25) and beef stroganoff (£5.20) are accompanied by a drop of Nix Wincott Two Henry's Bitter brewed in a neighbouring village. Lunch and dinner are also served in the rear dining extension which overlooks a delightful garden; fresh from it come the courgette flowers, artichokes and garden herbs which feature on seasonal menus. Leek sauce accompanies a terrine of pork and chicken, cucumber and dill dress the poached halibut and rack of lamb is garnished with home-made jellies. Sunday lunch is more traditional but no worse value (£12.50). Whitewood furniture and gaily patterned fabrics imbue the main house bedrooms with the country freshness their surroundings suggest; the bathrooms here are immaculately appointed. No less countrified, though rather plainer in decor, are the cottage bedrooms a stone's throw away at the heart of the village, just two minutes walk away from the magnificent grounds and gardens of Castle Ashby House. Home-made jams and jellies are again a memorable feature of the Falcon's hearty country breakfasts. *Bar Food* 7.15-9. *Restaurant Meals* 12.30-2, 7.30-9.30. *Vegetarian dishes. Children's portions. Free House.* *Beer Adnams, Hook Norton Old Hookey, Websters. Garden, outdoor eating.* *Accommodation* 14 bedrooms, all en suite, from £71.50 (single £56.50). Children welcome overnight, additional beds, cot available. Check-in all day. Access, Amex, Visa.*

Castle Cary   George Inn

Tel 0963 50761

Market Place Castle Cary Somerset BA7 7AH   Map 13 F2

Town-centre, listed 15th-century coaching inn, in part even older – the elm beam over the inglenook fireplace in the bar dates back a further 500 years. *Beer Butcombe Bitter, Websters Yorkshire, Wadworth 6X.*

Castle Combe   Castle Inn

FOOD
B&B

Tel 0249 782461

Castle Combe nr Chippenham Wiltshire SN14 7HN   Map 14 B2

Richard and Jean Spencer have recently become the new licensees of this splendid 12th-century inn in a picturesque, traditional village, with a fine medieval market cross and church. Exposed stone walls merge with fitted carpets in the two main bars and the vaulted former wine cellars have become a games room with skittles, pool and other pub games. The food is cooked by Jean and her bar food menu is appetising – soup (£1.95), breast of Melksham chicken in white wine, bacon and mushroom sauce (£6.25), Wiltshire spicy sausage stuffed with mature Cheddar and wrapped in sweet-cure bacon (£4.50), lemon sole (£5.50), T-bone steak (£10.25), poached pears in port (£1.95). Apart from lunch and supper, coffee is served all day and clotted cream teas (£2.75) in the afternoons. Cottagy bedrooms have carpeted bathrooms. According to Richard "warmth and hospitality percolate all day at the Castle". *Bar Food* 12-2.15, 7-9.30. *Vegetarian dishes. Children's portions. Free House.**Beer Wadworth 6X, Hook Norton, Marston Pedigree.* *Cider Scrumpy Jack. Patio, outdoor eating.* *Accommodation* 9 Bedrooms, all en suite, £45. Children welcome overnight. Under-10s free in parents room. Access, Amex, Visa.*

Castleton   Castle Hotel

B&B

Tel 043 362 0578   Fax 043 362 1112

Castle Street Castleton Derbyshire S30 2WG   Map 6 C2

Accommodation is a strong point at this pleasant old inn dating back in part to the 17th century. Comfortable bedrooms in the main house and stable-block annexe are all prettily decorated, with solid darkwood furnishings, including four-posters, and smartly tiled en-suite facilities (3 have whirlpool baths). Despite modernisation, the bars still offer plenty of old-world atmosphere – notably the Castle Bar with its flagstoned floors and low beamed ceilings. New

landlords. *Beer Stones, Bass. Garden, Children's play area.*
Accommodation 9 bedrooms, all en suite, £59 (single £39.50). Children welcome overnight, additional beds and cots available. Check-in by arrangement. Access, Amex, Diners, Visa.

Castleton   Nags Head

FOOD
B&B

Tel 043 3620248

Castleton Derbyshire S30 2WH

Map 6 C2

17th-century coaching house built of severe grey local stone, in a tiny village at the head of Hope Valley, under the hilltop site of Peveril Castle. Bar meals are served both lunchtime and evening with prawn and lobster soup (£1.55), paté-filled mushrooms (£3.10) or fresh codling in parsley sauce (£4.95) on offer; however, the emphasis is very much on the elegant two-tiered restaurant at night, where typical dishes could include deep-fried Brie and apple fritter (£4.50), followed by a rack of lamb for two (£19.50) or chicken with scampi and lobster sauce (£12.50) and for dessert, a brandy snap basket with fresh berries (£3.50). Bedrooms are also elegant, and furnished in a handsome period style, three with four-posters, all well-equipped. The most expensive offer spa baths; the cheapest shower and toilet only. A bright first-floor residents' lounge is done up in chintz and bamboo. *Bar Food 11.30-2.45, 6-10.45 (12-3, 7-10.15 Sun). Restaurant Meals 12-2 (2.30 Sun), 7-10. Vegetarian dishes. Children's portions. Free House. Beer Draught Bass. Cider Taunton. Accommodation 8 bedrooms, all en suite, £52 (single £39.50) Children welcome overnight, additional beds (charge according to age), cot available. Check-in all day. Access, Amex, Diners, Visa.*

Castleton   Moorlands Hotel

B&B

Tel 0287 660206

Castleton nr Whitby North Yorkshire YO21 2DB

Map 5 E3

With Baysdale Beck just east and Esk Dale minutes west Castleton can claim a rugged Moors pedigree, and the Moorlands has bedroom views to prove it. It is a small peaceful hotel at the head of the village with a homely lounge, small TV room and a bar. Bedrooms are simply decorated and offer TVs and tea-making facilities. Six bedrooms have their own compact shower rooms, while the others share two well-kept bathrooms. *Free House. Beer John Smiths Magnet, Tetley Bitter. Accommodation 10 bedrooms, 6 en suite, £38 (single £17). Children welcome overnight, additional beds (½ price over 3), cots available. Check-in all day. No dogs. Pub closed October-March. Access, Visa.*

Cauldon   Yew Tree

A ·

Tel 0538 308348

Cauldon Lane Cauldon nr Waterhouses Staffordshire ST10 3EJ

Map 6 C3

Enjoy Alan East's vast collection of antiques and bric-a-brac, the Persian rugs which overlay original quarry tiled floors, cast-iron copper-top tables, a working pianola and giant Victorian music boxes, which still operate for just 2p. Sleepy and undiscovered it is not, but worth a visit nevertheless: go in the evening and hear the landlord performing on the pianola. *Free House. Beer Bass, Burton Bridge. Family room.*

Cavendish   Bull

Tel 0787 280245

High Street Cavendish Suffolk CO10 8AX

Map 10 C3

Homely 500-year-old village pub run with great style, its mellow
atmosphere enhanced by wall timbers and beams, heavy settles and
lolling dogs. **Beer** *Adnams Bitter, Broadside. Garden.*

Cawston   The Ratcatchers

Tel 0603 871430

Eastgate nr Cawston Norwich Norfolk NR10 4HA

FOOD

Map 10 C1

A pleasantly old-fashioned free house in a rural spot just off the B1149,
one mile south of Cawston. Food's the thing here, and local produce is
a feature. Fish comes in a wide variety (monkfish in a pastry parcel
served on a bed of buttered spinach £8.95) and other choices might
include vegetable curry (£4.85), steak and kidney pie (the pub's
renowned for it) and duck with orange and brandy sauce (£9.95).
Puddings are also given due attention, treacle sponge being a favourite.
Bar Food *11.45-2, 6.30-10.15 (Sun 7-9.45). Vegetarian dishes.
Children's menu/portions. Children allowed in bar to eat. Free House.* **Beer**
Worthington Best, Adnams, Wadworth 6X. No credit cards.

Cerne Abbas   New Inn

Tel 0300 341274

14 Long Street Cerne Abbas Dorset DT2 7JF

B&B

Map 13 F2

A typical Dorset setting and a splendid old inn, a listed 15th-century
former monk's resting house, complete with original stone roof.
There's a priest-hole by the fireplace and charming window seats with
High Street views. Simple bedrooms have sloping floors and plenty of
character. **Beer** *Dorchester Bitter, Hardy Country, Royal Oak. Garden.
Family room.* **Accommodation** *5 bedrooms, sharing 2 bathrooms, £40
(single £25). Children welcome overnight, additional beds (under 12 £10,
over 12 £20), cots supplied. Check-in all day. Access, Amex, Diners, Visa.*

Cerne Abbas   Red Lion

Tel 0300 341441

Long Street Cerne Abbas Dorset DT2 7JF

Map 13 F2

Ancient, Grade II listed pub with a Victorian facade, thanks to a late
19th-century fire. There's also a beautiful 16th-century fireplace,
crackling with logs in winter, a de luxe ladies toilet, and a sheltered
south facing garden. **Beer** *Adnams Southwold, Ringwood Best, Smiles Best,
Wadworth 6X. Garden. Children's play area. Family room.*

Chaddleworth   Ibex

Tel 04882 311

Chaddleworth Berkshire RG16 0ER

FOOD

Map 16 B3

Landlord Colin Brown was once a professional jockey and rode Desert
Orchid in some of his early races. His enthusiasm for the sport,
coupled with the pub's proximity to racing stables, ensures plenty of
horsey talk in the bar – not to mention a television for watching the
racing. Restaurant and bar offer the same menu of imaginative fare
such as chicken livers in mustard and marjoram sauce (£3.25), good
steaks (£9.95), pork fillet in Dijon mustard and brown sugar sauce
(£7.95), and sturdy home-made English puddings featuring chocolate

crunch cake (£2.50) and various fruit crumbles (£2.25). *Bar Food and Restaurant Meals* 12-2, 7-9.30. *Vegetarian dishes. Children's portions. Beer Morland Old Speckled Hen, Old Masters and Original Bitter. Garden, outdoor eating. Family room. Access, Visa.*

Chadlington   Tite Inn

| Tel 060876 475 | **FOOD** |

Mill End Chadlington Oxfordshire OX7 3NY   Map 16 B1

From the outside, this warm 16th-century Cotswold-stone pub is as pretty as a picture, complete with cottage roses clambering up the walls. Inside, the original rough stone walls remain, but otherwise it is almost too neat and tidy, with its modern carpeted floor and wheelback chairs. A table displaying newspapers and magazines is a nice touch, though, and there is also a garden room which features bunches of grapes hanging from a vine covering the roof. The origin of the unusual name is uncertain but is thought to refer to the nearby springs which used to feed a mill pond. Michael Willis behind the bar looks after the real ales, which include the happily named Dr Thirsty's Draught from the local Glenny brewery, while Susan looks after the kitchen. Hearty home-made soups (£1.95) and succulent gammon sandwiches made with superior wholemeal bread are amongst the offerings listed on the regularly changing blackboard menu, although bobotie (£4.95 – a sweet and spicy meat loaf from South Africa) is, by popular demand, a permanent fixture, and there are always several vegetarian dishes available. At night, one end of the bar becomes a restaurant with dishes ranging from chicken breast in cider and honey sauce (£5.95) to duck sausages with Cumberland sauce (£5.95). A traditional roast is served on Sundays (£5.95). Popular puddings include fruit crumble (£1.95), hot sticky toffee pudding (£1.95) and chocolate and rum mousse (£1.95). The set menu is a little shorter in the evening. Children are made genuinely welcome and small portions are no problem. *Bar Food* (except Monday) 12-2, 6.30-9 (12-1.30, 7-8.30 Sun). *Restaurant Meals* 12-2 (Sun only), 7-9 (except Sun and Mon). *Vegetarian dishes. Children's portions. Beer Adnams Bitter, Glennys Bitter, Tanglefoot. Cider Blands. Garden, outdoor eating. Family room. No credit cards.*

Chale   Clarendon Hotel/Wight Mouse Inn

| Tel 0983 730431   Fax 0983 730431 | **FOOD** **B&B** |

Chale Isle of Wight PO38 2HA   Map 15 D4

This 17th-century coaching inn (on B3399) is a perennial favourite, for food, atmosphere, bed and breakfast and the genuine welcome to children: the Wight Mouse Inn was our 1990 Family Pub of the Year. Parents with children are treated like first-class citizens both inside and out. There are decent home-made bar meals too, featuring delicious local fish and seafood including smoked mackerel paté (£2.30), local crab cocktail (£3.10) and breaded cod (£3.60), and an astonishing 365 whiskies. The recently extended dining room has a set five-course dinner menu for £17 which includes dishes such as deep-fried Brie with raspberry sauce, chicken kebabs, stuffed trout and turkey escalopes with Jamaican banana and rum sauce. Nice bedrooms in the Clarendon next door successfully blend period and modern comforts, excellent family facilities and pretty views of the sea. One bedroom has a waterbed and there is also a luxury family suite. *Bar Food and Restaurant Meals* 11.30-10 (12-2.30, 7-9.30 Sun). *Vegetarian dishes. Children's menu/portions. Free House. Beer Burts, Marston Pedigree,*

Wadworth 6X. Family room (3 rooms). Outdoor play area, garden, outdoor eating. **Accommodation** *15 bedrooms, all en suite, £56 (single £28). Children welcome overnight, cots available. Check-in all day. Access, Visa.*

Chapel Amble   Maltsters Arms   ★

Tel 0208 812473	**FOOD**
Chapel Amble Cornwall PL27 6EU	Map 12 B2

This rambling pub isn't outstanding for its character, but the cooking is well above average. A central bar, warmed by a large open fire, has three rooms leading off; one of these is officially the dining area, but tables aren't laid until a food order is made. There are no frills, no tablecloths even, but taped Gilbert and Sullivan creates a civilised and jolly atmosphere and despite the non-restaurantry decor, it's the kind of pub where most customers come to eat. Owner Jeff Pollard does the cooking, while Vivienne runs the bar. Fine fresh ingredients place a particular emphasis on fish and seafood. Start with good home-made soups (£1.95), or grilled sardines (£5.50), followed perhaps by whole Cornish mackerel (£5.50) or a whole grilled plaice (£5.50). Carnivores aren't neglected either: try the home-made Cumberland sausage (£5.50) or breast of chicken (£5.50) from the delightfully varied lunchtime menu. The evening menu allows for choice in style and price too: salad leaves and feta cheese (£4.30) and fish soup (£4.10) are typical starters, and the main courses could include escalope of veal (£9.95), paella (£16.50) or rib steak (£9.95). Puddings are good too with a down-to-earth selection of favourites like bread-and-butter and treacle tart for around £2.75. There's a good range of bottled beers in addition to the rather ordinary draught selection, and Australian wines are now very popular on a notably ungreedy wine list. It's very busy indeed in summer, pretty quiet in winter, when the summer crowds have gone and the seasonal menu is more limited in scope. **Bar Food** *12-2.30, 7-9.30. Vegetarian meals. Children's menus. Free House.* **Beer** *John Smiths, Ruddles County, guest beer. Children allowed in bar to eat. Garden, outdoor eating. Family room. Access, Visa.*

Charing   Old Oak Hotel

Tel 0233 712307	
High Street Charing Kent TN27 0HU	Map 11 C5

Largish courtyard hotel in medieval North Downs village. The snug bar is properly pubby, and the upstairs restaurant is in the old malting room. **Beer** *Boddington, Brakspear, Shepherd Neame.*

Charlbury   Bell Hotel

Tel 0608 810278 Fax 0608 811447	**B&B**
Church Street Charlbury Oxfordshire OX7 3PP	Map 16 B1

Once a coaching inn, the Bell stands in the centre of town on the banks of the Evenlode. Day rooms, including a flagstoned bar dating from the year 1700, have a comfortable, traditional appeal, and bedrooms all have bath or shower rooms en suite. Small functions are catered for and fishing, gliding and hot-air ballooning are among the activities which the hotel can organise. Children up to 16 stay free in parents' room. *Free House.* **Beer** *6X, Hook Norton. Garden.* **Accommodation** *14 bedrooms, £75. Children welcome overnight, additional beds and cots supplied. Access, Amex, Diners, Visa.*

Charlestown   Rashleigh Arms

Tel 0726 73635

Harbourside Charlestown Cornwall PL25 3NJ   Map 12 B3

Large Georgian pub-hotel in charming Cornish port. Three bars. *Beer St Austell Tinners, Bass, Ruddles County, Wadworth 6X. Garden. Children's play area. Family room.*

Charlton   Horse & Groom

Tel 0666 823904   **FOOD**

Charlton nr Malmesbury Wiltshire SN16 9DL   Map 16 A4

Eminently civilised Grade II listed Cotswold stone pub, set well back from the main road. Open log fires, no music, small saloon bar and larger public. Everything is home-made by the landlady Virginia Hall – booking advised for restaurant. Popular bar food snacks include baked potatos with various fillings (£3.15), ploughman's (£3) and paté de campagne (£3.50). The restaurant menu offers pasta carbonara (£6.40), plaice Virginia (£8.85), chili con carne (£6.95) and coronation chicken (£7.95) with several puddings to follow: banoffi pie, lemon cheeseacke (both £2.50) or lemon and vanilla meringue (£3.50). *Bar Food 12-2, 7-9.30. Vegetarian dishes. Children's portions. Beer Archers, Moles, Tetley, Wadworth. Garden, outdoor eating, children's play area. Access, Visa.*

Chatton   Percy Arms Hotel

Tel 06685 244   **B&B**

Chatton Alnwick Northumberland NE66 5PS   Map 5 D1

Popular, pleasantly modernised roadside country inn in a sleepy village, excellent for anglers, with trout and salmon fishing rights on the rivers Tweed and Till. 24 malt whiskies are available in the L-shaped bar. *Free House. Beer Theakstons XB. Garden. Family room. Accommodation 7 bedrooms, 5 en suite, £40 (single £20). Children welcome overnight, cots available. Check-in all day. No credit cards.*

Chedington   Winyards Gap

Tel 0935 891244

Chedington nr Beaminster Dorset DT8 3HY   Map 13 F2

Ancient inn on unique site on the edge of the Dorset Downs, with views across the Axe valley. Pleasantly modernised inside. *Beer Whitbread, Marston Pedigree, Exmoor Ale. Garden. Children's play area. Family room.*

Chedworth   Seven Tuns

Tel 0285 720242   **A**

Chedworth Gloucestershire GL54 4AE   Map 14 C2

Cottagey and atmospheric old alehouse, lost in winding country lanes. Period charm, complete with original settles, hunting prints and log fire in the main bar; simpler public and family room has a games area attached. The lounge is "for adults only"; locals and visitors mix well. There's a waterwheel in the garden and a pretty walled garden across the lane. *Free house. Beer Courage Best and Directors, John Smith's Bitter, Smiles. Garden. Family room.*

Chelsworth   Peacock Inn

Tel 0449 740758

B&B

The Street Chelsworth nr Ipswich Suffolk IP7 7HU

Map 10 C3

Genuinely unspoilt 1470 cottage pub; it's easy to pass by and not
realise it's a pub at all. Inside is oak-timbered, inglenooked, and
attractively dotted with an eclectic mix of pictures, some of which are
for sale. Everything is immaculately kept, including the cottagey
bedrooms, which have washbasins, and share a beamed bathroom. *Free
House.* **Beer** *Adnams, Greene King, Mauldon. Garden.* **Accommodation**
*5 bedrooms, sharing a bathroom, £40 (single £30). Children over 10 yrs
welcome overnight. Check-in all day. No dogs. No credit cards.*

Chenies   Red Lion

Tel 0923 282722

Chenies Buckinghamshire WD3 6ED

Map 17 E2

There's a tiny family room, and equally cramped outdoor eating space.
The comfortably modernised and refurbished L-shaped bar has a
separate dining area to its rear. No music or machines. **Beer** *Ansells
Mild, Benskins Best, Tetley, Burton Ale. Family room.*

Cheriton Bishop   Old Thatch Inn

Tel 0647 24204

Cheriton Bishop nr Exeter Devon EX6 6JH

Map 13 D2

A nice old pub in the Dartmoor National Park and a useful detour
from the A30. No children. *Free House.* **Beer** *Fergusons Dartmoor Best,
Wadworth 6X, Burton Ale.*

Chesham   Black Horse

Tel 0494 784656

Chesham Vale Chesham Buckinghamshire HP5 3NS

Map 17 E2

Much extended village alehouse, its cosy black-beamed original bar
featuring a vast inglenook fireplace, and nice country furniture in the
newer bar, plus a converted barn and large garden to take the
overspill. **Beer** *Benskins, Adnams Best, Glenny Wychwood Best, Burton
Ale. Garden. Children's play area.*

Chesil   Cove House Inn

Tel 0305 820895

Chesil Beach nr Portland Dorset DT5 1AW

Map 13 F3

Gloriously positioned, beach-side pub with a bar and dining room of
subtle, simple, fishing pub atmosphere. Sit outside and enjoy the
sunsets. No children in the bar. **Beer** *Devenish Wessex, Marston
Pedigree, Wadworth 6X, Greene King Abbot.*

Chester   Albion Inn

Tel 0244 340345

2 Park Street Chester Cheshire CH1 1RN

Map 6 A2

Perhaps the last unspoilt Victorian corner pub in Chester, the Albion
is dedicated to the memory of World War I. **Beer** *Greenall Mild and
Bitter, Thomas Greenall Original.*

Chester   Ye Olde Kings Head

Tel 0244 324855	B&B
48/50 Lower Bridge Street Chester Cheshire CH1 1RS	Map 6 A2

Pristine black and white timbered 16th-century inn with overhanging upper storey. Bars are hotelly but retain much of the original woodwork. Many of the bedrooms have recently been updated and part-refurbished, 2 have four-posters. They are attractive and well-equipped with tea/coffee/chocolate making facilities, toiletries, TVs and trouser presses. *Beer Davenport, Greenall Original, Stones. Family Room. Accommodation: 8 bedrooms, all en suite, £50 (4-poster £60) (single £45). Children welcome overnight, additional beds (from £5), cots supplied. Check-in all day. Access, Amex, Diners, Visa.*

Chichester   Nag

Tel 024 378 5823	B&B
3 St Pancras Chichester West Sussex PO19 1FJ	Map 11 A6

This black and white timbered inn has recently been taken over by Prospects Group. There are plans for a major facelift both outside and in. The lively and friendly bar has a 'holy' feel as the seating is made out of old church pews. The bar is open all day and has a garden and patio. One bedroom has full en-suite bathroom, three others have showers and the rest have washbasins and share roomy public facilities. *Beer Flowers, Strongs, Wadworth 6X, Gales HSB. Accommodation 11 bedrooms, 1 en suite, £38 (single £22.50). Children welcome overnight, cots available. Check-in all day. Access, Visa.*

Chickgrove   Compasses

Tel 072 270 318	
Chicksgrove nr Tisbury Wiltshire SP3 6NB	Map 14 C3

Grade II listed pretty inn with a charmingly unspoilt bar; flagstones, inglenook, loads of old timber, and discreet modernisation. *Free House. Beer Adnams Best, Bass, Wadworth 6X and Guest Beers. Garden. Children's play area.*

Chiddingfold   Crown Inn

	FOOD
Tel 0428 682255 Fax 0428 685736	B&B
The Green Petworth Road Chiddingfold Surrey GU8 4TX	Map 11 A5

Built around 1258 as a guest house for pilgrims, the creeper-clad, timber-framed Crown is still offering hospitality to travellers. The soft furnishings in the main bar area may be a little tired but one's eye is taken by the massive old beams and huge inglenook fireplace. A panelled restaurant, of slightly later date, boasts an ornate plaster ceiling and examples of the stained glass for which Chiddingfold was famous during the 13th and 17th centuries. It's managed by a division of the Hall and Woodhouse brewery and refreshment comes in the form of ales with names like Tanglefoot and Badger. The inner man can feast on substantial fare like steak and kidney pie (£5.65), home-made soup (£1.95), beef and lamb hot-pot (£4.75) and sausage and mash with onion gravy (£3.95). More cosmopolitan offerings include spicy chicken in sweet and sour sauce (£4.50) and tagliatelle with mushrooms and peppers (£4.45). Sandwiches start at around £2.20. Creaking stairs and corridors lead to the bedrooms, four full of character with antique furniture (three with four-poster beds), and four lighter and more modern in style. All have remote-control TV,

direct-dial phones and trouser press. **Bar Food** *12-2.30, 7-9.30.*
Restaurant Meals (*except Monday*) *12-2.30, 7-9.30. Vegetarian dishes.*
Beer *Tanglefoot, Badger. Terrace, outdoor eating.* **Accommodation**
8 bedrooms, all en suite, from £57 (£47). Children welcome overnight,
additional beds and cots available. Check-in all day. Access, Amex, Diners,
Visa.

Chiddingly   Six Bells

Tel 0825 872227	A
Chiddingly nr Lewes East Sussex BN8 6HE	Map 11 B6

Highly atmospheric, old-fashioned pub with attractive window boxes,
roses in the garden, simple furnishings, three open fires, a pianola in
the back bar, and an overflow bar-cum-function room. Located where
the Weald Way crosses the Vanguard Way, walkers find this pub a
welcoming sight. Open fires in the winter. Extremely busy at
weekends. *Free House.* **Beer** *Courage Best and Directors, Harvey. Garden,*
outdoor eating.

Chieveley   Blue Boar Inn

Tel 063 524 8236 Fax 063 524 8506	B&B
North Heath Chieveley Newbury Berkshire RG16 8UA	Map 16 C3

Overlooking the Berkshire Downs, the Blue Boar is an attractive
16th-century thatched inn beside the B4494 with a homely,
welcoming feel in its low beamed main bar. Purpose-built bedrooms
surrounding a central courtyard can be reached by a separate entrance
and include both antique-furnished four-poster and half-tester rooms
and some compact singles. All offer carpeted bathrooms, TVs, tea-
makers, direct-dial telephones and radio-alarms. New owners. *Free*
House. **Beer** *Wadworth 6X, IPA. Garden.* **Accommodation** *15 bedrooms,*
all en suite, £57 (single £42). Children welcome overnight, additional beds
available. Check-in all day. Access, Amex, Diners, Visa.

Chilgrove   White Horse

Tel 0243 59219	FOOD
Chilgrove nr Chichester West Sussex PO18 9HX	Map 11 A6

Cottagey public house in a glorious Sussex Downs setting (not another
building can be seen from the pub) with an upmarket bar meal and a
most unusual, world-class wine list. There has to be a character behind
such an unusual setting and landlord (and oenophile extraordinary)
Barry Phillips fills the role admirably. His passion for wine has been
recognised around the world and his cellar now extends to 1800 bins.
What better place to sample a well-chilled bottle of rare Chateau
Grillet (there's even a choice of vintages!) with a snack in the small
bar or at a table on the green outside? Inside, the restaurant offers both
fixed-price meals and a good choice of daily specials – from pigeon to
lobster and salads to sweetbreads – at serious restaurant prices (£60+
for two, including wine and service). The cold buffet is a popular
summer attraction. The restaurant is recommended in our 1993 *Hotels*
& Restaurants Guide. You are as likely to encounter a rambler
challenging the Downs as you are a Chichester businessman matching
his company's expense account to the fruits of Barry's labour of love –
two large tomes of wines. No children are allowed indoors, but there's
plenty of room to let them enjoy themselves outside in good weather.
Free House. **Bar Food** *12-2 (not Mon), 6-10 (Tue-Fri). Vegetarian*
dishes. **Beer** *Courage Directors, King & Barnes Festive Bitter. Outdoor*
play area, garden, outdoor eating. Access, Visa.

Chillington   Chillington Inn

Tel 0548 580244

Chillington nr Kingsbridge Devon TQ7 2JS   Map 13 D3

Friendly old inn on the main road through the village. It changed
hands just as we went to press. *Garden, children's play area.*

Chinnor   Sir Charles Napier Inn

Tel 0494 483011   Fax 0494 484929

FOOD

Sprigg's Alley nr Chinnor Oxfordshire OX9 4BX   Map 17 D2

10 minutes from junction 6 of the M40, this is a distinctly
unassuming-looking country inn which offers a variety of menus in a
very restaurant atmosphere. Lunchtime during the week (preferably
taken on the terrace overlooking lawns and beechwoods) is the time
to enjoy the comparative bargain of a bar meal – grilled sardines with
herb butter (£4.50), cold rare rib of beef with salad (£8.50), pigeon
breast on a bed of spinach with port sauce (£8); evenings and
weekends are more formal – start with artichoke salad with rocket
and avocado (£4.75), linguine with anchovy, olives, chili and
breadcrumbs (£4.75), or half a Cornish lobster (£9), followed by
turbot with orange, ginger and red peppers (£13), best end of spring
lamb with leek sauce (£12.50) or grilled hare with brandy, grapes and
cream (£12), plus an English cheeseboard selection (£5.50) or home-
made puddings (all £4). Sunday lunch is particularly well-heeled (at
around £50 for two, it ought to be) – the choice of roasts could be
rib of beef (£9.50), Gressingham duck with sage, onion and apple
(£11.50) or Oxfordshire boar with apple sauce (£9.50). Evening
meals can easily notch up as much, if not more, but if you splash out,
go on a warm summer evening, when the tables on the terrace are
candle lit. Vegetarians can choose from 10 dishes on a separate menu.
Recommended in our 1993 *Hotels & Restaurants Guide*. **Bar Food**
*(except Sun and Mon) 12-2.30, 7.30-10.00. **Restaurant Meals** (except
Mon) 12-2.30 (12.30-3.30 Sun), 7.30-10.30. Children's portions.
Children allowed in bar to eat (lunchtime). Free House* **Beer** *Wadworth.
Garden, outdoor eating.* Amex, Diners.

Chipping Norton   Crown & Cushion

Tel 0608 642533   Fax 0608 642926

B&B

High Street Chipping Norton Oxfordshire OX7 5AD   Map 16 B1

The bar of this former coaching inn is full of character, with uneven
flagstones, an inglenook and blackened beams. Bedrooms range from
budget rooms in the annexe to suites with separate lounge, writing
desk, sofa and traditional cast-iron bath. A new leisure centre has been
added offering an indoor swimming pool, squash court, gym, solarium
and snooker. *Free House.* **Beer** *Morland Bitter. Garden.* **Accommodation**
*40 bedrooms, all en suite, £65 (single £39). Children welcome overnight,
additional beds, cots supplied. Check-in by arrangement.* Access, Amex,
Diners, Visa.

Chislehampton Coach & Horses

Tel 0865 890255 Fax 0865 891995

B&B

Chislehampton nr Oxford Oxfordshire OX9 7UX

Map 16 C2

Though pretty much modernised over the years, the Coach and Horses still keeps some traces of its 16th century beginnings. The bedrooms offer smartly kept, good practical accommodation with TVs and direct-dial phones. Showers are the norm, but a couple have bathtubs. The inn stands on the B480 south of Oxford. *Free House.* **Beer** *Morlands, Wadworth 6X. Garden.* **Accommodation** *9 bedrooms, all en suite, £69 (single £52). Children welcome overnight, additional beds (over 7 £10), cots available. Check-in all day. Access, Amex, Diners, Visa.*

Chorleywood Sportsman Hotel

Tel 0923 285155 Fax 0923 285159

B&B

Station Approach Chorleywood Hertfordshire WD3 5NB

Map 17 E2

The Sportsman was built on a hillside across the road from the railway station and dates from the late 19th century. Inside, comfortable bedrooms with darkwood furniture and brass light fittings all have fully-tiled bath/shower rooms and are provided with trouser presses, TVs, tea/coffee making facilities and direct-dial telephones. The Garden Bar with its plant-filled conservatory overlooking the garden and children's play area makes a bright and inviting spot for a drink. **Beer** *Bass, Worthington Best. Garden, children's play area. Family room.* **Accommodation** *14 bedrooms, all en suite, £62.50 (single £52.50). Children welcome overnight, additional beds and cots available. Check-in all day. Access, Amex, Diners, Visa.*

Christow Artichoke Inn

FOOD

Tel 0647 52387

B&B

Village Road Christow nr Moretonhampstead Devon

Map 13 D2

Very much the village local, the Artichoke is a white-painted, thatched pub with an unpretentious appeal. At one end of the bar there is a formally laid dining area, where regular favourites on a pleasing menu include smoked trout with prawn and crab filling (£5.50), home-made chicken and ham pie (£3.50) and peppered steak (£8.50). The fish comes regularly from Seaton, and lobsters are available with notice. Steaks and a splendidly fiery chicken curry provide more substantial meaty dishes. Vegetarians are well looked after and puddings feature home-made seasonal fruit pies and tarts (£1.80-£2.20). Sunday lunch – £4.50 dish, £6 3-course meal. The two bedrooms are modest but perfectly acceptable, and one has beds for a family of up to 4 (minimum two nights for this arrangement). Fluffy duvets with floral patterns match the curtains. **Bar Food** *(except Tue and Thur) 12-1.30, 7-9.* **Restaurant Meals** *(except Tue and Thur) 12-1.30, 7-9. Vegetarian dishes. Children's menu (£1.50 per dish).* **Beer** *IPA, Marston's Pedigree. Garden, outdoor eating.* **Accommodation** *2 bedrooms with shared bathroom, £30 (single £17.50), family bedroom (for 4) £45. Children welcome overnight, cots supplied. Check-in all day. No dogs. Accommodation closed 3 days Christmas. Pub closed Tuesdays & Thursdays. Access, Visa.*

Church Enstone   Crown Inn

Tel 0608 677262   **B&B**

Church Enstone Oxfordshire OX7 4NN   Map 16 C2

Accommodation is a strong point at the Crown, a Cotswold-stone inn standing in a quiet village near the A44. Bedrooms – all kept in apple-pie order – have pretty fabrics and furnishings, very comfortable beds, private bathrooms, TVs and tea-makers. The bar has an inglenook fire place and is usually full of lively chat, serves well-kept real ale and decent wines. *Free House. **Beer** Boddingtons, Flowers Original & Real, IPA. **Accommodation** 4 bedrooms, 3 en suite, £42 (single £30). Children welcomed overnight. Check-in all day.*

Church Knowle   New Inn

Tel 0929 480357

Church Knowle nr Wareham Dorset BH20 5NQ   Map 14 C4

Overlooking the Purbeck Hills, a partly thatched, very popular pub with a stylish public bar and comfortable lounge. ***Beer** Whitbread, Marston Pedigree. Garden. Children's play area.*

Churchstow   Church House Inn

Tel 0548 852237   **FOOD**

Churchstow nr Kingsbridge Devon TQ7 3QW   Map 13 D3

13th-century former Benedictine monks' house, complete with modern spin-offs like the Friars' Carvery; but lots of medieval atmosphere also remains, in the deep window seats and heavy stone walls, huge dark beams and enormous open fireplace. The long bar has lots of cushioned settles, and bar food from a screened-off servery at one end which serves, for example, a sausage basket (£2.25), cottage pie (£3.60) and sandwiches (from £1.35), with desserts such as cider apple pudding (£1.95) and banana shortcake (£1.95) on offer. There's also a conservatory-style bar at the back. The pub is on the A379. ***Bar Food** 12-1.30, 6.30-9. **Restaurant Meals** 7-8.45 (Wed-Sun) bookings required. Vegetarian dishes. Children's portions. Free House. **Beer** Bass, Ruddles County, Ushers Best. Garden, outdoor eating. Family room. No credit cards.*

Churchtown   Punchbowl Inn

Tel 0995 603360

Church Street Churchtown Lancashire PR3 0HT   Map 6 A1

Partly 15th-century pub in pretty village. Coal and log fires in the several cosy bar areas. ***Beer** Boddington, Tetley Bitter. Family room.*

Clanfield   Clanfield Tavern

Tel 036781 223   **B&B**

Clanfield Oxfordshire OX8 2RG   Map 16 B2

Charming 17th-century pub of Cotswold stone on A4095, with uneven flagstoned floors, low-beamed ceilings and a large open fire. At the time of going to press, renovations were due to be finished and luxury en-suite bathrooms installed (one with jacuzzi) to all bedrooms. Attractive views from the colourful small lawn. *Free House. **Beer** Hook Norton, Morlands, Morrells. **Cider** Stowfords. Garden. Family room. **Accommodation** 3 bedrooms, all en suite, £40 (single £35). Children welcome overnight, additional beds and cot available. Check-in by arrangement. Access, Visa.*

Clanfield   The Plough at Clanfield

FOOD
B&B

Tel 036 781 222   Fax 036 781 596

Bourton Road Clanfield Oxfordshire OX8 2RB

Map 16 B2

Occupying a central position in pretty Clanfield village, the Plough is a 16th-century Cotswold stone manor house that's more of an inn than a hotel. The lack of a residents' lounge restricts guests to either their bedrooms – all of which are of a good size and comfortably equipped (four have whirlpool baths) – or the bar, which is no real penalty as there's much original character in the form of old beams and a stone fireplace. In the 45-seat restaurant (recommended in our 1993 *Hotels & Restaurants Guide*), chef Stephen Parker uses select ingredients to produce dishes both modern and traditional, showing English and French influences. Mousseline of smoked haddock wrapped in smoked salmon on a chive butter fondue, paupiette of oyster and sole glazed with champagne and dill, and local pheasant braised with thyme, cranberries and chestnuts are typical choices. Puddings are a speciality. Lighter lunches (snacks and sandwiches) are also available. *Restaurant Meals 12-2, 7-10 (Sun to 9.30). Set L £14.50 Set D £22.95. Garden.* **Accommodation** *6 bedrooms, £80. No dogs. Access, Amex, Diners, Visa.*

Clare   Bell Hotel

B&B

Tel 0787 277741

Market Hill Clare Suffolk CO10 8NN

Map 10 C3

An imposing half-timbered 16th-century posting house with convivial, beamed bars, open fires and splendid carved furniture. Tasteful modernisation has brought a new conservatory, rear terrace and landscaping in the garden. Bedrooms are stylish and comfortable, traditionally furnished and strikingly decorated in the courtyard annexe; cottagey and simple in the main building. All the courtyard rooms are en suite, those in the main house are a mixture. *Free House.* **Beer** *Nethergate, Old Growler, Greene King IPA and Abbot, Tetley. Garden. Family room.* **Accommodation** *21 bedrooms, 18 en suite, £64.95 (single £43.50). Children welcome overnight, additional beds and cots available (no charge under 12 yrs). Check-in all day. Access, Amex, Diners, Visa.*

Clavering   Cricketers

FOOD

Tel 0799 550442

Clavering nr Saffron Walden Essex CB11 4QT

Map 10 B3

200 yards from the cricket green, this recently refurbished pub offers well-prepared home-made food with a menu that changes every 2-3 months. Tuesdays are seafood evenings (poached strips of salmon on crabmeat sauce (£7.50), deep-fried cod (£6.50), lobster most weeks) and a roast beef carvery (£6.50) is available on Wednesday and Sunday evenings (plus lunchtimes throughout winter). The restaurant has seating for 70, the bar for 120 and 75 can eat outside. Dishes include terrine of three vegetables (£3), chargrilled medallions of beef fillet with brandy and paprika sauce (£11.50), supreme of chicken stuffed with mushrooms in puff pastry (£7.50). The restaurant offers a 3-course meal with choice of 10 starters and main courses for £18. Paula, the resident pastry chef, cooks 12 desserts daily – treacle tart, lemon meringue pie, steam puddings (all £2.75). *Bar Food 12-2, 7-10.* **Restaurant Meals** *12-2 Sunday only, 7-10 (except Sun and Mon), Vegetarian dishes. Children's menu (£2.25 per dish). Free House.* **Beer**

Flowers IPA, Wethered Bitter, Boddingtons. Garden, outdoor eating.
Access, Visa

Claverley   Crown Inn

Tel 074 66 228

High Street Claverley Shropshire WV5 7DY   Map 6 B4

Lovely old pub in glorious picture-book village; Tudor styling and
heavy beams in three rooms. Good family garden. *Beer Hansons Mild,*
Banks Bitter. Children's play area.

Claygate   Swan Inn

Tel 0372 62582

2 Hare Lane Claygate Surrey KT10 9BT   Map 17 F4

In summer the Swan acts as the club house for the local cricket team;
its verandah handily overlooks the village green and pitch; Sunday
night jazz is often a feature after a match. The interior is charmingly
Edwardian in style, and books and prints abound. Food is
unpretentious and appetising – from bar snacks like sausage and fried
onion sandwiches (from £2.25) or filled jacket potatoes, to more
hearty restaurant meals that might include moules marinière (£3.75),
lemon sole (£5.50) and lamb brochettes (£5.25). Leave room for
home-made crème caramel (£1.95), hot chocolate fudge cake or kiwi
cheesecake (£2). Sunday roast (£5.50). *Bar Food & Restaurant Meals*
12-2.30, 6.30-9.30. Beer Youngs Ordinary, Wadworth 6X, Webster,
Samuel Smith. Patio, outdoor children's play area, outdoor eating.
Access, Visa.

Clayworth   Blacksmiths Arms

Tel 0777 817348

High Street Clayworth Nottinghamshire   Map 7 D2

A rather run-down looking creeper-clad village pub from the outside,
but clean and cottagey within, a stone-clad bar, fresh carpet tiling, and
framed antique mirrors; piped music's not too intrusive. *Beer*
Whitbread, Tetley, Bass.

Clearwell   Wyndham Arms

Tel 05948 33666   Fax 05948 36450   **B&B**

Clearwell nr Coleford Gloucestershire GL16 8JT   Map 14 B2

This splendid inn dates from the 1340s, but it's a modern annexe that
houses the 17 well-equipped bedrooms. Friendly staff and high
standards of housekeeping and the stylish touch of fresh flowers in all
rooms. *Free House. Beer Flowers Best Bitter, Bass. Garden.*
Accommodation 17 bedrooms, all en suite, £55 (single £30). Children
welcome overnight, additional beds, cots available. Check-in all day. Access,
Amex, Diners, Visa.

Cley-next-the-Sea   George & Dragon Hotel

Tel 0263 740652

High Street Cley-next-the-Sea Norfolk NR25 7RN   Map 10 C1

A salt marsh and sea-side village hotel with nice pubby bars. A
popular base for bird-watchers. *Beer Greene King IPA, Abbot and*
Rayments Special. Garden. Family room.

Cliffe   The Black Bull

Tel 0634 220893

186 Church Street Cliffe Kent ME3 7QP

FOOD

Map 11 C5

Late-Victorian pub on a historic tavern site. The three bars and 18th-century cellar restaurant specialise in Far Eastern cooking, mainly Malaysian. Tables in the 40-seat, non-smoking restaurant are booked only once in an evening, so there's no hurry to leave, especially as they have an extended licence to serve up to midnight. Starters are around £3; main courses (£12) comprise a number of dishes from which the customer makes his own assortment for one price. There's also a set meal (two starters, four main dishes, rice and dessert) for two. Lower prices in the bar (chili chicken £5.75, Lohan Chai Chinese mixed vegetables £5.60, the latter inspired by vegetarian Chinese monks). Changing guest beers and scrumpy ciders. *Bar Food 12-2, snacks 7-10. Restaurant meals 7-12. Vegetarian dishes. Children's portions on request. Free House. Beer real ales change fortnightly. Access Visa.*

Clifton   Duke of Cumberland's Head

Tel 0869 38534

Clifton nr Deddington Oxfordshire OX5 4PE

Map 16 C1

Thatched old stone-built pub on the B4031, complete with beams and inglenook fireplace. *Free House. Beer Jennings, Ruddles, Hook Norton, Wadworth 6X. Garden.*

Clifton Hampden   Barley Mow

Tel 086 730 7847

Clifton Hampden nr Abingdon Oxfordshire OX14 3EH

B&B

Map 16 C1

Jerome K Jerome mentioned the 14th-century Thames-side Barley Mow in his novel *Three Men in a Boat*. Low beams, oak panelling and button-back settees contribute to exceptional comfort. Bedrooms are pretty, though smallish, with Laura Ashley furnishings. One has en-suite facilities, the others share two smart bathrooms. All have toilets, TVs and telephones. New managers. *Free House. Beer Ruddles County, Wesbsters Yorkshire, Ushers Best. Garden. Accommodation 4 bedrooms, 1 en-suite, £56 (single £36). Children welcome overnight. No dogs. Check-in all day. Access, Amex, Diners, Visa.*

Clitheroe   Craven Heifer

Tel 0254 826215

Chipping Road Clitheroe Lancashire BB7 3LX

Map 6 B1

Well-organised Ribble Valley local. *Beer Tetley. Family room.*

Coatham Mundeville   Hall Garth

Tel 0325 300400

Coatham Mundeville nr Darlington Durham DL1 3LU

Map 5 E3

Unusual bar converted, as the name suggests, from the hotel's old stables; airy high-ceilinged, and in a useful spot for travellers, though the menu is routine enough. *Beer Theakston Best and XB, Bass, North Yorkshire Flying Herbert. Garden. Children's play area. Family room.*

Cockfield   Three Horseshoes

Tel 0284 828177
FOOD
Stows Hill Cockfield Green Suffolk IP30 0JD
Map 10 C3

Thatched 14th-century cottage pub, originally part of a hall house and
court, and an alehouse since the early 19th century. Period lounge and
lively locals' public bar. Try the horseshoe-shaped roll made with
bread specially baked in Lavenham and filled with salad, chopped
Suffolk ham mixed with mashed hard-boiled egg and mayonnaise
(£1.75). The Three Horseshoes is home to the Pudding Club, for
lovers of suety, custard-covered English puds Thursday evenings,
book early. *Beer Greene King IPA and Abbot. Garden.*

Cockleford   Green Dragon Inn   ★

Tel 0242 870271
FOOD
Cockleford Cowley Cheltenham Gloucestershire GL53 9NW
Map 14 C2

A wealth of good things awaits patrons of the Green Dragon, which
stands in deep countryside just off the A435. It dates from the 17th
century, and started life as a cider house. Beer drinkers today will
appreciate the traditional service of fine real ales direct from the cask;
there may be Hook Norton, Bass, Wadworth, Archers and Theakston
on any given day. Equally, even the most regular of diners will not
tire of Donald Campbell's weekly changing menus. Start, for instance,
with whole prawns and garlic mayonnaise (£2.50), or paté maison
(£2), and proceed to chicken with oranges (£5) or a steak (12oz
rump £10). Round it all off with strawberry meringue, banoffi pie,
or the intriguing Tracy's Tipsy Drizzle (all £1.95). For those of lesser
appetites, there's granary bread and cheese, various quiches, honey-
glazed ham, and a wide choice of cheese for ploughman's lunching.
The central bar serves as the fulcrum of much activity, with dining
room style seating at the upper level (book at weekends, when there's
waitress service) and a lower bar with rather more appeal to Cotswold
Way walkers. The old farriers' building, which once housed a
skittle alley, has been restored to create a function suite, which is
pressed into service on Sundays for a popular carvery lunch (main
course £6.50). Its pebbled patio – a lovely summer setting –
overlooks a trout stream and Cowley lake. Immensely popular all year
round, those in the know come early for the best fireside seats in
winter, or the pick of the summer spots on the flower-bedecked patio.
Service cannot be faulted here either, and there's always a cheery
welcome for strangers and regulars alike from Sue and Barry Hinton.
Bar Food 11.15-2 (12-2.15 Sun), 6.15-10 (7.15-10 Sun) (*carvery
12-2.30 Sun only*). *Vegetarian dishes, children's portions. Free House. Beer
Archers Golden, Butcombe Bitter, Hook Norton. Outdoor eating.
Access, Visa.*

Cockwood   Anchor Inn

Tel 0626 890203
FOOD
Cockwood Starcross Devon EX6 8RA
Map 13 E3

Large old harbourside pub, extended over the years but still admirably
traditional in spirit. The main bar divides into three areas, with a
comfortable little snug at one end dominated by a welcoming coal
fire. Black panelling, low ceilings and lots of private little alcoves lend
intimacy to a rambling space. Bar food favours the fishy with a half
pint of smoked prawns (£4.60), seafood mornay (£4.95), and shark
steak (£5.95) on the menu, while in the restaurant, the choice might

include prawns and crabmeat in mornay sauce (£5.45), a shellfish selection (£12.95) and grilled lemon sole (£9.95). *Bar Food & Restaurant Meals 12-2, 6-10. Vegetarian dishes. Children's menu. Beer Boddingtons, Draught Bass, Eldridge Pope Royal Oak, Marstons Pedigree, Whitbread Flowers Original. Cider Dry Blackthorne. Children allowed in bar to eat. Riverside patio/terrace. Access, Visa.*

Cockwood   Ship
Tel 0626 890373

Cockwood nr Starcross Devon EX6 8PA   Map 13 E3

Harbourside pub serving good fresh fish. *Beer Ushers Best & Founders, John Smith. Garden.*

Colchester   Foresters
Tel 0206 42646

Castle Road Colchester Essex   Map 10 C3

Busy local near the castle and Roman wall; daily changing home-cooked food, no printed menu. *Beer Whitbread, Marston Pedigree. Family room.*

Coleby   Bell
Tel 0522 810240

Far Lane Coleby nr Lincoln Lincolnshire LN5 0AH   Map 7 E2

Dining pub with three connecting carpeted bars, and open fires. *Beer Marston Pedigree, Courage Directers. Family room.*

Coleford   New Inn
Tel 0363 84242

Coleford Devon EX17 5BZ   Map 13 D2

Pretty thatched inn with a characterfully rambling interior in which ancient and modern blend successfully: fitted red carpets, fresh white walls, heavy beams, simple wooden furniture and settles, and a discreet variety of attractive brass and bric-a-brac. There's a stream-side patio. *Free House. Beer Flowers IPA, Original, Wadworth 6X, guest beers. Family room.*

Colesbourne   Colesbourne Inn

FOOD
B&B

Tel 0242870 376

Colesbourne nr Cheltenham Gloucestershire GL53 9NP   Map 14 C2

Cotswold country pub by the main A435; the 200-year-old inn is the same age as the road, built to service the increasingly fashionable spa town tourist trade. Panelled bars feature open fires and reliable bar food, for instance, home-made old fashioned pies (£6.25) or smoked trout fillets (£3.95). There's also Brambles Restaurant, serving deep fried Sharpham brie (£3.75) and scollops of salmon (£9.25). There are ten bedrooms in a converted stable block, with a mix of furniture, and well-equipped, with good en-suite facilities. *Bar Food and Restaurant Meals 12-2.30, 6.30-10 (7-10 Sun). Vegetarian Dishes, Children's portions. Beer Wadworth. Garden, outdoor eating. Accommodation 10 bedrooms, all en suite, £49 (single £29). Children welcome overnight, additional beds (£10), cot available. Check-in all day. Access, Amex, Diners, Visa.*

Coleshill   Red Lion

Tel 0494 727020

Village Road Coleshill Buckinghamshire HP7 0LN   Map 17 E2

Picturesque village pub in delightful spot close by the pond and
church. **Beer** *Ansells Mild, Benskins, Tetley. Garden.*

Colkirk   Crown

Tel 0328 862172

Colkirk nr Fakenham Norfolk NR21 7AA   Map 10 C1

Redbrick village centre pub with home-cooked food. What was the
restaurant is now a dining room with the same menu as the bar. **Beer**
Greene King XX Mild, IPA and Abbot, Guest Beer.

Collyweston   Cavalier Inn

Tel 078 083 288   **B&B**

Collyweston nr Stamford Northamptonshire DE9 3PQ   Map 7 E4

Previously the Slaters Arms, the pub here changed its name when the
slate mine closed and the workforce moved away. The inn itself is a
terrace of small 19th century cottages. Yet a glass window let into the
bar floor reveals a much earlier stone spiral stairway to a tiny cellar.
Bedrooms have been refurbished over the last 2 years. *Free House.*
Beer *Ruddles Best Bitter, County, Websters & guest beer. Garden.*
Accommodation *5 bedrooms, all en suite, £42 (single £28). Children
welcome overnight, additional beds. No dogs. Check-in by arrangement.
Access, Visa.*

Combe Hay   Wheatsheaf

Tel 0225 833504   **FOOD**

Combe Hay nr Bath Avon BA2 7EG   Map 13 F1

Narrowing twisting lanes lead to this charming village, hidden away
in a fold of hills to the south of Bath. Perched on a hillside looking
across a small valley, the Wheatsheaf dates back to the 17th century
and is as pretty as a picture, its black and white facade smothered in
flowers and pierced with the entrances to dovecots, built into the walls
and still inhabited. Well spaced rustic tables and benches in the large
sloping garden make the best of the views, an ideal spot for summer
eating and drinking. Inside there are rough stone walls, massive solid
wooden tables, and also a huge blackboard menu: food is important
here. There is something to suit just about every taste, from a home-
cooked Wiltshire ham salad (£5) to more adventurous and
sophisticated dishes, monkfish with root ginger and spring onion
cream sauce (£8.25), or breast of chicken filled with smoked salmon
mousse and wrapped in pastry (£7.25) among them. Deep-fried
mushrooms filled with brie make a good starter, the hot filling
spilling out to blend with surrounding provencale sauce. Home-made
puddings (£2.50) include bread and butter pudding, banoffi pie and
soufflés. Real ales are drawn direct from the barrel. There is no
background music as such, but a good deal emanates from the kitchen
where, to judge by the singing, they are clearly happy in their work.
Bar Food and Restaurant *12-2, 6.30-9 (6.30-9.30 Sun). Vegetarian
dishes.* **Beer** *Ash Vine, Courage. Garden, outdoor eating. Family room. No
credit cards.*

Compton   Coach & Horses
Tel 0705 631228

The Square Compton West Sussex PO18 9HA   **Map 15 D3**

Village local with licensee-cook and seasonally changing menus. Table-top mini barbecues of a superior kind are the house speciality. *Free House.* **Beer** *Theakston XB, Bass, Fullers ESB and London Pride. Garden.*

Compton   Harrow Inn
Tel 0483 810379

The Street Compton Surrey GU3 1EG   **Map 17 E4**

Four bedrooms were planned, permission pending, as we went to press, at this well-heeled commuter-belt dining pub. Outdoor dining by the car park. **Beer** *Tetley, Burton Ale.*

Compton   The Withies Inn
Tel 0483 421158

Withies Lane Compton nr Guildford Surrey GU3 1JA   **FOOD**
Map 7 A5

A delightful out-of-the-way setting, yet just two minutes off the A3. Light snacks are served in the bar of this friendly old-fashioned pub, with more substantial meals served à la carte in the 75-seat restaurant or large garden (a real treat in summer). **Bar Food** *11-2.30, 6-10.30 (except Sun eve).* **Restaurant Meals** *12-2.30, 7-10.30 (except Sun eve). Vegetarian dishes. Free House.* **Beer** *Bass, Sussex Real Ale, Tetley. Cider Addlestone. Garden, outdoor eating. Access, Amex, Diners, Visa.*

Compton Martin   Ring O'Bells
Tel 0761 221284

Main Street Compton Martin Avon BS18 6JE   **Map 13 F1**

Rambling, well-balanced village pub, with a busy local's bar, comfortable lounge with open fire, nice family room, and a large garden. Children are very well catered for. **Beer** *Butcombe, Bass, Wadworth 6X. Garden. Children's play area. Family room.*

Coningsby   Lea Gate Inn
Tel 0526 42370

Coningsby Lincolnshire LN4 4RS   **Map 7 E3**

Last of the once numerous Fen Guide Houses, places of safety on the treacherous eastern marshes. Traditional features, brick and beams, three open fires in the lounge areas, and garden room. The yew tree is the same age as the pub; the attractive garden also features a koi carp pond. **Beer** *Whitbread Castle Eden, Boddington, Marstons Pedigree, Timothy Taylors Landlord. Poolside garden. Children's play area.*

Coniston   Ship
Tel 053 94 41224

Bowmanstead Coniston Cumbria LA21 8HB   **Map 4 C3**

Easily missed, standing above the A593 on the Coniston side of Boxmanstead, reached up a narrow unmarked track. Near a large camp site. **Beer** *Hartleys XB. Family room.*

Constantine   **Trengilly Wartha Inn**

`Tel 0326 40332`

Constantine Cornwall TR11 5RP   **Map 12 B4**

Smart country inn, a mile from the village in a gloriously pretty area,
and with six acres of its own grounds. The bars are a delight, unspoilt
and simple, with exposed stone and beams, traditional furnishings, and
a good mix of locals and visitors. *Free House.* **Beer** *St Austell Tinners
and HSD, Exmoor Ale, Theakston XB, Courage Directors. Garden.
Children's play area. Family room.*

Corfe Castle   **Fox**

`Tel 0929 480449`

West Street Corfe Castle Dorset   **Map 14 C4**

Unspoilt 16th-century inn, with a snug very snug little front bar and
slightly less enchanting larger lounge. The Fox is especially appealing
in summer, though, and its mature, pretty garden has views of the
famous ruin. **Beer** *Whitbread. Garden. Family room.*

Cornworthy   **Hunters Lodge**

`Tel 080 423 204`

Cornworthy Devon   **Map 13 D3**

Unspoilt, simply refurbished country local with a cosy low-ceilinged
bar and attractive dining room, nice in winter when the log fire's
burning. *Free House.* **Beer** *Blackawton Special, Ushers Best. Garden.
Children's play area.*

Corscombe   **Fox Inn**

`Tel 0935 891330`   **FOOD**

Corscombe Dorset DT2 0NS   **Map 13 F2**

"Real Ale, Country Cooking. No Chips or Microwaves" it says on the
postcard, showing a pretty little thatched pub of stone and cob, built
in 1620. Equally neat and appealing inside, the small entrance lobby is
decorated with a wild flower and ivy mural painted directly on to the
walls. Beyond are two bars, one, with its hunting prints, reflecting
landlord Martyn Lee's favourite pastime, and other prettily furnished
with blue gingham curtains, tablecloths, banquette seat covers – even
the fabric covering the barrel stools. A huge old stone fireplace boasts
a real log fire in winter, while behind the bar a collection of plates,
copper and pewter ware is displayed. All is overseen by an array of
stuffed owls in glass cases. It's still verymuch a local's pub, complete
with local cricket team; fairly few tourists seem to find their way to
this quiet backwater. Most Friday nights and Sunday lunchtimes a
blues pianist entertains in a separate, newly opened stable conversion.
Foodwise, it's all down to Martyn's mother, who works alone in her
kitchen. The menu is, sensibly, not overlong. Dishes include soup
(£1.80), paté (£2.50), ham in cider (£4.50), beef casserole (£3.75)
and cauliflower cheese (£3). Fox's Favourite – a generous quantity of
chicken with peppers in a cream sauce (£3.75) – lives up to its name.
Evening brings a few changes to the menu with fillet trout (£5.25)
and gammon steak (£5.25) perhaps being added with desserts such as
treacle tart (£1.75) and meringue and cream (£1.75). **Bar Food &
Restaurant Meals** *12-2, 7-9. Vegetarian dishes. Free House.* **Beer** *Abbots,
Exmoor Ale.* **Cider** *Bridge Farm. Garden, outdoor eating, children's play
area. Family room. No credit cards.*

Corsham   **Methuen Arms Hotel**

Tel 0249 714867	**B&B**

2 High Street Corsham Wiltshire SN13 0HB   Map 14 B2

A 500-year history lies behind the Georgian facade of this fine old
family-run inn, seen to most dramatic effect in the heavily beamed
and stone-walled Long Bar. This part of the Grade II listed building
was a nunnery in the 15th century. Modernised bedrooms in the main
house sport pretty floral papers and fitted furniture; there is also more
luxurious accommodation in the converted coach house. TVs,
telephones and tea-makers are standard, and all the rooms have en-suite
facilities. Delightful walled garden. *Beer Gibbs Mew Wiltshire,
Salisbury Best, Bishops Tipple, Chairmans Choice.* **Accommodation**
*25 bedrooms, all en suite, £65 (single £47). Children welcome overnight,
additional beds, cots available. Check-in all day. Access, Visa.*

Cotherstone   **Fox & Hounds**

Tel 0833 50241	**FOOD**
	B&B

Cotherstone Co Durham DL12 9PF   Map 5 D3

North of Barnard Castle, on the B6277, the village of Cotherstone
stands in an area of outstanding natural beauty, where the Tees and
Balder rivers meet. The Fox & Hounds is back from the main road,
overlooking a small village green; a coaching inn for over 200 years,
it's been run for just the last few by the ever enthusiastic and amiable
Crawleys. A stripped-stone entrance hall leads into the main bar,
which has heavily beamed ceilings and rough painted walls. A brick
fireplace is hung with polished brasses; in summer it boasts fine dried
flower displays and polished copperware, in winter a fire that warms
the whole room. Window sills are crammed with pot plants and walls
hung with mainly hunting prints. Rustic benches and wheelback
chairs surround well-used wooden tables. Adjoining the bar, a small
dining area has polished ready-laid tables and pretty, cottagey curtains,
while at the other side of the entrance is a second eating area, again
with heavy beams and rustic-style furnishings. Quality bar food
produced with real enthusiasm by Patrick Crawley draws in the
crowds. In addition to the bar menu, which features venison in red
wine casserole (£7.95) or chicken and mushroom pancake (£5.95),
there is a specials board of more interesting dishes which allows him
to use what's best from the markets. Meat and vegetables come from
local suppliers, and fish arrives daily from Hartlepool. Fish is a
particularly strong point here: perhaps sole and smoked salmon
roulade with Sancerre sauce (£9.95). Quality local meat finds a
showcase in medallions of beef with a mushroom and Madeira sauce,
vegetables are fresh and well cooked, salads fresh and crisp. Added to
all of which, puddings are a must – strawberry pavlova with
raspberry couilis or a tulip basket filled with home-made water ice
and fresh fruit (£2.95). Naturally the dining areas get very busy,
especiallyat weekends. Bedrooms show a similar eye for detail to the
cooking. Designed and appointed by Jenny Crawley, and named after
local dales, the two doubles and single twin are furnished in country
style with fine pine furniture or solid period pieces, balanced by light
fresh furnishings and decor. Homely touches include ornaments,
mineral water and respectable local watercolours. Beds are firm and
comfortable, sheets crisp. Each room is en suite (one with a shower),
with carpets and practical fittings, though extractor fans are noisy.
Rooms are priced on a dinner, bed and breakfast rate. A homely

residents' lounge with exposed floorboards and big comfy armchairs is also home to the family parrot. *Bar Food & Restaurant Meals* *11.30-1.45, 6.30-9. Vegetarian dishes. Children's menu/portions. Free House.* *Beer* *Hambleton Bitter, John Smiths Bitter. Children allowed in bar to eat.* *Accommodation* *3 bedrooms, all en suite, £55 (single £40), price includes dinner. Children welcome overnight (minimum age 9). Check-in all day. No dogs. Access, Visa.*

Cousleywood   Old Vine

Tel 0892 782271	**FOOD**
Cousleywood nr Wadhurst East Sussex TN5 6ER	Map 11 B5

Long a favourite, this 16th-century typical old-English dining pub has inglenook fireplaces, beams, benches, farmhouse chairs, and climbing roses. The bar menu (which may be ordered in the restaurant) offers moules marinière (£3.00), soft roes on toast (£1.50), peppered chicken in cream (£4.75), and wild duck in black cherry sauce (£5.25), whilst the 3-course restaurant menu in the evening is priced according to choice of main dish (£10.95-15.95) – duck and orange terrine, avocado Waldorf, pork fillet in apricot sauce or chicken breast with prawns, cream and mushrooms. All puddings are home-made: chocolate cheesecake, sherry trifle and blackberry and apple pie are popular. Monday night is music night (a live trio). *Bar Food 12-2, 6.45-9.30 (music night menu only on Mon). Restaurant Meals 7-9.30. Vegetarian dishes. Children's portions. Beer Harvey, Flowers, Fremlins. Garden, outdoor eating. Access, Diners, Visa.*

Coventry   Greyhound

Tel 0203 363046	
Sutton Stop Hawkesbury Junction Coventry West Midlands CV6 6UF	Map 6 C4

Originally a farmhouse, the Greyhound's been a pub since 1822, when the North Oxford and Coventry canals were installed – they meet right outside the premises. *Beer Banks, Bass. Riverside garden. Children's play area.*

Coventry   William IV

Tel 0203 686394	**FOOD**
1059 Foleshill Road Coventry West Midlands	Map 6 C4

About three miles from the city centre, on the A444 Nuneaton road, the William IV looks extremely ordinary, a mock-timbered, redbrick, typical roadside city pub, and the distinctly unassuming interior, with its light modern wallpaper hung with prints, plush banquette seating and the obligatory fruit machine, do nothing to belie this view. But open the front door and the aromas that greet you are unmistakable, for the food here is authentic Indian, though there are also English dishes for the less adventurous. A printed menu offers a wide-ranging choice of competitively priced dishes, including the house specials, kadhai dishes (£3.99), biriyani (£4) and thalis (£4.85), accompanied by the usual side dishes. A fashionable addition to the menu is the marking out of some options as healthy, or rather, healthier, with the Look After Your Heart symbol; though as most of the dishes on the menu seem to have been awarded this honour, including all the puddings, it might be wise to treat the symbol with a pinch of Lo Salt. Currently proving very popular is the new balti menu with a choice of 80 dishes (all £3.90). A balti is a North Pakistani dish served in its own hot iron cooking dish. The pub is extremely busy, with a varied clientele; be prepared to share your table, and be prepared for a wait, as everything is cooked to order. On the whole the wait's worthwhile. Service is on the whole friendly. *Bar Food* (*except Sun*) *12-2.30, 6-10.30 (5-10.30 Fri/Sat). Vegetarian dishes. Children's portions. Children allowed in the bar to eat.* **Beer** *M&B Mild, Brew XI. Garden, outdoor eating. No credit cards.*

Coxwold   Fauconberg Arms

FOOD
B&B

Tel 03476 214

Main Street Coxwold North Yorkshire YO6 4AD

Map 5 E4

Located near Shandy Hall and Byland Abbey, this is a charmingly civilised, if invariably busy, place, with handsome old furnishings and an open fire. Bar food is adventurous and varied: cream of celeriac and coconut soup (£1.95), smoked salmon and watercress mousse (£3.65), pan-fried lamb with apple, mint and rosemary gravy (£6.55), seafood strudel in filo pastry (£5.95). The restaurant's 3-course table d'hote menu for Sunday lunch is £8.95 and in the evenings the à la carte menu offers choices such as prawns, scallions and almond quiche (£3.25), fresh Queenie scallops (£3.50), boneless quail wrapped in bacon, with ginger and orange gravy (£11.95) or medallions of monkfish (£11.95). Bedrooms have long been popular here too, and still look like good value. The setting is delightful, in a peaceful (despite the traffic) straggling village, and the church across the road is worth a look; Lawrence Sterne is buried there. *Bar Food and Restaurant Meals 12-1.45, 7-8.45. Vegetarian dishes. Children's menu (£1.95 per dish).* **Beer** *Tetley, Theakston Best, John Smith. Patio, outdoor eating.* **Accommodation** *4 bedrooms, one with shower, £45 (single £24). Children welcome overnight, additional beds (from £12) and cots available (£1.50). Check-in all day. Access, Visa.*

Cranborne   Fleur de Lys

FOOD
B&B

Tel 07254 282   Fax 07254 765

5 Wimborne Street Cranborne Dorset BH21 5PP

Map 14 C4

Historical connections are many at the Fleur de Lys: Thomas Hardy visited when writing *Tess of the D'Urbervilles*, Rupert Brooke wrote a poem on the premises, and Hanging Judge Jeffreys stayed the night. The pub itself is modernised and pleasant, with period features remaining. Bedrooms and bathrooms have been recently refurbished. Bedrooms are decorated in country-style with matching curtains and duvets. Tea and coffee kits, soap and hairdryers are supplied. Bar food is reliably good with steak pie (£4.75), rabbit pie (£4.65), beef provençale (£4.65) or lemon sole (£6.95) and outstanding puddings such as raspberry pavlova (£2.45), French fruit tart (£2.25) or a brandy snap basket with ice-cream and fruit (£2.25). *Bar Food 12-2, 7-9.30. Restaurant Meals 7-9.30. Vegetarian dishes. Children's portions.* **Beer** *Hall & Woodhouse Badger Best Bitter, Tanglefoot. Garden, outdoor eating, children's play area.* **Accommodation** *8 bedrooms, 7 en suite, £42 (single £24). Children welcome overnight, additional beds (from £5), cot available. Check-in all day. Access, Visa.*

Cranmore   Strode Arms

Tel 074 988 450

West Cranmore Cranmore Somerset   Map 13 F1

Mostly 15th-century coaching inn, formerly a farmhouse, opposite the
village pond. Delightfully rustic within, and run with imagination;
the daily papers laid out in the bars are a particularly welcome feature.
Vintage cars meet outside on the first Tuesday of the month. *Free
House.* **Beer** *Bunces Best, Wadworth IPA and 6X, Guest Beer. Garden.*

Crawley   Fox & Hounds

FOOD
B&B

Tel 0962 72285

Crawley Hampshire SO21 2PR   Map 15 D3

Splendid Tudorbethan style turn-of-the-century pub, its redbrick
exterior beautifully kitted out with convincing beams and
overhanging upper storeys, in a well-heeled, pretty village. Cosy main
bar with simple home-made food (hot Stilton and apple bake £3.25,
Mexican pork £5.95, rabbit pie £5.95) and good fresh fish (fresh
sardines £3.25, seafood pancake £5.95); main courses in the restaurant
are more ambitious – chicken Kiev (£8.25), medallions of pork
(£8.75) and tournedos Rossini (£11.95). A 3-course traditional
Sunday lunch is available in winter (£10.95). Three pristine bedrooms
are all en suite, attractively decorated, with light wood furnishings and
soothing colours. ***Bar Food and Restaurant Meals*** *12-2, 7-9.30.
Vegetarian dishes. Children's portions. Free House.* **Beer** *Gales BB,
Wadworth 6X.* ***Accommodation*** *3 bedrooms, all en suite, £55 (single
£45) Children welcome overnight, additional beds (from £10 if over
8 yrs). Check-in all day. Access, Visa.*

Cray   White Lion

Tel 0756 760262

Cray nr Skipton North Yorkshire BD23 5JB   Map 5 D4

Characterful stone-built Dales pub, popular with walkers. Beamed
ceilings, stone floors and a warming open fire in the main bar, which
also has farming bric-a-brac and a Ring the Bull game. *Free House.*
Beer *Theakston Best, Youngers Scotch, Moorhouses Premier, Pendle
Witches Brew. Riverside garden. Children's play area. Family room.*

Cromer   Bath House

Tel 0263 514260

The Promenade Cromer Norfolk   Map 6 C1

Handsome Regency inn with pleasant and welcoming bar in a likable
Victorian resort; a good place for windy walks and long weekends.
Beer *Bateman XB, Greene King IPA.*

Cromer Hyde   Crooked Chimney

Tel 0707 323832

Off B653 Cromer Hyde Hertfordshire AL8 7XE   Map 17 F2

Named after its own distinctly crooked chimney – a useful landmark
if lost and uncertain – a popular dining pub. **Beer** *Benskins, Ind Coope,
Tetley. Outdoor play area, garden.*

Croscombe   Bull Terrier

| Tel 0749 343658 | **B&B** |

Croscombe nr Wells Somerset BA5 3QJ   Map 13 F1

A lovely old pub, originally a priory and first licenced in 1612. Three
bars: the Inglenook, a red carpeted lounge with cushioned wall seats
and pretty beams; the Snug, leading off, and the Common bar, as well
as a family room. Owners of the eponymous dog tend to gather here,
but not usually in alarming numbers. *Free House.* **Beer** *Butcombe, Royal
Oak, Bull Terrier Best Bitter, Theakstons XB* **Cider** *Wilkins. Garden,
outdoor eating. Family room.* **Accommodation** *3 bedrooms, 2 en suite, £45
(single £22). No children under 16 overnight. Check-in all day. No dogs.
Access, Visa.*

Crowle   Old Chequers

| Tel 090 560 275 | |

Crowle Hereford & Worcester WR7 4AA   Map 14 B1

Extended, smartened-up country dining pub. No children indoors.
Beer *Ansells, Bass, Hook Norton. Garden.*

Cuckfield   The King's Head

| Tel 0444 454006 | **FOOD** |
| | **B&B** |

2 South Street Cuckfield West Sussex RH17 5JY   Map 11 B6

Popular and unspoilt village meeting place where banknotes of every
kind adorn one intimate, low-ceilinged bar, and the spacious, panelled
public bar leads out to the beer garden. Simple bar food is served at
lunchtime and in the evenings (except Saturday, Sunday and Monday)
– liver and bacon casserole (£3.25), spare ribs (£3.25), garlic paté
(£1.75), minted lamb (£3.25) but the big attraction is the menu in
the rustic, beamed restaurant – goat's cheese salad (£2.45), salmon
steak (£5.25), smoked chicken salad (£4.20), lemon cheesecake
(£1.75), caramel slice (£1.75); booking essential. Simply furnished,
good-sized bedrooms are warm and welcoming, with all the usual
little comforts. *Bar Food and Restaurant Meals 12.00-2.30, 5.30-9.00
(Tue-Fri only). Vegetarian dishes. Children's menu (£1.99 per dish). Free
House.* **Beer** *Harvey, King & Barnes. Garden, outdoor eating. Family
room.* **Accommodation** *9 bedrooms, 8 en suite, £55 (single £42).
Children welcome overnight, additional beds (from £10), cot supplied.
Check-in all day. Access, Amex, Visa.*

Cuddington   Crown

| Tel 0844 292222 | **FOOD** |
| | **B&B** |

Aylesbury Road Cuddington Buckinghamshire HP18 0BB   Map 17 D2

The cooking is solely in the hands of the landlady at the Crown, so
the daily menu, written up on a blackboard at one end of the bar, is
kept short and pleasingly unpretentious. The choice could include
Cumberland sausages (£4.25), potted shrimps (£3.30), cauliflower
cheese (£3.10), baked potatoes (from £2.75), chicken and asparagus
pasta bake (£4.95) or a vast, crisp, filled Yorkshire pudding (£4.95).
Salads are crisp and fresh, and puddings (all £2.10) simple, like bread-
and-butter pudding or gooseberries in filo pastry. This is real pub
home-cooking, honest, tasty, and always good value. The pub itself is
welcoming and white-painted, in the centre of a picturesque and
tranquil village, and has managed to preserve the friendly charm of a

real country local. Inside, one long room is dominated by a long
central bar counter with, to the left, a carpeted lounge end, to the
right a red tiled public bar area. Rustic roundback chairs surround
solid wood tables topped with little vases of fresh flowers, and two
huge inglenook fireplaces, one at each end, are topped by a fine old
beam. In winter, open fires warm the room, while in kinder weather
dried flower displays and other bits and pieces decorate the fireplace.
You can also sit outside if it's fine. It's quietish at lunchtime, busier in
the evening, and can positively heave at weekends. The licensees'
springer spaniel lives up to its name in a particularly springy way.
Overnight accommodation consists of just one cosy, twin-bedded
room, spotlessly kept, with creaking floorboards, sloping ceilings and
period furnishings. Books, magazines and a small black and white
television are provided. You share the licensees' neat bathroom. *Bar
Food* 12.30-2 *(except Sun)*, 7.30-9.30 *(except Sun, Mon, Tues eves)*.
Vegetarian dishes. Children's portions. **Beer** *Fullers ESB, London Pride,
Chiswick. Terrace, outdoor eating.* **Accommodation** *1 bedroom, sharing
facilities, £38.50 (single £19.25). No children overnight. Check-in by
arrangement. No dogs. No credit cards.*

Cullompton   Manor House Hotel

Tel 0884 32281 Fax 0884 38344	**B&B**
Fore Street Cullompton Devon EX15 1JL	Map 13 E2

Built as the town house for a rich wool merchant, this hotel-cum-inn
dates in part to 1603, and fine old casement windows jut out from the
freshly-painted black and white facade. Inside has an attractive mix of
styles, the knotty pine bar Victorian in feel (aside from the pair of
fruit machines). The appealing bedrooms are all individually
decorated, with stylish coordinating fabrics, nicely framed botanical
prints, and good freestanding furniture in mahogany or an orangey
pine finish. All the usual modern comforts. Carpeted bathrooms have
wooden toilet seats, good thermostatically controlled showers over the
baths, and nice touches like cottonwool balls and pot-pourri. Most
rooms are at the front of the building facing the main road (double-
glazing helps to reduce the traffic noise) and one of the two quieter
rooms to the rear has a pair of bunk beds for families. *Free House.*
Beer *Bass, Dorchester Ale, Hardys, Theakston. Patio/terrace. Family room.*
Accommodation *11 bedrooms, 10 en suite, £42.50 (single £35.50).
Children welcome overnight, additional beds, cots supplied. Check-in all day.
No dogs. Access, Visa.*

Dalton-in-Furness   Brown Cow

Tel 0229 62553	
Goose Green Dalton-in-Furness Cumbria LA15 8LQ	Map 4 C4

Atmospheric, resolutely traditional country pub in the town, a
surprisingly sleepy, village-like part of it, with a delightful garden.
Beer *Mathew Brown Bitter, Theakston Best and XB. Garden. Children's
play area. Family room.*

Dalwood   Tuckers Arms

Tel 040 488 342	
Dalwood Devon EX13 7EG	Map 13 E2

Picture-book pretty thatched pub in a delightful Axe Valley village,
beside the Corry Brook. Originally a manor house, parts of which
date back 700 years; the refurbished, relaxing interior has a mix of

chairs, original flagstoned floors, beams aplenty and a large inglenook fireplace. *Beer Boddington, Flowers Original, Marston Pedigree, Wadworth 6X. Garden. Family room.*

Dargate   Dove

Tel 0227 751360

Plum Pudding Lane Dargate Kent   Map 11 C5

An idyllic summer pub, with mature gardens and trees, dovecote, rockery and pool, and masses of cottage flowers. Inside is mellow, wood-panelled and attractively modernised. *Beer Shepherd Neame Bitter and Spitfire. Garden. Children's play area. Family room.*

Dartington   Cott Inn   **FOOD**

Tel 0803 863777   Fax 0803 866629   **B&B**

Dartington Devon TQ9 6HE   Map 13 D3

A delightful 14th-century thatched, stone and cob-built inn, continuously licensed since 1320, and severely damaged by fire in 1989, but now fully restored (they only closed for two days!). The English oak trusses newly replaced in the roof came courtesy of the great Kent hurricane. Now protected by the latest fire detection systems, and probably the safest thatched pub in England, as well as one of the longest, at 183 feet. Lunch is a hot and cold buffet with braised duckling in lime sauce (£6.95), rack of lamb redcurrant and rosemary sauce (£8.95) or fresh river dart Salmon (£8.95) on offer. Listed dishes are from the evening menu and includes monkfish with bacon, cream, mushroom, garlic and wine sauce (£11.50). No children under 10; no children overnight. *Bar Food 12-2, 6.30-9.30. Restaurant Meals 12 & 1.30, 7 & 9pm sittings. Vegetarian dishes. Children's portions. Free House. Beer Dartmoor Best, IPA, Palmers. Cider Churchwards Farmhouse. Garden, outdoor eating. Accommodation 6 bedrooms, 5 en suite, £62.50 (single £57.50). Check-in all day. No dogs. Access, Amex, Visa.*

Dartmouth   Cherub   **FOOD**

Tel 0803 832571

13 Higher Street Dartmouth Devon TQ6 9BB   Map 13 D3

Grade I listed 14th-century fishing pub with an extraordinary timbered exterior and busy, table-crammed small bar. The upstairs restaurant has a good reputation, with smoked salmon mousse (£4.50), brill stuffed with prawns (£10.95) poached fillets of sole (£9.95) or beef stroganoff (£12.95) listed on the menu; bar food is excellent at a fraction of the price offering dishes such as Stilton mushrooms (£3.50), soup (£1.75) and old English beef and ale stew (£4.95). *Bar Food 12-2, 7-10. Restaurant Meals 7-10. Vegetarian dishes. Children's portions. Free House. Beer Blackawton Bitter, Ind Coope Burton Ale, Whitbread Flowers Original. Cider Luscombe Farm, Farmers Old English. Children allowed in bar to eat. Access, Visa.*

Dartmouth   Royal Castle Hotel

Tel 0803 833033   Fax 0803 835445   **B&B**

The Quay Dartmouth Devon TQ6 9PS   Map 13 D3

Handsome Regency windows, overlooking the quay, conceal the Tudor heart of this finely restored hostelry. The Harbour Bar, popular with locals, has a pub feel, while the beamed Galleon Bar is more spacious and sports a weaponry display. Light, original bedrooms have period furnishings, four have four-posters and several enjoy river views. Two rooms have recently been refurbished and jacuzzi baths added. TVs, telephones, tea-makers and modern bath or shower rooms. *Free House.* **Beer** *Worthington, Whitbread Best Bitter, Bodingtons, Tennants, Flowers IPA. Family Room.* **Accommodation** *25 bedrooms, all en suite, £74 (single £48). Children welcome overnight, additional beds, cots available. Check-in all day. Access, Visa.*

Darwen   Old Rosins Inn
Tel 0254 771264

Treacle Row Pickup Bank Darwen Lancashire BB3 3QD   Map 6 B1

18th-century inn set in open moorland with panoramic views. *Free House.* **Beer** *Boddington. Flowers IPA, Timothy Taylors Landlord. Children's play area.*

Debden   Plough
Tel 0799 40396

High Street Debden Essex CB11 3LE   Map 10 B3

Nicely refurbished country local, just outside Saffron Walden; real fire; no music; good garden for families. **Beer** *Greene King IPA and Abbot. Garden. Children's play area.*

Dedham   Anchor
Tel 0206 323471

Heath Road Dedham Essex   Map 10 C3

Refurbished, peaceful pub with opened-out bar, new restaurant and a strong local following; large beer garden. **Beer** *Adnams, Greene King IPA and Abbot. Garden.*

Dedham   Marlborough Head Hotel   FOOD
Tel 0206 323250   B&B

Mill Lane Dedham Essex CO7 6DH   Map 10 C3

☺

Surrounded by picturesque Constable country, Dedham is a charming village, and the Marlborough Head, which occupies that most traditional of sites, directly opposite the church, has been dispensing hospitality for over 550 years. Woodcarving is a speciality here, outside on the black and white timbered upper storey of the building, inside above a massive old fireplace in the entrance lobby, as well as a particularly fine carved oak fireplace, original to the inn and now found in the family/coach party room. Several other rooms and bars, one featuring a heavily beamed ceiling, are furnished with good eating-height tables and the odd copper or brass ornament. Food orders are made at a leather-topped desk, quoting the number painted on a little stone on your table, from a long menu that runs the gamut from a simple jacket potato to the likes of noisettes of roedeer (£6.50) and fresh breast of chicken with garlic butter wrapped in filo pastry (£5.75). Not to be missed is the Marlborough soup made with vegetables and a proper beef stock. Try to leave room for pudding, too, perhaps a light chocolate roulade filled with raspberries or a fresh plum crumble. Spacious bedrooms, one double and two singles, are modestly but pleasantly furnished with a variety of pieces from the antiqueish and old pine to more modern bedside tables. Each has a few old timbers and sloping floors, and candlewick bedspreads add a homely touch. Two have compact, lino-floored en-suite shower rooms with toilets, and the double a proper bathroom. *Bar Food 12-2, 7-9.30 (10 Fri/Sat). Vegetarian dishes. Beer Adnams, Benskins. Garden, outdoor play area, patio, outdoor eating. Family room. Accommodation 3 bedrooms, all en suite, from £50 (single £32.50). Children welcome overnight, cots available. Check-in after 1pm. Access, Visa.*

Dent   Sun

| Tel 058 75 208 |

Main Street Dent Cumbria LA10 5QL   Map 5 D4

Delightfully old-fashioned village inn, pretty inside and out, with original timbers, comfortable furniture and a warming winter fire. They set up their own little brewery, a couple of miles down the road, in 1990, and now supply some other pubs in the area. *Free House. Beer Dent Bitter and Ramsbottom, Theakston XB, Youngers Scotch. Garden. Family room.*

Derby   Dolphin Inn

| Tel 0332 297741 |

6/7 Queen Street Derby Derbyshire DE5 1NR   Map 6 C3

The oldest pub in Derby, dating from the 16th century, in a conveniently central spot. No juke box or machines. *Beer M & B Highgate Mild, Bass. Garden.*

Dersingham   Feathers Hotel

| Tel 0485 540207 | **B&B**

Manor Road Dersingham Norfolk PE31 6LN   Map 10 B1

Fine stone-built carrstone pub not far from Sandringham and close to gentle woodland rambles. Also nearby are Dersingham and Snettisham Bird Reserves. The mellow oak-panelled main bar overlooks a splendid garden with solid wooden tables for summer drinking; there's also a cheery horse-brassy public bar. Accommodation comprises five bedrooms, none of them with en-suite facilities. *Beer Adnams, IPA. Children allowed in bar to eat. Garden, outdoor play area, summer barbecue. Family room. Accommodation 5 bedrooms, sharing 2 bathrooms, £40 (single £25). Children welcome overnight. Check-in all day. Access, Visa.*

Devizes   Bear Hotel

| Tel 0380 722444   Fax 0380 722450 | **FOOD**
B&B

Market Place Devizes Wiltshire SN10 1HS   Map 14 C3

Famous old town-centre coaching inn with an old-fashioned air, civilised, rambling and busy in typical market town style – hotelly rather than pubby, with a main lounge slightly reminiscent of an ocean liner bar. The parquet-floored Lawrence Room is smart and relaxing, and there's a splendid pea green sitting room. Good log fires in winter. A Bear Club triple decker (£2.95) is a popular bar food snack amongst other choices like beef in real ale (£3.95) or a Devizes pie with pickled egg (£2.25). Bar food is reliable, as is the beer in the home town of Wadworth brewery. More substantial dishes feature in the restaurant – roast rack of lamb with rosemary and mushrooms in a garlic cream sauce (£10.45) or pot-roasted quail, stuffed with herb forcemeat on a bed of shredded vegetables (£10.90). Bedrooms are floral, comfortable and well-equipped with proper sturdy furniture. Three have four-poster beds. *Bar Food 10-2.30, 7-9. Restaurant Meals*

12.30-2 (12.15-1.45 Sun), 7-9.30 (except Sun). Vegetarian dishes.
Children's portions. **Beer** *Wadworth. Patio, outdoor eating.*
Accommodation *24 bedrooms, all en suite, £60 (single £40). Children*
welcome overnight, additional beds (from £15), cots supplied. Check-in after
midday. Access, Visa.

Devizes   Moonrakers

Tel 038 072 2909	**B&B**

29 Nursteed Road Devizes Wiltshire SN10 3AJ   Map 14 C3

Homely overnight accommodation is provided at this mock-Tudor
inn standing less than a mile from Devizes town centre. The three
simple, well-kept bedrooms have their own shower cabinets as well as
TVs, tea-makers and cosy duvets, and share a public bathroom. An
open fire crackles beneath a copper-hooded fireplace in the plush
lounge bar, while the more modest public bar houses a pool table.
New Landlords. **Beer** *Wadworth 6X, IPA. Garden, Children's play area.*
Accommodation *3 bedrooms, not en-suite, £38 (single £20). Children*
welcome overnight, additional beds and cots available. Check-in all day.
Access, Visa.

Didsbury   Royal Oak

Tel 061-445 3152	**FOOD**

729 Wilmslow Road Didsbury Greater Manchester M20 0RH   Map 6 B2

Quantity and quality of cheese draw people here, for the landlord has
had a passion for it for 38 years. In his "old-fashioned pub in a time
warp", Arthur Gosling has covered the walls in theatre and play
posters and can therefore never redecorate! At lunchtime, the bar
counter is piled high with a huge selection of English, French and
Spanish cheeses. Enormous slices are served (£2.50 for choice of two)
with delicious wholemeal bread and bowls of onion and beetroot, or
olives. Several patés (£2.50) are also available. Doggy bags are on
hand for those who cannot do their portions justice. No children
allowed. **Bar Food** *12-2 (except Sat and Sun).* **Beer** *Marstons Pedigree &*
Best Bitter. Parking difficult. No credit cards.

Diggle   Diggle Hotel

Tel 0457 872741	**B&B**

Station House Diggle Greater Manchester OL3 5JZ   Map 6 C2

The village of Diggle is signposted off the A670. If approaching from
the north, you'll need to pass the junction and use the turning circle as
left turns are prohibited. Once through the village, watch out for signs
for the Diggle Hotel (by the school). The hotel itself, a dark stone
building by the railway line, dates back to 1789, and is close to the
(disused) longest canal tunnel in Britain, some three and a quarter
miles long. The owners of the Diggle, Gerald and Barbara Mitchell
and their daughter Dawn, gave up running a newsagents in Leeds to
take over this Free House some five years ago. The interior of the
building is neat and unpretentious. The main room (and adjoining
small room where children can sit) is full of polished brass and
copperware, and the plain walls decorated with a number of country
pictures. One wall has a display of bank notes and coins, both past and
present – it's interesting to see how the notes have shrunk (in size and
value!) over the years. Over the bar itself there's a collection of photos
of the locals. Upstairs there are three neat, unfussy double bedrooms,
two of them quite compact, the largest with views towards the

village. Modern fitted furniture is used in all rooms, as are duvets with pretty floral covers, and washbasins. The shared and carpeted bathroom also has a separate shower unit. A homely residents' lounge has fawn upholstered seating, books and games. The Mitchells are friendly and charming hosts, and staff equally pleasant. *Free House.* **Beer** *Whitbread. Garden. Family room.* **Accommodation** *3 bedrooms, sharing bathroom, £35 (single £25). Children welcome overnight, additional beds and cots supplied. Check-in all day. No dogs. Access, Visa.*

Disley   Dandy Cock Inn

Tel 0663 763712

Market Street Disley Cheshire SK12 2DT   Map 6 C2

Spick and span family-run village pub with restaurant and tremendous views across the neighbouring valley. **Beer** *Robinson's Mild and Best Bitter. Family room.*

Ditchling   Bull Hotel

Tel 0273 843147

2 High Street Ditchling East Sussex   Map 11 B6

Wonderfully atmospheric, historic old pub, with lots of original tavern features and handsome furnishings. **Beer** *Whitbread. Riverside garden. Family room.*

Docking   Pilgrim's Reach

Tel 0485 518383

High Street Docking Norfolk PE31 8NH   Map 10 C1

16th-century pub once much used by passing pilgrims; the barn they used for sleeping is now the main bar area. **Beer** *Adnams, Greene King IPA. Garden. Children's play area.*

Doddiscombsleigh   Nobody Inn

FOOD

Tel 0647 52394   Fax 0647 52978

B&B

Doddiscombsleigh Devon EX6 7PS   Map 13 D2

According to legend, a previous owner of this delightful old inn closed and locked the door against the knocking of weary travellers, pretending that there was nobody in, and it has remained the 'Nobody Inn' ever since. Today one can be sure that somebody's in, and of a warm welcome within its mellow bars. The mood is enhanced by a wealth of old beams, ancient settles and a motley collection of antique tables; horse brasses and copper pots and pans decorate the inglenook fireplace, and a real fire burns in winter. The varied bar menu includes a coarse duck liver paté with port and herbs (£2.60) and the special Nobody soup (£1.50), made with chicken stock, vegetables and fruit, resulting in a dark, consommé-like broth with a slightly sweet, spicy flavour. In the characterful restaurant, offerings range from Devon-cured venison (£2.80) and mussels from the Exe (£2.55) to snails bourguignon (£2.95) and fillet of beef with tarragon sauce (£10.50), and home-made puddings come with great dollops of real clotted cream. But ensure you leave a space for possibly the best collection of Devonshire cheese to be found anywhere. Six different cheeses can be chosen from a selection of more than forty, including cow's, goat's and ewe's milk cheeses, many of them unpasteurised, with wonderfully evocative names like Langleigh Meadow, Jacobstowe, Ticklemoor and Toatley. Even more impressive is the globetrotting wine list, which features over 700 bins and is particularly strong in the Loire. Sixteen wines are also offered by the glass at any one time and there are no less than 230 different whiskies to choose from. Four of the modestly comfortable bedrooms are in the inn itself, two with en suite shower and toilet, as well as tea-makers and a drinks tray bearing full bottles of brandy, gin and sherry -charged up by consumption, at bar prices. Three larger en-suite rooms are in a small early 17th-century manor house about 150 yards away, next to the church. These are traditionally furnished with old rather than antique pieces, and a ready-to-serve Continental breakfast is provided in the fridge. Alternatively, stroll up to the inn for one of their excellent cooked breakfasts. *Bar Food 12-2, 7-10. Restaurant Meals 7.30-9.15 (Tue-Sat). Vegetarian dishes. Free House. Beer Devon, Draught Bass, Glory, Nobody's Bitter, Whitbread Flowers IPA. Cider Grays Inch's Stonehouse. Garden, outdoor eating. Accommodation 7 bedrooms, 3 en suite, £53 (single £33). Additional beds (£6). Check-in all day. No dogs. Access, Visa.*

Donington-on-Bain   Black Horse

Tel 0507 343640

Main Road Donington-on-Bain Lincolnshire LN11 9TJ   Map 7 E2

On the Viking Way, as interior murals commemorate. The new 8-bedroomed motel opened recently. *Free House. Beer Adnams Bitter and Broadside, Ruddles Best, Websters Yorkshire. Garden. Children's play area. Family room.*

Dorchester-on-Thames   George Hotel

Tel 0865 340404	**B&B**

High Street Dorchester-on-Thames Oxfordshire OX9 8HH   Map 16 C2

With a history spanning more than 500 years, the George is one of the oldest inns in the land. Focal point of the public area is a fine beamed bar. Bedrooms in the main building have a solid, old-fashioned feel, some cosy and snug under oak beams, two with solid four-posters. Other rooms have less character but are still very adequate. *Garden. Accommodation 18 bedrooms, £85. Children welcome overnight. Closed 1 week Xmas. Access, Amex, Diners, Visa.*

Dorstone   Pandy Inn

Tel 0981 550273	**FOOD**

Dorstone Golden Valley Hereford & Worcester HR3 6AN   Map 14 A1

Located off the B4348, the Pandy is the oldest inn in Herefordshire, built in 1185 by Richard De Brito, a Norman knight, to house his workers while building Dorstone Church as atonement for his part in the murder of Thomas Becket. Vegetarians are well catered for on the daily changing menu, with a variety of dishes to choose from including spinach and mushroom lasagne (£4.95) and vegetable moussaka (£4.75). 'From the Sea & River' menu, the choices are rainbow trout (£6.35), fresh salmon with mushroom sauce (£7.50) or sole fillets stuffed with crab and scallops (£7.50). 'Light Bites & Starters' and meat dishes are not neglected either, with home-made hummus (£2.65), deep fried Camembert (£2.95), 10oz rump steak (£8.25) and wild rabbit pie (£5.25). Finally choose one of the seven desserts on the 'Puddings & Treats' menu (all £1.95). *Bar Food 12-2, 7-9.45. Vegetarian dishes. Children's menu (£1.95 per dish). Children allowed to eat in bar. Free house. Beer Bass, Charles Wells Eagle, Hook Norton. Cider Weston. Garden, outdoor eating, children's play area. Family room. No credit cards.*

Dowlish Wake   New Inn

Tel 0460 52413   **FOOD**

Dowlish Wake nr Ilminster Somerset TA19 0NZ   Map 13 E2

Well-loved little gem of a country pub – 15th-century, stone-walled,
village inn with a pleasingly old-fashioned air, a good mix of furniture
and a wood-burning stove. Cooking by the Swiss landlady (rösti fans
take note) is always good: choose either from a deceptively plain
typed bar menu – whitebait (£2.50), emincé of liver (£3.75), plaice
(£3.75) or a smarter à la carte – carpaccio £4), butterfly prawns
(£2.75), braised duck (£8.25), shoulder of lamb (£10.75) mixed and
matched with the bar menu in the evenings. They specialise in steaks
of all sorts and sauces. A delightful village, also home to Perry's Cider
Mill. Games are popular here – table skittles, skittle alley and darts.
Bar Food 12-2, 6.30-9. *Vegetarian dishes. Children's portions.* **Beer**
Butcombe Bitter, Wadworth 6X. Theakstons Old Peculier. **Cider** *Perrys.*
Garden, outdoor eating, children's play area. No credit cards.

Downham   Assheton Arms

Tel 0200 41227

Downham nr Clitheroe Lancashire BB7 4BJ   Map 6 B1

The focal point of an unspoilt stone-built old estate village. An
opened-up, red-carpeted bar has attractive furnishings and window
seats. **Beer** *Whitbread Castle Eden and Bently's Yorkshire, Marston
Pedigree.*

Downham Market   Cock Tavern

Tel 0366 385047   **FOOD**

43 Lynn Road Downham Market Norfolk PE38 9NP   Map 10 B2

Small, neatly-kept pub run with warmth and enthusiasm, often packed
with fans of the landlady's cooking which includes soup (£1.95),
baked avocado with chestnuts (£4.95), sea trout pie (£5) and honey
and almond tart (£1.95). Sauté potatoes are offered rather than the
ubiquitous chips. *Bar Meals* 12-1.45 *(not Sun)* 7-9.15. *Vegetarian
dishes. Children's portions.* **Beer** *Flowers Original, Tetley. Garden, outdoor
eating. Closed Tuesday, also Chrismas Day-New Year. No credit cards.*

Downham Market   Crown Hotel

Tel 0366 382322

Downham Market Norfolk PE38 9DH   Map 10 B2

17th-century coaching inn, worth trying for bed and breakfast. **Beer**
Batemans, Greene King IPA, Bass. Family room.

Downton   Royal Oak

Tel 0590 642297

Downton Hampshire   Map 14 C4

In the same family for 130 years, and traditionally run: no juke box,
no fruit machines. Bars immaculately kept, one of them no-smoking,
and there's a ramp for disabled access. Three open fires in winter. **Beer**
Whitbread. Garden. Family room.

Drakeholes   Griff Inn

FOOD
B&B

Tel 0777 817206

Drakeholes near Bawtry Nottinghamshire

Map 7 D2

Less of a hamlet than a multiple road junction, where the A631 meets the B6045, Drakeholes marks a right-angle turn on the Chesterfield canal where it tunnels for 150 yards under the road system. Standing above the basin, fronted by a large patio and canalside picnic tables, the Griff (once known as the White Swan) is built in the same distinctive red brick which characterises the estate village (both shopless and publess) of nearby Weston Hall. The 18th-century inn's interior echoes the grand style of an earlier age, with its marble-floored entrance foyer and bar, and intimate oak-panelled cocktail lounge. Grand eating is not, however, de rigueur, the extensive bar menu encompassing old-fashioned pies like steak and ale (£4.50); sandwiches start at £2. On Sundays there is a bar lunch (from £4.50) and weekend carvery (from £4.50). Separating the bar from the (non-smoking) restaurant, a bright breakfast room doubles as a gift shop, selling miniature pottery, pot pourri and hand-made candles. The restaurant itself combines table d'hote and a Sunday lunch with an ambitious à la carte, which is carefully cooked and neatly presented, perhaps seafood pancake (£4.60), Asia and Orient (£4.60), Calvados pork (£9.75), a 'Highland fling' (£11.60), or beef bourguignon (£9.75). The Griff is certainly useful to know for a quiet country stay in the Eden valley. Bedrooms are neatly appointed in pastel shades and varnished pine, which create a cottagey effect without frill or particular luxury. There are televisions but no phones. En suite bathrooms are spacious and airy with good, powerful showers for early morning invigoration prior to a substantial country breakfast. *Bar Food and Restaurant Meals* 12-2 (2.30 Sun), 7-10. *Vegetarian dishes. Children's menu. Free House. Beer Tetley, Whitbread. Children allowed in bar to eat. Garden, outdoor eating.* **Accommodation** *3 bedrooms, all en suite, from £45 (single £31.95). Children welcome overnight, cots available. Check-in all day. No dogs. Access, Visa.*

Drayton   Roebuck

FOOD
B&B

Tel 0295 730542

Drayton nr Banbury Oxfordshire OX15 6EN

Map 16 B1

Standing next to the A422 about a mile from Banbury is an attractive 16th-century stone pub which has built up a strong local following for its excellent food. The low-beamed bars with their rough, painted walls and solid wooden tables provide a cosily atmospheric setting for everything from the 'Roebuck Special' (£4.65 – fresh hot ham off the bone), liver and smoked bacon casserole (£4.75), savoury crepes (£4.50), and clam fries (£3.15) to lamb Shrewsbury (£8.70), scampi provencale (£12.25), cracked wheat casserole (£8.15) or tagliatelle in a cream sauce with vegetables (£8.15). Two neat, well-kept bedrooms, one with exposed beams and a sloping ceiling, have pretty floral fabrics and up-to-date furniture. They have a functional shower room and are both equipped with remote-control TVs, tea-makers and magazines. No dogs. **Bar Food** 11.30-2 (Sun 12-2), 6.30-9.30 (except Mon). **Restaurant Meals** 7-9.45 (except Sun and Mon). *Vegetarian meals. Children's portions. Free House. Beer Hook Norton, Waddingtons, Ruddles County, London Pride, Marston's Pedigree.* **Accommodation** *2 bedrooms with shared bathroom, £30 (£20 single). Children welcome overnight. Accommodation closed one week Christmas. Access, Visa.*

Driffield   Bell Hotel

| Tel 0377 46661   Fax 0377 43228 | **B&B** |

Market Place Driffield Humberside YO25 7AP

Map 7 E1

Period charm and modern amenities combine in a coaching inn that's more than 250 years old, but now very much a hotel. Conference and function facilities are in the restored Old Town Hall, and further conversion houses a leisure complex. Day rooms include the 18th-century wood-panelled Oak Room, the flagstoned Old Corn Exchange buffet/bar and a residents' lounge. Bedrooms boast antique furniture and up-to-date comforts. No children under 12. *Garden, indoor swimming pool, spa bath, steam room, sauna, solarium, squash.* **Accommodation** *14 rooms, £75. Closed 25-27 Dec. No dogs. Access, Amex, Diners, Visa.*

Dronfield   Old Sidings

| Tel 0246 410023 |

91 Chesterfield Road Dronfield Derbyshire S18 6XE

Map 6 C2

The extensive menu features an 11-strong vegetarian list at this popular dining pub, now run by the experienced Stanaways, previously at the Red House in Sheffield. **Beer** *Whitbread, Marston Pedigree, Bass. Family room.*

Droxford   Hurdles Inn

| Tel 0489 877451 |

Station Road Droxford Hampshire SO3 1QU

Map 15 D3

Well known food pub, cheap, cheerful, and usually packed with diners. Over 14s only. Book for weekend visits.

Duddington   Royal Oak Hotel

| Tel 078083 267 | **FOOD** |
| | **B&B** |

High Street Duddington nr Stamford Northamptonshire

Map 7 E4

The bar is modern, but by no means without character, due in part to plush banquette seating, lots of greenery and well-lit prints of Victorian scenes. At one end of the bar a winter fire burns; at the other an area is set up for eating, with smartly laid tables and waitress service. The food is home-made and unpretentious offering 4-5 'specials' every day – 20oz T-bone steak (£9.90), sliced turkey breast in mushroom and sherry sauce (£5.50), beef stroganoff with rice and green salad (£9.80) and vegetable pancake (£4.50). Soup and sandwiches (prawn £2.50) cope with lighter appetites, and there is a traditional roast lunch on Sundays (main course £4.75, 3-course meal £7.95). A garden, patio and children's play area are available for taking refreshment under the sun. Decent-sized bedrooms, attractively done out in pastel shades, have antique-style reproduction pieces, Victorian prints and very comfortable beds with brass bedsteads. TVs, phones and tea-maker alarm clocks are standard, and the bathrooms are carpeted and fully tiled. **Bar Food and Restaurant Meals** *12-2, 6.30-10 (7-10.30 Sun). Vegetarian dishes. Children's portions. Free House.* **Beer** *Abbotts. Garden, outdoor eating & children's play area.* **Accommodation** *5 bedrooms, all en suite (4 with shower, 1 with bath), £40/£45 (single £28.50/£32). Children welcome overnight, additional beds (£8), cots supplied. Check-in all day. No dogs. Access, Visa.*

Dummer   The Queen

Tel 0256 397367	**FOOD**
Dummer nr Basingstoke Hampshire RG22 2AD	Map 16 C4

If you didn't know that you were in the village where the Duchess of
York grew up, a visit to The Queen would soon enlighten you!
Several rooms have been opened up to make one bar area, with beams
and fireplaces. A daily changing blackboard menu offers a variety of
sandwiches (including enormous double-deckers), poached salmon
(£8.95), chicken (£6.95) or vegetarian tikka (£5.95), grilled fish,
together with a choice of home-made puddings (£2.25 – £3.20) –
summer pudding, different cheesecakes, chocolate mousse. 4-course
Sunday roast lunch £8.95. Live light music entertainment on Sunday
evenings. *Bar Food 12-2.30, 6-10. Vegetarian dishes. Children's portions.*
Beer Courage Best, Directors, guest bitter every month. Garden, outdoor
eating. Access, Amex, Visa.

Dunsfold   Sun

Tel 048 649 242	**FOOD**
The Common Dunsfold Surrey GU8 4LE	Map 11 A5

Charming village-green Georgian-fronted pub with a 17th-century
barn interior. Old fishing rods and horse tack decorate the walls. The
bar food and restaurant menu are one and the same although there is a
separate dining area and additional 'specials' are available on Friday and
Saturday evenings. Start with deep-fried Brie (£3.75) or spicy samosas
(£3.75), followed by home-made steak and kidney pie (£5.75) or
lamb noisettes (£7.95) and finish with death by chocolate (£2.50) or
treacle tart (£2.50). *Bar Food and Restaurant Meals 12-2.15 (12-2*
Sun), 7-10 (7-9.30 Sun). Vegetarian dishes. Children's portions. Children
allowed in bar to eat. Beer Harvey, Ind Coope. Garden, outdoor eating.
Access, Amex, Diners, Visa.

Dunston   Cottage Inn

Tel 0665 576658	
Dunston nr Alnwick Northumberland NE66 3SZ	Map 5 D2

A conversion of five cottages, white-painted and creeper-strewn, in a
sleepy little village. Pleasant panelled lounge; public bar has pool, and
film star cut-outs; also black and white tiled conservatory. Eight acres
of grounds: the garden is lovely for outdoor eating and completely
safe for children. *Beer Ruddles Best and County. Garden. Children's play*
area. Family room.

Dunwich   Ship Inn

Tel 072873 219	**FOOD**
	B&B
St James Street Dunwich Suffolk IP17 3DT	Map 10 D2

Well-loved old smugglers' inn overlooking the salt marshes and sea.
The delightfully unspoilt public bar offers nautical bric-a-brac, a
wood-burning stove in a huge brick fireplace, flagged floors and
simple wooden furnishings. There's also a plain carpeted dining room.
A fine Victorian staircase leads to simple homely bedrooms, light and
clean with pretty fabrics and period touches, but no televisions. Good
simple food in generous portions, too: the restaurant menu applies
throughout the pub in the evenings; bar meals menu lunchtime only.
Choose at lunch from home-made soup (£1.25), cottage pie (£3.10),
steak and mushroom pie (£3.95) and in the evening, hot garlic

prawns (£4.25), crispy Camembert parcels (£3.75), rump steak (£7.25), fish of the day (£7.25) or escalope of pork (£6.50), followed by home-made desserts such as boozy bread-and-butter pudding, apple crumble (both £1.60) or apple and cider flan (£2.20). *Bar Food and Restaurant Meals* 12-2, 7.30-9.15. *Vegetarian dishes. Children's portions. Beer Adnams Bitter and Broadside, Greene King. Garden, outdoor eating. Familyroom. Accommodation 3 bedrooms, 1 en suite, £48 (single £19). Children welcome overnight, additional beds (£12), cots supplied. Check-in by arrangement. No credit cards.*

Duxford   John Barleycorn

Tel 0223 832699

Moorfield Road Duxford Cambridgeshire CB2 4PP   **Map 10 B3**

Well-kept thatched pub which is glorious with hanging baskets tubs and borders in high summer. Softly lit main bar with country furniture; additional seating in a converted barn. *Beer Greene King Mild, IPA and Abbot. Garden.*

Dyke   Wishing Well Inn

Tel 0778 422970

Dyke Bourne Lincolnshire PE10 0AF   **Map 7 E3**

Done-up, opened-out village inn, a relaxing venue with its candlelight, heavy beams, exposed stone and wishing well. *Free House. Beer Tetley, Burton Ale, Greene King Abbot. Garden. Children's play area.*

Dymock   Beauchamp Arms

Tel 035 185 266

Dymock Gloucestershire GL18 1LP   **Map 14 B1**

Pretty garden and popular for lunchtime bar food. Dynmock single Gloucester cheese is worth sampling. *Beer Wye Valley Hereford Bitter, Whitbread, Marston Pedigree. Garden. Children's play area.*

Eardisland   White Swan

Tel 05447 565

Eardisland nr Pembridge Hereford & Worcester   **Map 14 A1**

A relaxing, pretty pub, traditionally styled, with real fires, and the daily papers laid out for customers in the low-beamed cosy lounge; basic, lively public bar. Glorious village. *Beer Marston Pedigree. Garden. Children's play area.*

Earl Soham   Victoria

Tel 0728 685758

Earl Soham nr Woodbridge Suffolk IP13 7RL   **Map 10 C3**

Superb little country pub with an Icelandic landlord well-known for his passion for good home-brewed beer. Simple old-fashioned furnishings, lots of wood on floors and walls, open fires and Queen Victoria pictures. *Free House. Beer Earl Soham Gannet Mild, Victorian Bitter and Gannet Ale. Garden.*

Easebourne   Olde White Horse

Tel 0730 813521

Easebourne Street Midhurst Easebourne West Sussex GU29 0AL   **Map 11 A6**

Neat stone pub with modernised, comfortable lounge, bigger public bar and locals' tap room. *Beer Greene King IPA and Abbot. Garden.*

Easington   The Mole & Chicken

Tel 0844 208387

Easington Aylesbury Buckinghamshire HP18 9EY

FOOD

Map 17 D2

Between junction 7 of the M40 and Aylesbury; take the B4011 from Thame past Long Crendon (2 miles), following the Chilton road outside the village and turn left at the top of Carters Lane (opposite the Chandos Arms), then straight on for half a mile. Newly renovated and with a new landlord, Johnny Chick, this pretty pub has magnificent views of the Oxfordshire/Buckinghamshire countryside and has quickly become established. Inside, the ragged washed walls are hung with hunting prints and candle lighting; a low, beamed ceiling and hand-painted floor in the Tuscany style are complemented by two roaring log fires. There's seating for 60 people at oak and pine tables, and half a ton of French oak on bricks forms the attractive bar. Good home-cooked food such as half shoulder of lamb with honey and provençale sauce (£7.95), fresh sardines from Billingsgate (£3.95) and roast crispy duck with orange and a sauce made with beef stock (£7.50). Three-course Sunday lunch (£10.50) is served in the separate restaurant area. *Free House.* **Bar Food** *11.30-2.30, 6.30-10.30. Children's portions.* **Beer** *Hook Norton, Bass, Adams, Burton, monthly guest beers. Garden. Outdoor eating. Access, Visa, Amex.*

East Dereham   King's Head Hotel

Tel 0362 693842

Norwich Street East Dereham Norfolk NR19 1AD

B&B

Map 10 C1

Locals fill the bar, which looks out on to a bowling green edged with flowerbeds and a pretty patio which are both attractive summer features. The inn was built in the 17th century, and has been modernised to provide comfortable bedrooms in a converted stable block as well as in the main building. All are centrally heated and offer TVs, tea-makers and direct-dial telephones, as well as good en suite bath/shower rooms. **Beer** *Ruddles Best Bitter, Websters Yorkshire Bitter, Norwich Bitter. Garden.* **Accommodation** *15 bedrooms, 12 en suite, £46 (single £35). Children welcome overnight, additional beds, cots available. Check-in all day. Access, Amex, Diners, Visa.*

East Down   Pyne Arms

Tel 0271 850207

East Down Devon EX31 4LX

Map 13 D1

Little pebbledash pub. Traditional interior has lots of nooks and crannies, plus a small galleried loft area. *Free House.* **Beer** *Flowers IPA.*

East Haddon   Red Lion

Tel 0604 770223   Fax 0604 645866

East Haddon Northamptonshire

B&B

Map 15 D1

Civilised little hotel of golden stone in a country location not far from the M1. Pleasant, relaxing lounge bar with a mix of furnishings, china and pewter, smaller, plainer public bar. Recommended for its cottagey, well-kept bedrooms (two twins, two doubles and a single) with handbasin in each room. **Beer** *Charles Wells. Family room. Garden.* **Accommodation** *5 bedrooms, sharing 2 bathrooms, from £39 (single £29). Children welcome overnight, cot available. Check-in by arrangement. No dogs. Access, Amex, Diners, Visa.*

East Ilsley   Swan

Tel 063 528 238

High Street East Ilsley Berkshire RG16 0LF

Map 16 C3

Lovely old village pub which has belonged to local brewers Morlands for over 150 years. The opened-out, refurbished interior still retains lots of nooks and crannies, different areas with different styles and customers, and the fruit machine and piped music don't intrude on the civilised mood too much. *Beer Morlands Original and Old Masters. Garden. Children's play area. Family room.*

East Lulworth   Weld Arms

Tel 092 941 211

East Lulworth Dorset BH20 5QQ

Map 14 B4

Distinctive and relaxing thatched old pub with a welcoming fire, a mix of attractive furnishings including large country kitchen tables, and nautical memorabilia, thanks to the yachtsman licensee. Lovely garden. *Beer Devenish Royal Wessex. Garden. Children's play area. Family room.*

East Ruston   Butchers Arms

Tel 0692 650237

Oak Lane East Ruston Norfolk NR12 9JG

Map 10 D1

Friendly family-run free house which makes good use of local fish. *Free House. Beer Morlands, Tetley, Woodfordes Broadsman. Garden. Children's play area. Family room.*

East Witton   Cover Bridge Inn

Tel 0969 23250

East Witton nr Leyburn North Yorkshire DL8 4SQ

Map 5 D4

Old, proprietor-run country inn, a good base for Dales visits. *Free House. Beer John Smiths Yorkshire, Theakston Best. Garden. Children's play area.*

Eastergate   Wilkes Head

Tel 0243 543380

FOOD

Church Lane Eastergate West Sussex PO20 6UT

Map 11 A6

An 18th-century flagstone-floored pub with two well-worn bars, homely and relaxing – a useful stopping place en route to Goodwood or Fontwell Races. Simple, honest home cooking by the landlady: ground beef lasagne is recommended (£3.95) and but other choices could be chili (£3.95), mixed grill (£5.25), chicken Kiev (£6.90) or fillet steak (£9.95); eat in the riverside garden in fine weather. Steaks and fish dominate the straightforward restaurant menu. Food is only served until 8.30pm on winter Sunday evenings in order to make space for the pub's quiz night. *Bar Food 12-2, 7-9.30 (7-8.30 winter Sun). Vegetarian dishes. Children's menu (£1.95 per dish). Free House. Beer Ballards, Gales, Burton, Benskins. Garden, outdoor eating. Access, Visa.*

Eastling   Carpenter's Arms

| Tel 0795 890234 | **FOOD** |

Eastling near Faversham Kent ME13 0AZ   Map 11 C5

The mellow redbrick Carpenter's Arms dates back to the 14th century
and is teeming with character. An old inglenook fireplace in the
brick-floored restaurant has an old baking oven; corn dollies decorate
the old timbers and beams, and a host of flowers and pot plants add a
homely touch. The red carpet-tiled bar features lots of old photos, a
collection of old bottles, and pew seating around draw-leaf dining
room tables. The bar menu is not over-long, featuring hearty home-
made soups (£1.50), burgers, ham and eggs, ploughman's and
sandwiches. Steaks and simple fish dishes are to be found in the
restaurant, including smoked salmon (£3.75), Dover sole £10.50) and
beef and ale pie (£7.50), served with a selection of fresh vegetables.
All is freshly cooked to order. Older children are only allowed inside
if eating in the restaurant, but there are a few tables in the garden and
small portions are available of suitable dishes. Meanwhile, next door in
a typically Kentish white clapperboard house are four peaceful
bedrooms, two of them rather on the small side, with shower cabinets
and toilets en suite. The best room is much more spacious with a full
en suite bathroom. All have the same floral curtains, which contrast
rather oddly with abstract patterned duvets, as well as TVs and radio
alarms. Good breakfasts are served in the restaurant. *Bar Food 12-2
(1.30 Sun), 6.30-8.30 (except Sun).* **Restaurant** *12-2.30 (1.30 Sun),
7-10.30 (except Sun). Vegetarian dishes. Children's portions.* **Beer** *Master
Brew, Shepherd Neame, Spitfire. Garden, outdoor eating.* **Accommodation**
*(no children under 12) 3 bedrooms, all en suite, £40 (single £32). Check-
in all day. No dogs. Access, Amex, Visa.*

Eccleshall   St George Hotel

| Tel 0785 850300   Fax 0785 861452 | **B&B** |

Castle Street Eccleshall Staffordshire ST21 6DF   Map 6 B3

New landlords have taken over this carefully restored 250-year-old
coaching inn which enjoys a central crossroad position in Eccleshall.
The oak-beamed bar, which is open all day, has an opaque glass 'smoke
room' panel and red-brick inglenook, and there is also a relaxing little
lounge. Cottage-style bedrooms, many with open fires, exposed beams
with vaulted ceilings and canopied or four-poster beds, are
thoughtfully equipped and all have private facilities. *Free House.* **Beer**
Tetley, Bodingtons, Burtons, guest beer. **Cider** *Scrumpy Jack.*
Accommodation *10 bedrooms, all en suite, £55, (single £40). Children
welcome overnight, additional beds and cots available. Check-in all day.
Access, Amex, Diners, Visa.*

Edburton   Tottington Manor Hotel

| Tel 0903 815757 | **FOOD** |
| | **B&B** |

Edburton nr Henfield West Sussex BN5 9LJ   Map 11 B6

A Grade II listed 17th-century inn-cum-hotel in its own grounds at
the foot of the South Downs, with lovely views. The bar is simple and
properly pubby, with country furniture and an open fire hogged by
an assortment of animals. Good bar food – jacket potatoes (£4),
sandwiches (£2.60), ploughman's (£3.80); prices are just a little
higher in the restaurant whose £15, 3-course menu includes half a
bottle of wine. Breast of French duckling with honey and fig sauce,
roast South Down lamb and a wide variety of fresh fish are some of

the main courses, and several vegetarian dishes are always available. Bedrooms are pretty, with soothing colours and good sturdy furniture, and en-suite bathrooms have proper guest toiletries. The residents' lounge is also rather fine. *Bar Food* 12-2, 7-9.15. *Restaurant Meals* 7-9.15 (except Sun). *Vegetarian meals. Children's portions. Free House.* *Beer* Adnams,Bateman 4X, Fullers London Pride. *Cider* Stowford Press. *Garden, outdoor eating.* **Accommodation** 6 bedrooms, all en suite, £60 (single £42). Children welcome overnight, additional beds (£12), cot supplied. Check-in all day. Pub closed on Sundays from January to end March. Access, Amex, Diners, Visa.

Effingham   Plough

| Tel 0372 458121 | **FOOD** |
| Orestan Lane Effingham Surrey KT24 5SW | Map 17 F4 |

Smartly rustic, family-run pub with reliable food. No smoking area. Simply cooked food – avocado and bacon pasta (£3.40), fresh vegetable crumble (£3.40), Greek lamb casserole (£3.40) in addition to steak & kidney pie, beef sandwiches, savoury crepes and on Sundays, a traditional 2-course lunch for £5.95. *Bar Food* 12-2, 7-9.15 (not Sun eve). *Vegetarian dishes. Children's portions.* **Beer** Youngs Best Bitter, Porter. Garden, outdoor eating, children's play area. No credit cards.

Eggleston   Three Tuns

| Tel 0833 50289 | |
| Eggleston Durham DL12 0AH | Map 5 D3 |

Get here early for one of the coveted window seats in the Teesdale Room, with splendid views across the valley. The traditionally furnished, civilised bar has old oak settles and an open fire. *Free House. Garden. Children's play area.*

Eglingham   Tankerville Arms

| Tel 066 578 444 | |
| Eglingham nr Alnwick Northumberland NE66 2TX | Map 5 D1 |

Plush banquette-modernised stone-built village pub with two coal fires. *Free House.* **Beer** Stones, Tetley. Garden. Children's play area. Family room.

Egton Bridge   Horseshoe Hotel

| Tel 0947 85245 | |
| Egton Bridge nr Whitby North Yorkshire YO21 1XE | Map 5 E3 |

Delightful old stone pub in pretty Esk-side spot. Lots of black panelling, simple wood furniture. Wines by the glass include the English Lamberhurst. *Free House.* **Beer** John Smiths, Tetley, Theakston Best. Riverside garden. Children's play area. Family room.

Elkesley   Robin Hood Inn

| Tel 077 783 259 | |
| High Street Elkesley Nottinghamshire DN22 8AJ | Map 7 D2 |

Opposite the 13th century village church, a popular dining pub with cooking by the licensee. **Beer** Whitbread. Garden. Children's play area.

Ellerker   Black Horse

Tel 0430 423270

Church Lane Ellerker Humberside HU15 2DN

Map 7 E1

Farmhouse cottage overlooking two village greens, and which aims for a continental bistro atmosphere. Quiet at lunchtimes early in the week, but booking is essential every evening. *Free House. Children's play area. Family room.*

Ellisfield   Fox

Tel 0256 381210

FOOD

Green Lane Ellisfield Hampshire RG25 2QW

Map 16 C4

Excellent village pub, at the end of a tangle of quiet country lanes. Enjoyable honest, unpretentious cooking – steak and kidney pie (£5.95), hot chili and French bread (£4.50), T-bone steak (£13.50), beef in beer, Neapolitan pasta (£4.50); real fire, no music. No children indoors. *Bar Food 12-1.45, 7-9.30 (except Mon eve). Vegetarian dishes. Children's portions. Free House. Beer Gales HSB, Marston Pedigree, Wadworth 6X. Garden. Access, Visa*

Elsenham   Crown

Tel 0279 812827

High Street Elsenham Essex

Map 10 B3

Not only a pub but also the local cricket club headquarters. *Beer Benskin. Garden.*

Elslack   Tempest Arms

Tel 0282 842450

Elslack nr Skipton North Yorkshire BD23 3AY

Map 6 B1

Traditional stone roadside inn with simple traditionally furnished bar and other civilised areas leading off, plus Bonaparte Restaurant; despite the location, this is a French-run establishment. *Free House. Beer Tetley Mild and Bitter, Thwaites, Youngers Scotch. Riverside garden. Children's play area. Family room.*

Elstead   Woolpack

Tel 0252 703106

FOOD

The Green Elstead Surrey GU8 6HD

Map 17 E4

On an old wool trading route, the tile-hung Woolpack was in fact originally built as a wool-bale store in the 18th century, and only later developed into a hostelry. Now comfortably countrified, various artefacts dotted about the place still hint at the pub's previous use: bobbins and spindles of yarn, a lamb's fleece, an ancient pair of scales and a partly woven rug. Today folk flock here (no pun intended) to enjoy the notably, famously generous portions of home-cooked dishes chosen from a long blackboard menu, which ranges from baked goat's cheese on toast with garlic and mango sauce (£4.25) to duck breast in pear, brandy and peppercorn sauce (£8.25) and steak and kidney pie (£6.25). The pie in question is noteworthy for featuring properly cooked on-top-of-the-pie pastry, and not a pre-cooked square stuck on top as the pie leaves the kitchen, a practice all too common in pubs these days. Genuinely home-made puddings are something of a cottage industry here, with the landlord's mother-in-law and other local ladies contributing to the selection, which might include Mrs. Swayne's pudding (layers of a mix of cake and breadcrumbs, chocolate chips and cream (£2.50) or apple strudel. Children can have smaller portions at smaller prices, or opt for baked beans and tinned spaghetti on toast. A children's room has nursery rhyme murals on the walls and bunches of flowers hung up to dry from the ceiling; there's also a slide in the pretty garden. Landlord Kevin Macready, who used to work as an area manager for a brewery, takes good care of the beers, which are drawn directly from barrels racked behind the bar. *Bar Food 12-2, 7-9.45. Vegetarian dishes. Children's portions. Beer Greene King IPA, Wadworth 6X. Garden, outdoor eating, children's playing area. Family room. Access, Visa.*

Elsted   Elsted Inn

Tel 0730 813662	FOOD
Elsted Marsh nr Midhurst West Sussex GU29 0JT	Map 11 D3

It would be very easy to drive past this unprepossessing Victorian roadside pub, but that would be to miss out on some good food and a warm welcome. It was built to serve the railway in the steam age, when there was a station here, but was later left stranded by Dr Beeching's 'axe' in the 1950s. This explains the old railway photographs that adorn the thankfully unmodernised and unpretentious bars, in what is very much a local community pub, free of background music and electronic games but with plenty of traditional pub pastimes like shove ha'penny, darts, cards, dominoes and even conversation. There are two small bars with lots of original wood in evidence, original shutters and open fires. A small dining room, candle-lit in the evening, boast an old pine dresser and colourful cloths on a few dining tables surrounded by a motley collection of old chairs. Tweazle Jones and her partner Barry Horton have between them a varied catering background, including cooking in a Scottish school, chefing on luxury liners and working in directors' dining rooms in the city; Tweazle even spent a period as an inspector for Egon Ronay (who else!). The result is a globetrotting menu – always home-made and based on good local produce – with the likes of osso buco from Italy, coq au vin from France or Mexican tacos. England is also well represented though, with dishes like braised oxtail, mutton with caper sauce and sandwiches closely resembling door stops; vegetarians are well served, too, with lentil bakes and vegetable roulades. Children can have half portions at half price, and there's a car tyre hanging from a plum tree in the shady garden to keep them amused, plus pétanque for the adults. Dogs are welcome or at least tolerated by the house hounds, Truffle and Sam, and an area of the garden is fenced off to keep dogs and children apart. The pub is no longer owned by the local brewers, Ballards, but their Best, Trotton and Wassail ales are still served here, along with Marston Pedigree and various guest beers. *Bar Food 12-2.30, 7-10 (9.30 Sun). Vegetarian dishes. Children's portions. Beer Admans, Ballards, Batemans, Mitchells. Family room. Outdoor play area, garden, outdoor eating, summer barbecue. Access, Visa.*

Elsted   Three Horseshoes

Tel 073 085 746	FOOD
Elsted nr Midhurst West Sussex SU29 0JX	Map 11 D3

Bowed walls, terracotta-tiled floors, gnarled beams and mellow stained plasterwork all create an atmosphere of genuinely unspoilt charm in this popular Tudor inn, romantically candle-lit at night. Food is as hearty and rustic as the surroundings, and fish is a speciality,

particularly at weekends – try the fried clams if available. ***Bar Food***
*12-2, 6.30-9.30; bar snacks both sessions. Vegetarian meals, children's
portions.* ***Beer*** *Ballards, Batemans, Fullers, Ringwood. Children allowed in
bar to eat, garden.*

Elsworth   George & Dragon

Tel 095 47 236

41 Bosworth Road Elsworth Cambridgeshire CB3 8JQB   Map 15 F1

Attractive, unusual pub with a panelled bar and separate dining area.
Beer *Whitbread, Greene King IPA. Garden. Children's play area. Family
room.*

Elterwater   Britannia Inn

Tel 09667 210   **B&B**

Elterwater Ambleside Cumbria WA22 9HP   Map 4 C3

Well-loved old Lakeland perennial, white-painted and inviting, in a
glorious spot, and very popular with walkers. The little beamed bar is
simple to the point of spartan, in keeping with farming and rambling
traditions, with other drinking rooms leading off; the atmosphere is
informal and relaxed, particularly in winter when the crowds have
subsided, and the log fires are crackling. Head for the new outdoor
drinking area on a sunny day. There's a chintzy comfortable residents'
lounge and dining room. Bedrooms are clean, bright and pretty, with
charming views. *Free House.* ***Beer*** *Jennings Mild, Bitter, Marston
Pedigree, Boddingtons.* ***Cider*** *Bulmers. Patio/terrace.* ***Accommodation***
*9 bedrooms, 6 en suite, £58. Children welcome overnight (half price up to
12), additional beds, cots available. Check-in all day. Access, Visa.*

Emery Down   New Forest Inn

Tel 0703 282329

Emery Down Hampshire SO43 7DY   Map 14 C4

Prettily set in woodland, the building of the inn was the result of the
first successful establishment of squatter's rights on Crown land, in the
early 18th century. Much extended since, it has a big, busy open-plan
bar and fairly modern seating and style, with effective country touches
and real fires. A pub known for its genuine welcome. ***Beer*** *Whitbread,
Flowers Original, Wadworth 6X. Garden. Family room.*

Empingham   White Horse

Tel 078 086 221   Fax 078 086 521   **FOOD**
B&B

2 Main Street Empingham nr Oakham Leicestershire   Map 7 E3

Roger Bourne's civilised pub, a stone's throw from serene Rutland
Water, is the centre of village life, a centre for walkers and
birdwatchers and central for access from the A1 at Stainford and the
market town of Oakham. In attempting to be all things to most callers
its day stretches from morning coffee and croissants through lunches
and cream teas to late evening suppers. Central to the three eating
areas, which include a family room, is the food counter displaying
cold meats and home-made sweets backed by a blackboard of daily
dishes, lamb curry and spotted dick, perhaps, quiche and self-served
salads and junior pizzas, virtually on demand. Two menus accompany:
garlic hoagies with mozzarella (£2), steak, kidney and Guinness pie
(£5.45), oven-baked Rutland trout (£7.50) and vegetarian lasagne
(£4.25) constitute substantial bar meals. A la carte 'coquilles St Jacques
Riviera' (£11.95) and 'médaillons de veau au crabe gratinée' (£12.75)

command heftier prices. The bedrooms, too, are popular. Fittingly, the best are in the stables, kitted out in varnished pine and each with its own well-appointed bathroom. In the main building, recently spruced-up rooms are bright and neat though nonetheless more modest, with shared bathing facilities. *Bar Food* 12-2, 6.30-10 *Restaurant Meals* 7.15-10 (not Sun). *Vegetarian dishes. Children's portions. Beer John Smiths, Courage. Garden. Family room. Accommodation 13 rooms, 8 en suite, £49, single £38. Children welcome overnight, extra beds charged, cots supplied. Access, Amex, Diners, Visa.*

Eskdale Green	Bower House Inn	FOOD
Tel 09467 23244		B&B
Holmbrook Eskdale Green Cumbria CA191TD		Map 4 C3

A perennial favourite, this unspoilt country inn, built as a farmhouse in the 17th century, has the advantage of a location in perfect and unimproved peace, in good walking country. There's also a warm welcome in the cosy beamed bar, with its polished darkwood furnishings and open log fire, and the separate pretty restaurant. Good food such as deep-fried Camembert (£3.25), lasagne (£4.50), gammon with eggs (£4.75), and guinea fowl with fresh herbs (£6.75), and good accommodation too: best bedrooms are in the converted barn and garden cottage annexes, modern and well-equipped, with excellent bathrooms. Older, simpler, not en-suite rooms in the main building. Comfortable, recently redecorated residents' lounge. *Bar Food* 12-2, 6.30-9.30. *Restaurant Meals* 7-9.30. *Vegetarian dishes. Children's portions. Children allowed in bar to eat. Free House. Beer Ruddles, Theakston. Riverside garden, outdoor eating, children's play area. Family room. Accommodation 22 bedrooms, all en suite, £53.50 (single £39.25). Children welcome overnight, additional beds (£5.50), cots available. Check-in all day. No dogs. Access, Visa.*

Eton	Christopher Hotel	
Tel 0753 852359 Fax 0753 830914		B&B
110 High Street Eton Berkshire SL4 6AN		Map 17 E3

Former coaching inn on the High Street. Best bedrooms are in the main house, others in courtyard chalets that are being redecorated. There are two bars and a patio. Children up to the age of 12 are free in their parents' room. Dogs in courtyard rooms only. *Accommodation 34 bedrooms, £80. Access, Amex, Diners, Visa.*

Ettington	Houndshill	
Tel 0789 740267		B&B
Banbury Road Ettington Warwickshire CV37 7NS		Map 14 C1

A pubby little bar and plain but bright dining room feature in this handsome white hotel on the A422. The bedrooms are light and attractive, with lemony cream walls, fitted grey carpets, pretty fabrics and pine furniture. All have excellent bath/shower rooms, too. *Free House. Beer Theakston. Garden, outdoor eating, children's play area. Accommodation 8 bedrooms, all en suite, £48 (single £29). Children welcome overnight, additional beds (from £5), cots supplied. Check-in all day. Access, Visa.*

Euxton   **Euxton Mills**

Tel 0257 264002

Wigan Road Euxton Lancashire PR7 6JD

Map 6 B1

18th century low-beamed pub which specialises in daily roasts. *Beer Burtonwood.*

Ewen   **Wild Duck Inn**

Tel 0285 770310

Drakes Island Ewen nr Cirencester Gloucestershire GL7 6BV

B&B

Map 14 C2

Lovely Cotswold village pub near the Water Park. The dimly-lit Post Horn bar is nicely poised between traditional and smartened up; the restaurant has red walls, candles in bottles, and simple pine furniture, and bedrooms (particularly the two four-poster ones in the oldest part of the building) are decent, though the extension-housed remainder might seem surprisingly modern in style. The Grouse Room residents' lounge, a haven of peace overlooking the pretty gardens, is also open to diners. *Free house.* **Beer** *Bass, Duck Pond Bitter (specially brewed), Theakston 6X and Old Peculier, Wadworth 6X. Garden.* **Accommodation** *9 bedrooms, all en suite, £65 (single £48). Children welcome overnight, additional beds and cots available. Check-in all day. Dogs permitted by prior arrangement only. Access, Visa.*

Ewhurst Green   **White Dog Inn**

Tel 0580 830264

Ewhurst Green nr Robertsbridge East Sussex TN32 5TD

FOOD

Map 11 C6

Enjoying a lovely village setting near the parish church, with fine views over the Rother Valley to Bodiam Castle, this old tile-hung pub has recently opened up its fenced garden at the back and in summer months hosts local theatre productions (seats 200) and organises theme nights. Inside, a huge inglenook dominates the attractive beamed bar where light snacks are served (8oz steak sandwich £3.95, home-made soup £1.75). The chef offers an interesting blackboard restaurant menu regularly featuring fresh fish (sea bream £8.95) and steaks, Indonesian chicken curry (£5.25) and in winter months only, the traditional Sunday lunch (£5.25 main course) is a feast. *Bar Food and Restaurant Meals 12-2, 7-9 (Mon-Thur), 7-9.30 (Fri-Sat), 7-8.30 (Sun). Vegetarian dishes. Children's menu (£2.50 per dish). Free House.* **Beer** *Worthington, Harvey, Bass, London Pride. Garden, outdoor eating. Access, Visa.*

Exeter   **Double Locks**

Tel 0392 56947

Canal Bank Exeter Devon EX2 6LT

FOOD

Map 13 D2

The Double Locks isn't easy to find but it's well worth the effort. First find the Marsh Barton Trading Estate and drive through it to the council incinerator – don't worry, the pub is some way yet – until you reach the plank canal bridge, which is made for vehicles, although it may not appear to be. Once across, turn right, and a single-track road will bring you to the red-brick Georgian Double Locks. Equally popular with business people and students, this is the perfect summer pub: there are swans on the canal next to the eponymous lock, a large garden shaded by huge pine trees, and a barbecue both lunchtime and evening in summer, weather permitting. There's even a small marquee in which to shelter from errant showers. Inside is very informal.

Several rooms have black and white tiled floors, draw-leaf domestic dining-room tables and lots of posters advertising local events. Chess, draughts, monopoly, scrabble and bar billiards are all keenly played. A huge blackboard displays the day's offerings, featuring almost as many options for vegetarians as for carnivores. Start with mushroom and coriander soup (£1.40), garlic mushrooms and Stilton on toast (£3.40) or a selection of garlic breads with Cheddar, Stilton or goat's cheese topping (ranging from £1.25-£2.65 respectively), followed perhaps by turkey and mushroom pie (£3.30), lasagne (£3.30), baked potatoes with a variety of toppings (ranging from £1.25-£3.80) or vegetarian and meat crepes (£3.85). Breakfasts here mean a traditional fry-up, either meat or vegetarian, plus a pint of the beer of your choice at the all-in price of £4. There is no special children's menu but most things also come in smaller portions at smaller prices, and several rooms can be used by families, who are made genuinely welcome. **Bar Food** *11-10.30 (Mon-Sat),12-2, 7-10 (Sun). Vegetarian dishes. Free House.* **Beer** *Broadside, Greene King Abbot Ale, Marstons Pedigree.* **Cider** *Grays, Inch's. Riverside garden, outdoor play area, outdoor eating, summer barbecue. Family room. No credit cards.*

Exford   The Crown

Tel 064383 554	**B&B**
Exford nr Minehead Somerset TA24 7PP	Map 13 D1

A favourite of the huntin', shootin' and fishin' set, the 17th-century Crown stands by the green in a lovely Exmoor village. Lots of traditional charm in the comfortable lounge and rustic bar, and pretty bedrooms of varying sizes, individually furnished, with excellent modern bathrooms. Thoughtful touches range from fresh fruit and a welcoming glass of sherry to hot water bottles, tea-makers, trouser presses and hairdryers. All bedrooms have recently been redecorated and dining-room and lounge revamped. Stabling available for 15 horses. *Free House.* **Beer** *John Smith, Ruddles. Riverside garden. Family room.* **Accommodation** *18 bedrooms, all en suite, £80 (single £45). Children welcome overnight, additional beds (nominal fee charged), cots supplied. Check-in all day.*

Eyam   Miners Arms

Tel 0433 630853	**B&B**
Water Lane Eyam Derbyshire S30 1RG	Map 6 C2

Run by the Cooks for almost 30 years, pleasant 17th-century picturesque village inn with original leaded light windows, mock Tudor beams and open fires. Refurbished bars. Some of the simply appointed bedrooms are in an annexe. *Garden.* **Accommodation** *5 bedrooms, 1 en suite, £30 (single £25). Children welcome overnight, cot supplied. Check-in all day. No credit cards.*

Eyam   Rose & Crown

Tel 0433 630858	**B&B**
Main Road Eyam Derbyshire S30 1QW	Map 6 C2

Beautifully situated in the romantic 'plague village' of Eyam, in the National Park. The Rose & Crown provides modest country-house style overnight accommodation at modest prices. Bedrooms have direct dial phones, alarm clocks, TVs, trouser presses and tea/coffee kits. New licensees plan total refurbishment. *Free House.* **Beer** *Stone, Tetley.* **Cider** *Olde English. Garden, outdoor play area.* **Accommodation**

3 bedrooms, 2 en suite, £35 (single £25). Children welcome overnight, cot available. Check-in by prior arrangement. No dogs. No credit cards.

Eynsham   Newlands Inn

Tel 0865 881486

Newland Street Eynsham Oxfordshire

Map 16 B2

Nice old pub with traditional interior and its own smokery. *Free House.* **Beer** *Tetley, Wadworth 6X, Hook Norton. Children's play area.*

Faccombe   Jack Russell Inn

FOOD

B&B

Tel 026 487 315

Faccombe nr Andover Hampshire SP11 0DS

Map 16 B4

Faccombe is a tiny, out-of-the-way village owned by the 'big house' it surrounds, and almost entirely occupied by estate workers. The story goes that when the new estate owner decided to renovate the old village pub, it just fell down, so he had to rebuild it. In any event, the present simple redbrick building dates from 1983 but is quickly being mellowed by a spreading Virginia creeper and hanging baskets of flowers. The modest bar boasts a few rural artefacts and has already developed the yellow patina of cigarette smoke on walls and ceiling. The best place to eat is in the large conservatory, which looks out onto the garden with its duck pond and rustic climbing frame which is provided for children, who are tolerated rather than encouraged. A daily changing blackboard lists the mostly home-made dishes which offer a good varied choice including Cumberland sausage (£4.50) and mixed grill (£7.50). The individual steak and kidney pudding (£4.50) with accompanying freshly steamed vegetables can't fail to satisfy the largest appetite. The food trade is highly organised: when ordering food at the bar, you are given a little plastic table number so that the waitress can find you easily, and booking is advisable, particularly at weekends and for the traditional Sunday lunch. Three simple bedrooms, just one with en suite bathroom, offer good clean accommodation with functional melamine furniture, poly-cotton bedding and the usual tea/coffee-making kit. There are televisions, but no telephones. **Bar Food** *12-2, 7-9.30 (7-9 Sun). Vegetarian dishes. Children's menu/portions. Free House.* **Beer** *Ringwood Fortyniner. Garden, outdoor eating, children's play area.* **Accommodation** *3 rooms, 1 en suite, £40 (single £25). Children welcome overnight. Small dogs permitted (by prior arrangement only). Check-in by arrangement. Access, Visa.*

Falmouth   Pandora Inn

FOOD

Tel 0326 372678

Restronguet Creek Mylor Bridge Falmouth Cornwall TR11 5ST

Map 12 B4

A thatched riverside pub with a first-floor restaurant, three cosy bars, a patio and a pontoon for fine weather. The chef puts an emphasis on fish (mostly from Newlyn and Falmouth, plus oysters from Helford), the exact menu depending on the local catch. Often very busy in summer, the restaurant is sometimes closed in winter. Ask for directions when booking. **Restaurant Meals** *Dinner only 7-10 (Sun to 9.30). Access, Visa.*

Falstone   Blackcock

Tel 0660 40200

Falstone Northumberland   Map 5 D2

Useful stop when visiting Europe's largest man-made forest, not far
from the equally superlative Kielder Water. Welcoming stone-built
walkers' favourite with period coal fires, and a Beatonette stove;
handsome dining room. Grand piano in the residents' lounge. *Beer
Greenwalls. Garden. Family room.*

Far Sawrey   Sawrey Hotel

Tel 053 94 43425

Far Sawrey nr Windermere Cumbria LA22 0LQ   Map 4 C3

Attractive white-painted 18th century rural inn, the main bar
converted from the old stable block with bedrooms above. *Beer
Jennings Bitter, Theakston Best & Old Peculier. Garden. Children's play
area. Family room.*

Faringdon   Bell Hotel

Tel 0367 20534   Fax 0367 241824   **B&B**

Market Place Faringdon Oxfordshire SN7 7HP   Map 16 A2

The new manager at this 16th-century posting house has plans to turn
the restaurant into a dining bar, hoping to create an atmosphere for
relaxed dining and to provide live entertainment. This is also a
courtyard garden for summer sipping. The original bar has rustic
furniture and a mural of local scenes. Bedrooms are currently being
refurbished and all have en-suite facilities. *Beer Wadworth 6X,
Tanglefoot. **Accommodation** 9 bedrooms, all en suite, £42 (single £35).
Children welcome overnight, additional beds and cots available. Check-in all
day. Access, Amex, Diners, Visa.*

Farnah Green   Bluebell

Tel 0773 826495

Hazelwood Farnah Green Belper Derbyshire DE5 2UP   Map 6 C3

Smartened up dining pub with a separate restaurant which is redolent
of a well-heeled city Indian restaurant in decor. *Beer Bass. Garden.
Family room.*

Faugh   String of Horses Inn

Tel 0228 70297   Fax 0228 70675   **B&B**

Faugh Cumbria CA4 9EG   Map 4 C2

Substantial white-painted old inn, with a beamed and panelled lounge
and a 'Cocktail' bar, also oak panelled, which is reserved for restaurant
diners. White-painted bedrooms, well-maintained rather than stylish,
have modern prints, carpets, wallpaper and matching floral fabrics,
although three have four-posters and exciting bathrooms. A
swimming pool and sauna for residents' use add to the attraction of
staying here at the heart of a tiny hamlet off the A69. *Free House.
Beer No real ales. Patio/terrace. **Accommodation** 14 bedrooms, all en suite,
£65 (single £58). Children welcome overnight, additional beds, cots
available. Check-in all day. Access, Amex, Diners, Visa.*

Felbridge   Woodcock
Tel 0342 325859
Woodcock Hill Felbridge Surrey   Map 11 B5

Leaded windows and original beams in the original bar, a handsome
lounge leading off, elegantly decorated, and a chaise-longue-strewn
Victorian parlour. Upstairs, meanwhile, is a smart restaurant, candle-lit
in the evenings. Altogether a stylish, individual pub. *Free House.* **Beer**
Harveys, Ringwood Old Thumper, Greene King Abbot, Wadworth 6X.
Family room.

Fen Drayton   Three Tuns
Tel 0954 30242
High Street Fen Drayton Cambridgeshire CB4 5SJ   Map 15 F1

Characterful timbered old pub, originally the local trade or guild hall.
The present bar is outwith the original building, but brims with
atmosphere: heavy moulded beams, inglenook fireplaces, oak
furnishings, and lots of quality bric-a-brac. It gets extremely busy.
Beer *Greene King IPA & Abbot. Garden. Children's play area. Family*
room.

Fenstanton   King William IV
Tel 0480 62467
High Street Fenstanton Cambridgeshire PE18 9JF   Map 15 F1

Attractive white-painted roadside inn, once three separate houses, next
to the old clock tower, and very much the hub of village life. Its
popularity is such that a glass roof has just been fitted to the patio area
adjoining the restaurant, to provide more all-weather table space. The
original bars are still reserved for drinkers, with newer extended areas
for diners. Capability Brown is buried in the village churchyard. **Beer**
Greene King.

Fingest   Chequers Inn
Tel 0491 63335
Fingest nr Henley-on-Thames Oxfordshire RG9 6QD   Map 17 D3

Charming 15th-century redbrick village pub, traditionally furnished
inside, and with French windows opening onto a delightful garden.
Roaring log fires in winter.

Finglesham   Crown Inn
Tel 0304 612555   **FOOD**
The Street Finglesham nr Deal Kent CT14 0NA   Map 11 D5

The makers of road maps seem to have overlooked Finglesham, and
there are no signposts either, but if you take a left by the Shell garage
on the A258 about two miles north of Deal you will find the village
and, more importantly, the Crown. The freshly painted, rendered
exterior belies its age, the oldest part dating back to the 1500s, but
inside exposed brick walls and old timbers give character while red
plush upholstery provides the comfort. The whole place is very well
kept, and fresh flowers and a warm welcome from the Virtues
provide the finishing touch. There is a separate restaurant area and
menu (steaks and straightforward sauced dishes) but in fact one can eat
from any menu anywhere. Bar meals are written up on a blackboard
and might include a hearty Stilton, celery and chicken soup (£1.50),
corn on the cob (£1.75), beef goulash (£5.25), whole grilled plaice

(£5.75) and a crunchy-topped vegetarian bake (£4.50) – all served in generously sized portions. Sandwiches start at £1.10. *Bar Food 12-2, 7-10. Vegetarian dishes. Children's portions. Free House. Beer Ruddles County, Shepherd Neame Master Brew. Garden, outdoor eating, children's play area. Access, Amex, Visa.*

Fir Tree   Duke of York

FOOD

Tel 0388 762848

Fir Tree nr Crook Durham DL15 8DG

Map 5 D3

This large 18th-century inn by the A68 is a very popular stop-off for both locals and tourists, especially at weekends. Both an interesting collection of stone-age flints and letters from celebrity visitors hang on one wall of the entrance, which leads into two bar areas. One, to the right, is furnished with roundback chairs, bench seating and solid wooden tables; its beamed ceiling and walls are hung with horsey pictures, plates and bottles on high shelves. The other bar is more homely, with wing chairs, curtains and stools, all tapestry-upholstered. Mementoes of the landlord's time in Africa include fearsome spears, hunting rifles and photographs, grouped around the stone fireplace, and a juke box stands alongside the bar counter. Adjoining this area is an unfussy dining room with rough white walls and polished ready-laid tables. Blackboards in each bar list the food on offer. The top bar tends to be more bar-foody, the bottom one restauranty, but often the two converge and overlap. Prices are a little above the average for the area, but the cooking (in the hands of Marilyn Suggett) is reassuringly good. Fish is fresh and meat all comes from a dependable local butcher. The choice is wide, from salads and open sandwiches to cream of cauliflower soup (£1.95), garlic mushrooms (£2.50), buttered gourmet scampi (£7.95), beef bourguignon (£7.95), fresh plaice (5.95) and sirloin in Stilton sauce (£10.50). All dishes come with a selection of potatoes and fresh vegetables. Puddings are also good with hot apple pie and Caribbean slice both at £2.25. At the back of the inn are a pleasant garden, bordered by trees, and a paddock. *Bar Food 12-2, 6-10.30. Restaurant Meals 6-10. Vegetarian dishes. Children's menu/portions. Free House. Beer Bass, Stones. Children allowed in bar to eat. Garden, outdoor eating, children's play area. Access, Visa.*

Firle   Ram Inn

FOOD

B&B

Tel 0273 858222

Firle nr Lewes East Sussex BN8 6NS

Map 11 B6

The road runs out once it eventually reaches Firle village at the foot of the Downs. It's a quiet backwater now, but this, almost unbelievably, was once a main stage-coach route and the Ram an important staging post. Built of brick and flint and partly tile-hung, the inn displays a fascinating mixture of periods. The Georgian part was once the local courthouse. Other parts are older, and the kitchen dates back nearly 500 years. The main bar is a simple, unpretentious affair with a motley collection of tables and chairs, and old photos. A no-smoking snug bar is similarly modest. Michael Wooller had spent 20 years as a farm management consultant when the tenancy of the Ram, his local, came up a few years ago, and he leapt at the chance to indulge his interest in food a little closer to the consumer. Helped by his son Keith and daughter-in-law Christine, he produces daily-changing menu choices with the likes of ploughman's (£4.95), Sussex-style pork chops (with cream cheese and garlic bread £7.95), Dover sole

(£8.25), courgette and broccoli bake (£6.95), chicken in Stilton (£8). There are popular home-made puddings (all £2.75) – banana and toffee pie, blackberry and apple pie. Vegetarians are well catered for here and fish is always fresh rather than frozen. Around six wines are available by the glass, including Berwick Glebe from the local vineyard and an organic white Sussex wine, and a charming walled garden with rustic tables makes an idyllic spot for summer drinking and playing of a local Sussex game 'Toad in the Hole'. Simple bedrooms are bright and fresh, with a variety of antique furniture and new beds topped by duvets. The largest room features a shower cabinet and en- suite toilet; the remaining four share a neat shower room. All rooms have tea and coffee-making kits but, as a matter of policy, no televisions or radios. *Bar Food 12-2, 7-9. Vegetarian dishes. Children's portions. Free House. Beer Palmers Best Bitter (summer), Bass Charrington, Harvey. Garden, outdoor eating. Family room. Accommodation 4 bedrooms, 1 en suite, £60 (£45 not en suite, single £25). Children over 14 welcome overnight. Check-in all day. Access, Visa.*

Fittleworth   Swan

Tel 079 882 429 Fax 079 882 546	**B&B**
Lower Street Fittleworth nr Pulborough West Sussex RH20 1EW	Map 11 A6

Wayside Inns (Whitbread) have recently taken over this 14th-century inn, where you can luxuriate in the peaceful beauty of the lovely garden of flowers and herbs (with play area) and see where the river Arun meets the Rother by taking a peaceful river walk. Inside the log fire dominates the bar with its display of policemen's truncheons and brass and copper trinkets hung from beams. Villagers enjoy darts in the small public bar. Laura Ashley- style bedrooms have modern bathrooms and many amenities including trouser presses. Three share two smart bathrooms. *Beer Wadworth 6X, Boddingtons, Flowers and guest beers. Accommodation 10 Bedrooms, 7 en suite, £55 (single £37.50). Children welcome overnight, additional beds and cots available. Check-in all day. Access, Amex, Diners, Visa.*

Flaunden   Bricklayers Arms

Tel 0442 833322	
Long Lane Hog Pits Bottom Flaunden Hertfordshire HP3 0PH	Map 17 E2

Pretty village pub with a pleasant modernised interior and reminders of ancient origins, plus a good summer garden with mature trees. Massively popular locally for food, and a new restaurant shows definite signs of ambition. They offer set menus for parties of ten or over. There's a garden salad bar, weather permitting. Children allowed in restaurant. *Beer Adnams, Brakspears, Fullers London Pride & guest beers. Garden.*

Fleetwood   North Euston Hotel

Tel 0253 876525	
Esplanade Fleetwood Lancashire FY7 6BN	Map 6 A1

There's a large pubby bar within this Victorian crescent hotel, by the Blackpool tram terminus. Good views of ships and Lake district hills. *Beer Bass, Ruddles, Websters. Family room.*

Fletching   **Griffin**

FOOD
B&B

Tel 0825 722890

Fletching nr Uckfield East Sussex TN22 3SS

Map 11 B6

The last real excitement in this sleepy Sussex village was in 1264 when Simon de Montfort's army camped outside the church prior to the Battle of Lewes. These days visitors with a more peaceful intent are made more than welcome at the 16th-century Griffin Inn, which is at the heart of Saxon Fletching's picturesque main street, and is everything a village local should be. The main bar has old beams and wainscot walls, a copper-hooded brick fireplace and a motley collection of old pews and wheelback chairs; the public bar provides a pool table and fruit machine for the amusement of the local youth and there's a pretty Laura Ashley-decorated restaurant. Good home-made food is a major attraction, with one daily-changing menu, written out at night, with a shorter version available at lunchtime, applying to both the bar and restaurant. An eclectic choice ranges from Griffin spare ribs (£4.95) or salmon fishcakes (£5.50) through stuffed aubergines with ratatouille (£5.25) to bruschetta with olive paste (£2.95), scallops and monkfish moneybags (£7.95) or rack of lamb with mint and herb crust (£7.95). There are also char-grills, homely puddings and ploughperson's lunches large enough to cope with the sharpest appetite. Gourmet evenings offer a regular sample of the food and wines of different countries and regions, including a Beaujolais Nouveau dinner the weekend after Nouveau Day. Children are made very much at home, with suitably-sized portions of adult dishes from the menu, and in summer the garden offers an outstanding view of the South Downs, as well as tables for al fresco eating. An excellent wine list, featuring some invigorating examples from the burgeoning Sussex vineyard scene, owes a good deal to family connections with the Ebury Wine Bar in London. There are four charming, beamed bedrooms, three with a four-poster bed, purpose-built to counteract the sloping floors and so ensure a level night's rest. Tea and coffee-making kits are provided, and the substantial breakfasts are worth getting up for. An excellent stopover on the way to Newhaven, some sixteen miles distant, and the Dieppe ferry. **Bar Food** *12-2.30, 7-9.30.* **Restaurant Meals** *12-2 (12-2.30 Sun), 7.30-9.15 (except Sun). Vegetarian dishes. Children's menu/portions.* **Beer** *Hall & Woodhouse Tanglefoot, Harvey, King & Barnes. Garden, outdoor eating. Family room.* **Accommodation** *4 bedrooms, all en suite, £45-65 (single £40). Children welcome overnight, additional beds and cots supplied. Check-in all day. No dogs. Access, Amex, Visa.*

Flixton   **Foxhound Inn**

Tel 0723 890301

Flixton North Yorkshire YO11 3UB

Map 5 F4

Large roadside white-painted inn, much extended and modernised, with a 100-seater dining room. **Beer** *Scottish & Newcastle, Tetley, Theakston. Family room.*

Fonthill Bishop   **King's Arms**

FOOD
B&B

Tel 074789 523

Fonthill Bishop nr Salisbury Wiltshire SP3 5SH

Map 14 B3

A smart little redbrick pub (converted from an old farm building) standing by the roadside offers value for money and good eating in a comfortable dining area with waitress service. A blackboard

announces the day's specials, starting perhaps with garlic mushrooms
(£2.50) then moving on to mixed grill (£6.50) or poached salmon
(£6.50). The printed menu offers soup (£1.75), sandwiches (£1.80)
and steaks – including 10oz sirloin, cooked in garlic butter and
accompanied by onion rings, mushrooms, tomatoes and chips galore
(£8.50) – and there are home-made desserts such as blackcurrant
cheesecake, chocolate fudge cake and apple pie (all £1.95). Sunday
lunch is popular (main dish £4.25), and there is a children's menu.
This is a popular stopover for horseriders, who have the use of a
paddock behind the pub. Simple accommodation. *Bar Food* 12-2,
*7-10. Vegetarian dishes. Children's menu/portions. Free House. Beer
Strongs of Romsey, Wadworth 6X, Flowers. Garden, outdoor eating.
Family room. **Accommodation** 4 bedrooms, sharing facilities, £30 (single
(£15). Children welcome overnight, additional bedrooms (£5 if under
7 yrs), cots supplied. Check-in all day. No credit cards.*

Fonthill Gifford   Beckford Arms
Tel 0747 870385
Fonthill Gifford Tisbury Wiltshire SP3 6PX   Map 14 B3

Relaxing 18th-century country pub, recently completely refurbished,
next door to Fonthill Vineyard. Nice log fire in winter. *Beer Courage,
John Smiths Yorkshire, Wadworth 6X. Garden. Family room.*

Foolow   Lazy Landlord
Tel 0433 30873
Foolow Derbyshire S30 1QR   Map 6 C2

Old beamed Peak District pub, in a scenic village complete with duck
pond, village green and old stone cross. A second room has a more
relaxed atmosphere than the often bustling main bar, with a variety of
seats, a high ceiling, and open fire. *Beer Darley Thorne Dark Mild,
Ward Sheffield Best.*

Ford   Dinton Hermit
Tel 0296 748379   **FOOD**
Ford nr Aylesbury Buckinghamshire HP17 8XH   Map 17 D2

15th-century stone cottage pub named after John Briggs, clerk to one
of the judges who condemned Charles I to death. Two bars: a
modernised log-fire-warmed lounge, and characterful public bar;
pretty garden for sunny days. Hearty home cooking draws the crowds
– cauliflower cheese (£3), steak and mushroom pie (£5.50),
medallions of lamb in white wine and caper sauce (£5.50), rump steak
(£9.75). Cheery waitress service helps. *Bar Food* 12-2, *7-9.30.
Vegetarian dishes. Beer Bass, ABC, Tetley. Garden. No credit cards.*

Ford   Plough
Tel 0386 73215   **A**
Temple Gutting Ford Gloucestershire   Map 16 A1

Long a favourite of Cotswold ramblers and lovers of the traditional
English pub everywhere, the interior of the idyllic little 13th-century
Plough has all the atmosphere you could wish for. *Beer Donnington
BB & SBA. Garden.*

Ford   White Hart at Ford

| Tel 024 978 2213   Fax 024 978 3075 | **B&B** |

Ford nr Chippenham Wiltshire SN14 8RP   Map 14 B2

Nestling beside a trout stream overlooking the Weavern valley, this fine 16th-century inn offers character and comfort galore. The new owners Mrs & Mrs Phillips have lightened and refurbished the bar area, with antique furniture maintaining a mellow mood. Half the bedrooms (some with four-posters) have recently been refurbished and plans are under way for the remainder. The bedrooms all have en-suite facilities and also offer TVs, radios and tea-makers. Swimming pool available. *Beer Wadworth 6X, Tanglefoot, Hook Norton, guest beers. Free House. **Accommodation** 11 bedrooms, all en suite, £59 (single £43). Children welcome overnight, additional beds and cots available. Check-in all day. Access, Visa.*

Fordwich   Fordwich Arms

| Tel 0227 710444 | **FOOD** |

King Street Fordwich nr Canterbury Kent CT2 0DB   Map 11 C5

Located next to the smallest, half-timbered medieval town hall in the country, the Fordwich Arms is a solid Tudor-style village pub, with a rather handsome but not intimidatingly smart interior – standard enough furnishings with a parquet floor, green hessian walls, open fireplaces and lovely arched windows. The menu is the same in the bar as in the restaurant, with dishes like smoked haddock mornay (£5.75), lamb chops in redcurrant sauce (£5.25) and chicken fusilli (£5.50). The terrace is a civilised spot, as is the garden next to the narrow river Stour. *Bar Food 12-2, 6.30-10 (not Sun eve). Vegetarian dishes. Beer Boddingtons Pedigree, Fremlins, Marston, Whitbread. Garden, outdoor seating. Family room. No credit cards.*

Forty Green   Royal Standard of England

| Tel 0494 673382 | **A** |

Forty Green nr Beaconsfield Buckinghamshire HP9 1XS   Map 17 E3

Famous old pub, named by the decree of Charles II after he had been given sanctuary in the high rafters of what is now the food bar. Tremendous interior with superb array of collectors' items, now overlaid by a cheap and cheerful food operation lunchtime and evening, and huge crowds including coach parties. Go in winter. *Free House. Beer Eldridge Pope, Marston. Garden. Family room. No credit cards.*

Fosse Cross   Hare & Hounds

| Tel 0285 720288 | |

Fosse Cross nr Chedworth Gloucestershire GL54 4NW   Map 14 C2

Family dining pub, 300 years old, built of Cotswold stone, and with warming log fires. Caravan site next door. *Free House. Beer Hook Norton, Marston Pedigree, Theakston Old Peculier, Wadworth 6X. Garden. Children's play area.*

Fossebridge   Fossebridge Inn

FOOD

Tel 0285 720721

B&B

Fossebridge Northleach Gloucestershire GL54 3JS

Map 16 A2

Standing square on to the Fosse Way (now the A429), the ivy-clad Cotswold-stone inn marks the spot where once the Roman road crossed the river Coln. A-gaggle with geese, the rear garden borders the river, with picnic tables for summer use. The Stable Bar is rightly the pub's focal point with its unique stonework, flagstone floors and heavy oak beams. Real ales are in good condition and plenty of carefully produced snacks are available in the bars: North Cerney goat's cheese salad (£3.20), chicken liver paté (£3), prawn club sandwiches (£3.70) and blackcurrant crumble with cream (£2). Blackboard specials are served both here and in the attached restaurant: moules marinière (£3.20); veal escalope with garlic and paprika butter (£8.90); red bream fillet with basil and tomato dressing (£8.90); crème caramel with exotic fruit salad (£3). "Fossebridge" label house wines accompany. Bedrooms, all en suite, are located well apart in the main house, which has its own residents' lounge and breakfast room. To the rear are restful views down the garden: top-floor front bedrooms look out through dormer windows across the road and 20th-century bridge down the wooded Coln valley. *Bar Food* 12-2, 7-8. *Restaurant Meals* 12-2, 7-9.30. *Vegetarian dishes. Children's portions. Free House. Beer Hook Norton, Wadworth 6X, Marstons Pedigree. Garden, outdoor eating. Accommodation 9 bedrooms, all en suite, £55 (single £40). Additional beds (£10), cots supplied. Check-in all day. Access, Visa.*

Fotheringhay   Falcon Inn

Tel 08326 254

FOOD

Peterborough Northants PE8 5HZ

Map 7 E4

The Falcon is a splendidly relaxed and relaxing country pub, which feeds its customers and looks after them very well. A pretty stone building, surrounded by tiny outhouses and rambling farmyard, embellished with flowers and greenery, its colourful, carefully tended garden, complete with tables on its patio and lawn, and open-ended double conservatory are good omens for summer lunch. The river Nene is a short walk away through a field. Within, it's brightly painted and carpeted throughout. Prints of historic Fotheringhay Castle, a memorial to the ancient "College of the Blessed Virgin", and the wrought-iron 18th-century bell clappers from the village church all reflect the owners' interest in local folklore. A very popular food pub, the Falcon also remains a busy village local, with a populous public bar where personalised pewter pots hang, darts and dominoes are played, and contributions are invited to the church's floodlighting fund. The reason most people come, though, is to eat, and after many years' practice the Stewarts can make justifiable claims to be past masters. Each day the menu offers up to twenty starters, just as many main dishes – rabbit in cider with apples and walnuts (£5.40), roast duckling with apple and rosemary stuffing (£6.40), carbonade of beef £7.90) and a dozen or more puddings, mostly cold and fruity in summer, hot and comforting on long winter nights (spiced apple and hazelnut crumble £2). This is prodigious production of fresh food, coming from a kitchen so small (with no microwaves and precious little use of the chip fryer) that three is a crowd. The need to book can't, therefore, be over-emphasised, but once you're seated and provided with menus, everything will proceed smoothly – if not always rapidly – from that point. *Bar Food 12.15-2, 6.45-9.45 (7-9 Sun). Vegetarian dishes. Children's portions. Free House. Beer Adnams, Elgoods, Cambridge Bitter, Greene King, Ruddles County. Children allowed in bar to eat. Garden, outdoor eating. Family room. Access, Visa.*

Fovant   Cross Keys

Tel 0722 70284	**B&B**
Fovant nr Salisbury Wiltshire SP3 5JH	Map 14 C3

15th-century coaching inn by the A30 road, standing beneath the Fovant Emblems, regimental badges carved into the hillside by First World War soldiers. Handsome furnishings, low ceilings, nice fire, grandfather clock and friendly atmosphere. Bedrooms are warm and cottagey, with rough whitewashed walls. *Free House. Beer Adnams Southwold, Wadworth 6X. Garden, outdoor eating. Family room. Accommodation 4 bedrooms, sharing 2 bathrooms, £35 (single £17.50). Children welcome overnight (minimum age 3), beds available (from £7.50). Check-in by arrangement. No dogs. Access, Visa.*

Fovant   Pembroke Arms

Tel 072270 201	**B&B**
Fovant nr Salisbury Wiltshire SP3 5JH	Map 14 C3

Formerly the shooting lodge of the Earl of Pembroke, now a creeper-covered Georgian pub, all the Pembroke's past is currently relegated to its collection of World War One memorabilia. A certain sombreness reigns, and the bars are simple, the only luxuries being a large open fire and a warm welcome. The bedrooms are smart, comfortable and well-heated. Bathroom facilities are shared with the owners. *Free House. Beer King Alfred, 6X, Flowers Original, Fullers London Pride. Garden. Accommodation 2 bedrooms, bathroom facilities shared with owners, £30 (single £15). Children welcome overnight, additional beds, cots available. Check-in all day. No credit cards.*

Fowlmere   Chequers Inn

Tel 0763 208369	**FOOD**
High Street Fowlmere Cambridgeshire SG8 7SR	Map 15 F1

The Chequers was already a popular travellers' halt when Samuel Pepys stayed the night in 1659. There's still plenty of period charm, and the pub is still noted in many a diary as a good place to pause for refreshment. It's comfortably furnished, with a civilised, relaxing atmosphere, and eating, whether in bar or restaurant, is very much the thing. Food is reliably good and choices range from Vietnamese chicken (£6.85) and turkey escalope with cream and mushrooms (£6.20) in the bar to blinis with smoked salmon and crème fraiche (£5.70), bouillabaisse (£13.40) or trio of filo parcels on tomato and basil coulis (£8.80) in the restaurant. Specialities on the cheeseboard include Golden Cross, Jacobs, Stowe and Bronchester Medium. There's a traditional 3-course Sunday lunch for £14.25. The newly built Archer Room is an attractive conservatory extension big enough to house a small wedding party. *Bar Food & Restaurant Meals 12-2 (12-2.30 Sun), 7-10 (7-9.30 Sun). Vegetarian dishes. Children's portions. Free House. Beer Tolly Best & Original. Garden, outdoor eating. Access, Amex, Diners, Visa.*

Fowlmere   Queens Head

Tel 0763 208288

Long Lane Fowlmere Cambridgeshire SG8 7SZ

FOOD

Map 15 F1

Thatched white-painted pub with half a dozen picnic tables in the garden. Inside, black-painted beams, formica-topped tables, and a lino-floored lounge. The speciality of the house is twenty or so varieties of cheese; the Continental and unpasteurised varieties commanding the higher prices, and all served with cottage cob or other local bread, salad garnish and pickles. *Beer Tolly Best & Original. Garden. Family room.*

Fownhope   Green Man

Tel 0432 860243   Fax 0432 860207

Fownhope Hereford & Worcester HR1 4PE

B&B

Map 14 B1

Located approximately 7-8 minutes walk from the River Wye, this enormous, towering black and white Tudor inn is recommended for its bed and breakfast. Inside is more modernised manorial than strictly pubby. Bedrooms are well kept (courtyard rooms are smaller); ask for one of the two oldest, in the main building. Afternoon tea on the gracious lawns in summer. *Free house Beer Hook Norton Best, Marston Pedigree, Samuel Smith. Cider Weston Scrumpy. Garden, children's play area. Family room. Accommodation 20 bedrooms, all en suite, £47 (single £31). Children welcome overnight, additional beds (under 5 yrs free, 5-12 yrs £10), cots supplied. Check-in all day. Dogs permitted (£2.50). Access, Amex, Visa.*

Fradley   Fradley Arms Hotel

Tel 0283 790186   Fax 0283 791464

Fradley nr Lichfield Staffordshire WS13 8RD

B&B

Map 6 C3

Standing beside the busy A38, this family-run inn makes a very convenient overnight stop and is especially popular with business visitors. The six double-glazed bedrooms are well co-ordinated and include TVs, tea-makers and telephones. There is a peaceful residents' lounge overlooking the garden, and a convivial bar. A new addition is a conference room which can seat 200 people. *Free House. Beer Ansells Best Bitter, Mild, Tetley Bitter, Samson. Garden, children's play area. Accommodation 6 bedrooms, all en suite, £52 (single £38). Children welcome overnight, cots available. Check-in all day. Access, Amex, Diners, Visa.*

Framlingham   White Horse

Tel 0728 723220

27 Well Close Square Framlingham Suffolk IP13 9DT

Map 10 D2

Refurbished old coaching inn with original timbers surviving. *Beer Ruddles Best, Websters Yorkshire. Garden. Children's play area. Family room.*

Frampton Mansell   Crown Inn

Tel 028 576 0601

Frampton Mansell Stroud Gloucestershire GL6 8JB

B&B

Map 14 B2

A fine old village pub in a quiet setting just off the A419 from Stroud to Cirencester with wonderful views over the Golden Valley. Inside, the place oozes rural charm with exposed Cotswold stone walls, open fires and beamed ceilings. The stylish accommodation is in a purpose-built block to the rear, where guests can make themselves comfortable in attractive rooms with pastel schemes, contemporary fabrics, darkwood fitted furniture, brass light fittings and smart en-suite bathrooms. New owners. *Free House. Beer Wadworth 6X, Adnams. Accommodation 12 bedrooms, all en suite, £50 (single £40). Children welcome overnight. Check-in by arrangement. Access, Visa.*

Framsden   Dobermann

Tel 0473 890461

The Street Framsden Suffolk IP14 6HG

FOOD

Map 10 C3

Once called the Greyhound, now renamed for reasons incautious customers may discover should they chance their arm over the bar, this is a relaxing, well-kept, attractive 16th-century thatched inn. Two rooms are divided by a central log fire, and there's a good mix of furnishings, as well as prizes and pictures of the owners' dogs. A variety of home-made dishes is available (some vegetarian); chicken liver paté (£3.25), savoury pies (£6.25-8.50), chicken breast St. Etienne (£7.95), nut loaf with spicy tomato sauce (£4.75), brandy cordon bleu cake (£2.50), gooseberry pie (£2.50). No children indoors. *Bar Food 12-2, 7-9.30 (7-8 Sun). Vegetarian dishes. Beer Adnams, plus three guest beers. Garden, outdoor eating. No credit cards.*

Frant   Abergavenny Arms

Tel 0892 75233

Frant Road Frant East Sussex

Map 11 B5

Pleasant pub on Tunbridge Wells to Eastbourne road, in the pretty village of Frant. *Beer Clarks, Wells, Harveys Best, Hopback. Family room.*

Freeland   Shepherds Hall Inn

Tel 0993 881256

Witney Road Freeland Oxfordshire OX7 2HQ

B&B

Map 16 B2

Originally a 13th-century shelter for shepherds and drovers and once known as the 'Shepherds All', the green-shuttered inn today offers plain and practical accommodation. The bar is simple, with wheelbacked chairs, and a collection of plates adorns the walls. Six bedrooms (three of which are in an annexe) are clean, comfortable and modern in style, and include TVs, telephones and tea-making facilities. The annexe rooms have neat tiled shower rooms, and the pub rooms have private bathrooms. *Free House. Beer Whitbread Poacher, Wethered, Flowers IPA, Wadworth 6X. Garden, children's play area. Family room. Accommodation 6 bedrooms, all en suite, from £38 (single £30). Children welcome overnight, additional beds, cots available. Check-in all day. Access, Amex, Diners, Visa.*

Freshwater   Red Lion

Tel 0983 754925

Church Place Freshwater Isle of Wight PO40 9BP

Map 14 C4

Good country interior with flagged floors, rustic tables and reproduction settles. *Beer Flowers Original, Gales HSB, Marston Pedigree. Garden. Children's play area. Family room.*

Frilford Heath   Dog House Hotel

Tel 0865 390830   Fax 0865 390860

Frilford Heath nr Abingdon Oxfordshire OX13 6QY

B&B

Map 16 C2

A pleasant 300-year-old tile-hung inn which commands a lovely view over the Vale of the White Horse. The bar is spacious, and incorporates a central stone fireplace with a real winter fire. All bedrooms have en-suite facilities, TVs, telephones, hairdryers and pine furniture. Top of the range is the four-poster bridal suite. *Beer Morland PA Bitter, Best Bitter, Old Masters, Old Speckled Hen, Revival Mild. Garden, children's play area. Accommodation 19 bedrooms, all en suite, £62.50 (single £50). Children welcome overnight, additional beds, cots available. Check-in all day. Access, Amex, Diners, Visa.*

Frilsham   Pot Kiln

Tel 0635 201366

Yattendon-Bucklebury Road Frilsham Berkshire

Map 16 C3

Remote country pub, delightful in summer in the pretty little garden with its soothing woodland views. The name derives from this being the site of old brick kilns, abandoned after the war, and the building is, appropriately, of attractive redbrick construction. Inside is distinctively old-fashioned, with simple wooden furnishings (take a cushion), a warming open fire and a good, relaxing atmosphere, with a successful mix of locals and passing ramblers. There's live folk music some Sunday evenings; otherwise, peace. *Free House. Beer Arkells BBB, Morlands Original & Old Speckled Hen. Garden. Family room.*

Frithelstock   Clinton Arms

Tel 0805 23279

off Bideford Road Frithelstock Devon EX38 8JH

Map 12 C2

Diners' and family pub with a jolly atmosphere, its front lawn, also the village green, a perfect spot for relaxing summer meals. The priory ruins are opposite, in this sleepy affluent village. Children can be safely let off the leash in the walled rear garden. *Beer Bass. Garden. Children's play area. Family room.*

Fulking   Shepherd & Dog

Tel 0273 857382

Fulking nr Henfield West Sussex BN5 9LU

FOOD

Map 11 B6

Attractive pub in a truly glorious setting. Formerly a coaching house, it boasts inglenook fireplaces, polished oak tables and fresh flowers, and a good, varied selection of bar meals. There's usually a queue at the food servery where lighter food is served at lunchtime: steak and kidney pie (£5.25), wings of skate (£6.10), fresh poached salmon (£5.95), tiramisu (£2.25), real ice cream (£2.25), while hot specials in the evening could be roast duck (£7.95), scrumpy chicken (£6.75) or salmon feuilleté (£7.95). *Bar Food 12-2, 6.30-9.30. Vegetarian dishes. Children's portions. Beer Harvey, Ruddles, Directors. Cider Addlestones. Garden, outdoor eating, children's playing area. Access, Visa.*

Fullers Moor   Copper Mine
Tel 0829 782293

Nantwich Road Fullers Moor nr Broxton Cheshire CH3 9JH

Map 6 A3

A conservatory with six additional tables has just been added to this civilised, spacious country-style pub, whose bars are littered with copper mining memorabilia. Spacious grounds, open fires. *Beer Bass, Burtonwood. Garden. Children's play area.*

Fyfield   White Hart
Tel 0865 390585

Main Road Fyfield nr Abingdon Oxfordshire OX13 5LN

Map 16 B2

500 year old ex-chantry house with a 30-foot-high gallery and four family rooms. The landlord is also the cook. *Free House. Beer Boddington, Hook Norton, Morlands Original, Ruddles County, Wadworth 6X. Garden. Family room.*

Ganton   Greyhound
Tel 0944 70116

Main Street Ganton North Yorkshire YO12 4NX

Map 5 F4

Popular dining pub on the A64, not far from the championship golf course. *Beer McEwan, Tetley Bitter. Ganton.*

Gillingham   Swan
Tel 0502 712055

Loddon Road Gillingham Norfolk NR34 0LD

Map 10 D2

Full name the Swan Motel, on a roadside with five acres of grounds. Modernised, airy and well-kept; plush and frilly-curtained bar and dining room. *Beer Adnams Bitter & Broadside, Bass, Marston Pedigree. Garden. Children's play area. Family room.*

Gisburn   White Bull
Tel 0200 445233

Main Street Gisburn Lancashire BB7 4HE

Map 6 B1

18th-century pub on A59, by the foot of Pendle Hill, of Pendle Witches fame. *Beer Boddington, Whitbread. Garden. Children's play area. Family room.*

Glastonbury   Mitre Inn
Tel 0458 31203

27 Benedict Street Glastonbury Somerset BA6 9NE

Map 13 F1

A traditional, friendly urban local. *Beer Courage, John Smiths. Garden. Children's play area. Family room.*

Glemsford   Black Lion
Tel 0787 280684

Lion Road Glemsford Suffolk CO10 7RF

FOOD

Map 10 C3

Despite the unremarkable exterior, the Lion turns out to have a treasure of a Tudor interior complete with half-timbered walls and rehabilitated timbers, which today serve to frame and support the bar. With this noble lineage is a mixed decor of distinctly Edwardian feel; quarry-tiled floors, country prints, leather armchairs and bay-window seats, all of which is at once both uncluttered and charming. In June

1992, Anne White and Averil Hemingway arrived as the new licensees. They take it in turns in the kitchen and concentrate on producing good home cooking: lasagne (£3.75), chicken pie (£3.50), bangers & mash (£2.20) are good examples on the bar food menu. There's a wider choice of dishes in the restaurant but the cooking remains uncomplicated: garlic mushrooms (£2.70), mackerel and dill paté (£1.95), steak and kidney pie in Abbot Ale (£5), grilled salmon (£6.80). Their fruit pies and toffee apple tart are home-made (all £1.75). 3-course traditional Sunday lunch £5. *Bar Food 12-2.30, 6.30-9.30 (except Sun eve). Vegetarian dishes. Children's portions. Beer Greene King IPA, Abbot Ale. Garden, outdoor eating, children's play area. Access, Visa.*

Glooston   Old Barn

FOOD
B&B

Tel 085 884 215

Main Street Glooston Leicestershire LE16 7ST

Map 7 D4

On the route of the Old Roman road called the Gartree, the Old Barn stands at the centre of a tiny hamlet and just across the road from a picture postcard row of stone terraced cottages; the pub's 16th-century frontage of tiny leaded windows framed by flowering boxes and hanging baskets also makes a summer picture. Within, the premises readily divide into two separate sections, a postage-stamp-size cocktail bar and restaurant to the front, its tables forming booths thanks to high-backed pews and brass-ringed curtaining, and at a lower level to the rear, a cellar bar largely devoted to snacks and bar meals, in which stripped pine tables and kitchen chairs are gathered in front of a winter log-burning fire. Prominently displayed blackboard specials run from home-made soup through to turkey and pheasant pie (£6.25). Restaurant meals follow a more formal menu, changed fortnightly, which offers three courses at £14.95, and an à la carte added on Friday and Saturday nights. Medallion of duck breast, poached darne of salmon and tournedos Rossini, all make use of the freshest produce available; vegetarian dishes are specially prepared to order, and the puddings are home-made, crumbles and fruit flans coming from the kitchen of the lady next door. The bedrooms – two doubles and a twin, are well fitted out, with duvets, trouser press and hairdryer, small televisions and bedside radio. Owing to lack of space, the modular fitted shower rooms are a practical, if cramped, solution, but the towels could certainly be bigger. Host Charles Edmondson-Jones and chef/partner Stewart Sturge add a final ingredient of good service and genuine friendliness which many could learn from; the Old Barn is one of those pubs to which people keep coming back. *Bar Food and Restaurant 12-1.45 (restaurant Sun only), 7-9.30. Vegetarian dishes. Children's menu/portions. Free House. Beer Adnams, Batemans, Theakston. Children allowed in bar to eat. Garden, outdoor eating. Accommodation 3 bedrooms, all en suite, £42.50 (single £37.50). Children welcome overnight, cot available. Check-in by arrangement. Pub closed Sun eve & Mon lunch. Access, Visa.*

Goathland   Mallyan Spout

Tel 0947 86206

Goathland Whitby North Yorkshire YO22 5AN

Map 5 E3

Splendid old hotel built of local stone, overlooking the green in remote, romantic moorland village. Modernised, rather smart interior. Good walks nearby; lovely view from garden. *Beer Malton Double Chance. Children's play area. Family room.*

Godstow   Trout Inn

Tel 0865 54485

Godstow Road Lower Wolvercote nr Oxford Oxfordshire OX2 8PN   Map 16 C2

This famous medieval pub situated on the River Thames at Godstow
still attracts thousands of visitors every year. In summer, the cobbled
terrace beside the fast-running river with its weir makes a restful place
to watch the peacocks meandering round the terrace and catch a
glimpse of the chub (not trout as is widely believed) in the clear
water. The bridge across to the private island is now sadly falling
apart but it is still possible to to the island with its famous
stone lion, and on to the now ruined Godstow Nunnery where the
fair Rosamund (Henry II's mistress) was imprisoned. Inside the Trout
you find flagged stone floors, beamed ceilings, bare floorboards and
welcoming open fires in winter. Be warned, the Trout can get very
busy in the summer, but is well worth a visit. *Beer Bass, Charringtons
IPA. Garden. Family room. Access, Amex, Visa.*

Goldsborough   Bay Horse Inn

Tel 0423 862212   **B&B**

Goldsborough nr Knaresborough North Yorks HG5 8NW   Map 5 E3

A delightful, well-maintained 450-year-old inn, quietly situated off the
A59. It is spotless inside with gleaming copper-topped tables and
furnishings in muted autumnal colours. Summer window boxes and
an award-winning garden complete the setting for the simple rooms
in the annexe. All have washbasins, TVs, duvets and tea-makers, and
two public bathrooms are pristine. The rooms are small but the
service and housekeeping are impeccable. There are plans this year
make all bedrooms en suite and extend the accommodation. *Beer
Bodingtons, Trophy, Castleden, Murphys. Garden. **Accommodation**
5 bedrooms, not en suite, £37 (single £18.50). No children under 5. No
dogs. Check-in by arrangement. Access, Visa.*

Goldsithney   Crown

Tel 0736 710494

Fore Street Goldsithney Cornwall   Map 12 A4

Relaxing and informal village pub with a Cornish flavour, busy with
hungry locals when not mobbed by summer tourists. *Beer St Austell
Mild & Tinners. Garden.*

Goosnargh   Bushells Arms

Tel 0772 865235   **FOOD**

Church Lane Goosnargh Lancs PR3 2BH   Map 6 B1

Just 4 miles from Junction 32 of the M6, this modernised Georgian
building offers a splendid alternative to the expensive plastic food of
the motorway service areas. To reach the pub, follow the A6 North
and turn onto the B5269; once in the village, take the left turn
opposite the post office, and you'll find the Bushells Arms about a
quarter of a mile along on the right. It's run by the experienced David
and Glynis Best, who have written a book on the business side of pub
catering, using much of their own experience. Certainly the food at
the Bushells is first rate; cooking is in the hands of Glynis, who
produces a long, wide and cosmopolitan selection of specials,
blackboard-listed behind the food counter, as well as those on the
distinguished printed menu. A truly international menu includes

spring rolls (£2) and falafel (£2) for starters with Greek stifado (£6)
and chicken Kiev (£6) or chili con carne (£4.50) to follow. British
dishes aren't forgotten either: a steak, kidney and Murphy's pie (£5) is
admirably handled. There are fine accompaniments, too, like O'Brien
potatoes, a delicious mix of diced potato with cream, peppers, spices,
garlic and Parmesan cheese. Great care and enthusiasm are evident
throughout, and the wine list is constantly being reviewed. The
interior of the pub itself is cleverly divided into a number of alcoves
and by using effective wooden screens and exposed sandstone columns
and walls. There's also lots of greenery, not all of it real. Seating is
mainly on plush red button banquettes and stools, arranged around
unfussy wooden tables, and a couple of the areas are non-smoking.
Brasses and watercolours in a real mix of styles hang on the walls, and
there's piped music. To the rear is a well-maintained garden with
white plastic patio furniture, useful in summer when the pub gets
extremely busy. Staff are noticeably welcoming and friendly. The
village, incidentally, is pronounced Goozner. *Bar Food* *12-2.30, 7-10.*
Vegetarian dishes. Children's portions. *Beer* *Boddingtons, Tetley. Children*
allowed in bar to eat. Garden, outdoor eating. No credit cards.

Goostrey   Crown

Tel 0477 32128	
111 Main Road Goostrey Cheshire	Map 6 B2

Handsome 16th-century pub in popular village, with an attractively
furnished double-room lounge, traditional tap room, rear dining
room-cum bistro, and upstairs overspill dining room when not
booked by private parties. This is the nearest pub to Jodrell Bank
Radio Telescope. No music, real fires. *Beer* *Marston Pedigree.*

Goring Heath   King Charles Head

Tel 0491 680268	
Goring Heath nr Reading Oxfordshire RG8 7RL	Map 17 D3

Rambling, characterful old brick cottage in a romantic woodland
setting. Several rooms lead off the central bar; two real fires. A
modern extension bar leads into two and a half acres of lovely garden.
No juke box or background music. *Free House.* *Beer* *Adnams Broadside,*
Brakspears Mild & PA, Glenny Wychwood, Hook Norton. Garden.
Children's play area.

Gosberton   Five Bells

Tel 077 584 0348	B&B
Spalding Road Gosberton Lincolnshire PE11 4HL	Map 7 E3

On the A16 Boston-Spalding road stands this simple pebbledash pub.
There are just three bedrooms, which are being renovated by the new
landlords, offering TVs and tea-making facilities and sharing a
bathroom. Downstairs, the public bar has a pool table while the main
bar is rather smarter and decorated with much brass and copperware.
Beer *John Smith Magnet, Directors. Garden. Children's play area.*
Accommodation *3 bedrooms, not en suite, £30 (single £15).*
Check-in all day. Access.

Gosforth   Wasdale Head Inn

Tel 09467 26229   Fax 09467 26334

B&B

Wasdale Head Gosforth Cumbria CA20 1EX

Map 4 B3

The world's greatest liar and rockclimbing pioneer, Will Ritson, founded this unique inn around 1856, siting it close to England's highest peak, Scafell Pike, deepest lake, Wastwater, and smallest parish church, St Olaf's in the dale head. A walkers' and climbers' paradise, it's six or so miles from the village post office. You'll not arrive here by accident, nor expect to be disturbed by TV, radios or passing traffic noise; cascading Mosedale Beck apart, the silence by night is complete. First-class cask-conditioned ales are the highlight in the flagstoned bar, whose atmosphere is enhanced by converted gas mantles, varnished oak pews and Victorian mountaineering memorabilia. For residents, a diary logs their daily walks ("please tick when you return") and there's a clothes-drying room and abundant hot water on tap at the end of the day. Carefully segregated from the pub proper are a quiet, comfortable lounge stacked with magazines and board games, and a private garden. The pine-panelled bedrooms are snug and unfussy, with small, practical bathrooms; two have WC/shower only. A five-course dinner is included in the quoted price; a recent visit, however, produced little about which to get excited – the captive market (half-board terms only) seems to be poorly served. Big plans are afoot for 1993 and include extensions to the adjacent self-catering facilities. No service charge is levied and gratuities are not accepted. *Free House.* **Beer** *Yates, Jennings, Theakston XB & Old Peculier. Garden. Family Room.* **Accommodation** *10 rooms, all en suite, £106 (half-board only), single £55. Children welcome overnight, additional beds £10 (ages 2-8); over-8s £46.50. Cots supplied. Check-in all day.* Access, Visa.

Goudhurst   Star & Eagle

Tel 0580 211512

B&B

High Street Goudhurst Kent TN17 1AL

Map 11 B5

Behind the splendid timbered facade vintage charm and modern comfort blend harmoniously in a fine 14th-century hostelry owned by Whitbread. Beams, bricks, vaulted stonework and inglenooks make great appeal in the public rooms, while creaking floors and odd angles are the order of the day in the bedrooms. These vary in size and shape and the majority are furnished in pine, though the four-poster room has some antiques. Nine rooms have carpeted bathrooms en suite. **Beer** *Harveys, Flowers, Fremlins Bitter. Garden.* **Accommodation** *11 bedrooms, 9 en suite, £45 (single £30). Children welcome overnight, additional beds and cots available. Check-in all day.* Access, Amex, Visa.

Grange Moor   Kaye Arms

Tel 0942 848385

29 Wakefield Road Grange Moor West Yorkshire WF4 4BG

Map 6 C1

Run by the same family for over 20 years, and recently bought from Tetley Brewery, the Kaye Arms is now blossoming into an interesting foodie pub, with all the cooking and serving done by various Coldwells.

Great Barrington   Fox

Tel 045 14 385

Great Barrington Gloucestershire   **Map 16 A2**

Genuinely unspoilt little Cotswold pub, run by the same people for
many years; its charm is of the simple alehouse sort, and not tweely
countrified, take note. Low ceilings, stone walls, rustic furnishings,
open fires, a skittle alley, and outdoor tables by the pretty river
Windrush. No music. *Beer Donnington BB & SBA. Garden.*

Great Budworth   George & Dragon

Tel 0606 891317

High Street Great Budworth Cheshire CW9 6HF   **Map 6 B2**

Picturesque local at the heart of a delightful village, opposite the
church. Cosy, rambling wood-panelled lounge; lively public bar. *Beer
Burton Ale, Tetley.*

Great Chesterford   Plough

Tel 0799 30283

High Street Great Chesterford Essex CB10 1PL   **Map 10 B3**

Delightful village pub with a traditional, unspoilt interior and a
pleasant atmosphere. Superb garden. No children indoors. *Beer Greene
King IPA & Abbot, Rayments Special. Garden. Children's play area.*

Great Clacton   Robin Hood

Tel 0255 421519

211 London Road Great Clacton Essex CO15 4ED   **Map 11 C4**

The pub was a row of farm cottages until 1960 when Bass
Charrington converted it. Cosy beamed local and, now, a popular,
homely dining pub with two open fires. *Beer Adnams, Bass. Garden.
Children's play area. Family room.*

Great Eversden   Hoops

Tel 0223 262185

High Street Great Eversden Cambridgeshire   **Map 15 F1**

17th-century village local with a Jacobean fireplace, original timbers
and a stone-flagged floor; there's also a simpler, noisy public bar. The
garden is large and child-friendly. *Beer Charles Wells, Mansfield.
Garden.*

Great Hampden   Hampden Arms

Tel 0494 488255

Great Hampden nr Great Missenden Buckinghamshire HP16 9RQ   **Map 17 E2**

Two-roomed pub on a corner of Hampden Common. Friendly service
from popular licensees. *Beer Ansells, Tetley, Greene King IPA. Garden.*

Great Henny   Henny Swan

Tel 0787 269238

Great Henny nr Sudbury Essex CO10 7LS   **Map 10 C3**

Ex-barge house by a weir on the river Stour, once called simply the
Swan. There's a pleasant dining lounge, and a Victorian style
conservatory which extends from the restaurant and leads onto a
patio/barbecue area. *Beer Greene King IPA & Abbot. Riverside garden.*

Great Kimble   Bernard Arms

FOOD
B&B

Tel 08444 6172

Risborough Rd Great Kimble nr Aylesbury Buckinghamshire HP17 0XS   Map 17 D2

On the A4010 about three miles north of Princes Risborough. Part
13th-century, antique plates and soda syphons decorate the walls,
currency from around the world covers the bar shelves. It takes at
least six blackboards to list the food and drinks available. Only ten
portions are available of each dish on the bar menu; once served, they
are replaced by others. All the food is home made using herbs from
their own garden: goat's cheese salad (£3.75), Chiltern game pie
(£7.50), loin of pork (£7.50), plum crumble or Bakewell tart (both
£2.50). A separate restaurant offers two table d'hote menus (2-course
£14.50, 3-course £17.50) with choices such as Cornish crab or tartine
of duck liver mousse, followed by grilled mullet or osso buco with a
home-made cheesecake to finish. A 3-course traditional Sunday lunch
is also served (£14). The seating is comfortable, the service good, and
the portions huge. Large car park and garden. Five bedrooms with
showers and basins share two toilets; TVs, tea/coffee-making facilities
and telephones are provided. *Bar Food and Restaurant Meals 12-2,
7-9.30. Vegetarian dishes. Children's portions. Beer Wadworth 6X, Tetley,
Benskins Best. Garden, outdoor eating, children's play area.*
*Accommodation five bedrooms, sharing facilities. Children welcome
overnight, additional beds available. Check-in all day. No dogs. Access,
Visa.*

Great Limber   New Inn

Tel 0469 60257

High Street Great Limber Lincolnshire   Map 7 E2

Spacious, popular pub dominating an estate village; Brocklesby Park,
nearby, is the seat of the Earl of Yarborough, who still owns the New
Inn. Traditional lounge free of music and electronic games, but with
real fires. *Beer Bateman XB, Tetley, Wards. Garden.*

Great Missenden   George

Tel 024 06 2084

94 High Street Great Missenden Buckinghamshire HP16 0BG   Map 17 E2

A listed ancient monument, its 15th-century timbers intact: there are a
dozen foot-thick beams on the bar parlour ceiling alone. The most
attractive room is upstairs, a spacious chamber complete with huge
Gothic oak arch. Pleasant surroundings and service. *Beer ABC Bitter,
Fullers London Pride, Greene King IPA, Wadworth 6X. Garden.
Children's play area.*

Great Offley   Green Man

Tel 0462 76256

High Street Great Offley Hertfordshire SG5 3AR   Map 17 F1

Busy, rambling country pub with good views from the well-organised
garden. *Free House. Beer Boddington, Banks & Taylors Shefford, Greene
King IPA & Abbot, Marston Pedigree. Garden. Children's play area.*

Great Offley   Red Lion

Tel 0462 76281

Kings Walden Road Great Offley Hertfordshire SG5 3DZ   Map 17 F1

Now properly known as the Red Lion and Lodge Hotel, an almost roadside redbrick pub. *Beer Boddington, Brakspears, Castle Eden, Marston Pedigree. Garden. Children's play area. Family room.*

Great Rissington   Lamb   ★   FOOD
B&B

Tel 0451 20388

Great Rissington Gloucestershire GL54 2LP   Map 16 A1

Originally a farmhouse, the oldest part of the Lamb dates back nearly 300 years, the newest just a couple of years. That it is difficult to tell the difference is a tribute to the skill and craftsmanship of the appropriately named landlord Richard Cleverly, formerly a builder, who has done all the most recent work himself. The charming restaurant, for instance, with its candles and lacy tablecloths, is housed in a new extension, but makes imaginative use of old timbers and stonework. It fits in well with the stone-walled bar, where incidentally, hangs a plaque to the memory of the airmen who died when their Wellington bomber crashed in the garden here during the Second World War; part of a propeller is displayed above the wood burning stove. Kate Cleverly is no less talented than husband Richard, taking justifiable pride in the fact that everything on the menu is genuinely home-made; even the chicken en croute is cooked to order, starting from scratch with raw chicken breast. The daily changing blackboard bar menu carries starters like chicken liver paté (£3.25), followed by steak and mushroom pie (£5.50) and sherry trifle (£2.25). The restaurant menu also applies in the bar, giving an even wider choice, such as mushrooms in cream and garlic sauce (£3.50) and duck breast in raspberry sauce (£10.75), and they can usually find some fishfingers or baked beans on toast for children with a hankering for convenience foods. Richard and Kate's skills have combined in the creation of charming bedrooms which include built-in wardrobes made with salvaged timbers, and a splendid four-poster bed, testifying to his skills as a wood carver. Kate's contribution is the pretty decor, each room highly individual in style, with coordinating fabrics and wall coverings. Most of the furniture is antique and all but two rooms, which share a shower room, have en-suite bathrooms (five with showers rather than baths). They make a virtue out of not having television or radios in the rooms but addicts will find them in the cosy residents' lounge, as well as in the best guest room, a quite luxurious suite. A heated indoor swimming pool in the delightful garden, which also boasts an aviary, summer house and play area, is a luxury all residents can share in the summer months. *Bar Food 12-1.45, 7-9 (7-9.30 Fri/Sat). Restaurant Meals 7-9 (7-9.30 Fri/Sat, 7-8.30 Sun). Vegetarian Dishes. Children's menu (£2.50 per dish). Free House. Beer Hook Norton, John Smith, Theakston. Garden, outdoor eating. Accommodation 12 bedrooms, 10 en suite, £46 (single £35). Children welcome overnight, additional beds (£10.50), cots available (£3.50). Check-in all day. Access, Visa.*

Great Ryburgh   Boar Inn

Tel 032 878 212

B&B

Great Ryburgh nr Fakeham Norfolk NR21 0DX

Map 10 C1

If you are looking for peaceful and quiet accommodation within handy reach of the Norfolk coastline, the Boar Inn, a white-washed pub nestling near the river Wensum in a sleepy village, is the place to go. On chilly nights a log fire crackles in the huge inglenook fireplace in the low-beamed bar and there are more beams upstairs in the cottagey bedrooms. Each room has a washbasin, TV and tea-making facilities and they share a shower and toilet. *Free House.* **Beer** *Tolly Cobbold Original, Wensum Bitter, Adnams Bitter, Sam Smith. Garden.* **Accommodation** *3 bedrooms with shared facilities, from £32.80 (single £20.50). Children welcome overnight, cots available. Check-in all day. Access, Visa.*

Great Stainton   Kings Arms

Tel 0740 30361

The Green Great Stainton Durham TS21 1NA

Map 5 E3

Large, comfortable saloon and busy locals' bar. **Beer** *Castle Eden, Flowers Original, Whitbread. Family room.*

Great Tew   Falkland Arms

FOOD

Tel 060883 653   Fax 060883 656

B&B

Great Tew Oxfordshire OX7 4DB

Map 16 B1

Great Tew must be one of the prettiest of Cotswold villages and has the inestimable advantage of being a bit out of the way and not on the main tourist trail. Despite the ambition implied by its name, it's actually rather a small place, with barely a score of mostly thatched cottages, a small general store and, naturally, in its rightful place opposite the church, the village inn. Dating back to the 16th century, the creeper-clad Falkland Arms must be close to everybody's ideal country pub, with high-backed settles, a flagstone floor and a prized collection of hundreds of jugs and mugs hanging from the old beams. A pretty garden shaded by a large hornbeam tree is complete with dovecote, whose occupants seem to spend most of the day perched on the pub's stone-tiled roof cooing to each other. The regular real ales are supplemented by an ever-changing selection of guest beers (some 250 in a full year) and 50 malt whiskies and 14 country wines are also available. They sell snuff, and even clay pipes ready-filled with tobacco. Food is served at lunchtimes only from a short but varied blackboard menu that changes daily but always includes a vegetarian dish (the landlord John Milligan eats not of meat), along with ploughman's and perhaps a rook pie (well at least it wasn't dove). Everything is home-made, from a cod and prawn crumble (£4.80), pork and Stilton hot pot (£5), or duck and apricot pie (£5.50) to sponges and crumbles (£1.60). Four cottage bedrooms, two with four-poster beds and two with old iron bedsteads, are furnished with antiques and decorated with pretty co-ordinating fabrics and wall coverings. The largest, under the eaves, has a pitched ceiling, exposed timbers and its own en-suite bathroom. Others have showers and, all but one, their own toilets. Televisions and tea /coffee facilities are standard, and you can help yourself to fresh milk from the kitchen. Breakfast is at 9 o'clock prompt (9.30 on Sundays) and they like the rooms vacated by 10.30 on the day of departure. Bookings must be confirmed in writing with a 50% deposit. **Bar Food** *12-2 (Tue-Sat*

*only). Vegetarian dishes. Children's portions. Children allowed in bar to
eat. Free House. **Beer** Donnington, Hook Norton, Wadworth, guest beers.
Cider Weston. Garden, outdoor eating, children's play area.
Accommodation 4 bedrooms, all en suite, £45 (single £25). Children
welcome overnight. No dogs. Check-in by arrangement. No credit cards.*

Great Wolford   Fox & Hounds
`Tel 0608 74220`
Great Wolford nr Shipston-on-Stour Warwickshire CV36 5NQ   Map 16 A1

Cotswold stone pub, traditionally run by the proprietors, with
traditional public bar games and discreet piped music in the main
room. Furnishings are simple and various, and there's a log fire. *Free
House.* **Beer** *Boddington, Castle Eden, Flowers IPA, Marston Pedigree,
Wadworth 6X.*

Greta Bridge   Morrit Arms Hotel   **FOOD**
`Tel 0833 27232`   **B&B**
Greta Bridge Co Durham DL12 9SE   Map 5 D3

Old-fashioned peace and quiet are promised in the Dickens Bar of this
well-loved old coaching inn, the bar so named because the novelist
stayed here while researching *Nicholas Nickelby* in 1838. A substantial
and imposing building, run personally by its proprietor twin brothers,
the interior has a homely, unashamedly unmodernised feel,
particularly evident to residents. The bar (there's also a quite separate
public bar) has high ceilings, traditional furnishings and views out
over the lawn. Standard bar food includes carrot and ginger soup
(£1.80), jumbo sausages (£4), fish and chips (£5), sandwiches (from
£2), and ploughman's (£3.75); while in the restaurant the set £19.75
menu is a bit more upmarket with leek and pineapple soup, grilled
rumpsteak, poached salmon, and noisettes of lamb featuring. Bedrooms
vary: many are quite modestly furnished, though others have brass
bedsteads and one sports a four-poster. A good base for the North
Country tour. *Bar Food* 12-2 (3pm cold food). 6-9. *Restaurant Meals
12.30-1.15 (Sun only), 7-8.45. Children's portions. **Beer** Butterworths
Bitter. Garden, outdoor eating, children's play area. **Accommodation**
17 bedrooms, all en suite, £64 (single £50). Children welcome overnight,
additional beds (£12), cots supplied. Check-in all day. Access, Amex,
Diners, Visa.*

Gretna   Gretna Chase Hotel
`Tel 0461 37517`   **B&B**
Gretna Carlisle Cumbria CA6 8JB   Map 4 C2

Patrons of the first marriage house over the Scottish border used the
nearby Gretna Chase for stabling their horses. That function has long
since ceased, but today's honeymooners can install themselves in a
splendid four-poster suite. All rooms (with TVs, but discreetly
phoneless) feature quality furniture and fabrics, and most overlook the
award-winning garden of 2½ acres. There is a spacious Victorian
reception hall, plenty of bar space and a little lounge. *Beer Youngers
Scotch, Dark Mild. **Accommodation** 9 bedrooms, 6 en suite, £60 (single
£38). Children welcome overnight, additional beds, cots available. Check-in
all day. No dogs. Pub closed January. Access, Amex, Diners, Visa.*

Gretton   Royal Oak

Tel 0242 602477	**FOOD**

Gretton nr Winchcombe Gloucestershire GL54 5EP

Map 14 C1

Excellent for people with children in tow, the Royal Oak has a
particularly large, safe garden for small people to explore, with a
proper play area. At the bottom of the garden is the GWR steam
railway, which runs from Toddington a few miles away, and brings a
lot of trade. The pub itself is a mixture of ancient and modern, with
flagstone floors, beams, stripped oak, pine tables and a conservatory
dining room, and visitors are equally diverse, a mix of locals,
holidaymakers and day-trippers enjoying varied bar food from a long
blackboard list and proper pub restaurant: Cheddar and potato soup
(£1.80), baked crab and mushroom pot (£2.95), lamb and apricot
curry (£4.50) and perhaps a home-made choc-fruit and biscuit cake
(£1.80). Live folk music on Wednesday evenings. *Bar Food 12-2,
7-9.30. Vegetarian dishes. Children's menu (£2.95). Children allowed in
bar to eat. Free house.* **Beer** *Courage Best, John Smith, Eldridge Pope,
Thomas Hardy Country, Ruddles, Wadworth 6X. Garden, outdoor eating,
summer barbecue, children's play area, tennis court open to public. Access,
Visa.*

Grimsthorpe   Black Horse Inn

Tel 077 832 247	**FOOD**
	B&B

Bourne Grimsthorpe Lincolnshire PE10 0LY

Map 7 E3

Imposing Georgian coaching inn with a distinctive style, run by the
Fishers for many years. It has a well lived-in look and slightly
eccentric charm. There's a pleasant beamed bar and dining room (with
polished tables and fresh flowers), where all meals are served, leaving
the bar a drinkers' haven. Good reliable food with a pleasing English
and local emphasis including home-made soup (£1.99) and
Lincolnshire lamb baskets (£4.95). Mrs Beeton's beefsteak, kidney and
mushroom pie (£4.95) remains a favourite. Good bed and breakfast
too, in three spacious chintzy bedrooms with peaceful parkland views.
*Bar Food 12-1.30, 7-9.30. Vegetarian dishes. Children's portions. Free
House.* **Beer** *Tetley. Family room.* **Accommodation** *3 bedrooms, all en
suite, £52 (single £26). Children welcome overnight (minimum age 7).
Check-in by arrangement. Pub closed Sunday. Access, Amex, Visa.*

Grimston   Black Horse

Tel 0664 812358	

Grimston nr Melton Mowbray Leicestershire LE14 3BZ

Map 7 D3

The garden is the village green and the interior awash with cricket-
abilia, including over 80 autographed bats. No children under 14. *Free
House.* **Beer** *Marston Pedigree. Garden.*

Grindleford   Maynard Arms

Tel 0433 630321 Fax 0433 630445	**B&B**

Grindleford Derbyshire S30 1HP

Map 6 C2

The tastefully refurbished early Victorian inn, with comfortable and
spacious bedrooms, three of them 'superior', two with four-posters, the
rest attractive with decent laminate furnishings. Two relaxing bars and
charming lounge. On B6521, north of the village. **Beer** *Boddingtons,
Stones and guest beer. Garden.* **Accommodation** *13 bedrooms, all en suite,
£79.50 (single £63). Children welcome overnight, additional beds (£10),
cots supplied. Check-in all day. Access, Amex, Diners, Visa.*

Grindon   Cavalier

Tel 0538 8285

Grindon Staffordshire   Map 6 C3

Just a mile from the Manifold Valley, a partly-carpeted, partly-tiled, rustically furnished and decorated old pub, a popular walkers' halt. *Beer Marston Pedigree, Ruddles County & guest ales. Garden, children's play area. Family room.*

Groombridge   Crown

Tel 089 286 4742

Groombridge on B2110 Kent   Map 11 B5

Quaint Elizabethan Kentish tile-hung pub, rambling and characterful, with period square-panelling. Be early to get a seat in the cosy main bar. Outdoor seating on the front terrace or village green. On the B2110. *Beer Brakspear, Harveys, Marston. Family room, patio/terrace.*

Guisborough   Fox Inn

Tel 028 763 2958   **B&B**

10 Bow Street Guisborough Cleveland TS14 6BP   Map 5 E3

One of the two spotless bars is decked out in green plush to complement the copper-topped tables, and the other is similarly furnished but in red and with mock beams and rough plaster walls. The exterior is pebbledashed, and the Williamsons make you welcome as soon as you step through the door. High standards of cleanliness extend to the bedrooms, simply furnished with lightwood units, TVs and tea-makers. Two public bathrooms and four toilets serve the rooms. *Beer Scottish & Newcastle Exhibition, Youngers Scotch, McEwans 80. Accommodation 7 bedrooms not en suite, £34.50 (single £19). Children welcome overnight, cots available. Check-in all day. No dogs.* Access, Visa, Amex.

Guisborough   Moorcock Hotel

Tel 028 763 2342   Fax 028 766 31631   **B&B**

West End Guisborough Cleveland TS1 6RL   Map 5 E3

On the outskirts of town, a modern redbrick pub offering functional overnight accommodation in six neatly fitted bedrooms. The new landlords have recently refurbished the bedrooms, which all have their own shower cubicle, TV and and tea-makers; they share two public bathrooms. Downstairs is the large, split-level main bar which provides entertainment most evenings. *Beer Boddingtons, Castleden, guest beers. Garden, adventure playground. Family room. Accommodation 6 bedrooms, not en suite, £35 (single £20). Children welcome overnight, additional beds and cots available. Check-in all day.* Access, Visa.

Guiting Power   Olde Inne

Tel 0451 850392   **FOOD**

Winchcombe Road Guiting Power Gloucestershire GL54 5UX   Map 16 A1

Located in one of the prettiest Cotswold villages, this 16th-century pub has endless views over the fields. The dining room has recently been redecorated and the lounge bar is heated in winter by a roaring log fire in the inglenook fireplace. The straightforward menu includes marinated Danish herring (£3.25), asparagus gratiné (£2.95), chicken

Stilton with leeks (£7.25), honey-roast duck (£8.50) steak and kidney
pie (£4.95) with Ye Olde Inne pudding (£1.95) to follow. Well
worth a visit. *Bar Food and Restaurant Meals* 12-2, 7-9
*(7-9.30 Fri/Sat). Vegetarian dishes. Children's menu (£2.50 per dish).
Children allowed in bar to eat. Free House. **Beer** Hook Norton Bitter,
Marstons Old Peculier. Garden, outdoor eating. No credit cards.*

Gunnislake   Cornish Inn

| Tel 0822 832475 | **B&B** |

The Square Gunnislake Cornwall Pl18 9BW   **Map 12 C3**

Just off the A390, and a five-minute walk from the River Tamar, this
white-painted village inn has a simple, spacious, spick and span bar and
a cosy-first floor residents' lounge. Plain-painted walls give a bright
feel to the modest but comfortable rooms. Three have functional en-
suite bathrooms; the other two (with washbasins) share a bathroom.
All have colour TVs and tea-makers. *Free House.* **Beer** *Cornish
Original, Boddingtons Bitter, Newquay Steam Bitter, Murphy Stout,
Whitbread Best and Mild.* **Accommodation** *5 bedrooms, 3 en suite, £37
(single £22). Children welcome overnight, additional beds, cots available.
Check-in all day. Access, Amex, Visa.*

Hallaton   Bewicke Arms

| Tel 085 889 217 | **FOOD** |
| | **B&B** |

1 Eastgate Hallaton Leicestershire LE16 8UB   **Map 7 D4**

Neil Spiers' 400-year-old country inn stands above the Welland valley
in the heart of fine Leicestershire countryside. Hallaton itself is locally
renowned for the parish church's Norman tower, the conical butter
cross on the village green – right across the road from the pub – and
the tiny village museum which offers a unique insight into its rural
past. The Bewicke has three bedrooms and two bathrooms, and the
accommodation is available for weekly self-catering in its entirety;
failing that, the bedrooms are let individually for bed and breakfast.
The pub below is a cracking good local and a predictable printed
menu lists the usual steaks and grills, ploughman's and sandwiches –
look to the specials board for more adventurous options. Starters
typically include garlic mushrooms, deep-fried Camembert, and
mussels baked in pastry (£3.60), while top-sellers among the main
courses include a beery beef casserole (£6.20) and chicken Boursin
(£7.40). Vegetarians get a good look in, too, with risotto, lasagne and
a cauliflower, courgette and mushroom bake topped with Stilton
crumble, and there's a fair choice of home-made puddings of the
cheesecake, pavlova and treacle sponge and custard genre. Wines
offered by the bottle are more interesting than the house beers; a
printed, largely European list is backed by a wines of the month
board, typically featuring Australian and Chilean specials. The pub is
consistently busy and the more recently added Bottom Room, stone
clad with a bow window, Austrian blinds and an effective library
theme, opens when demand dictates. At weekends it's almost certain to
be full, so better book. *Bar Food* 12-2, 7-9.45. *Vegetarian dishes.
Children's menu. Free House.* **Beer** *Marston Pedigree, Ruddles Best,
Websters Yorkshire Bitter. Garden, outdoor play area, patio/terrace, outdoor
eating. Family room.* **Accommodation** *3 bedrooms, 2 en suite, £39 (single
£32). Children welcome overnight, cot available. Check-in by arrangement.
Access, Visa.*

Haltwhistle   Grey Bull

Tel 0434 320298

Main Street Haltwhistle Northumberland NE49 0DL   Map 5 D2

The young and hugely energetic Heavisides smoke their own fish, cheese, sausage and chicken, catch their own trout, grow their own vegetables and herbs, and make pies, bakes and casseroles, many with a modern twist. Eat in the pleasant bar of this old coaching inn, or in the separate dining room (closed winter lunchtimes). *Free House. **Beer** Hadrian Centuries, Jennings, Marston Pedigree, Theakston Best. Garden. Children's play area.*

Haltwhistle   Milecastle Inn

Tel 0434 320682   **FOOD**

Military Road Haltwhistle Northumberland NE49 9NN   Map 5 D2

Just 500 yards from Hadrian's Wall, a small, traditional 17th-century country pub with a vast collection of brass and copper, good log fires and a separate restaurant. No music, machines or pool table. Good reliable food ranges from garlic breaded mushrooms (£2.30), wild boar and duckling pie (£5.85) to roast venison (£9.90) and jugged hare (£10.95). ***Bar Food** 12-2 (except Mon & Tues), 6.30-9 (except Sun & Mon). Children's portions. Free House. **Beer** Theakston, Sampsons, Websters. Children over 5 allowed in bar to eat. Garden, outdoor eating. Access, Diners, Visa.*

Hambleden   Stag & Huntsman

Tel 0491 571227

Hambleden nr Henley-on-Thames Buckinghamshire RG9 6RP   Map 17 D3

Unassuming three bar pub in delightful village; real fires; nice garden. *Free House. **Beer** Brakspears PA & SPA, Wadworth 6X & Farmers Glory. Garden.*

Hampstead Marshall   White Hart Inn

Tel 0488 58201   **FOOD**
                                              B&B
Hampstead Marshall nr Newbury Berkshire RG15 0HW   Map 16 B4

The splendid herbaceous borders around the neat lawn at the front of this 16th-century inn are very English, and the pride and joy of Dorothy Aromando, but inside the Latin influence of husband Nicola predominates in the White Hart's Italian menu. A few old beams, mingling with some newer ones, give clues to the age of the building, but the decor is basically simple: red plush in the bar, red cloths on the tables of the restaurant leading off it. The same handwritten menu serves for both bar and restaurant. Nicola makes his own pasta and consquently there's a selection of pasta dishes (all £6.50) alongside meat dishes. Two favourites are quadroni (ravioli) with wild mushrooms and spinach fettucine with small lamb meatballs stuffed with mozzarella cheese in a wine, mushroom and cream sauce. Otherwise the menu offers soup of the day (£2.75), goat's cheese grilled with garlic and yoghurt (£4.50), Dover sole (£14), chicken breast with ham and asparagus (£9.50) and spinach and ricotta pancake. Amongst the home-made puddings, the crème caramel (£3.50) is outstanding, freshly cooked and with the topping caramelised to just the right degree. An old barn to the rear of the pub has been converted into six uncluttered bedrooms with pine furniture and good cotton bedding. All have neat en-suite bathrooms with

showers over their bathtubs. Get one of the two large rooms under
the eaves, if you can, which have sloping ceilings and exposed timbers,
as well as an extra bed for family use. The two single rooms are very
compact. Good freshly cooked breakfasts set you up for the day ahead.
*Bar Food 12-2, 7-10. Vegetarian dishes. Children's portions. Beer Hall &
Woodhouse, Wadworth. Garden, outdoor eating.* **Accommodation**
*6 bedrooms, all en suite, £50 (single £40). Children welcome overnight,
additional beds (£10 if over 18). No dogs. Check-in by arrangement. Pub
usually closed in August. Access, Amex, Visa.*

Hanwell Moon & Sixpence	**FOOD**
Tel 0295 730544	**B&B**
Hanwell nr Banbury Oxfordshire OX17 1HW	Map 16 B1

A short distance from 17th-century Hanwell Castle, the Moon &
Sixpence describes itself as a restaurant with rooms rather than an inn,
especially since the restaurant (with à la carte menu) can seat up to 100
people. Choose from sautéed king prawns in garlic butter (£6.95),
monkfish with saffron (£10.95) or 'mother's special' – sirloin steak

baked in the oven and filled with mortadella and mozzarella (£10.55).
Old bar meal favourites like steak and kidney pie are still available,
though. Two table d'hote menus (2 courses £9.80, 3 courses £12.65)
are served in the bar. There is a vast selection of English and Italian
cheeses, an extensive wine list and over 30 malt whiskies to choose
from. The "new, improved" bar now leads out on to a patio. Children
are allowed in both dining areas. *Bar Food 12-2 (except Sat and Sun).
Restaurant Meals 12-2 (except Sat and Sun), 7-9.45 (except Sun).
Vegetarian dishes. Children's portions. Beer Flowers IPA & Best,
Boddingtons.* **Accommodation** *(closed August) 3 bedrooms, sharing a
bathroom, £50 (single £37). Children welcome overnight, additional beds
(nominal charge). Check-in all day. No dogs. Access, Visa.*

Happisburgh Hill House	
Tel 0692 650004	
The Hill Happisburgh Norfolk	Map 10 D1

Next to a church with an elegant bell tower, the Hill House was a
Tudor stonemason's cottage and still has lots of old-time character. The
sea is just 500 yards away. Off B1159. *Beer Adnams. Garden.*

Harberton Church House Inn	
Tel 0803 863707	
Harberton nr Totnes Devon TQ9 7SF	Map 12 D3

Tucked away by the village church, and originally a chantry house for
monks, one of whom is said to be still lurking on the premises, the
Church House didn't pass out of clerical hands until 1950. The
carefully removed plaster of centuries has revealed ancient fluted oak
beams, a magnificent medieval oak screen, a Tudor window frame
and 13th-century glass. The open plan bar and restaurant were once
the great chamber, and are now furnished with old pews and settles.
*Free House. Beer Bass, Courage Best & Directors, Wadworth 6X & guest
ales. Family room.*

Hardway   Bull Inn

Tel 0749 812200

Hardway nr Bruton Somerset BA10 0LN   Map 13 F2

A remote and charming pub on the Somerset plains. **Beer** *Butcombe, Wadworth 6X. Garden, children's play area.*

Hare Hatch   Queen Victoria

Tel 0734 402477

Blakes Lane Hare Hatch Berkshire RG10 9TA   Map 16 D3

The pub is a convivial, low-ceilinged 17th-century two-roomed village local with a fruit machine and video game, as well as a good selection of more traditional pursuits. Real fire, no music. **Beer** *Brakspears Mild, Bitter, Special and Old Ale. Garden.*

Harlington   Carpenters Arms

Tel 052 55 2384

Sundon Road Harlington Bedfordshire LU5 6LS   Map 17 E1

Early 17th-century pub with beamed bars and separate upstairs restaurant, and a fine inglenook fireplace. **Beer** *Ruddles Best & County, Websters Yorkshire. Garden, children's play area.*

Harome   Star Inn

Tel 0439 70397   **FOOD**

Main Street Harome nr Helmsley North Yorkshire YO6 5JE   Map 5 E4

The Star is a little gem of a pub. Originally a 14th-century long house, the single thatched building is picture-postcard pretty outside and no less delightful within, with its low beamed ceiling, high-backed settles, 'Mousey' Thompson rustic furniture (somewhere on each piece he made he carved a small mouse), and, by the fireplace, a rack of magazines to browse through and a box of Lego and other toys for those customers not yet of reading age. That the cottage garden to the rear is just a little unkempt serves only to enhance its charm. Add a friendly landlord (Thomas Blackburn), good beer, classical music in the background and good food, and one has what for many would be the ideal pub. The menu has something to suit most appetites and tastes from sandwiches (for which they are well known), Stilton paté (£2.95) and vegetarian crepe (£2.95) to a plate of fresh poached salmon with chives and cream (£4.95), jacket potatoes (from £2.95) croque monsieur (£4.95), savoury mince with Yorkshire pudding (£5.95), Gressingham duck in port, black cherry and cream sauce (£9.95) and home-made puddings (all at £2.50) like apple crumble and mincemeat and brandy tart, and a children's menu. At night there is also an especially attractive restaurant and above in the 'loft' a coffee lounge (also used by families at lunchtime) that comes complete with playing cards and board games to keep you amused over post-prandial drinks. **Bar Food** *12-2.30, 7-9.* **Restaurant Meals** *7-9. Vegetarian dishes. Children's menu/portions. Free House.* **Beer** *Tetley, Theakstons Old Peculier, Best, Timothy Taylors Landlord. Garden, outdoor eating. Family room. Access, Visa.*

Harrietsham Ringlestone Inn

Tel 0622 859900 **A**

Between Harrietsham and Wormshill Kent **Map 11 C5**

Splendidly atmospheric old inn, remotely tucked away by the
Pilgrim's Way. Brick floors and walls, low beamed ceilings, intricately
carved settles and an magnificent oak dresser. *Free House.* **Beer**
Fremlins, Spitfire, Shepherd Neame, Bishop's Finger. **Cider** *Beddenden,
Theobalds. Children allowed in bar to eat. Garden, outdoor eating, outdoor
play area.*

Hascombe White Horse

Tel 048 632 258

Hascombe nr Godalming Surrey GU8 4JA **Map 11 A5**

Grade II listed, 16th-century pub in a beautiful corner of Surrey. **Beer**
Burton Ale, Friary Meux, Fullers London Pride. Garden. Family room.

Haselbury Plunkett Haselbury Inn

Tel 0460 72488

Haselbury Plunkett Somerset **Map 13 F2**

Characterful pub with an unusual bar, half given over to a chintzy
sitting area, complete with television half traditionally furnished, its
tables candle-lit at night. *Free House.* **Beer** *Butcombe, Charles West
Bombardier, Exmoor, Smiles Best, Wadworth 6X. Garden.*

Hastingwood Common Rainbow & Dove

Tel 0279 415419 **A**

Hastingwood Common Essex CM17 9JX **Map 11 B4**

Charming old rose-covered 16th-century pub very close to junction 7
of the M11 motorway, its name a reference to Noah's Ark (and it gets
almost as crowded inside). Oak beams, open fires, and a snug decorated
with jugs and golf clubs. **Beer** *Ansells, Tetley Bitter. Garden, outdoor
play area.*

Hatherleigh George Hotel

Tel 0837 810454 **B&B**

Market Street Hatherleigh Devon EX20 3JN **Map 13 D2**

Cob and thatch inn, originally a monk's retreat. The main bar is in the
converted brewhouse, with an extended area reserved for non-
smokers. The inn's original bar, atmospherically laden with original
beams, heavy stone walls, an enormous open fire and a pleasing variety
of comfortable seats and sofas, is now largely confined to residential
use. The market baracross the way is opened on Tuesdays only and
there's a fine cobbled courtyard drinking area. Bedrooms have direct-
dial phones and TVs and some have four-poster beds. The hotel has an
outdoor swimming pool. *Free House.* **Beer** *Draught Bass, Flowers
Original, Pompey Royal, Whitbread Boddingtons Bitter.* **Cider** *Stone
House, Jack Scrumpy. Garden. Family room.* **Accommodation**
*11 bedrooms, 9 en suite, £60 (single £46). Children welcome overnight,
additional bed (£6), cots supplied. Check-in all day. Access, Amex, Visa.*

Hatherleigh   Tally Ho

Tel 0837 810306

14 Market Street Hatherleigh Devon EX20 3JN   **Map 13 D2**

A regenerated old pub, 'discovered' in 1983 by its present Italian
owners, and gradually improved in the intervening years. Nice old
furnishings, a partly exposed brick floor, warming working stoves,
and relaxing touches like candles in bottles. *Free House.* **Beer** *Potboilers,
Own Brew – Tally Ho Beers. Garden, children's play area.*

Hatton   Waterman Inn

Tel 0926 492427

Birmingham Road Hatton Warwickshire CV35 7JJ   **Map 14 C1**

Restaurant and traditional country inn located by the Hatton locks on
the Grand Union Canal. **Beer** *Greenalls. Riverside garden, children's play
area. Family room.*

Hawkedon   Queen's Head

Tel 028 489 218

Main Street Hawkedon Suffolk   **Map 10 C3**

Foodie pub with eccentric touches, such as the Roo's Tours coach (an
old jalopy) which transports parties here and back – the pub is
Australian-owned. **Beer** *Greene King IPA & Abbot, Nethergate. Garden.*

Hawkhurst   Oak & Ivy

Tel 0580 753293

Rye Road Hawkhurst Kent TN18 5DB   **Map 11 C6**

Traditionally-run 15th-century pub with low beams and polished
brass, once the haunt of the smuggling Hawkhurst Gang. **Beer** *Flowers
Original, Fremlins, Harveys PA, Whitbread. Garden, children's play area.
Family room.*

Hawkshead   Drunken Duck Inn

FOOD
B&B

Tel 05394 36347

Barngate Hawkshead Cumbria LA22 0NG   **Map 4 C3**

There are fabulous views towards Ambleside from this white
pebbledash pub, which stands in splendid isolation in glorious
Lakeland countryside, the perfect peace spoilt only by the occasional
low-flying military jet. Despite its seclusion, the pub is extremely
popular with walkers and tourists, and weekends can get especially
hectic. In good weather, they spill out on to the rustically furnished
small front patio, and the grass over the narrow road. The country-
style interior, a main bar with three adjoining rooms, features original
beams, open fires, ladderback chairs and lots of landscape and sporting
prints. Main bar walls are covered with snarling fox heads, displays of
fishing flies (the pub has its own trout-filled tarn), deer skulls and
other local memorabilia. Justly popular bar food, blackboard-listed in
the bar, has a bistro-style feel, changes daily, and makes good use of
fresh local produce. A good selection of patés precedes dishes like
braised beef and vegetables, lasagne and minted lamb casserole (all
£5.25). Fruit crumble, sticky toffee pudding, and treacle tart (all
£2.50) are typical of the sturdy pudding choice. It's reasonably priced,
reasonable cooking. Ten excellent en-suite bedrooms are all
individually designed using Laura Ashley style wallcovering and
fabrics in soft, restful shades. Furniture varies from room to room,

stripped wood and units in some, antique pieces in others. All the usual modern creature comforts include impeccable bathrooms with fluffy towels and good lighting. Service is young, willing and friendly. Barngate is 2 miles north of Hawkshead – follow the signs from B5286. *Bar Food* 12-2, 6.30-9 (Sun 7-9). *Restaurant Meals* 8pm Fri/Sat (residents only). *Vegetarian dishes. Children's portions. Free House. Beer Jennings, Marston, Theakston, Yates. Garden, outdoor eating. Family room. Accommodation 10 bedrooms, all en suite, £65 (single £32.50). Children welcome overnight, additional beds (£12), cots supplied. Check-in all day. Access, Visa.*

Hawkshead   Queen's Head Hotel

FOOD

Tel 0539 436271

B&B

Hawkshead Cumbria LA22 0NS

Map 4 C3

Pretty white-painted Elizabethan inn in an attractive village street. Bigger than it appears from the outside, opening out into two panelled bar areas, comfortable rather than characterful, and a neat rear dining room. Food ranges from light bites and sandwiches to paella (£5.25), lamb hotpot (£5.50), pan-fried scampi and Stilton steak. Low beams and simple furnishings characterise the main-house bedrooms; cottage rooms are all en suite and the two newest ones have Beatrix Potter-inspired decor. There are three family rooms with bunk beds. Plushly comfortable residents' lounge. *Bar Food* 12-2.30, 6.15-9.30. *Restaurant Meals* 6.15-9.30. *Vegetarian dishes. Children's portions. Beer Hartleys, Robinsons. Patio/terrace, Outdoor eating. Family room. Accommodation* 13 bedrooms, 9 en suite, £55 (single £38). *Children welcome overnight. Check-in all day. No dogs. Access, Visa.*

Haworth   Old White Lion Hotel

Tel 0535 642313

Main Street Haworth West Yorkshire BD22 8DU

Map 6 C1

Brontë village hotel with a pleasant modernised bar. *Beer Ruddles, Websters Yorkshire.*

Haydon Bridge   General Havelock

Tel 0734 6843

FOOD

Ratcliffe Road Haydon Bridge Northumberland NE47 6ER

Map 5 D2

The dark green exterior of the General Havelock certainly helps it stand out from neighbouring cottages. It was named after Sunderland-born General Henry Havelock, who relieved the Indian town of Lucknow in the late 1880s. The interior of the pub is also dark green. In the front bar area there are wrought-iron-legged tables, stripped wood and padded benches, and some brilliant wildlife photographs taken by a local photographer. The pub's main draw, though, is its dining room in the converted stables to the rear, a high-ceilinged room with exposed beams, natural stone walls, ready-set polished tables and watercolours of local scenes. The cooking is in the accomplished hands of self-taught chef Angela Clyde, who prides herself on using only fresh produce: meat comes from a local butcher in Hexham, and fish is delivered twice a week from North Shields. The short lunchtime menu includes soup like Stilton and onion or a terrine (£3.60) amongst the starters, followed by a daily roast and a fish dish. In the evenings a set price four-course menu (£16.50) has a more upmarket feel with the likes of smoked North Shields cod or tarragon chicken. Cooking is of a high standard, and the puddings are also first-class: Danish chocolate bar and a splendid plum tart (with very good pastry) are typical. Service is friendly, casual but efficient. To the rear of the dining room is a paved patio which runs down to a lawn and the River Tyne. Though the pub has its regulars who use the bar for a drink, this is really more of a dining pub, and people travel some distance to eat here. Weekends (including a popular Sunday lunch at £10.50) can be very busy, so booking is advised. They close all day Monday and Tuesday. *Bar Food 12-2. Bar snacks lunchtime. Restaurant 12-2 (except Mon & Tues), 7.30-9 (except Sun, Mon, Tues). Vegetarian dishes. Children's portions. Free House. Beer Tetley Bitter. Children allowed in bar to eat. Riverside garden, outdoor eating. Closed 2 weeks Sept, 3 weeks Jan. No credit cards.*

Haytor Vale   Rock Inn

| **FOOD** |
| **B&B** |

Tel 0364 661305

Haytor Vale Devon TQ13 9XP

Map 13 D3

Sturdy old pub in a tiny, wuthering Dartmoor village; a characterful traditional interior, complete with lovely old furnishings and open fires, and reliably good bar food, with a particularly strong list of light meals and snacks, and the promise of fresh local vegetables. Dishes range from omelettes (£3.95) to fresh Devon salmon (£7.95) and peaches and cream (£1.95), and in the restaurant a £17.95 set menu could feature fresh mussels in garlic butter and roast Devonshire duckling in orange and brandy sauce. *Bar Food 11-2, 7-9.30. Restaurant Meals 7.30-9. Vegetarian dishes. Children's portions. Free House. Beer Dorchester Bitter, Eldridge Pope Best, Thomas Hardy Country, Royal Oak. Garden, outdoor eating. Accommodation 10 bedrooms, 8 en suite, £49 (single £37.95). Children welcome overnight, additional bed, cots supplied. Check-in all day. No dogs. Access, Amex, Visa.*

Heath   King's Arms

Tel 0924 377527

Heath Common Heath West Yorkshire WF1 5SL

Map 7 D2

Part of the five-pub-strong Clark's brewery empire, a stone-flagged gaslit 18th century pub full of unspoilt character, surrounded by a hundred acres of common grassland, yet only five minutes from the motorway. Oak settles, cast-iron framed tables and a working kitchen range in the main bar, and a sympathetic modern extension, plus three further rooms. *Beer Clarks Bitter & Hammerhead, Tetley, Timothy Taylors Landlord. Garden. Family room.*

Heathton   Old Gate Inn

Tel 074 66 431

Heathton Claverley Shropshire WV5 7EB

Map 6 B4

Restored old pub in splendid rural setting. Real fire. No music. *Beer Holts, Taylor Walker. Garden, children's play area. Family room.*

Heaton Norris   Nursery Inn

Tel 061-432 2044

Green Lane Heaton Norris Greater Manchester

Map 6 B2

Suburban 1930s pub with a traditional layout: vault, smoke room, lobby lounge; wood-panelling, and a manicured bowling green at the rear. *Beer Hydes Anvil Mild & Bitter. Garden.*

Heckington — Nag's Head

Tel 0529 60218	**B&B**
34 High Street Heckington Lincolnshire NG34 9QZ	Map 11 E3

In the centre of a village by the Lincolnshire Fens, the Nag's Head offers agreeable overnight accommodation. The atmosphere is warm and relaxing in the bar. Upstairs there is a residents' lounge and the three simple bedrooms have quaintly old-fashioned furniture, pretty floral wallpaper, TVs and tea-makers. One room has en-suite facilities, the others have washbasins and share a bathroom. *Beer Draught Bass, Wards Sheffield Best Bitter, Samson Bitter. Garden.* **Accommodation** *3 bedrooms, 1 en suite, £32 (single £22). Children welcome overnight, cots available. Check-in all day. Access, Visa.*

Hedon — Shakespeare Inn

Tel 0482 898371	
9 Baxtergate Hedon Humberside	Map 7 E1

Cosy, friendly one-roomed pub with 3000 beermats adorning the ceiling, in the formerly busiest port on the Humber, with 14th-century origins. *Beer Vaux, Wards Sheffield Best. Family room.*

Helford — Shipwrights Arms

Tel 032 623 235	**FOOD**
Nr Helston Cornwall TR12 6JX	Map 12 B4

Stunningly located on the banks of the Helford estuary, its approach road so narrow that in summer it's restricted to pedestrian use only. But it's worth the effort, particularly in the busy summer months, when barbecues are held in the magical terraced gardens. The interior is quite special too, staunchly traditional, with lots of nautical bits and pieces, and lots of yachting types swapping unlikely stories too. The simple lunchtime bar food and smarter, fishier evening fare is also reliably good; it gets extremely busy. *Bar Food 12-1.30, 7-9 (not Sun nor Mon eves winter). Vegetarian meals. Children's portions. Beer Cornish Original. Children allowed in bar to eat. Garden.*

Helmsley — Feathers Hotel

Tel 0439 70275	**B&B**
Market Place Helmsley North Yorkshire YO6 5BH	Map 5 E4

On the handsome market square of this most typical of North Yorkshire's affluent small market towns. It's part 15th-century cottage – the venue for the traditional little bar – and part elegant 18th-century house. Bedrooms are simply appointed, and en-suite facilities functional. *Free House. Beer Tetley, Theakston, Scottish & Newcastle. Garden. Family room.* **Accommodation** *18 bedrooms, 16 en suite, £53 (single £31.50). Children welcome overnight, additional beds and cots supplied. Check-in all day. Access, Amex, Diners, Visa.*

Helmsley — Feversham Arms

Tel 0439 70766	
1 High Street Helmsley North Yorkshire YO6 5AG	Map 5 E4

Golden stone building by the church, much modernised inside, and rather garishly decorated. Good facilities: tennis, heated outdoor pool for residents. *Beer Tetley, Theakston Best.*

Hempstead   Hare & Hounds

Tel 0263 713285

Hempstead nr Holt Norfolk NR25 6LD   **Map 10 C1**

Simple, old country pub run by the owners with no extra staff.
Popular with locals all year, tourists in the season. The nice old-
fashioned interior has tiled floors topped with rugs, a variety of
furnishings, cottage windows with deep sills, and a woodburning
stove. No machines or music. "No whisky drinkers", so no malts.
Free House. **Beer** *Adnams, Bass, Batemans. Garden. Family room.*

Hengoed   Last Inn

Tel 0691 659747

Hengoed Shropshire   **Map 6 B3**

Homely country pub with various rooms and a beer connoisseur dog.
Beer *Bass, Marston, Woods. Garden. Family room.*

Henley-on-Thames   Argyll

Tel 0491 573400   **FOOD**

15 Market Place Henley-on-Thames Oxfordshire RG9 2AA   **Map 17 D3**

Behind its mock Tudor facade, squeezed in between some shops in the
main street of town, the Argyll lives up to the Scottishness of its name
with tartan carpet, and prints of Scottish soldiers around the panelled
walls along with the odd sporran, stag's head and battered breast plates.
New managers, Denise and Steve Lothian, run things in a friendly
fashion more as a drinking than an eating pub – there's no food at
night – but lunches from the little buffet are popular. The small
selection of traditional pub dishes is likely to include steak and kidney
pie (£3.95), seafood lasagne (£3.95) and cottage pie (£3.75), all
served with fresh vegetables, plus a few salads – beef, gammon or
quiche (£3.75) and puddings like cherry pie and sherry trifle (all at
£1.95). A selection of sandwiches starts at £1.50. Sunday brings a
traditional roast lunch at £4.95. Everything is home-made although
the odd 'tin' is used , as in the fruit for the trifle, and generous portions
ensure that nobody goes away hungry. **Bar Food & Restaurant Meals**
12–2. Children's portions. **Beer** *Morland. Patio, outdoor eating. Access,
Visa.*

Henley-on-Thames   Little Angel

Tel 0491 574165   **FOOD**

Remenham Lane Henley-on-Thames Oxfordshire RG9 2LS   **Map 17 D3**

Just over the bridge, on the Berkshire side of the river, the 17th-
century Little Angel (not to be confused with The Angel public house
on the town side of the bridge) is very much an eating pub. The same
extensive menu operates both in the pubby bar with its dark red
ceilings and in the beamed restaurant beyond with crisply clothed
tables. There are also a couple of function/private dining rooms. Eat
outside and on summer weekends you get the added attraction of
being able to watch the local cricketers, whose pitch is right next
door. Sherried kidneys (£3.50), Stilton and walnut tagliatelle (£4),
sausage and mash (£4.95), fillet of haddock 'bonne femme' (£6.50),
chicken chasseur (£8.95) and beef stroganoff (£9.50) demonstrate the
range with the addition of sandwiches (from £2.25) and ploughman's
(from £3) served in the bar area. Smart young men in white shirts

and bow ties provide efficient service. *Bar Food & Restaurant Meals*
*12-3, 6-10. Vegetarian dishes. **Beer** Brakspear. Terrace, outdoor eating.*
Access, Amex, Diners, Visa.

Henstridge   Virginia Ash

Tel 0963 62267

Henstridge nr Templecombe Somerset BA8 0PL

Map 13 F2

Homely, popular, energetically-run pub, welcoming to families. ***Beer***
Courage, Wadworth 6X. Garden, children's play area.

Henton   Peacock Hotel

Tel 0844 353519   Fax 0844 353891

Henton nr Chinnor Oxfordshire OX9 4AH

B&B

Map 17 D2

Very pretty black and white timbered, thatched inn, some 600 years
old, in a sleepy village just off the B4009. Peacocks roam the grounds;
the bar is comfortable and immaculately kept. Some bedrooms are in
the extension, which also houses the residents' lounge. There are now
20 in total and all are smart and well equipped. *Free House.* ***Beer***
*Brakspear. Patio, outdoor eating. **Accommodation** 20 bedrooms, all en*
suite, £45 (single £42). Children welcome overnight. Check-in by
arrangement. No dogs. Access, Amex, Visa.

Hermitage   Fox

Tel 0635 201545

Hermitage nr Newbury Berkshire RG16 9RB

FOOD

Map 16 C3

Set on a hill on a bend in the road, The Fox has a large terrace in
front with a car park below at road level. Inside, there are three bars –
two for drinking only and the third primarily for eating. A very large
blackboard menu is in the centre room with an 'extras' board close to
it. Horse brasses and prints decorate the walls in the low, beamed bar.
Food is kept warm on a hotplate and the portions are large: home-
made soup (£1.95), frog's legs (£2.25), bubble and squeak with eggs
and bacon (£3.95), lasagne (£4.95) 10oz rump steak (£7.75). A
traditional roast (£5.75) is served on Sundays. *Bar Food 12-2,*
6.30-9.30. Vegetarian dishes. Children's portions. Free House. ***Beer*** *No*
Name Bitter, Theakston. Terrace, outdoor eating. Access, Visa.

Hermitage   Sussex Brewery

Tel 0243 371533

36 Main Road Hermitage West Sussex PO10 8AU

Map 15 D4

A fresh carpet of sawdust is laid daily at this Grade II listed pub-
brewery, and open fires are continually alight from October to Easter.
There's no jukebox or fruit machine, not even a cigarette machine.
Free House. ***Beer*** *Eldridge Pope, Hall & Woodhouse, Morlands. Garden.*

Hesket Newmarket   Old Crown

Tel 069 98 288

Caldbeck Hesket Newmarket Cumbria

Map 4 C3

Friendly little fell-side pub whose simple main bar has assorted tables,
a little counter, and old floor coverings, lots of books, and beam-hung
mugs. Country café style dining room. Home-brewed beers. Worth a
visit also for the delightful village. ***Beer*** *Own Brew Beer – Blencathra,*
Skiddaw Special & Doris's 90th Birthday Ale. Garden. Family room.

Hessenford   Copley Arms

Tel 050 34 209

Hessenford nr Torpoint Cornwall PL11 3JH

Map 12 C3

This boxy white-washed roadside pub is utterly transformed in
summer, when the window boxes, hanging baskets and pavement
flower tubs are a riot of pinks and reds, front and back, and the paved
riverside drinking terrace really comes into its own. **Beer** *St Anstell
Tinners & HSD. Riverside garden. Chidlren's play area. Family room.*

Hetton   Angel Inn

Tel 0756 730263

Hetton nr Skipton North Yorkshire BD23 6LT

FOOD

Map 6 C1

Be early for a seat at this increasingly popular 400-year-old dining
pub. The four interconnected rooms are full of character with 16th-
century nooks, crannies and beams, comfortably furnished, and
overrun by diners at mealtimes; fresh flowers, attractive pictures and
sepia photographs add charm, and it's immaculately kept. The very
cheerful gourmet licensees, Denis Watkins and John Topham, are
responsible for the cooking of the reliably good food on the extensive
menu. Their 5am visits to Manchester market, as well as the daily
deliveries from Fleetwood, ensure a good variety of fresh fish and
seafood which is now a daily speciality. On any one day, you may be
able to order salmon with beurre blanc (£6.50), bouillabaisse with
rouille and fresh Parmesan (£9.95), salmon en croute with lobster
sauce (£7.50) or steamed halibut with white wine sauce, tomatoes,
fresh asparagus, cucumber and dill (£7.50). Popular bar food choices
are an AWT – crusty bread open sandwich with cream cheese,
smoked salmon and bacon with fresh mango chutney (£4.85),
bresaola – their own home-cured and air-dried beef (£4.35), or confit
of duck with orange sauce (£6.85). The restaurant is open in the
evenings for a 4-course table d'hote menu only (£20.70) with all
dishes cooked to order – a money-bag purse of filo pastry filled with
seafood with lobster sauce, insalata calda alla tuscana (chargrilled lamb
served on a bed of rucola with chargrilled aubergine, fresh Parmesan,
pesto and sun-dried tomatoes), Oriental marinated duck breast served
with spring rolls or baked halibut steak with asparagus and tomato
sauce. Space should be left for the home-made puddings (all £2.75) –
summer, sticky toffee, mango and raspberry sherry trifle, langue de
chat tulip with fresh berries. The pub stands off the B6265. **Bar Food**
12-2 (12-2.30 Sat/Sun), 6-10 (6-9.30 Winter Sun). **Restaurant Meals**
*12-2 (Sun only), 7-9.30 (except Sun). Vegetarian dishes. Children's
portions. Free House.* **Beer** *Landlord, Theakston, Timothy Taylor. Patio,
outdoor eating. Access, Visa.*

Heydon   King William IV

Tel 0763 838773

Chishill Road Heydon Cambridgeshire SG8 8PW

A

Map 15 F1

Unremarkable on the outside, but an Aladdin's Cave within,
overflowing with agricultural oddities and equipment, including a
plough, as well as giant bellows, cast-iron cauldrons, stuffed animals in
glass cases, lamps, casks, plates – even a copper font with a gothic-style
wooden top. Other more traditional features include heavy beams and
rustic tables, some of them suspended by chains from the ceiling; also
not so traditional piped music and fruit machines. Lots of animals in
the garden. *Free House.* **Beer** *Bateman, Greene King, Abbot, Adnams.
Garden. Family room.*

High Roding   Black Lion

Tel 0371 87847

High Roding Essex CM6 1NP   **Map 11 B4**

Black and white timbered Tudor roadside pub. Intimate bar full of
old beams, brick-built bar counter, and cosy rustic atmosphere; a
second bar is less atmospheric, with pool table and fruit machine, and
doubles as a family room. **Beer** *Ridleys Mild & IPA.*

Higher Burwardsley   Pheasant Inn   ★   **FOOD**

Tel 0829 70434   **B&B**

Higher Burwardsley nr Tattenhall Cheshire CH3 9PF   **Map 6 A3**

Tucked into the hillside amongst the Peckforton hills, the Pheasant is
best located by following signs to the candle factory from the A534.
It's plain to see, on arrival, that the place was once a farm, and the
more surprising, therefore, to find that there has been a pub here since
the 17th century. The oldest part, a half-timbered sandstone
farmhouse, is the venue for the bar, which claims to house the largest
log fire in Cheshire. The adjacent Highland Room generally known as
the Bistro, was once the kitchen and retains the old cast-iron range.
The most recent addition is an imposing conservatory of striking
modernity, which overlooks a tiered patio and, beyond this, right
across the Cheshire plain towards North Wales. The old barn,
formerly the centre of the village life with its regular weekend barn
dances, has now been skilfully converted into six very comfortable
bedrooms, equipped to the highest pub standards, with televisions,
clock radios, hairdryers, mini-bars and roomy, if poorly lit,
bathrooms. Stonework interiors are eye-catching, and nights tranquil.
Two further bedrooms, housed in the pub proper, boast original
beams and brighter bathrooms, as well as memorable views. There are
three quite distinct aspects to the food operation. A self-service counter
in the conservatory is useful for a quick lunch, perhaps of chicken
provençale, mushroom stroganoff or a Sunday plate of roast beef and
Yorkshires (all at under £5), with a special children's menu (£1.95
main course and pudding), and extended hours at weekends. In the
bar, blackboards display a daily changing list for those requiring a
little more comfort and exclusivity: smoked trout fillets (£2.05),
avocado with seafood cocktail (£2.10), fillet of salmon with fresh
ginger, garlic and spring onion (£5.50), or pan-fried fillet of beef with
burgundy sauce (£5.95) typify the offerings here. The Bistro,
meanwhile, comes into its own at night (and for Sunday lunch in
winter). A further elaboration of the other menus, it offers more
substantial fare, with more vegetables and fewer chips, in an informal
and intimate setting. Space is limited; booking is advised. Landlord
David Greenhaugh has an unusual and passionate interest, namely his
prize-winning herd of pedigree Highland cattle. It's not surprising
therefore to find a certain bias towards meat dishes, amongst which
the steaks are outstanding (sirloin £9.50, fillet £11.95), especially
when one of "the family" is on offer! The winter menu offers dishes of
equal merit, including pheasant casserole (£5.25) or roast haunch of
venison (£8.95). Amongst the home-made 'to follows' (all £1.80), the
bread and butter pudding and banoffi pie come out tops, so, too, do a
friendly bunch of staff who go out of their way to be pleasant and
helpful. **Bar Food and Restaurant Meals** *12-2 (12-2.30 Sun), 7-9.30.
Vegetable dishes. Children's portions. Free House.* **Beer** *Bass, Worthington.*

Garden, outdoor eating. **Accommodation** *8 bedrooms, all en suite, £60 (single £40). Children welcome overnight, additional bed available, cot available. Check-in all day. No dogs. Access, Amex, Diners, Visa.*

Hilton   Falcon Inn

Tel 0642 592228

off A19 Hilton Cleveland TS15 9LB   Map 5 E3

Spacious, chintzily civilised dining pub serving the Middlesbrough business community, among others. *No real ales. Garden. Family room.*

Himley   Crooked House

Tel 0384 238583   **A**

Coppice Mill Himley West Midlands DY3 4DA   Map 6 B4

In keeping with the name, heavy mining subsidence has left the Crooked House sloping alarmingly away from right to left. And you haven't had anything to drink yet. Located off the B4176 to the east of Himley, the interior is Victorian rustic, half-panelled, red-tiled with an imposing brick fireplace and another of cast iron, plus lots of period decoration. The two original bars are joined by a newer extension, prettily done with exposed bricks, country paper and fine antique pieces. **Beer** *Banks's Mild, Bitter. Patio. No credit cards.*

Hindon   Lamb at Hindon

FOOD

Tel 0747 89573   **B&B**

High Street Hindon nr Salisbury Wiltshire SP3 6DP   Map 14 B3

Wisteria clings to one corner of this mellow 17th-century coaching inn. At its height, 300 post horses were kept here to supply the great number of coaches going to and from London and the West Country. Prime Minister William Pitt was apparently most put out to find no fresh horses available when he stopped off in 1786. But there have also been less reputable visitors. Silas White, a notorious smuggler said to be leader of the Wiltshire Moonrakers, used the Lamb as the centre of his nefarious activities. These days, things in Hindon are rather more peaceful and the Lamb limits itself to providing honest hospitality to modern travellers who bring their own horsepower in four-wheeled form. The bar is slightly disappointing, a less characterful room than the build-up suggests, although there is a splendid old stone inglenook fireplace, and the atmosphere is enhanced by an ever-changing collection of paintings by local artists both here and in the rather smarter restaurant, which features splendid dark green tartan curtains. The blackboard bar menu is sensibly not over-long, but still manages to offer a reasonable choice – rabbit and pigeon pie (£4.95), cod steak and prawn mayonnaise (£5.50) or puff pastry case with asparagus. The emphasis is fishy on Tuesdays and Fridays, when the fishmonger calls, and in winter there's also plenty of game, from the estate of the local landowner who bought the inn just a couple of years ago. In the restaurant a 3-course table d'hote menu (£18.95) is available with such choices as roast guinea fowl in strawberry sauce, chicken breast with Stilton or fillet of beef with wild mushrooms. Overnight accommodation is also offered – standards are variable. **Bar Food** *12-2, 7-10. Vegetarian dishes. Children's portions. Free House.* **Beer** *Wadworth 6X, Smiles, Stonehenge. Patio/terrace, outdoor eating.* **Accommodation** *13 rooms, all en suite, £55 (single £38). Children welcome overnight, additional beds (£12), cots supplied. Check-in all day. Access, Amex, Diners, Visa.*

Hinton Charterhouse   Rose & Crown

Tel 0225 722153

Hinton Charterhouse Avon BA3 6AN   Map 13 F1

Late Victorian oak-panelled pub in quaint village not far from Bath.
Friendly and relaxed. Seperate cellar restaurant. *Beer Bass, Burton Ale,
Marston Pedigree, Wadworth 6X. Garden.*

Hinton St George   Poulett Arms

Tel 0460 73149

Hinton St George Somerset   Map 13 F2

Smartly plush dining pub, with original stripped stone walls and
fireplace, heavy timbers, and two little anterooms, plus a rear drinkers'
public. *Free House. **Beer** Courage Best, Flowers Original. Garden. Family
room.*

Hinton St Mary   White Horse

Tel 0258 72723

Hinton St Mary Dorset DT10 1NA   Map 13 F2

Attractively extended and modernised pub in lovely village. *Beer
Wadworth 6X. Garden, children's play area.*

Hollington   Red Lion

Tel 0335 60241

Hollington nr Ashbourne Derbyshire DE6 3AG   Map 6 C3

Eating pub whose central bar serves two little eating areas; village
pool room bar at rear. Lino floors, bentwood chairs, formica table
tops, café-style and very popular. *Beer Marston Pedigree. Garden,
children's play area. Family room.*

Holt   Old Ham Tree

FOOD

B&B

Tel 0225 782581

Holt nr Trowbridge Wiltshire BA14 6PY   Map 14 B2

Cleanly modernised, beamed and pleasant 18th-century inn
overlooking the village green. Reliably good, simple food in the form
of steak and Guinness pie (£4.50), pan-fried cod (£4.75), bean goulash
(£4.25) or monkfish sautéed with garlic and chili (£6.95). The
blackboard also advertises the new extended fish menu. The restaurant
has recently been refurbished and the varied menu offers poussin and
pecan sauce (£7.95), Ham Tree fillet of beef with mustard (£10.45),
pork marsala (£7.50) or ham in Chablis sauce (£5.95). Bedrooms are
centrally heated, clean and airy, white-painted with matching
furniture, pretty floral fabrics, and a modern shared bathroom.
Residents' television lounge above the bar. *Bar Food 12-2, 7-10.
Vegetarian dishes. Children's menu/portions. Free House. **Beer** Young
Special, Marston Pedigree. Garden, outdoor eating. **Accommodation**
5 bedrooms, 1 en suite, £42 (single £22.50). Children welcome overnight.
Check-in by arrangement. No dogs. Access, Amex, Diners, Visa.*

Holywell   Old Ferry Boat Inn

Tel 0480 63227

B&B

Holywell Huntingdon Cambridgeshire PE17 3TG

Map 10 B2

A thousand years of history at this delightful thatched and wisteria-draped riverside inn, originally a monastic ferry house. Situated by the River Ouse where there is ample mooring, the Old Ferry Boat has a particularly charming panelled alcove off the main bar, and good views from the sun terrace. It is haunted by Juliet, a young victim of unrequited love, so don't go on March 17th unless you want to join the ghost hunters! The seven bedrooms are individually decorated with floral wallpaper and curtains. Two have four-poster beds and two overlook the river. Tea/coffee-making facilties and TVs are provided. *Free House.* **Beer** *London Pride, Bass, Broadside, Abbot, Adnams. Riverside garden, outdoor eating.* **Accommodation** *7 bedrooms, all en suite, £49.50 (single £40). Children welcome overnight, additional beds (from £5), cots supplied. No dogs. Check-in by arrangement. Access, Visa.*

Holywell Green   Rock Inn Hotel

Tel 0422 379721

B&B

Holywell Green nr Halifax West Yorkshire HX4 9BS

Map 6 C1

Enjoying a peaceful rural setting, yet conveniently near junction 24 of the M62, this pub converted from a row of 17th-century cottages has a warmly welcoming air. Open fires, beams and original stonework walls characterise the bars, while pine-ceilinged bedrooms in a rear extension are contrastingly modern. All have mahogany furniture and brightly tiled bathrooms, as well as TVs, radios, direct-dial telephones, tea/coffee-making facilities, hairdryers, drinks trays and trouser presses. *Free House.* **Beer** *Tetley, Theakston Best, Cromwell, McEwan, Younger No. 3. Patio/terrace.* **Accommodation** *18 bedrooms (3 with four-posters), all en suite, £65 (£46 weekend), (single £55, £36 weekend). Children welcome overnight, additional beds (£10), cots supplied. Check-in all day. Access, Amex, Diners, Visa.*

Hope   Poachers Arms

Tel 0433 620380

FOOD

B&B

Castleton Road Hope Derbyshire S30 2RD

Map 6 C2

Copper-topped tables, beams, plaster walls, and a pair of stuffed fox heads characterise this Peak District National Park pub. Reliably good bar food includes steak and kidney pie (£4.95), game casserole (£5.25) and cod mornay (£4.95). The separate dining room features dishes like roast pheasant (£16), steak au poivre (£16.50) or three fillets of pork, beef and lamb in a red wine sauce (£16). Bedrooms are variously sized, some very large; white woodchip or patterned walls, furniture generally modest reproduction, with the odd antique mixed in. *Free House.* **Bar Food** *12-2, 6-10.* **Restaurant Meals** *12-2, 7-10. Vegetarian dishes. Children's portions.* **Beer** *Courage Directors; John Smiths Bitter. Children allowed in bar to eat. Family room.* **Accommodation** *6 bedrooms, all en suite, £52 (single £39). Children welcome overnight, additional bed (£15), cot available. Check-in all day. No dogs. Access, Amex, Visa.*

Hopesgate   Stables Inn

Tel 0743 891344

Hopesgate nr Minsterley Shropshire SY5 0EP

FOOD

Map 6 A4

Country lanes signposted from the A488 eventually lead to the
Hardings' tiny, secluded inn, set in glorious countryside above the
Hope valley. It's a distinctly traditional pub, whose attraction, in
addition to the good food and beer, is an atmosphere in which good
company can be enjoyed, in the absence of intruding gaming machines
or juke boxes. The bar is L-shaped, its blackened oak beams hung with
pottery mugs, and the imposing open stone fireplace burns logs in
winter. The mood is intimate and friendly; summer talk is largely of
cricket, and the exploits of the pub's new team. Four draught beers on
handpumps include the local Wood's Special, and in summer a choice
of draught ciders. Lunchtime choices, posted on the blackboard, range
from home-made soup (£1.80) and hot local sausages (£3.75) to beef,
Guinness and walnut casserole (£5.50) tomato and aubergine bake
(£4.60). Evening eating (Wednesday to Saturday only) is a mite more
serious. Booking is strongly advised as there are only four tables in the
dining room (so diners usually overflow into the adjacent snug).
Debbie's cooking makes the best use of local supplies and seasonal
produce, skilfully combining Cumberland sauce with grilled lamb
steaks (£7.50) or fresh whiting fillets with cheese and prawns (£7.20).
A simpler choice is roast chicken. They're substantial eaters in these
parts, so there's no shortage of takers for puddings (all £2.20): treacle
sponge with custard, the landlady's now celebrated bread-and-butter
pudding, or seasonal fruit crumble served with local farm ice cream.
*Bar Food 12-1.30 (except Mon). Restaurant Meals 7-8.30 (except Sun,
Mon, Tue). Vegetarian dishes. Children allowed in bar to eat. Free House.
Beer Woods Special, Hancock, Tetley. Cider Addlestones, Westons.
Patio/terrace. No credit cards.*

Hopton Wafers   Crown Inn

Tel 0299 270372

Hopton Wafers nr Cledbury Mortimer Shropshire DY14 0NB

FOOD

B&B

Map 6 B4

Two and a half miles from the peak of Clee Hill, nestling in a wooded
valley, is the Norman hamlet of Hopton Wafers. The creeper-clad
Crown is set in its own garden which slopes down to one of the many
streams (crossed here by the A4117) which flow down to the Tewe
valley. Bounded on three sides by terraces of tables with their
colourful summer parasols, it's a splendid spot for al fresco eating, but
parents with little ones should watch out for the duckpond, as perilous
as it is picturesque. Inside, the Rent Room, where once local villagers
came to pay their rents, houses an atmospheric and intimate bar where
talk is frequently of the shootin' and fishin' sort over a pint. Snacks
and bar meals have a strongly fishy emphasis: sauté of calamares
(£3.50), fresh dressed crab (£3.95), grilled shark steak (£7.25),
poached salmon (£6.50), lemon sole with prawns (£6.50). But meat-
eaters aren't forgotten, with hearty steak and mushroom pie (£5.50),
or duck breast with oyster and chili sauce (£6.50), which come with
three fresh vegetables and a choice of potatoes. Nor are vegetarians
neglected: decent meatless meals include celery and cashew risotto, or
tagliatelle verdi with tomato and basil (£4.25), and children's portions
of virtually anything for £2.95 will please many parents. Puddings,
home-made daily (£2.50) include treacle tart, peach and apple pie, or
a banana and rum trifle. Behind a central stone chimney, in which

huge log fires burn at both sides in winter, the newly-named restaurant, The Hopton Poacher, serves a three-course dinner (£19.50, from Tuesday to Saturday) and Sunday lunch, for which you should book. Market-fresh fish (seafood thermidor), medallions of beef fillet in mushroom and claret sauce, roast guinea fowl with redcurrant and orange sauce, and grilled steaks, with or without pepper sauce, are typical main courses. Recent reorganisation has increased to eight the bedrooms, whose decor and character are commendable. Unsuspecting overnighters are in for a treat of exposed rafters, sloping corridors and creaky floorboards – with which the automatic trouser press and bathroom telephone extensions seem faintly at odds; all, nonetheless, are assured a high degree of comfort, a warm welcome and the convivial company of a fine country inn. *Bar Food 12-2, 6.30-10.* *Restaurant Meals 7-9.30 (except Sun and Mon). Vegetarian dishes. Children's portions (£2.95). Children allowed in bar to eat. Free House. Beer Bass, Flowers, Boddingtons, Brains Dark Mild. Riverside garden, outdoor eating. Accommodation 8 bedrooms, all en suite, £50 (single £35). Children welcome overnight, additional beds (£15), cots supplied. Check-in all day. No dogs. Access, Visa.*

Horndon　　Elephants Nest

Tel 0822 810273

Horndon Devon PL19 9NQ　　　　　　　　　　Map 12 C3

Named after a landlord of great size and/or possessed of a great nest of a beard – the mythology is a little confused. Window seats, old rugs and flagstones and an open fire make this a good pub for winter weather. *Free House. Beer Boddingtons, Palmers IPA, St Austell HSD, Websters Yorkshire. Garden. Family room.*

Horndon on the Hill　　Bell Inn

Tel 0375 673154

High Road Horndon on the Hill Essex SS17 8LD　　　Map 11 B4

A hot cross bun is nailed to a ceiling beam at the Bell every Good Friday, and the collection of shrunken, fossilised old buns is now pretty spectacular. A sporty, friendly community pub, free from music, gaming machines and pool tables, it has an opened-up bar, lots of old wood and stone, and an attractive garden. *Beer Bass, Charrington IPA.*

Horningsea　　Plough & Fleece

Tel 0223 860795

FOOD

High Street Horningsea Cambridgeshire CB5 9JG　　Map 10 B3

A grade II listed building, built in the Dutch style so popular in the East Anglia of the late 18th century when Dutch engineers came to advise on the draining of the Fenlands. The generally very busy Plough & Fleece owes its great popularity to old-fashioned regional cooking, which is often given a modern interpretation. Come here for homely, comforting hot-pots (£4.50), cottage pie (£3.30) and cockles (with garlic £2.60), as well as more contemporary treatments of dinner-partyish food, like honey-roast guinea fowl (£8.25), or a perfect poached salmon (£9.10). Puddings (all £2.10) are suitably gorgeous and cream-laden; the Northamptonshire chocolate pudding in particular has an informal international fan club but there are at least seven others to choose from. All this means the pub can get crowded and a new dining room extension has been built to take the strain, providing a welcome haven for non-smokers. In addition to the traditional roast on Sunday (£5.50 main course), the Romany rabbit pie (£7.75) proves equally as popular. The atmosphere is homely and traditional in feel, especially so in the unspoilt public bar, with its ancient settles, tiled floor, elm tables and custard-coloured walls. The lounge is comfortable rather than characterful and invariably packed with bar meal diners. Arrive early at lunchtime to beat the scrum. No children indoors. *Bar Food and Restaurant Meals* 12-2 (12-1.30 Sun), 7-9.30 (except Sun/Mon eves). Vegetarian dishes. *Beer* Greene King IPA. Patio, outdoor eating. Access, Visa.

Horningsham   Bath Arms

Tel 098 53 308

Horningsham nr Longleat Wiltshire BA12 7LY   Map 14 B3

Splendid country hotel close to Longleat, in a 'best-kept' village. *Beer* Bass, Eldridge Pope, Wadworth 6X. Garden.

Horringer   Beehive

Tel 0284 735260   **FOOD**

The Street Horringer Suffolk IP29 5SD   Map 6 C3

Genuine home-made food is served throughout the bar areas here, and tables can be booked: the ratio of reservations to casual droppers-in is usually about 50/50. A printed menu is much more imaginative than most, and a specials board with delicious fresh fish makes the choice even more difficult. The fish is cooked simply – grilled with butter and wine (£7.95-8.95). Other choices are home-made taramasalata (£3.25), slivers of sesame roast chicken with nutty blackcurrant dressing (£3.95), scrambled eggs and smoked salmon (£4.95) and from eight home-made puddings (all £1.95): banoffi pie, Beehive tart (sponge, butter and raisins), treacle tart. Rambling, traditionally furnished little rooms radiate off a central servery, warmed by a wood-burning stove. *Bar Food* 12-2, 7-10 (not Sun eve). Vegetarian dishes. Children allowed in bar to eat. *Beer* Greene King Abbot. Garden, outdoor eating. Access, Visa.

Horsebridge   Royal

Tel 082 287 214   **FOOD**

Horsebridge nr Tavistock Devon PL19 8PJ   Map 12 C3

Three excellent reasons for a detour to Terry Wood's informal and relaxing pub: to look at the ancient Tamar Bridge, to sample their own home-brewed ales (of which it is reported that no one has been able to drink more than five pints!) and to try the landlady's cooking, including herby home-made bread with the ploughman's and the imaginative salads. There is also sherried kidneys (£5.95), chicken and broccoli bake (£4.50) and seafood slice (£5.50); no chips. *Bar Food* 12-2, 7.15-9 (9.30 Sat) No food Sun eve. Vegetarian dishes. Free House. *Beer* Own home brew, Bass, Royal Oak. Garden, outdoor eating. No credit cards.

Horsell Common   Bleak House

Tel 0483 760717

Chertsey Road Horsell Common Surrey GU21 5NL   Map 17 E4

Well-known and exceedingly lively village local in good walking country; live jazz or blues on Monday evenings; famous visitors have included the Bedser twins, John McCarthy, and Martians from outer space, who landed their craft outside during the filming of War of the Worlds. *Beer Ind Coope, Tetley, Youngs. Garden. Children's play area.*

Horton   Horton Inn   FOOD B&B

Tel 0258 840252

Horton nr Wimborne Dorset BH21 5AB   Map 14 C4

Attractively refurbished 18th-century country inn at a crossroads on the B3078, in downland countryside. Proprietor-run with enthusiasm; good eating to be had in the convivial bar, or garden in summer. Bar food includes fisherman's pie, lasagne and ham and asparagus mornay. In the restaurant dishes may include medallions of beef fillet au poivre or rack of lamb with Cumberland sauce. Bedrooms are bright and fresh, and extremely spacious; all feature comfy easy chairs, and three have their own bathrooms. First-floor residents' lounge. *Bar Food 12-2, 7-10. Restaurant Meals 12-2, 7.30-9.30 (closed Sun/Mon eves). Vegetarian dishes. Beer Courage, Directors. Garden, outdoor eating, children's play area. Accommodation 5 bedrooms, 3 en suite, £37.50 (single £15). Children welcome overnight, additional beds, cot available. Check-in by arrangement. Visa.*

Horton-in-Ribblesdale   Crown Hotel   B&B

Tel 0729 860209

Horton-in-Ribblesdale nr Settle North Yorkshire BD24 OHF   Map 5 D4

A genuine Yorkshire welcome awaits visitors to this most unpretentious of pubs, a limestone building standing right on the Pennine Way, near the river Ribble. This is walking country par exellence, and walkers join local characters for a chat in the beamed bars; residents can join in, or watch TV in one of the homely lounges. Bedrooms are smallish, clean and quite modest, with modern utility furniture. Two rooms have full en-suite facilities, five have showers and washbasins, the remaining two have washbasins and share two bathrooms. Two cottages are suitable for families. *Beer Theakston Best Bitter, XB, Mild, Old Peculier. Garden. Accommodation 9 bedrooms, 2 en suite, £45.80. Children welcome overnight, additional beds, cots available. Check-in all day.*

Hose   Rose & Crown

Tel 0949 60424

Bolton Lane Hose Leicestershire   Map 7 D3

An interesting, changing range of beers is available in a comfortable popular Vale of Belvoir pub. *Free House. Beer Bass, Batemans XXXB, Wadworth 6X. Garden.*

Houghton Conquest   Knife & Cleaver   B&B

Tel 0234 740387   Fax 0234 740900

Houghton Conquest nr Ampthill Bedfordshire   Map 17 E1

Opposite the parish church in a sleepy village three miles from Ampthill and equidistant from junctions 12 and 13 of the M1. The Knife & Cleaver is more an inn than a pub. The accommodation, however, is especially pleasing, in spacious brick-built garden rooms standing alongside a mature orchard. In addition to TVs, telephones, radio-alarm clocks and beverage facilities, the mini-fridge in each room is thoughtfully stored each day with fresh milk. The less mobile are especially well catered for by wide, paved bedroom access and ramps into the pub proper. Food was disappointing on our last visit.

Free House. **Beer** Batemans XB Bitter, Banks & Taylor, Shefford Bitter.
Garden. Family room. **Accommodation** 9 bedrooms, all en suite, £53,
£41 single. Children welcome overnight, extra beds and cots supplied.
Check-in all day. Access, Amex, Visa.

Hoxne   Swan

Tel 037 975 275

Low Street Hoxne Suffolk   Map 10 C2

The village is pronounced Hoxon. The Swan, a Grade II listed 15th
century inn was built by the Bishop of Norwich as the guest quarters
to his now defunct summer palace, and has been a hostelry since at
least 1619: the original part of the building features high ceilings and
fluted oak joists and there's a large, walled garden bordered by mature
trees. You can play croquet. **Beer** Adnams, Greene King Abbot. Garden,
children's play area.

Hubberholme   The George Inn

Tel 0756 760223

Kirkgill Hubberholme North Yorkshire BD23 5JE

FOOD

B&B

Map 6 B1

The fells rise up steeply on each side of a hamlet by the river Wharfe,
deep in the Yorkshire Dales. Opposite the church, which owned the
inn until 1965, the George is a pleasingly unspoilt, unmodernised
(there is central heating in the simple bedrooms, though), 17th-century
inn with flagstoned floors, copper-topped tables, rough stone walls
and, in one room, a couple of untrimmed tree trunks providing the
ceiling beams. The pub has been on the market for a while now (and
may be for some time), but as long as landlord John Fredrick remains
here in his kitchen the standard of cooking is unlikely to falter.
Chicken and steak and kidney pies (both £4.40) are the only hot
dishes at lunchtime, when there is also a ploughman's (£2.65) and
large crusty rolls with a variety of fillings. At night, the printed menu
includes prawn cocktail (£3.40), good, fresh ravioli in a rich tomato
sauce (£1.65), corn on the cob (£1.65), gammon steak with egg or
pineapple (£6.50), 1½lb Scotch steaks (from £9.30), Barnsley chops
(£9.25) plus a selection of vegetarian dishes (all at £5.50). A
blackboard offers specials of the day like salmon with asparagus sauce
and venison in red wine (both £8.50). For the sweet-toothed there's
treacle sponge (£2), butterscotch and walnut fudge cake (£1.80) and
sticky toffee pudding (£2). You can eat either in the bar or in the
small pew-furnished dining room. Four modest, but decent-sized
bedrooms are neat and well kept, sharing a tiled bathroom and
separate loo. A table in the hallway offers tea and coffee-making kit
plus a selection of magazines. **Bar Food** 12-1.50, 7-8.45. Vegetarian
dishes. Free House. **Beer** Youngers. **Accommodation** 4 rooms, not en suite,
£36. No children under 8. Check-in all day. No credit cards.

Hurley   Dew Drop

Tel 062 882 824327

Near Hurley Berkshire   Map 16 D3

Well-loved, tucked-away, genuinely unpretentious cottage pub. Food
is very much secondary to the atmosphere and rural peace; the
garden's delightful in summer, and it's a real hideaway of a place in
winter, when the twin log fires in the main bar are crackling. No
children indoors. **Beer** Brakspears PA & Old Ale. Garden, children's play
area.

Ickham   Duke William

Tel 0227 721308

The Street Ickham Kent CT3 1QP

FOOD

Map 11 C5

Comfortable, welcoming old village pub built in 1611 and close to
the A257. Full meals tend to be of the restaurant sort (half leg of
lamb £10.85) with simple snacks in the front bar (large mixed salads,
lots of ways with avocado and always plenty of pasta). Burgers and
fish fingers are banned, even for children. There is a large
conservatory reserved for non-smokers and adults with children. *Bar
Food 12-2.30, 6-10. Vegetarian dishes. Children's portions. Free House.
Beer Adnams, Fullers, Harveys, Youngs. Cider Biddenden. Family room.
Garden, outdoor eating, children's play area. Access, Amex, Diners, Visa.*

Iddesleigh   Duke of York

Tel 0837 810253

Iddesleigh Winkleigh Devon EX19 8BG

FOOD

Map 13 D2

Originally built to house the stonemasons working on the 13th-
century church next door, the thatched Duke of York is the ideal
village pub, with real food, real ale and a real welcome. Scrubbed
wooden tables sport fresh flowers and candles in wax-encrusted
bottles, and an open log fire burns. The blackboard-listed menu offers
the usual, with home-made soup (£1.85), melon and prawns (£1.85)
or deep-fried mushrooms (£1.85) for starters, and 8oz rump steak
(£7.95), poached salmon (£5.95) or pan-fried chicken (£4.80) for
main course. It's worth leaving a little space for the puddings, which
come with real, thick, yellow farmhouse clotted cream, such as sticky
toffee pudding (£1.85), chocolate cheesecake (£1.85) or banoffi pie
(£1.85). From Wednesday to Saturday evenings, a short, fixed-price
menu is also on offer in the beamed dining room. Children are made
welcome and provided with smaller portions at smaller prices. The
cottage garden is very pretty. New licensees arrived in July 1992. *Bar
Food all day. Restaurant Meals 6.30-9.30 Wed-Sat (booking essential).
Vegetarian dishes. Children's portions. Free House. Beer Cotleigh Tawney
Bitter, Old Hookey. Cider Store House. Garden, outdoor eating. Family
room. No credit cards.*

Ightham Common   Harrow Inn   ★

Tel 0732 885912

Common Road (off A25) Ightham Common Kent TN15 9ER

FOOD

Map 11 B5

Coloured lights around the door offer a welcome at this Virginia
creeper-hung stone inn on a country lane. In the small front bar a
couple of stuffed birds in glass cases and old motor racing photos are
mounted above dado pine panelling, and there's a pair of old leather
armchairs and a pool table in the room next door; the whole effect
wobbles on the very fine line between characterful and seedy. Boxes
of board games and newspapers laid out on a side table are a nice
touch, and the landlord and his friendly staff soon dispel any doubts.
Gerard Costelloe has an impressive catering background, and the
cooking is excellent. Well-balanced soups arrive in large tureens from
which one helps oneself (£2.10), along with a whole freshly baked
rye loaf on its own bread board. There are always a couple of pasta
dishes (from £3.95), at least one of them vegetarian, as well as the
likes of baked red snapper (£6.50) and venison sausage (£4.50). It's

worth saving a little space for pudding, like a classic summer pudding
(£1.75), properly made, its bread thoroughly soaked in the juice of
soft fruits. The bars are not really suitable for children but they are
welcome (particularly for Sunday lunch) in the cottagey restaurant, its
conservatory extension complete with grape vine. The menu here
tends to be the somewhat more adventurous, with the likes of chicken
parmigiana (£7.95) and fillet of beef chanterelles (£12). *Bar Food
12-2.30 (till 2 Sun), 7-10. Restaurant Meals 12-2.30 (3.30 Sun), 7-9.30
(except Sun eve). Vegetarian dishes. Children's portions. Free House. Beer
London Pride, Shepherd Neame, Sussex Brewery. Garden, outdoor eating.
Family room. Pub closed Monday. Access, Amex, Visa.*

Ilmington   Howard Arms

Tel 060882 226

Lower Green Ilmington Warwickshire CV36 4LN

FOOD
B&B

Map 16 A1

Ilmington is typical of the small local villages which delight visiting
tourists, and the mellow Cotswold-stone Howard Arms, a rambling
building overlooking the village green, is equally admired. Outside,
there are five arched and bay windows and large hanging baskets
brimming with flowers in summer. Inside is immaculately maintained
and full of period character. Splendid flagstone floors are covered with
colourful rugs, rustic oak tables, settles and round-back chairs. There
are huge, heavily-beamed ceilings and a wall of exposed stone. Other
walls are hung with hunting and sporting prints. The blackboard
menu offers good quality food from fresh produce and includes simple
dishes like lamb and rosemary pie (£5) and crispy cod (£4.75) as well
as a couple of more substantial choices like good-quality rump or
sirloin steak comes with a robust green peppercorn sauce (£9.95) or
fresh poached salmon (£6.95), served with a well-flavoured cream and
fresh basil sauce, and a pretty, crisp panaché of fresh vegetables. Good
puddings (all £2.25) like damson crumble and bread and butter. Then
there's the restaurant, up a couple of steps from the bar with light-
painted walls, and tablecloths. Regularly changing menus here show a
good deal of thought and effort at a reasonable set price (currently
£16 for three courses and coffee). Typical starters might include
melon and redcurrants or duck and bacon terrine; to follow, scallops
of pork with Parma ham and sage, or braised pheasant in red wine.
Sundays see a traditional roast menu (£10.75). There's nice service and
a quiet civilised atmosphere throughout, but at times it gets very busy.
It's best to book for the restaurant. *Bar Food 12-2, 7-9
(7-9.30 Fri/Sat). Restaurant Meals 7-9 (9.30 Fri/Sat). Vegetarian dishes.
Children's portions. Free House. Beer Marston IPA and Pedigree. Garden,
outdoor eating, children's play area. Accommodation 2 bedrooms, both en
suite, £40 (single £25). Children welcome overnight, additional beds and
cots available. Check-in by arrangement. No dogs. Access, Visa.*

Inkpen   Swan Inn

Tel 0488 668326

Lower Inkpen nr Hungerford Berkshire RG15 0DX

FOOD

Map 16 B4

Colourful window boxes and hanging baskets of flowers adorn the
front of this long, low, white-painted 17th-century country pub.
Inside, there are lots of old beams and timbers, some of them salvaged
from a nearby barn, pew seating at one end and pink-clothed tables in
the restaurant area at the other. After his return from 14 years out
East, landlord John Scothorne thought Singaporean cooking and real
ales would go well together; five years on, the experiment has proved

a great success, and pints of good English bitter have proved fine partners for dishes like spicy lamb keema (£5.55) or sweet and sour fish (£5.95), from a fairly extensive menu available in both the bar and, more formally, the restaurant at night. Mock chicken drumsticks made from chicken wings seasoned in sherry, crushed garlic and honey (£4) make particularly good, if rather sticky, finger food. For those with less exotic tastes, a traditional 'pub grub' menu at lunchtime features ploughman's (£3.75), home made steak and kidney pie (£4.75), beef and venison pie (£5.50) and the like. The house wines are all bottled by a friend of John's (who also happens to be his partner in a French hotel) at his chateau just east of Bordeaux. The range includes Bordeaux Sec, Bordeaux Supérieur and a sweet dessert wine called Cadillac, while the nine other listed wines include a New Zealand Chardonnay, Australian Shiraz, Spanish Rioja and low alcohol American wine, plus champagne from the Widow Clicquot if you are in a celebratory mood, or experimenting with bold new accompaniments to Singaporean cooking offered in the evenings. **Bar Food** *12-1.45, 7-9.30. Vegetarian dishes. Free House.* **Beer** *Brakspear, Hook Norton, Boddingtons, Ringwood.* **Cider** *Addlestones. Patio/terrace, outdoor eating. Access, Visa.*

Ivy Hatch   Plough   ★

Tel 0732 810268	**FOOD**

Coach Road Ivy Hatch Kent TN15 0NL   Map 11 B5

Quite apart from its outstandingly good cooking, the Plough is the kind of pub just about everyone would love to have as their local. A large mid-18th-century roadside inn dominating this little hamlet, it's just enough off the beaten track, although well signposted. Within, it's peaceful and genuinely unspoilt, with dark pitch pine-lined walls and inky-dark polished furniture which glows mahogany in the light of a crackling log fire, and candlelight by night. By way of contrast, the conservatory dining extension, home to the justifiably well-regarded Le Chantecler restaurant, is light and fresh, with its soft pink linens, cane furniture and decorative greenery. But you don't have to opt for formal restaurant dining to enjoy excellent food at the Plough, because the bar food here is also a cut above the ordinary. From the blackboard listed menu, choose an excellently flavoured soup (the fish soup is particularly good), perhaps salmon grilled with Cajun spices (£10.50) or a warm salad of scallops with ginger and coriander (£7.50), finishing with a classic, tangy tarte au citron. Or stick patriotically to some good old English specialities: a broccoli and Stilton soup, warming oxtail stew, jugged hare (£8.50), or liver and onions. Inspiration from further afield is shown in bresaola with roasted peppers and chili salsa (£5), mozzarella with red onion and plum tomatoes (£3.50), and warm salad of scallops with ginger and coriander (£7.50). Puddings (£3.25), the same list shared by restaurant and bar, also cross the Channel and back; perhaps a delicate crème brulée, bread-and-butter pudding, sticky toffee pudding or strawberry tuile; all show a lightness of touch and substantial skill. Tables can't be booked in the bar, so be early, or be patient; tables *are* bookable in the restaurant. **Bar & Restaurant Food** *12-2, 7-10 (not Sun eve). Vegetarian dishes. Children's portions.* **Beer** *Brakspears, Marston, Larkins. Children allowed in bar to eat. Garden, outdoor eating. Access, Visa.*

Ixworth   Pickerel Inn

Tel 0359 30398

High Street Ixworth Suffolk IP31 2HH   Map 10 C2

A new licensee is in place at the Pickerel, an atmospheric, rambling, old-fashioned pub in a village just off the A143. *Beer Greene King. Children's play area. Family room.*

Kegworth   Cap & Stocking

Tel 0509 674814

20 Borough Street Kegworth Leicestershire DE7 2FF   Map 7 D3

Traditional hostelry less than a mile from J24 of the M1. *Beer Bass. Garden. Children's play area. Family room.*

Keinton Mandeville   Quarry Inn

Tel 0458 222367

Keinton Mandeville nr Somerton Somerset TA11 6DZ   Map 13 F2

As the name suggests, this was once the quarrymaster's residence. It's early Victorian and roomy, if not exactly quaint. *Beer Oakhill Bitter, Wadworth 6X. Garden. Children's play area.*

Kelston   Old Crown Inn

Tel 0225 423032

Kelston nr Bath Avon BA1 9AQ   Map 13 F1

Old coaching inn with stone floors, wood panelling, settles; one room once served as a mortuary for bodies washed up from the Avon; upstairs was used as a magistrate's court. *Free House. Garden.*

Keswick   Pheasant

Tel 07687 72219   **B&B**

Crosthwaite Road Keswick Cumbria CA12 5PP   Map 4 C3

Homely little inn just off the A66, about a mile from the town centre. A nice old-fashioned bar has walls decorated with colourful cartoons. Bedrooms are neat and simple, with washbasins and individual heating. *Beer Jennings Bitter. Patio/terrace. **Accommodation** 3 bedrooms, sharing bathroom, from £39 (single £22.50). Children welcome overnight, cots supplied. Check-in all day. No credit cards.*

Kew   Kings Arms Taverna

Tel 081-940 3182   **FOOD**

Kew Bridge Road Kew Surrey   Map 17 F3

This converted pub, overlooking Kew Green, is now part of the Kleftiko Restaurant Group (June 1992). It still has outside picnic-style tables and a bare bar for drinking only, but the main attraction is the transformed lounge bar and conservatory which is now a large dining room area. This is the fourth venture for brothers Michael and Andreas, who have been serving Greek food in West London for over twenty years. Regular items on the menu (£5.50-£7) include stifado (lean beef cooked in wine and vinegar), keftedes (meatballs deep-fried and topped with tomato and mushroom sauce) moussaka and charcoal grills. Specialities on offer are kleftiko (joint of lamb cooked in oven for three hours) (£6.50) and the mini meze (£7) – a collection of 12-13 hot and cold dishes. The set-price menu offers three courses and coffee for £10.95. Burgers and fish fingers feature on the children's menu (£3.50-£4.50) should Greek cooking not be to their liking. *Restaurant Meals 12-3, 6-11. Vegetarian dishes. Children's menu. Beer Courage Directors and Best. Garden, patio/terrace, outdoor eating. Access, Amex, Visa.*

Keysoe   Chequers Inn

Tel 0234 708678

Pertenhall Road Keysoe Bedfordshire MK44 2HR   **Map 15 E1**

Two beamed bars, one with an unusual pillared fireplace; log fires in cold weather. *Free House. Garden. Children's play area. Family room.*

Keyston   Pheasant Inn   ★

Tel 08014 241   **FOOD**

Village Loop Road Keyston nr Bythorn Cambridgeshire OE18 0RE   **Map 7 E4**

The latest addition to the stable of Ivo Vannocci from *The George of Stamford*, the Pheasant is a true thoroughbred. Black and white painted with a low thatched roof and original interior beams, the pub promises much in character and atmosphere which the food lives up to in admirable fashion. Nick Steiger, manager and chef, oversees menus which range from the simplest bar snack, be it soup and bread (£1.90) or toasted Brie (£3.25), through to monthly speciality evenings featuring regional food and wines – from Piedmont, say, or Alsace – which are fully booked at around £20 per head. Menu boards up-dated daily offer a comprehensive range: spicy chicken wings (£2.25), trout terrine with red pepper sauce (£3.25), penne with smoked chicken, tomato and herbs (£6.45), baked haddock in white wine sauce (£6.45), pigeon breast with red cabbage and poivrade (£7.45). Nightly dinners progress on a seasonally evolving menu to ravioli of duck, thyme and ginger sauce (£4.25), fillet of sea bass with braised fennel (£15.50) and a hot Galliano soufflé served with vanilla cream (£4.50). Careful segregation of dining areas ensures nonetheless that the Pheasant remains at heart a well-kept, friendly village pub, as deservedly popular for its range of well-kept cask-conditioned ales as for its wines, of which an even dozen may be ordered by the glass. In terms of popular acclaim the Pheasant is breaking new ground in East Anglia. *Bar Food 12-2, 6-10 Restaurant Meals 12-2, 7-10. Vegetarian dishes. Children's portions. Free House. Beer Adnams, Batemans, Banks's & Taylor Midsummer Ale, Fullers ESB. Cider Scrumpy Jack. Garden, outdoor eating. Family room. Access, Amex, Diners, Visa.*

Kidmore End   New Inn

Tel 0734 723115   **FOOD**

Chalkhouse Green Road Kidmore End Oxfordshire RG4 9AU   **Map 17 D3**

Ordering a meal here is a high-tech affair: you choose from a regular printed menu and order at the bar, where a 'light pen' is passed over a special bar-coded copy for the order to be printed out automatically in the kitchen. The food itself is rather more traditional; steak, mushroom and Murphy's pie (£5.45), scampi in breadcrumbs (£5.75), vegetable lasagne (£5.15) and entrecote steak platter (£8.90) plus more exotic monthly specials like chicken tikka (£6.45) and lamb cutlets in blackcurrant (£6.80). Along with the good fresh vegetables go for the super 'chips' that are satisfyingly chunky, golden and piping hot. On the snack front French bread sandwiches start at about £2.15 and there are salad platters based on mature farmhouse

Cheddar (£4.20) or Long Clawson Stilton (£4.65). Decor is typical of an English country pub with low beams and wheelback chairs. A large tree-shaded garden provides for summer eating and drinking. Off the A4074, north of Reading. *Bar Food & Restaurant Meals 12-2, 6.30-9.30 (7-9.30 Sun). Vegetarian dishes. Children's menu (£2.20 per dish)/portions. Beer Brakspear. Garden, outdoor eating. Family room. Amex, Visa*

Kilnhurst   Ship

Tel 0709 584322

1 Hooton Road Kilnhurst South Yorkshire S62 5TA   Map 7 D2

Built in 1752, the Ship is the oldest building in the village, close to railway and canal; a homely country inn boxed in by the urban landscape. Bar room entertainment most evenings. *Beer Castle Eden, Whitbread. Garden, children's play area. Family room.*

Kilve   Hood Arms

FOOD

B&B

Tel 027874 210

Kilve nr Bridgwater Somerset TA5 1EA   Map 13 E1

Pristine 17th-century white village coaching inn at the front of the Quantock hills, a mile from the sea with log fires, a large collection of horse brasses and a complete set of a show harness above the fireplace. Modernised, comfortable interior, with wood-burning stove in carpeted main bar, which is bistro-like in the evenings. The menu varies from prawn cocktail (£2.75), chicken and broccoli mornay (£4.50) and National Trust pie (£4.50) to Dover sole (£11), chicken Kiev (£8) or spinach and garlic lasagne (£4.50). Puddings are the old favourites (all £1.60) – treacle tart, sherry trifle, rum tipsy cake. Also smaller, cosy lounge. Pleasant garden. Friendly, welcoming service. *Bar Food 12-2 (12-1.30 Sun), 6.30-10 (7.15-9.30 Sun). Restaurant Meals 7-9.30 (except Sun, Mon and Tue). Vegetarian dishes. Free House. Beer Whitbread, Boddingtons, Flowers Original. Garden, outdoor eating. Accommodation 5 bedrooms, all en suite, £56 (single £28). Children welcome overnight (minimum age 7). Check-in all day. Access, Visa.*

Kingscote   Hunters Hall Inn

FOOD

Tel 0453 860393

Kingscote Tetbury Gloucestershire GL8 8XZ   Map 14 B2

Unusually spacious, comfortably genteel old inn, continuously licensed since the 15th century. High ceilinged, connecting rooms hold a pleasing variety of furniture, both squashy and elegant, exposed stone walls, and open fires. An upstairs Gallery (that families can use) takes more diners, and there's also a quite separate, quite different, low-ceilinged locals' public bar where you'll find over a dozen malt whiskies. Bar food is buffet-servery style, with hot dishes listed on a blackboard: home-made soups (£2.20), steak and kidney pie (£4.95), loin of pork (£5.95), lamb and red wine casserole (£5.10); Sunday roast (£5.95). The restaurant menu extends to mushroom and blue cheese tartlets (£3.85) or devilled chicken livers (£3.90) to start, followed by rack of lamb (£10.90) and pigeon breast (£8.95); apple and rhubarb pie (£2.30) or rich chocolate mousse (£2.30) to finish. Recommended for family expeditions. *Bar Food 12-2, 7-9.45. Restaurant Meals 7.30-9.45 (Mon-Sat). Vegetarian Dishes. Cheese. Beer Draught Bass, Hook Norton Bitter, Uley Old Spot, Wadworth 6X.*

Family room. Outdoor play area, garden, outdoor eating, summer barbecue.
Accommodation *12 bedrooms, all en suite, £54 (single £44) children welcome overnight, cots available, check-in all day. Access, Amex, Diners, Visa.*

Kingskerswell **Barn Owl**	**FOOD**
Tel 0803 872130	**B&B**
Aller Mills Kingskerswell Devon TQ12 5AN	Map 13 D3

Look out for a sign on the A380 to the Barn Owl Inn, which offers decent food, good bedrooms and a friendly welcome. Lovingly restored by the Warners, the original (16th- century) farmhouse has a neat if unremarkable exterior which makes its characterful interior even more of a surprise. Old beams, rough stone walls and flagstoned floors have been uncovered, and real log fires warm each of the three bars in winter. One room features an inglenook fireplace, another an ancient blackleaded range, while in the largest bar, oak panelling and an ornate plasterwork ceiling are rather grander than might be expected of a modest farmhouse. Fresh flowers on all the tables add to the general charm of the surroundings. A printed bar menu offers a good range of steaks (from £6.25), fresh fish (from £5.25), hot jacket potatoes (from £2.95) and sandwiches with fillings including some excellent home-boiled ham carved off the bone, in good granary bread (from £2.30). In addition, a blackboard menu lists the dishes of the day, which always include a vegetarian special. Remember to bring your appetite: portions are generous. In the evenings, the French-inspired à la carte is offered in a converted barn restaurant. Six bedrooms within the original farmhouse combine considerable charm with conveniences like television and direct-dial phones. Extensive sound-proofing effectively eliminates any noise from the bars below. Rooms are cottagey in style with black beams, white plaster walls, dark-stained pine furniture locally made in solid country style and their own individual floral fabrics, perhaps red poppy, honeysuckle or sweet pea. This 'signature' design is also used above dados in the bathrooms and in panels on the doors, the outsides of which are covered with old floorboards, thus cunningly concealing the modern fireproof doors within. Bowls of fruit and mineral water add the final homely touch. No children under 14 are permitted in either bars or bedrooms, but they are tolerated in the small garden. **Bar Food** *12-2, 7-10.* **Restaurant Meals** *6.30-9.45 (closed Sun). Vegetarian dishes. Children's portions. Free House.* **Beer** *Dartmoor. Garden, outdoor eating.* **Accommodation** *6 bedrooms, all en suite, £62.75 (single £47.50). Check-in all day. No dogs. Access, Amex, Visa.*

Kingsteignton **Old Rydon** ★	
Tel 0626 54626	**FOOD**
Rydon Road Kingsteignton Devon TQ12 3QG	Map 13 D3

Hermann Hruby (pronounced Ruby) is still producing some of the best pub food in the south west, and in that respect little has changed since the Hrubys bought the Old Rydon in 1978 except for the building of a splendid, and large, heated conservatory, leafy with vines, jasmine, bougainvillaea and other plants. It's a Grade II listed former farmhouse, converted in the 1960s with an original old cider loft forming an attractive part of the bar, previously the farm stables. Underneath the plank and beam ceiling adorned with pewter mugs is a raised log fire; the whitewashed stone walls are hung with antlers and horns. Tables here are drinking style, too small and cramped for relaxed dining, and many of the seats are converted barrels. Separate from the bar, a comfortable diners' lounge leads through to the little restaurant, in the oldest part of the building. Most visitors come for the delicious and interesting food which includes seafood in garlic butter (£2.95), satays (£2.65) or fresh mussels (£4.35) for starters, followed by fettuccine with pesto (£2.25), braised lamb (£5.45) or paella (£5.65). The blackboard specials menu embraces poached Scotch salmon (£4.65), herring fillets (£4.20), farmhouse chicken (£11.35) and charcoal-grilled duck (£12.60). In addition to this there are imaginative side salads and starters that make good lunchtime snacks on their own (though they don't serve sandwiches). Succulent puddings served with clotted cream could include summer pudding (£1.95), profiteroles (£2.50) or pancakes (£1.95). Aside from the conservatory, the sheltered walled garden makes an ideal summer venue for lunch. To find the pub; take Longford Lane off the A381; Rydon Road is on the left. *Bar Food 12-2, 7-10 (9.30 Sun).* *Restaurant Meals 7-9.30 (closed Sun). Vegetarian dishes. Children's portions. Free House. Beer Bass, Wadworth 6X, guest beer. Garden, children's play area. Family room. Access, Amex, Diners, Visa.*

Kingston   Juggs

| Tel 0273 472523 | **FOOD** |

The Street Kingston nr Lewes East Sussex BN7 3NT

Map 11 B6

Just off the A27, a short distance from Brighton, you will find this picturesque little 15th-century inn made from two tiny cottages. The name 'Juggs' originates from the leather jugs the women used to carry on their heads to collect fish from the market. The main bar is particularly characterful with its low ceilings, rough black timbers, rustic benches and yellowing walls; there's also a small no-smoking dining area (same menu in both). The home-made steak and kidney puddings have a reputation for being enormous and good value (£7.25), the Sussex bangers are made by a local butcher and served with chips (£2.95), and puddings are also local – Sussex plum pudding or a summer fruit special soaked in redcurrant wine (both £2.50). *Bar Food 12-2, 6-9.30. Vegetarian dishes. Children's portions. Free House. Beer Harveys Best, King & Barnes Broadwood Festive. Garden, outdoor eating, children's play area. Family room. Access, Visa.*

Kintbury   Dundas Arms

| Tel 0488 58263   Fax 0488 58568 | **FOOD** |
| | **B&B** |

Station Road Kintbury nr Newbury Berkshire RG12 0UT

Map 16 B4

Reached via Halfway, past the Kintbury turnoff from the Hungerford-bound A4, this well-loved, reliable old-fashioned waterside inn, by the Kennet and Avon canal, has been run by the Dalzell-Pipers since the 1960s. The civilised bar has a striking display of blue patterned plates entirely covering one wall. The riverside patio is very popular on summer lunchtimes. The comfortable dining-room with canal views is the stage for owner David's cooking. Fresh local ingredients are prepared with skill, confidence and a notable lack of fuss. These talents show up well in dishes like paté-stuffed quail with peppered red jelly and grilled red mullet with a lively citrus sauce which appear on the 3-course (£16.50) lunch menu, or roast partridge with fried cabbage and smoky bacon which is on the 3-course (£24) menu. The bread and butter pudding and treacle tart are both moist, well-executed, old-fashioned desserts. The Dalzell-Pipers are proud of their particularly interesting wine list, which admirably complements the large cheeseboard. Pleasant bedrooms are in a converted stable block, with French windows opening on to a quiet private terrace, where garden furniture is provided for each room. *Bar Food 12-2, 7-9.15. Restaurant Meals 12.30-1.30, 7.30-9.30. Vegetarian dishes. Children's portions. Beer Eldridge Pope Hardy Country Bitter, Fullers London Pride, Morland OB. Riverside patio/terrace, outdoor eating. Accommodation 5 bedrooms, all en suite, £65 (single £55). Children welcome overnight, additional beds available. Check-in by arrangement. Access, Amex, Visa.*

Kirkby Lonsdale   Snooty Fox Tavern

Tel 05242 71308

Main Street Kirkby Lonsdale Cumbria LA6 2AH   Map 4 C4

A pristine white-painted, town-centre Jacobean inn; traditional bars with lots of wood, stone and bric-a-brac. *Free House. Garden. Children's play area. Family room.*

Kirkby Stephen   King's Arms Hotel   FOOD
                                                        B&B
Tel 0930 71378

Market Street Kirkby Stephen Cumbria CA17 4QN   Map 5 D3

Small convivial hotel bar, with open fire and panelled walls, as well as simple bar food like steak and kidney or shepherd's pie. The lunchtime dining room is probably a better bet, prettily laid and decorated, with fresh fish, steaks, roasts and salads, and good cheeses to follow. Booking essential for the traditional Sunday lunch. Bedrooms are traditional in style with lacy bedspreads and solid period furniture. *Bar Food & Restaurant Meals 12-1.45, 7-8.45. Beer Whitbread. Children allowed in bar to eat. Garden Accommodation 9 bedrooms, 3 en suite, £50. Children welcome overnight. Check-in all day. Access, Visa.*

Kirkbymoorside   George & Dragon Hotel

Tel 0751 31637   Fax 0751 33334   B&B

17 Market Place Kirkbymoorside North Yorkshire YO6 6AA   Map 5 E4

Flowers and a fresh coat of paint give a good first impression at this 17th-century town- centre inn. The bar has a beamed ceiling and old stone fireplaces but is less atmospheric than one would expect with rough plaster walls (Italian restaurant style) and red leatherette upholstery. The bedrooms are in two separate buildings to the rear, reached via very pretty and peaceful gardens. Those in the 'Rectory' are larger and more comfortable than those in the 'Corn Exchange' but all are similarly decorated with plain walls and attractive, floral matching duvet covers and curtains. All have TV (of varying ages), direct-dial telephone and tea and coffee making kits. *Bar Food 12-2.15, 7-9.15. Vegetarian dishes. Children's menu/portions. Free House. Beer Theakston. Garden, outdoor eating. Family room. Accommodation 22 bedrooms, all en suite, £55 (single £30). Children welcome overnight, additional beds, cot available. Check-in all day. Access, Visa.*

Knapp   Rising Sun

Tel 0823 490436   FOOD

Knapp North Curry nr Taunton Somerset TA3 6BG   Map 13 E2

Very much a dining pub, pretty, white-painted and cottagey, and totally refurbished, though many original features remain in this "most perfect example of a Somerset longhouse open to the public", dated 1480. On the edge of the Somerset Levels, it was originally a cider house; it has retained some period features including two inglenook fireplaces which provide open log fires in winter. Fish from Brixham predominates – the board can feature over 30 different dishes: tiger prawns, spicy fish soup (£3.50), wild salmon, scallops in vermouth with Dijon mustard (£10.50), red mullet with fennel, rosemary and anchovy butter (£11.50) are but a few. For non-fish eaters, ribeye steak (£7.50), garlic chicken (£8.50) or duck in orange sauce (£9.75) are available. Vegetarians can choose from two or three dishes. *Bar Food 12-2. Restaurant Meals 7-9.30. Vegetarian dishes. Children's portions (½ price). Free House. Beer Bass, Exmoor, Boddingtons. Cider local farmhouse cider in summer. Patio, outdoor eating. Family room. Access, Visa.*

Knightwick   Talbot Hotel

FOOD
B&B

Tel 0886 21235

Bromyard Rd Knightwick nr Worcester Hereford & Worcester WR6 5PH   Map 14 B1

Prettily set, attractive white inn, originally 14th-century. The old bar, with modern carpets and curtains, is dominated by its vast open fireplace; the oak-panelled dining room is romantically gloomy, warmed by a wood-burning stove. Food is imaginative and tempting – home air-cured smoked beef (£3.95), fresh sweetcorn soup (£1.50), smoked haddock mornay (£3.95), chicken stuffed with cream cheese in filo pastry (£9.50), steak and kidney pie (£6.95). Puddings (£3) are equally imaginative: gooseberry and elderflower crumble, chocolate truffle ice cream cake or carrot cake and cinnamon cream. A traditional 3-course Sunday lunch is available for £9.95. Main-building bedrooms are best, though three have no bathrooms attached; extension-housed rooms, all en suite, are simple and cottagey in style. The residents' lounge is comfortable and modern rather than quaint and beamy. *Bar Food 12-2, 6.30-9.30. Vegetarian dishes. Children's portions. Children allowed in bar to eat. Free House. Beer Banks's, Bass, Marston Pedigree. Patio/terrace, outdoor eating. Family room. Accommodation 10 bedrooms, 7 en suite, £52.50 (single £29). Children welcome overnight, additional beds (£10), cots supplied. Check-in all day. Access, Visa.*

Knowle Hill   Seven Stars

Tel 062 882 2967

Bath Road Knowle Hill Berkshire   Map 17 D3

Large 16th-century coaching inn, popular for wedding receptions. Beyond the Georgian frontage is a series of comfortable panelled rooms with warming open fires; good for families – children are welcome until 9pm, and there are tree houses in the large garden. No music. *Beer Brakspear. Garden. Children's play area. Family room.*

Knowstone   Masons Arms

FOOD

Tel 03984 231

Knowstone Devon EX36 4RY   Map 13 D2

Thatched 13th-century inn in the sort of truly tranquil spot where dogs fall asleep in the middle of the road. A good place for a drink and the food's not at all bad either: cheese and leek pie (£3.95), home-made soup (£1.50), curries (£5.50) and puddings, sticky toffee (£1.75) and apricot flan (£1.75) are particularly good. *Free House. Bar Food 12-2, 7-9.30 (12.30-2, 7-9 Sun). Restaurant 12.30-2 (Sun only), and 7-9 (not Sun). Vegetarian dishes. Beer. Cotleigh Tawny Bitter,*

Hall & Woodhouse Badger Best Bitter. Garden, outdoor eating. Family room. No credit cards.

Lacock   At the Sign of the Angel   **FOOD**

| Tel 0249 730230   Fax 0249 730527 | **B&B** |

6 Church Street Lacock nr Chippenham Wiltshire SN15 2LB   Map 14 B2

A 15th-century wool-merchant's house situated in a National Trust village and run by the Levis family since 1953. Beams, creaking floors, huge fireplaces and heavy oak furniture offer plenty of character in the main-house bedrooms; a couple of rooms are in the annexe, reached by a little bridge across the garden stream. The lounge is shared by residents and diners. In the two dining rooms a traditional roast, with a fish alternative, is the centrepiece of set dinners served by candlelight. Typical starters are scallop, bacon and prawn au gratin, duck liver terrine with pickled oranges and tomato and marjoram soup. To finish, perhaps crème brulée, spiced bread-and-butter pudding or meringues with clotted cream (this is hearty food, not for serious weight-watchers!). Cold food only Saturday lunch & Sunday dinner (the latter for residents only). *Restaurant Meals 1-1.30, 7.30-8.15. Closed L Sat & Mon, D Sun. Set L £16 Set D £22.50-£30. Accommodation 10 bedrooms £93, single £70. Children welcome overnight (under-5s free in parents' room). Garden. Closed 22 Dec-1 Jan. Access, Amex, Visa.*

Lacock   The George Inn

| Tel 0249 730263 | **FOOD** |

4 West Street Lacock nr Chippenham Wiltshire SN15 2LH   Map 14 B2

The virtual epitome of the traditional village pub. The George could scarcely be in a more ideal spot than the National Trust village of Lacock. Starting life in 1361 as the *Black Boy* with its own brewery in farm buildings to the rear, its many modernisations have preserved and reutilised many of the original timbers. Central to the bar is a unique mounted dog-wheel built into the open fireplace and used for spit-roasting in the 16th century (the dog was not roasted, but trained to rotate the wheel). Today's pub lives well alongside such idiosyncrasy with its close-packed tables on odd levels set beneath a wealth of old pictures at many an odd angle. From a menu of firm favourites, traditional steak and kidney pie (£4.50) sells by the 50.9 kilos (hundredweight to you) alongside fresh dressed Cornish crab (£4.25), chicken breast in white wine, cream and garlic (£7.65) and a vegetarian spinach and blue cheese crumble (£4.25). The large garden stretches out on both sides of the rear car park; beyond it is a safe play area for youngsters, close by an old stocks to restrain the most troublesome. True to its long-standing identity as a family concern, the licensees' family not only provides overnight farmhouse accommodation nearby but also lays on complimentary transport to and from the pub. Enquiries should be addressed to the pub. *Bar Food & Restaurant Meals 12-2, 6-10 (7-10 Sun). Vegetarian dishes. Children's menu/portions. Beer Wadworth Henry's IPA, 6X and Farmer's Glory. Garden, outdoor eating, children's play area. Access, Visa.*

Lacock   Red Lion

| FOOD |
| B&B |

Tel 0249 730456

High Street Lacock nr Chippenham Wiltshire SN15 2LQ   Map 14 B2

Scarcely the loveliest building in the village, the Grade II listed Red
Lion is opposite the entrance to Lacock Priory. Its bars are a mixture
of uneven flagstones and bare boards with scatter rugs, divided into
sections by beams and panels, high-backed settles and old agricultural
implements. Blackboard menus follow a similarly mixed formula. All-
day snacks include ploughmans various, smoked trout mayonnaise,
vegetarian moussaka (£4.60) and English cream teas (£2.25).
Lunchtimes add home-made soup, beef mushroom and ale pie £5.50),
and chicken and ham bake, with, to follow, walnut and treacle pie,
cream fudge gateau and apple strudel (£2.25): not all are made on the
premises. From 7pm the menu board is reversed to present diners with
cauliflower and blue cheese soup (£2.05) and garlic mushrooms
(£2.90) ahead of whole baked lemon sole (£6.95) and loin of lamb
with port and redcurrant jus (£6.75). Dispensing the full range of
Wadworth beers and some rather indifferent wines, the pub progresses
to a lively late venue with refuge from the musically-included hubbub
to be found in a gravelled rear garden of abundant shrubs and flowers,
picnic tables and colourful umbrellas. The buildings historic listing
still hampers the brewery's plans to develop and upgrade the
bedrooms. Still, they're of generous size with big comfortable beds and
easy chairs: unencumbered by TVs or phones, they make for a restful
overnight stay. The addition of en suite facilities should, in time, add
greater comfort to their obvious character. *Bar Food & Restaurant
Meals 12-2.30, 7-9.30. Vegetarian dishes. Children's menu/portions. Beer
Wadworth Henry's IPA, 6X and Farmer's Glory. Garden, outdoor eating,
children's play area. Family room. Accommodation 3 bedrooms, 1 en suite,
£40 (single £32). Additional beds (£5 if over 5 years). Cots supplied.
Check-in all day. Access, Visa.*

Lamarsh   Red Lion

Tel 0787 227918

Lamarsh Essex   Map 10 C3

Best in winter when the log fire's lit, a little tiled Essex pub,
comfortably modernised, originally timbered, and much used by
locals. On the Bures-Sudbury road. *Free House. Garden, children's play
area.*

Lamport   Lamport Swan

Tel 060 128 555

Market Harborough Road Lamport Northamptonshire NN6 9EZ   Map 7 D4

Large, extremely busy, extended pub enthusiastically owned and run
by unflagging Canadians. Opposite Lamport Hall. *Beer Whitbread,
Flowers IPA. Garden, children's play area. Family room.*

Lanchester   Queen's Head

Tel 0207 520200

Front Street Lanchester Durham DH7 0LA   Map 5 D3

Grade II listed pub at the heart of the village. Welcoming and
warmed by open fires. *Beer Vaux Double Maxim.*

Lane End   Old Sun

Tel 0494 881235

Church Road Lane End Buckinghamshire HP14 3HG   Map 17 D3

The huge old ex-fireplace in this cosy, relaxing pub was once a bakery, and now seats eight people around its large table. There are three inter-connected rooms with wall benches, private recesses, and plenty of distinctive bric-a-brac. Two real fires in winter. An enormous garden has lots of play equipment and good views. *Beer Whitbread. Garden. Children's play area.*

Langdale   Old Dungeon Ghyll Hotel

Tel 096 67 272

Langdale Cumbria   Map 4 C3

Cosy and attractive walkers' bar with coveted window seats cut into the monumental stone walls, a warming open fire, and good views, in a popular inn spectacularly set in excellent fell-walking country. *Free House. Garden.*

Langley Marsh   Three Horseshoes

Tel 0984 23763

Langley Marsh Somerset   Map 13 E2

Handsome village inn with a stylish rear bar, complete with piano, and noisier locals' public at the front with a fruit machine and music. Lovely in summer, on the lawn or verandah. *Free House. Garden, children's play area. Family room.*

Lavenham   Angel Inn

Tel 0787 247388

Market Place Lavenham Suffolk CO10 9QZ   Map 10 C3

A delightful early 15th-century inn, overlooking the medieval marketplace and guildhall. The interior and gardens have been refurbished, and the bar opened up, preserving, of course, the rare Tudor shop window uncovered in earlier renovations. Live classical piano some lunchtimes and evenings. *Free House. Garden, children's play area. Family room.*

Laxfield   King's Head

Tel 0787 247388

Gorams Mill Lane Laxfield Suffolk IP13 8DW   Map 10 D2

Unspoilt, rethatched, repainted traditional old pub with a good mix of country furnishings and a real fire. Locals know it as the Lowhouse. There's no bar – too new-fangled a feature! Instead beer is served from the barrels in the tap room. Some of the fine old settles are themselves listed and protected. Summer brings Morris dancers and there's often live folk music. *Free House. Garden. Children's play area. Family room.*

Laxton   Dovecote

Tel 0777 871586

Laxton nr Newark Nottinghamshire NG22 0NU   Map 7 D2

Redbrick village pub in England's last remaining open field village; visitors' centre behind the building. Pleasant interior, friendly and cosy. *Free House. Children's play area. Family room.*

Ledbury   The Feathers

Tel 0531 5266   Fax 0531 2001   **B&B**

High Street Ledbury Hereford & Worcester HR8 1DS   Map 14 B1

A classic timber-framed former coaching inn dating from 1565 with
oddly-shaped, en-suite, double-glazed bedrooms (including one with a
four-poster), uneven, creaky floors and drunken staircases. Remote-
control TV, bedside tea-tray and hairdryers are standard. Good snacks
in the hop-bedecked Fuggles bar. *Accommodation* 11 bedrooms, £79.
Access, Amex, Diners, Visa.

Ledbury   Ye Olde Talbot Hotel

Tel 0531 2963   **B&B**

New Street Ledbury Hereford & Worcester HR8 2DX   Map 14 B1

The 16th-century building with its striking half-timbered exterior is   ☺
being excellently maintained both inside and out by its new landlords.
You enter through a massively heavy oak door into the neat and
simple bar, and darkly old-fashioned dining room, used for breakfast.
In keeping with the age of the pub, the charming little bedrooms have
low doorways, low beamed ceilings, oak furniture and pretty
bedspreads. *Free House.* **Beer** *Ansells, Burton, Wye Valley Hereford
Supreme.* **Cider** *Stowford Press. Courtyard garden, children's play area.*
Accommodation 7 *bedrooms, 3 en suite, £49 (single £32). Children
welcome overnight, additional beds and cots available. Check-in all day.
Access, Amex, Diners, Visa.*

Ledsham   Chequers Inn

Tel 0977 683135

Ledsham nr South Milford West Yorkshire LS25 5LP   Map 7 D1

Old-fashioned village pub with lots of little rooms leading off a central
panelled servery; real fires, low beams, cosy corners, and lots of
customers. No music. *Free House. Garden.*

Leeds   Whitelocks

Tel 0532 453950   **A**

Turks Head Yard Briggate Leeds West Yorkshire LS1 6HB   Map 6 C1

A real Yorkshire institution, tucked away in an alley off the shopping
area; the original bar is long and narrow, with an unspoilt Edwardian
atmosphere. The less exciting overspill bar further along the yard has
been kitted out in Victorian style. *Beer* *Youngers.*

Leek   Three Horseshoes Inn

Tel 053 830 296   Fax 053 830 320   **B&B**

Blackshaw Moor Leek Staffordshire ST13 8TW   Map 6 C3

A large mock-Tudor-style pub located on the A53 north of Leek.
Inside, the bar has recently been redesigned to offer an open-plan style
but still retain its traditional old-world charm. The bedrooms have
been refurbished in a cottagey style and offer TVs, tea-makers and en-
suite bath/shower rooms. *Free House.* **Beer** *McEwans 80/-, Theakston
XB & Old Peculier, weekly guest beers. Garden. Family room.*
Accommodation 6 *bedrooms, all en suite, £46 (single £40). Children
welcome overnight, additional beds and cots available. Check-in by
arrangement. Access, Visa.*

Lees Moor   Quarry House Inn

Tel 0535 642239

Bingley Road Lees Moor West Yorkshire BD21 5QE   Map 6 C1

Family-run ex-farmhouse high above Keighley, with superb views of
the Worth valley and its famous steam railway. Cricket ground next
door. **Beer** *Ind Coope, Tetley. Garden. Family room.*

Leicester   Welford Place

Tel 0533 470758

FOOD

9 Welford Place Leicester Leicestershire LE1 6ZH   Map 7 D4

This striking Victorian building, designed by Joseph Goddard in 1876,
stands at a convenient city-centre intersection between the High Street,
Cathedral, Castle Park and Granby Halls. Formerly home to the
private members Leicestershire Club, Welford Place is operated by the
Hope family, who have so successfully run Lincoln's now-famous *Wig
& Mitre* (qv) for over twelve years. Their latest classy operation
promotes itself both as a watering hold for the seriously intentioned
and a haven of peace. There are no music noises and, they hope, no
pretension, so a set-up which opens for breakfast and morning coffee,
offers a Specials menu which purports to change twice daily, and
promises its à la carte will be available all day throughout the premises
until 11pm. Thus, in the bar – a striking semi-circular room with
high windows overlooking Welford Place itself and furnished with
leather armchairs and glass-topped tables – a light, relaxing lunch
might start with avocado and smoked salmon, followed by roast duck
with red cabbage and end with bread-and-butter pudding, all washed
down with a creamy pint of Ruddles. Salmon fishcakes (£7.50),
lasagne (£5) and chicken liver paté (£3.75) also feature. Across the
grand parquet-floored hall, the restaurant, a stolid, square room in
blues and russets, appears perhaps a little more formal than it's
intended to be, with an à la carte menu extending to warm lobster
and brill paté (£6.50), lamb cutlets (£10), sautéed calf's kidneys
(£11), home-made sorbets (£2.50) and hazelnut gateau (£2.50). The
new Welford Place adjoins the recently reconstructed Leicester
magistrates courts, from which it appears destined to draw much
trade, as a kind of laborious lawyers' canteen. **Bar Food and
Restaurant Meals** *all day. Vegetarian dishes. Free House.* **Beer** *Ruddles.
Family room. Access, Amex, Diners, Visa.*

Lenham   Dog & Bear Hotel

Tel 0622 858219   Fax 0622 859415

B&B

The Square Lenham nr Maidstone Kent ME17 2PG   Map 11 C5

This attractive coaching inn dates from 1602. Splendid oak beams
combine with a new up-to-date decor and comfortable seating in the
bar, and there is a welcoming little foyer-lounge. Centrally heated
bedrooms with darkwood furniture and bright contemporary fabrics
all have direct-dial telephones, TVs, tea-making facilities and neatly
kept en-suite bathrooms. **Beer** *Shepherd Neame Master Brewer, Spitfire.*
Cider *Pilgrim.* **Accommodation** *25 bedrooms, all en suite, £45 (single
£35). Children welcome overnight, additional beds and cots available.
Check-in by arrangement. Access, Amex, Visa.*

Lewknor   Leathern Bottle

Tel 0844 51482

1 High Street Lewknor Oxfordshire OX9 5TH

Map 17 D2

Homely country pub with Cromwellian connections. Close to
junction 6 of the M4 motorway. *Beer Brakspear. Garden, children's play
area. Family room.*

Ley Hill   Swan

Tel 0494 783075

Ley Hill nr Chesham Buckinghamshire HP5 1UT

Map 17 E2

16th-century pub overlooking the golf course, village cricket ground
and common land. There's a rambling bar of character, with wall and
window seats, an old cooking range, and no-smoking area. *Beer
Benskins. Garden. Children's play area. Family room.*

Lickfold   Lickfold Inn

Tel 0798 5285

Lickfold nr Petworth West Sussex GU28 9EY

Map 11 A6

Splendid interior with a vast open fire, handsome furnishings and a
rug-strewn floor. Unusual and attractive gardens. No children. *Free
House. Garden.*

Lidgate   Star Inn

Tel 0683 500275

The Street Lidgate Suffolk CB8 9PP

Map 10 B3

Beware of ducks when approaching this beamed old inn – a lively
village local; they may be leisurely in crossing the road to the pond.
Beer Greene King IPA, Abbot. Garden. Children's play area.
Map

Lincoln   Wig & Mitre

Tel 0522 535190

FOOD

29 Steep Hill Lincoln Lincolnshire LN2 1LU

Map 7 E2

The Hope family's trendy city-centre pub is not the historic ale-house
it purports to be, but is nonetheless a classic. Its really rather ordinary
exterior, a glass shop front under a flower-laden cast-iron balcony,
stands between the Lincoln Vintner and Chantilly's bridal shop;
Lincoln cathedral is just a stone's throw away across cobbled streets
where once the Roman *via principalis* ran, and its echoing hourly
chimes are almost deafening. The pub's interior -which also has a rear
access from Drury Lane – won a Business and Industry Award in
1978 for the meticulous restoration of its genuine Tudor timbers,
between which sections of 13th-century daub and wattle walls are still
visible. Connected by three staircases, there's a warren of rooms in
which to eat, two bars dispensing Sam Smith's Old Brewery bitter and
oak-casked Museum ale, and a tiny rear patio, as well as a table from
which you can pick up the day's papers for a browse. The menu
encourages all comers to eat as little or as much as they'd like at any
time throughout the premises, thus encompassing every taste and
pleasing all pockets, and the catering is ambitious: breakfast starts at
8am with the papers and food's served through to midnight. There are
two daily blackboard menus, one taking over from the other at
around 4pm. From this, perhaps a watercress and oyster mushroom
soup (£2), tuna and lemon paté (£2), ratatouille with garlic bread

(£3.55), and cheesy potato bake (£3.50), baked cod with a garlic crust (£6.95), beef braised in Sam Smith's beer (£5.25) or, stepping up a level, a steamed panaché of brill, monkfish and salmon (£12). In addition, an all-day à la carte extends the selection with a salad of sweetbreads and oyster mushrooms (£4.95), marinaded beef fillet with parmesan (£6.50), and pork fillet sautéed with Calvados and cream. Daily puddings could include chocolate biscuit cake, raspberry parfait with fruit coulis, meringue nests with ice cream and butterscotch or chocolate roulade. Staff are especially smart and courteous, and there are plenty of them in evidence even at the busiest times. *Bar Food 8am-Midnight. Vegetarian dishes. Free House. Beer Samuel Smith Old Brewery Bitter, Museum Ale. Patio/terrace, outdoor eating. Access, Amex, Diners, Visa.*

Linley Brook　　Pheasant Inn

Tel 0746 762260

Linley Brook nr Bridgnorth Shropshire WV16 4RJ　　Map 6 B4

Traditional country pub complete with honeysuckle round the door. Not a pub for families -very much an adult hideaway. Real fires. No music. *Beer Mitchells, Holden. Garden.*

Linthwaite　　Bulls Head

Tel 0484 842715　　**FOOD**

Blackmoorfoot Linthwaite nr Huddersfield West Yorkshire HD7 5TR　　Map 6 C1

The Bulls Head is a sombre stone free house standing high above Linthwaite on a wild and wuthering hillside. There's no easy way to find it, but having reached the village on the A62, look for signs to Blackmoorfoot (if you can find any) and proceed up the hill towards the Moors. If lost, flag down a passing local. To the front of the pub is a paved area with wooden tables. A stained-glassed door leads you into the main bar area, which has been decorated in contemporary style with two-tone wallcoverings. Cast-iron-legged tables are well spaced, surrounded by stools and smartly upholstered bench and banquette seating. A smaller seating area to the right of the entrance has a fine iron fireplace. Large parlour plants and some exposed stonework also feature, and a collection of old irons is displayed in the main bar. Blackboards display the day's choice of regularly changing bar food, for which the pub is well known and which the new licensees didn't much change. You order from the bar and pay the waitress when she appears. The local speciality, Yorkshire pudding (£1.60), features prominently, along with roast topside of beef (£4.20) and leg of lamb (£4.20), both served with fresh vegetables and roast potatoes. There's also a fine choice for vegetarians, with dishes like aubergine, mushroom and butterbean bake. Bakes are another house speciality (£3.75-£4): try the tuna, pasta and sweetcorn variety, or cauliflower, ham and courgette croustade. Lighter meals include roast beef and Yorkshire pudding sandwiches (£1.60), and home-made soup (£1), while daily specials might include a chicken, broccoli and pasta bake (£3.90). It can get very busy, and the service is friendly and efficient. A separate dessert list features mainly home-made items. There's a fruit machine and piped music. *Bar Food 11.30-10 (Mon-Fri), (Sat: 11.30-3, 6.30-10), (Sun: 12-2.30, 7-10). Vegetarian dishes. Children's portions/menu. Beer Boddingtons, Stones, Whitbread. Patio, outdoor eating. Family room. Access, Visa.*

Linton   Bull Inn

FOOD

Tel 0622 743612

Linton Hill Linton Kent ME17 4AW

Map 11 C5

If you love fresh fish, this is the pub for you. Delivered regularly from Rye, Hastings and Folkestone, the choice includes plaice (£6.25), haddock, cod, brill and huss, grilled or fried in a good light batter. Other dishes on the menu include Scottish salmon, dressed crab (£6), sautéed monkfish, fisherman's pie and skate wings. Lasagne, steak and kidney or shepherd's pie is on the menu for those who really don't want fish. Home-made apple crumble for pudding. *Bar Food* 12-2 *(Sun to 2.30)*, 7-9.30 *(times vary day by day)*. *Restaurant Meals* 12-2 *(Sun only)*, 7-9.30 *(Wed-Sat only)*. *Beer* Fremlins, Harveys. Children allowed in bar to eat. Garden, outdoor eating. Access, Visa.

Linwood   High Corner Inn

FOOD

B&B

Tel 0425 473973   Fax 0425 480015

Linwood Ringwood Hampshire BH24 3QY

Map 14 C4

Early 18th-century inn set in seven acres of the New Forest; bar food, carvery, restaurant, stable room, barbecue area, public squash court, Lego room and bedrooms. A quiet hideaway in winter, mobbed in high summer. A long list of bar snacks ranges from whitebait (£3.25) or game paté (£3.45) to baked local trout with tomato mayonnaise (£5.25) and mixed grill (£9.95), plus a good selection of ploughman's lunches (£3.25-£3.95). The restaurant offers the likes of baked egg au gratin (£2.45) or smoked mackerel and apple tart (£3.15) to start, followed by steak au poivre (£8.75-£11.50), roulade of lemon sole and smoked salmon (£8.95); top it all off with home-made puddings – from sherry trifle (£2.10) to banana mess (£2.25). There are also eight rooms for accommodation. *Bar Food* 12-2, 6.30-10 *(summer Sats)*. *Restaurant Meals* as per bar meals, but also all day Sunday. *Beer* Wadworth 6X, Marstons Pedigree, Boddington. Garden, outdoor play area. Family room *(three rooms)*. *Accommodation* 8 bedrooms, all en suite, £66 *(single £45.50)*. Children welcome overnight, cots available. Check-in all day. Access, Amex, Diners, Visa.

Little Bedwyn   Harrow Inn

FOOD

B&B

Tel 0672 870871   Fax 0672 870401

Little Bedwyn nr Marlborough Wiltshire SN8 3JL

Map 16 B3

Effectively owned and operated by Little Bedwyn's villagers, who purchased the abandoned property in 1991, the Harrow is run by husband and wife cooks Sean and Louize Juniper: accordingly the emphasis in this tiny three-roomed pub is strongly on the food. Daily snacks, lunch and evening, are prominently displayed on a blackboard behind the bar. Soup might be cream of watercress (£1.95); the main courses kidneys with marinated vegetables (£3.95), pasta with smoked salmon and avocado (£4), and for vegetarians, a Greek salad with feta and olives (£2.50). Evening meals, from Wednesday to Saturday inclusive, and Sunday lunches are more elaborate and the cooking, too, is stylish. Start with veal, pigeon and pistachio terrine (£4.95) or filo parcels of goat's cheese and herbs (£2.50). Main courses may be calf's liver with smoked bacon and mushrooms (£9.50), Wahoo steak with coriander and coconut cream (£9) or cabbage leaves filled with wild mushrooms (£6.50) followed by a selection of home-made desserts. In addition to Hook Norton Bitter, there's always a guest ale or two: the house wines only are sold by the glass, but there's an interesting list of predominantly New World bottles. Decor is minimal in the open-plan bar and dining area which leads through to an enclosed rear garden: size, however, dictates advance booking at weekends. Those wishing to stay have choice of a single, twin or double bedroom, each with en-suite bathroom, colour TV and beverage tray – but mercifully free of telephones and traffic noise. *Bar Food 12-2, 7-9.* *Restaurant Meals 12-2 (Sunday only), 7-9 (except Sun, Mon and Tue). Vegetarian dishes. Children's portions.* Free House. *Beer Hook Norton, Bateman's Premium, Brakspear, plus weekly changing guest beers. Garden, outdoor eating.* *Accommodation 3 bedrooms, all en suite, £35 (£20). Additional beds and cots available. Check-in by arrangement. No dogs.*

Little Braxted   Green Man

Tel 0621 891659

Kelvedon Road Little Braxted Essex   Map 11 C4

Secluded, unspoilt little brick and tiled pub with comfortable lounge and traditional public bar. *Beer Ridleys. Garden.*

Little Compton   Red Lion Inn

FOOD
B&B

Tel 060784 397   Fax 060874 521

Little Compton nr Moreton-in-Marsh Warwickshire GL56 0RT   Map 16 A1

David and Sarah Smith run their charming 16th-century village inn with warmth and pride, offering good plain cooking to match the simple surroundings of exposed stone walls, beams and sturdy wooden furnishings. Follow thick, spicy mulligatawny soup (£1.95) or mushrooms in garlic butter (£2.95) with a huge helping of moist pheasant casserole (£6.25) or home-made lasagne (£5.50) or rump steak cut from the joint to your own specification (£8.60). Ploughman's platters and filled granary rolls make lighter bites and there are puddings like Scotch whisky trifle and raspberry meringue. Upstairs, the three bedrooms overlook the attractive garden and share a spacious carpeted bathroom, and each has its own washbasin and tea-making facilities. Two rooms feature original beams and two have open stone walls. Garden and play area. *Bar Food and Restaurant Meals 12-2 (12-1.30 Sun), 7-8.45 (7-9.30 Sat). Vegetarian dishes. Children's portions. Beer Donnington BB and SBA. Garden, outdoor eating. Accommodation 3 bedrooms, share bathroom, £32 (single £20). Children over 8 years welcome overnight, additional beds (£10). Check-in by arrangement. No dogs. No smoking in bedrooms.* Access, Visa, Amex.

Little Driffield   Downe Arms

Tel 0377 42243

Little Driffield Humberside YO25 7DX   Map 7 E1

Completely refurbished white corner pub, with some original beams and character intact. No music. *Beer Tetley Bitter. Garden.*

Little Eccleston   Cartford Country Inn & Hotel

Tel 0995 70166

Cartford Lane Little Eccleston Lancashire   Map 6 A1

Prettily located on the river Wyre. Lots of character and comfort within. *Beer Taylor, Whitbread. Garden. Family room.*

Little Hadham   Nag's Head

Tel 0279 771555

The Ford Little Hadham Hertfordshire SG11 2AX

Map 15 F1

Built of old ships' timbers in around 1500, on the once busy old London to Cambridge road, but now a reasonably quiet country local. *Beer Greene King Abbot Ale.*

Little Hampden   Rising Sun

Tel 0494 488393

Little Hampden Buckinghamshire

Map 17 E2

Fairly smart, refurbished dining pub in sleepy village lane. The plushly upholstered, opened-out interior is warmed by a woodburning stove, in cold weather. Good local walks, but muddy shoes and boots are frowned upon. *Beer Adnams. Garden.*

Little Longstone   Packhorse

Tel 062 987 471

Little Longstone nr Monsal Head Derbyshire

Map 6 C2

18th-century village cottage tavern, full of old-fashioned charm, very popular with walkers. Real fires, no music, animals in the steep little garden. *Beer Marston. Garden.*

Little Milton   Lamb Inn

Tel 0844 279527

On A329 Little Milton Oxfordshire OX9 7PU

Map 16 C2

Thatched and golden stone 17th-century pub with rustic, characterful bars (windows at stooping height). *Beer Ind Coope, Tetley. Garden.*

Little Milton   Plough

Tel 0844 278180

Thame Road Little Milton Oxfordshire OX9 7QD

Map 16 C2

17th-century village pub full of character. *Beer Bass, Morells. Garden, outdoor play area.*

Little Missenden   Red Lion

Tel 024 06 2876

Little Missenden Buckinghamshire

Map 17 E2

Unspoilt village local, simply furnished with old kitchen range, nice coal fire and no music. Friday and Saturday evenings bring a singalong by the piano, and the traditional pub game Shut the Box is also keenly played. There's a small riverside garden. *Beer Benskins, Ind Coope, guest beers. Garden. Family room.*

Little Odell   Mad Dog

Tel 0234 720221

212 High Street Little Odell Bedfordshire MK43 7AR

Map 15 E1

Thatched pub close to the Harrold-Odell country park. Real fire in inglenook, no music, and a roundabout for the children in the garden (though they are not allowed indoors). The name comes from a supposed cure for the bite of mad dogs which 18th-century landlords took in payment of a debt. *Beer Greene King, Rayments. Garden. Children's play area.*

Little Stretton   Green Dragon

Tel 0694 722925

Ludlow Road Little Stretton Shropshire SY6 6RE   Map 6 A4

Good walkers' pub, at the foot of the Long Mynd Hills; comfortably refurbished lounge with open fire and fine views. *Free House. Garden.*

Little Washbourne   Hobnails Inn

Tel 0242 620237   **FOOD**

Little Washbourne Gloucestershire   Map 14 C1

The licensee's family have run Hobnails for almost 250 years, which must be some kind of record. The front bar is simply and traditionally furnished, with a quarry-tiled floor and low beams; there's also a modernised, carpeted rear lounge and a skittle alley. A printed menu features a vast selection of intriguingly filled baps (from £1.80), as well as a choice of 35 puddings. A separate menu carries a short list of hot specials – from goujons of chicken in garlic butter (£3.30) to lemon sole (£7), wild salmon (£7.80) and lamb casserole (£5.60). *Bar Food and Restaurant Meals 12-2, 7-10.30 (9.30 restaurant). Vegetarian dishes.* **Beer** *Wadworth 6X, Whitbread, Flowers Original IPA. Garden, outdoor eating, children's play area. Family room. Access, Visa.*

Litton   Red Lion

Tel 0298 871458

Litton Derbyshire SK17 8QU   Map 6 C2

16th-century pub overlooking the village green. Open coal and log fires, oak beams, stone walls, fresh flowers, and a strong local following. **Beer** *Boddingtons. Children's play area.*

Liverpool   Philharmonic

Tel 051-709 1163   **A**

36 Hope Street Liverpool Merseyside L1 9UX   Map 6 A2

Extraordinary cathedral of Victorian confidence and excess. Glorious tiling, carving, panelling and etched glass – a social museum piece but with modern intrusions like a juke box and fruit machine. Remarkable Victorian toilets (ornate with marble and tiles)! **Beer** *Jennings, Burton, Tetley.*

Llanfair Waterdine   Red Lion Inn

Tel 0547 528214

Llanfair Waterdine nr Knighton Shropshire LD7 1TU   Map 6 A4

Comforting little tap room and rambling lounge at a delightful riverside inn with lovely garden. *Free House. Garden. Children's play area, no children indoors.*

Llanymynech   Bradford Arms

Tel 0691 830582   **FOOD**

Llanymynech Oswestry Shropshire SY22 6EJ   Map 6 A3

Village pub (the building is in England, but entry is via Wales through the front door!) with above-average food in its spotless, comfortably traditional bar. The menu ranges from smoked meat platter (£3.95) and deep-fried halloumi salad (£2.75) to escalope of veal (£11.50) and fillet steak dijonnais (£11.95). Very good puddings – rum and walnut gateau, peach and nut pie (£1.95). **Bar Food** *12-2,*

*7-10. **Restaurant Meals** 7-10. Vegetarian dishes. Children's portions. Free House. **Beer** Marston Pedigree. Children allowed in bar to eat. Patio, outdoor eating. No credit cards.*

Lodsworth   Halfway Bridge Inn

Tel 07985 281	**FOOD**
Lodsworth nr Petworth West Sussex GU28 9BP	Map 11 A6

On the A272 midway between Petworth and Midhurst, the mellow, red-brick Halfway Bridge was originally built as a coaching inn in 1740. Today, run by the friendly Hawkins family, it's still catering to travellers with real ales and real food from an extensive blackboard menu that ranges from moules marinière (£3.50) and prosciutto and melon (£3.95) to toad-in-the-hole (£4.25) and beef curry (£4.25). If you're really hungry go for either the half shoulder of lamb or half duck (each at £7.95), both roasted to order and served with fresh vegetables. The same menu operates both in the country-style restaurant (set in the old stables) and in a number of cosy interconnecting rooms that form the bar. Real fires (one room features an old kitchen range) offer a warm welcome in winter; in summer there are tables out on the lawn and on the small patios. For celebrations try a bottle of the local Gospel Green méthode champenoise cyder (sic). **Bar Food** *12-2, 7-10. Vegetarian dishes. Free House. **Beer** Brakspear, Flowers, Marston Pedigree. Garden, outdoor eating. Access, Visa.*

Long Rock   Mexico Inn

Tel 0736 710625	**FOOD**
Long Rock nr Penzance Cornwall TR20 8JL	Map 12 A4

The name comes from one Bill Trewarthan, a mining engineer who returned from the silver mines of Mexico in 1794 to open a silver mine near the present pub. The mine flooded in 1799, but the Mexico Inn is still here, a typical Cornish terrace pub, originally the counting house where Trewarthan paid his miners and for which he obtained a licence to sell beer, a brilliant tactical move which both kept the workers happy and recouped most of the wages he had just paid out. It's a friendly, characterful place with rough granite walls, wheelbacked chairs around scrubbed wooden tables, and exposed joists and ceiling boards – the floorboards of the upper floor, painted black and red. Although the bar is small, the menu is anything but, a long and eclectic list that ranges from burgers to squid salad (£2.45), as well as traditional Mexican chilied chicken with chocolate. Long menus do not usually bode well for standards, but virtually everything here is home-cooked, including the particularly succulent ham generously sliced into wholemeal bread sandwiches. Vegetarians are well looked after too, with the likes of nutty stuffed mushrooms, and cauliflower and almond au gratin. It's not a pub for children – there's no indoor family area and no children's menu – although a small corner of the car park at the rear has been screened off and furnished with a few rustic tables and benches. **Bar Food** *12-2.30, 6-9.30. Vegetarian dishes. Children's portions. Free House. **Beer** Bass, Worthington real ale. Family room. Patio, outdoor eating. Access, Amex, Visa.*

Long Wittenham   Machine Man

Tel 086 730 7835

Fieldside off High Street Long Wittenham Oxfordshire OX14 4QP   Map 16 C2

Cheery, popular local in a conservation village. *Beer Eldridge Pope, Exmoor Ales. Children's play area.*

Longframlington   Granby Inn

Tel 066570 228

Longframlington Northumberland NE65 8DP

B&B
Map 5 D2

On the A697, cosy, attractively modernised little 18th-century inn with colourful window boxes. Main building bedrooms are small, neat and modern. Garden chalets incorporate a small sitting area, fridge and bathroom, and standards of housekeeping are reliably high everywhere. Good breakfasts; try the kippers. *Accommodation 5 bedrooms, all en suite, £53.50 (single £26.55). Children welcome overnight. Check-in all day. Access, Amex, Visa.*

Longhorsley   Linden Hall

Tel 0670 516611

Longhorsley nr Morpeth Northumberland NE65 8XF   Map 5 D2

Part of the Georgian Linden Hall hotel, or rather in a converted granary behind it. *Free House. Garden, children's play area.*

Longworth   Blue Boar

Tel 0865 820494

Tucks Lane Longworth Oxfordshire OX13 5ET

FOOD
Map 16 B2

Pretty thatched pub in the centre of a small village. Inside are two log fires and quarry tiles on the floors – lots of atmosphere with old wooden skis hanging from the ceiling. Very popular with the young and for good-value food; typical dishes include grilled king prawns (£3.50), beef and Guinness pie (£4.90), large bowl of creamy moules marinière (£3.75) and vegetable lasagne (£3.75). Three-course Sunday lunch (£7.95). *Bar Food 12-2, 7-10. Garden, outdoor eating. Family room. Beer Morrell. Access, Amex, Visa.*

Lostwithiel   Royal Oak

Tel 0208 872552

Duke Street Lostwithiel Cornwall PL22 1AO   Map 12 C3

13th-century inn just off the main road in the original capital of Cornwall. There are two bars. The saloon is the local meeting place. *Free House. Garden. Family room.*

Louth   Masons Arms

Tel 0507 609525

Corn Market Louth Lincolnshire LN11 9PY

B&B
Map 7 F2

Useful to know in an area not highly blessed with accommodation pubs is the Masons, a former posting inn dating from the 18th century. Right in the centre of the Cornmarket, the inn has been given a new lease of life by resident proprietors Mike and Margaret Harrison, who have refurbished throughout and created five new bedrooms complete with well-equipped en-suite facilities. Two further double bedrooms share a restored Victorian bathroom and separate WC. Bars are open all day with fastidiously tended Bateman XB and

XXXB on handpump. A welcoming, friendly inn. *Free House. Beer Salem Porter, Marston Pedigree, Bateman. Accommodation 10 rooms, 5 en suite, £40 (single £20). Children welcome overnight, extra beds and cots supplied. Check-in all day.*

Low Catton   Gold Cup Inn
Tel 0759 71354

Low Catton Humberside YO4 1EA   Map 7 D1

An old favourite in the York area. Modernised but pleasant and relaxing, with two real fires in the rambling three-room lounge; there's also a noisier games room at the rear. The beer garden features lots of little farm animals to delight children, and access to the river bank. *Free House. Garden, children's play area.*

Lowdham   Springfield Inn
Tel 060 266 3387   Fax 060 266 4840   **B&B**

Old Epperstone Road Lowdham Nottinghamshire NG14 7B2   Map 7 D3

We hope the new landlords will maintain the high standards of housekeeping and comfort which have prevailed here, in a converted private house set back from the A6097 amid acres of green fields. Mock beams adorn the handsomely furnished main bar and relaxing lounge bar. Most of the 10 attractively refurbished bedrooms have pretty floral soft furnishings and simple white unites, while all offer good private facilities plus TVs, direct-dial telephones, radio-alarms and tea-makers. *Beer Trophy, Marstons Pedigree, Boddingtons. Garden, putting green, children's play area. Accommodation 10 bedrooms, all en suite, £50 (single £36). Children welcome overnight, additional beds and cots available. Check-in all day. No dogs. Access, Visa.*

Lower Ashton   Manor Inn
Tel 0647 52304

Lower Ashton Nr Christow Devon EX6 7QL   Map 13 D3

Traditional Teign Valley local, keen on pub games. *Beer Bass, Cotleigh Tawny Bitter. Garden.*

Lower Froyle   Prince of Wales
Tel 0420 23102

Lower Froyle Hampshire   Map 17 D4

Extremely popular, usually bustling Edwardian village pub. *Beer Courage, Theakston. Garden.*

Lower Peover   Bells of Peover
Tel 0565 722269   **A**

The Cobbles Lower Peover nr Knutsford Cheshire WA16 9PZ   Map 6 B2

Recommended primarily for its atmosphere: originally a home for monks, a lovely, creeper-covered old pub by the church, at the end of a cobbled lane off the B5081. Toby jugs of all sizes and styles make amusing company in the snug, where the bar counter is to be found; the barless main room has a motley collection of old tables and chairs, copper and brass and decorative blue plates. *Beer Greenall Original and Ordinary. Patio/terrace, outdoor eating.*

Lower Swell   Golden Ball
Tel 0451 30247
Lower Swell nr Stow-on-the-Wold Gloucestershire GL54 1LF   Map 16 A1

Simple, friendly two-room village pub, with a real fire and traditional pub games. No children under 14 inside. *Beer Donnington BB & SBA. Garden. Children's play area.*

Lower Wick   Pickwick
Tel 0453 810259
Lower Wick nr Dursley Gloucestershire GL11 6DD   Map 13 F1

Totally refurbished 18th-century pub with open fires and a large car park, close to M5 motorway link. *Beer Bass, Theakston. Garden. Children's play area.*

Lower Wield   Yew Tree Inn
Tel 0256 389224
Lower Wield nr Alresford Hampshire SO24 9RX   Map 15 D3

Cosy whitewashed pub off the B3046 at Preston Candover, in a remote rural spot opposite the cricket ground; Sunday matches are taken very seriously. *Beer Marston Pedigree. Garden. Children's play area.*

Loweswater   Kirkstile Inn
Tel 090 085 219   **B&B**
Loweswater nr Cockermouth Cumbria CA13 0RV   Map 4 C3

A very quaint little inn overlooking the River Parkbeck, in a quiet Lakeland valley which has everything – lakes, mountains, pastures and forest. The beamed bars attract locals and climbers alike, and they are made pleasing by pot plants, wooden tables and settles and a Buttermere slate shove-ha'penny board. The compact bedrooms are clean and functional with simple furniture, individual heaters, duvets and tidy bathrooms with good towels and soaps; there is also a cosy residents' lounge and a dining room. *Free House. Beer Jennings Bitter, Youngers Scotch. Garden. Accommodation 10 bedrooms, 8 en suite, £48 (single £30). Children welcome overnight, additional beds (£7), cots available. Check-in all day. Access, Visa.*

Lowick   Black Bull
Tel 0289 88228
2/4 Main Street Lowick Northumberland TD15 2UA   Map 5 D1

An old village inn, popular with locals and as an off-the-A1 stopping point. There's a peaceful back snug and livelier locals' bar. *Beer McEwans. Garden.*

We do not necessarily recommend food in pubs that do not carry the FOOD symbol against their entry.

We always welcome new recommendations from readers. Please use the form provided at the back of this Guide.

We do not accept free meals or hospitality – our inspectors pay their own biils and never book in the name of Egon Ronay's Guides.

Other Egon Ronay's Guides available:

Egon Ronay's Cellnet Guide 1993 Hotels & Restaurants £13.99
Egon Ronay's Just a Bite Guide 1993 £8.99 (published Mar '93)
Egon Ronay's Guide 1993 ...and Baby Comes Too £8.99 (published Mar '93)

Lowick   Snooty Fox

Tel 080 12 3434

Lowick Northamptonshire NN14 3BS   Map 7 E4

17th-century long house inn with a nicely renovated double roomed lounge, oak beams, exposed stone walls, two open fires and an extraordinary carved bar counter. Children are genuinely welcome. *Free House. Garden, children's play area.*

Ludlow   Church Inn

Tel 0584 872174

Church Street Buttercross Ludlow Shropshire SY8 1AW   Map 6 A4

Pleasant rather than characterful old pub in the centre of an ancient Marches town, a good base for touring the Border country. *Free House.*

Lurgashall   Noah's Ark

Tel 0428 78346

Lurgashall nr Petworth West Sussex GU28 9ET   Map 11 A6

450-year-old pub right on the village green which doubles as a cricket pitch. Inglenook fireplaces in both bars; 90 hanging baskets in summer. **Beer** *Greene King IPA, Abbot Ale. Family room. Garden.*

Luxborough   Royal Oak

Tel 0984 40319

Luxborough nr Dunster Exmoor National Park Somerset TA23 0SH

FOOD
B&B

Map 13 E1

Nestling by a stream at the bottom of a steep-sided valley, deep in Exmoor's Brendon Hills, the Royal Oak is a truly rustic, 14th-century rural inn. No piped music, no fruit machines, no posh fixtures and fittings have intruded here – and the partly thatched roof is really rather mangy. In short, no attempt whatsoever to tart the place up for the holidaymakers, which is perhaps why so many flock here during the summer months. The several rooms have flagstoned or cobbled floors, low beams, old kitchen tables and hardly a pair of matching chairs. Besides uncontrived charm, there are a couple of other good reasons for a visit here: a splendid choice of well-kept real ales, with an ever-changing selection of guest beers to supplement the regular names, and the food, prepared by alumni from the local catering college. An extensive menu ranges widely, from sandwiches and jacket potatoes to home-made soups (£1.75), partnered by great wedges of crusty bread, and substantial main dishes like beef and Beamish pie (£4.45) with tender, lean meat in a rich gravy cooked beneath a square of toothsome pastry. There's always a vegetarian dish, and the ubiquitous fishfingers are offered to children. Steaks and fish (Dover sole £10.55) and a few other extras (fillet of pork £9.25) appear for the additional evening menu. It's still very much a locals' pub: Tuesday night is quiz night, and every Friday a folk club takes over the back room, which has a pool table and sadly unworkable old harmonium. Two bedrooms are available for overnight guests but, being above the bars, are probably not suitable for families with children or others with an early bedtime. Rooms are perfectly clean and respectable but this is not luxury accommodation: a bed and a couple of sticks of old furniture is about it. The large shared bathroom is in good order but there is no shower. **Bar Food** *12-2, 7-10. Vegetarian dishes. Children's menu/portions. Free House.* **Beer** *Cotleigh*

Tawny Bitter, Eldridge Pope Royal Oak, Exmoor Gold. Children allowed in bar to eat. Family room. Garden, outdoor eating. No credit cards.

Lyddington   Marquess of Exeter Hotel

Tel 0572 822477 Fax 0572 821343	**B&B**
Main Street Lyddington near Uppingham Leicestershire LE15 9LT	Map 7 E4

Nice old stone inn in a prosperous village. Now a Best Western hotel targeting business traffic, and rather dull 'masculine taste' bedrooms reflect this. The main bar is pleasant enough, with exposed stone and red plush chairs and stools. *Free House.* **Beer** *Batemans XXXB, Ruddles Best Bitter & County, Theakston XB. Family room.* **Accommodation** *17 bedrooms, all en suite £69 (single £60). Children welcome overnight, cots available. Check-in all day. Access, Amex, Diners, Visa*

Lydford   Castle Inn

	FOOD
Tel 082 282 242	**B&B**
Okehampton Lydford Devon EX20 4BH	Map 12 C3

Pink-washed, with wisteria entangled in its small front verandah, the Castle is certainly a pretty little pub, but it's not until you go inside that you realise how old it is. Much is 12th-century, with various later additions, and it just oozes atmosphere, with its slate floor and low sagging ceilings turned a deep amber colour by time and smoke. The place is literally crammed with bits and pieces collected by landlords over the years, including several marvellous old high-backed settles (some with little roofs), dozens of decorative plates, numerous old photos and handbills and a fine collection of Hogarth prints. At least one former owner was a strong royalist to judge by the many commemorative plates; there's even an illuminated speech, made by Elizabeth I to her troops at Tilbury in 1588. Seven of only 31 remaining Lydford pennies minted by Etherlred the Unready in the 10th century are on display too, the rest being held by the British Museum. The Castle's reputation for good food and a friendly welcome is safe in the hands of owners Mo and Clive Walker. A blackboard bar menu covers the usual ground and features fish which comes fresh from Plymouth three times a week. At lunchtime, this menu applies throughout the inn, but at night it's limited to the smaller bar and snug, when the main bar becomes a restaurant. Here, an à la carte menu features the likes of gingered prawns, smoked salmon and mussel chowder for starters (ranging from £2.50-£4.95). For main course perhaps whiskeyed steak (£13.50) or coronation chicken (£9.95). Notable among the puddings is a lovely rum and raisin chocolate crunch cake. Booking is advisable. The bedrooms have been, or are about to be, redecorated. Six of the rooms are en suite (one with a plastic shower cubicle and WC), while the others share a perfectly acceptable bathroom. There is quite a lot to see in the vicinity of the pub. Immediately next door is the castle with its rather gruesome history; local folklore has it that even to this day the birds, sensing its evil, will not go near the place. Rather more welcoming, the church boasts some fine wood carving on no less than 69 pew ends, featuring all manner of birds, fish, flowers and animals as well as a very fine rood screen. Just a short walk away is the famously picturesque Lydford gorge and its wooded walks. **Bar Food** *12-2.30, 6.30-9.30 (not Sun eves).* **Restaurant Meals** *6.30-9.30. Vegetarian dishes. Children's portions. Free House.* **Beer** *Bass, Dartmoor Best, Palmer IPA, guest beer. Garden, outdoor eating, children's play area. Family room.* **Accommodation.** *8 bedrooms, 6 en suite, £45 (single £35). Children welcome overnight, cots supplied. Check-in all day. Access, Amex, Visa.*

Lyme Regis   Pilot Boat Inn

Tel 029 74 443157

Bridge Street Lyme Regis Dorset DT7 3QA   Map 13 E2

The front bar, modernised in blue plush, is still very much a fishing haunt; a lounge at the back overlooks the river. *Beer Palmer.*

Lynmouth   Rising Sun

Tel 0598 53223   **B&B**

The Harbour Lynmouth Devon EX35 6EQ   Map 13 D1

Hugo Jeune has spent a great deal of money in lovingly restoring his 14th-century thatched pub and adjacent cottages which climb steeply up the slope from the Lynmouth breakwater. The bedrooms boast individual decor, stylish fabrics, pine furniture, colour TV, direct-dial phones and spotless bathrooms, and the top cottage, where Shelley spent his honeymoon in1812, has been decked out for modern newly-weds. There's another literary connection: R.S. Blackmore wrote part of *Lorna Doone* here. *Free House. Beer Ruddles County/Best, Usher Best, Webster Yorkshire. Garden. Accommodation 16 bedrooms, all en suite, £70 (single £43). No children under five. Closed January. Check-in day. Access, Amex, Diners, Visa.*

Lyonshall   Royal George Inn

Tel 05448 210   **B&B**

Lyonshall Kington Hereford & Worcester HR5 3JN   Map 9 D4

Originally 17th-century one-storey pub with later upper-floor extension. Cosy beamed lounge, public bar, games room and country restaurant. Snug bedrooms are simply furnished. *Beer Whitbread IPA, Woods Best. Garden, children's play area. Accommodation 4 bedrooms, sharing 2 separate bathrooms, £15 per person. Children welcome overnight, additional beds and cots available. Check-in all day. No dogs. Access, Amex, Diners, Visa.*

☺

Macclesfield   Sutton Hall

Tel 0260 253211   Fax 0260 252538   **FOOD**

Bullocks Lane Sutton Macclesfield Cheshire SK11 0HE   **B&B**

Map 6 B2

Proprietors Robert and Phyllida Bradshaw see Sutton Hall as pub (first and foremost), restaurant and hotel, in that order, and their priorities, thus set, are significant. Central to the building, a wood and stone-built 16th-century mansion in use as a nunnery until just 30 years ago, is the pub itself, which has a really stunning interior. The black oak beams, gnarled and knotted, which frame the bar are certainly of much older origin than the rest of the structure, there having been a manor house on this site since 1093, and a unique atmosphere is created by the combination of oak panelling, exposed stonework, leaded windows and two large log-burning fireplaces, one of them guarded by a medieval knight in armour. The fiercely traditional bar menu is thus much in keeping with its surroundings. Starters and snacks are of the deep-fried button mushrooms stuffed with cream cheese (£3.25), Welsh rarebit (£2.95) and chicken liver paté (£3.25) variety, while the main dishes – veal cordon bleu (£5.25), steak and kidney pie topped with oysters (£5.25) and perhaps a lasagne, all served with salad, chips or boiled potatoes are good value for money. Vegetarian dishes are done to order – stir-fry vegetables (£4.95). The adjacent restaurant, kitted out in flock wallpaper with polished mahogany tables, takes itself a little more seriously, with a weekly three-course lunch at £10.75 (£11.95 on Sunday including an extra course) and a whole baby plaice or home-made steak and kidney pie are decidedly substantial, as are the cold desserts dispensed from the inevitable sweet trolley. Evening diners can enjoy a 4-course table d'hote menu (£19.65). Bedroom conversion by the present owners has seen the installation of bathrooms throughout, plus modern day amenities like remote-control televisions, trouser presses, and hairdryers. The antique flavour, however, is well preserved in lace-covered four-poster beds and deep leather easy chairs, although (a penalty of antiquity) there's a distinct shortage of natural daylight through their leaded Gothic windows, further dimmed by heavily overhanging eaves. The Hall's immediate environs, backing on to a working farm at the rear, appear so close to ramshackle as to cause some initial concern, but the warmth of the interior and the casual tomfoolery between landlord, staff and regulars suggest that such imperfection and incompleteness are not, perhaps, entirely accidental. *Bar Food and Restaurant Meals* 12-2.30, 7-9.45. *Vegetarian dishes. Free House.* **Beer** *Bass, Burton Traditional, Stones, Worthington. Garden, outdoor eating. Family room (weekend lunch).* ***Accommodation*** *9 bedrooms, all en suite, £85 (single £69). Children welcome overnight, cots available. Check-in all day. Access, Amex, Visa.*

Maidensgrove   Five Horseshoes
Tel 0491 641282
Maidensgrove nr Stonor Oxfordshire RG9 6EY   Map 17 D3

Creeper-clad, 17th-century pub standing alone in Chiltern countryside. Walkers use the public bar. **Beer** *Brakspear. Garden.*

Mamble   Dog & Duck
Tel 029 922 291
Mamble Hereford & Worcester   Map 6 B4

Rejuvenated old country pub, run by the people who made the Crispin at Stourbridge in the Midlands so popular. **Beer** *Hook Norton. Garden. Family room.*

Manaccan   New Inn
Tel 0326 623323
Manaccan Cornwall

FOOD

Map 12 B4

Visitors are welcome at this thatched, cottagey pub deep in Daphne Du Maurier country (the original Frenchman's Creek is nearby), but the atmosphere is very much that of the locals' village pub. The actual age of the New Inn isn't clear, but it certainly predates Oliver Cromwell, to whose soldiers it was quite specifically placed out of bounds during the Civil War. The interior, with boarded walls and exposed ceilings, isn't much changed in a hundred years, and Paddy the landlord aims to keep it that way. The air of tradition extends to pub games: shove ha'penny, chess, backgammon and cards among them, which all help the regulars while away the long winter evenings. As does the range of well-kept beers, still drawn direct from the barrel on a rack behind the bar. This isn't really a pub for children, but there are plenty of tables outside in the extensive garden for summer family visits. A short lunchtime blackboard menu offers robustly cooked typical pub dishes like cottage pie, together with some inventive soups served with great wedges of wholemeal bread. The evening menu has a wider horizon: garlic prawns, chicken fricassee with pasta, plus oysters and lobsters, if given prior notice. Baked plaice costs £4, duck casserole £5, an 8oz sirloin steak £8. Good puddings come generously accompanied by wonderful thick clotted cream; the chocolate strawberry roulade is particularly unmissable. To walk it off, take a stroll up to the village church, where a remarkable 200-year-old fig tree is literally growing out of the wall. Its other claim to fame, incidentally, is that Captain Bligh was imprisoned in the vestry for a time, mistaken for a French spy when he landed here after being cast adrift from the Bounty. Manaccan was put firmly on the world map for a time when a mineral (manaccanite) was discovered nearby which in its heyday enjoyed a monopoly as an additive for strengthening metal alloys. *Bar Food 12-2, 6.30-9.30 (12.30-1.45, 7-9 winter). Vegetarian meals. Children's portions. Beer Cornish Original, Marston Pedigree. Children allowed in bar to eat. Garden, Outdoor play area. Outdoor eating. No credit cards.*

Manchester   Lass O'Gowrie

Tel 061-273 6932

36 Charles Street Manchester Greater Manchester M1 7DB   Map 6 B2

Simply furnished and decorated in a successful alehouse style, with bare brick walls, hopsack-strewn high ceilings, wooden floors and genuine gas lighting. *Beer Whitbread, Home-brewed. Family room.*

Manchester   Mark Addy

Tel 061-832 4080

Stanley Street Salford Manchester Greater Manchester   Map 6 B2

Deeply smart waterside pub with a distinctly unpubby smoked glass facade and brick-bayed and boothed interior with an elegant modern air. Canalside drinking area. *Free House. Patio/terrace.*

Manchester   Mr Thomas's Chop House

Tel 061-832 2245

52 Cross Street Manchester Greater Manchester M2 7EA

FOOD

Map 6 B2

Richard Davis and Richard Tatlow re-opened the pub's splendid dining room after it had spent long years of use as offices. Standing on one of Manchester's busy shopping streets (close to the Arndale Centre), the pub has an unassuming and deceptively small frontage. Thought to be the last surviving Victorian pub in the city, its small, narrow front bar features fine oak panelling, a mosaic-tiled floor (which spreads throughout) and Victorian-style lamps and decor. Walk through this room and an apparently small space quite suddenly opens out into the splendid dining area. Here, original and impressive wall tiles combine splendidly with the mosaic floor, and pink-clothed tables bearing small vases of fresh flowers are well spaced and invariably full. Sandwiches (made to order) are available in the bar, including a wonderful hot roast beef one, the meat freshly roasted each day. But the dining room is where most people eat. A printed menu offers a varied list, including recently-introduced tapas dishes like fried monkfish, braised squid and beef meatballs. On the regular menu, robustly prepared starters include black pudding with mustard sauce, deep-fried mushrooms or king prawns in garlic butter. Follow these with a perfectly-cooked Barnsley chop (superb meat), a northern mixed grill, grilled gammon or lamb's liver with bacon and onions. Puddings are reassuringly traditional, with old favourites like rice pudding, fruit crumble and bread and butter pudding. Expect to pay around £30 for two for a full 3-course lunch, or opt for tapas or just a single dish and you can spend a lot less. Service is friendly and informal. Weekends bring a younger and noisier crowd, as well as loud music...the landlord makes sure he has weekends off. **Bar Food** *11.30-3, 5-8 (not Sat eve, no food Sun).* **Restaurant** *11.30-4 (till 3 Sat, no food Sun)* **Beer** *Boddingtons Bitter, Castle Eden Ale. Access, Visa*

Marbury   Swan Inn
Tel 0948 3715
Marbury nr Whitchurch Cheshire SY13 4LS   Map 6 B3

In a small pretty Cheshire village which regularly wins 'best kept' awards. *Garden. Children's play area.*

Market Drayton   Corbet Arms Hotel
Tel 0630 652037   Fax 0630 652961   **B&B**
High Street Market Drayton Shropshire TF9 1PY   Map 6 B3

This creeper-clad 16th-century coaching inn located in the centre of this a market town has been the town's major meeting place for over 200 years. Exposed timbers (and creaky floorboards) have been retained in smartly decorated bedrooms, fully equipped with all modern hotel facilities. Under-5s stay free in their parents' room. Staff are cheerful. *Free House.* **Beer** *Boddingtons Bitter, Marston's Pedigree. Family room.* **Accommodation** *11 bedrooms, all en suite, £49.50 (single £39.50). Children welcome overnight, additional beds (£10), cots supplied. Check-in all day. Access, Amex, Diners, Visa.*

Market Overton   Black Bull
Tel 0572 83677   **FOOD**
Market Overton Leicestershire LE15 7PW   Map 7 E3

Having bought a semi-derelict, part-thatched ale-house in 1985, John and Valerie Owen set single-mindedly about planning the conversion work needed to create what they were really after – a relaxed local pub with good-value dining. The bar's agreeable interior of blue banquettes, polished tables, poker-back chairs and background popular music (there are speakers everywhere, even in the loos!) creates a chatty, relaxed atmosphere in which to engage in banter with the landlord and enjoy the beer. Across a central area of original flagstone floor is the dining room, converted from a garage, which offers the likes of sweet and sour chicken (£5), half a roast duck (£8.95), home-made soups (£1.45), salmon poached in a seafood sauce (£6.25) and blackboard specials like pork medallions or pork tandoori (£6.50). Sticky toffee meringue (£1.90) or profiterole mountain cake (£1.90) to finish. Upstairs, one en-suite double and a twin are equipped with televisions and a tea tray, whilst in a mews row just off the village green the Owens rent out their lovely stone-built country cottage (two up, two down) on a weekly self-catering basis but – sorry – please don't bring the children. **Bar Food** *12-2, 7-10 bar snacks both sessions. Vegetarian dishes.* **Beer** *Bass, Ruddles, Courage. Children allowed in bar to eat. Patio/terrace, outdoor eating. Visa.*

Market Weighton   Londesborough Arms

| Tel & Fax 043 087 2219 | **B&B** |

High Road Market Weighton Humberside YO4 3AH   Map 7 E1

The new landlord has been renovating the Londesborough Arms, a
red-brick Georgian hotel, restoring it to its former glory. His success is
shown by his design awards and Hotel of the Year (Yorkshire Tourist
Board). There are three good bars, including the Bradley Bar
commemorating the town's 18th-century patron. The bedrooms have
all been refurbished and feature Victorian bath suites, TVs and direct-
dial telephones. *Free House. Beer Tetley. Accommodation 14 bedrooms,
all en-suite, £70 (single £50). Children welcome overnight, additional beds
and cots available. Check-in all day. Access, Amex, Diners, Visa.*

Marsh Benham   Water Rat

| Tel 0635 582017 | **FOOD** |

Marsh Benham nr Newbury Berkshire RG16 8LY   Map 16 B4

Kenneth Graham's immortal *Wind in the Willows* was reportedly
inspired by the countryside around here and the book is the
inspiration behind the new name (it was formerly called the Red
House) and decor of this recently reopened, thatched pub. The interior
has been opened up into two areas; one, with exposed brick walls,
becomes the restaurant at night, the other has walls covered with
murals of riverside scenes; there is even an overgrown stream at the
bottom of the garden where, with a little imagination, one might
picture Ratty and his pals 'just messing about in boats'. Foodwise there
is a nice varied selection ranging from steak and kidney pie (£4.50),
prawns with garlic dip (£2.95) and deep-fried plaice (£5.50) to
vegetable tempura (£3.95), gravad lax with dill mustard sauce
(£3.95) and spinach and feta cheese strudel (£4). The restaurant menu
is in similar vein and offers a good cheeseboard with about 10 or 12
British cheeses, some of which appear on the bar menu in the guise of
ploughman's (which comes with a bowl of French onion soup from
£4.50) or a cheese plate for afters. Cheese list includes Stilton, smoked
Wedgemore, Devon Oke, Cloisters, Napoleon Golden Saye, Isle of
Mull Cheddar. *Bar Food 12-2.30, 7-10. Restaurant Meals 7-10.
Vegetarian dishes. Children's menu/portions. Free House. Beer Belchers
Marsh Ale and Best, Theakstons Best. Cider Westons Old Rosie. Garden,
Outdoor eating, Children's play area (Wendy house, sand pit and climbing
frame). Family room. Access, Visa.*

Marshside   Gate Inn

| Tel 022 786 498 | **FOOD** |

Chisley Marshside nr Canterbury Kent CT3 4EB   Map 11 C5

Delightfully set, with a duckpond in the garden. Indoors, it's rustic and
wholly unpretentious, and prides itself on still being "a talker's pub", in
tandem with a thriving bar meal trade. Fresh, local produce is used to
produce homely, honest English fare (spicy sausage hot pot
£3.50, garlic mushrooms £1.60), along with burgers and a famous
black pudding sandwich (£1.15) served with mango chutney. The
menu has two sides, one of which is green, listing healthier dishes.
Free-range eggs and local vegetables are also sold over the bar. A good
log fire in winter. Live jazz every Tuesday; quiz night is Thursday
night (when there's also a special menu). *Bar Food all open hours.
Vegetarian dishes. Children's portions. Beer Shepherd Neame. Family
room. Outdoor play area, riverside garden, outdoor eating, summer barbecue.
No credit cards.*

Masham   King's Head Hotel
Tel 0765 689295

Market Place Masham North Yorkshire HG4 4EF   **Map 5 E4**

Popular bed and breakfast inn with an imposing facade and position.
A modernised, opened-up lounge bar interior. Machines and pop
music. **Beer** *Theakston.*

Mashbury   Fox Inn
Tel 0245 31573

Fox Road Mashbury Essex   **Map 11 B4**

Remote country pub run by a Swiss-trained chef, particular about
details. Traditional pub dishes in modern dress a speciality. **Beer**
Adnams, Ridley. Garden.

Matfen   Black Bull
Tel 0661 886330

Matfen Northumberland NE20 0RP   **Map 5 D2**

Pretty creeper-covered stone-built roadside pub with open fires.
Overlooking village green and river Pont. **Beer** *Theakston, Younger.
Family room.*

Mayfield   Rose & Crown

FOOD

B&B

Tel 0435 872200

Fletching Street Mayfield East Sussex TN20 6TE   **Map 11 B6**

Delightful 16th-century pub in a historic village, alongside what was
the original London-Brighton road, now a quiet village lane. Unspoilt
bars, particularly the two small front ones, have ochre walls, beams,
and inglenook fireplace, two log fires, and an atmosphere in which
shove ha'penny and cribbage are still keenly played. Strong traditions
have now been matched by forward-looking ambitions: there's a new
car park, refurbished restaurant and newly landscaped gardens to front
and rear. The same menu applies both in the bar and restaurant – 6
starters, 9 main courses and 6 puddings. Start, perhaps, with char-
grilled duck breast with cider and honey dressing (£3.50) or smoked
chicken and quail's egg salad (£3.45), move on to fillets of Perthshire
venison with green peppercorn sauce (£7.10), char-grilled hake with
lime and tarragon sauce (£6.25) or carbonara pasta bake with garlic
bread (£3.95), followed by one of the home-made puddings (all
£2.25) – crumbles, steamed puddings, Bakewell tart or cheesecake.
The vegetables are organic from the farm next door. The five quaint,
beamed bedrooms have recently been redecorated. The furniture is
pine and the rooms are equipped with tea/coffee making facilities,
TVs, and trouser presses. **Bar Food** *12-2, 7-9.30. Vegetarian dishes. Free
House.* **Beer** *Adnams Best, Harveys Best, Abbot Ale, guest ale. Garden,
outdoor eating.* **Accommodation** *5 bedrooms, all en suite, £48 (single
£38). Children welcome overnight (minimum age 7). Check-in by
arrangement. No dogs. Access, Visa.*

Meavy   Royal Oak   ★

| Tel 0822 852944 | **FOOD** |

Meavy Yelverton nr Plymouth Devon PL20 6PJ

Map 13 D3

Narrow, high-banked Devon lanes lead to the Royal Oak, fronted by a thousand-year-old oak tree planted, as was the custom, to shade the 'preaching stone' that was here centuries before the church next door was built in 1540. Inside, old beams, deep-set windows and rustic tables are the setting for Graham and Carolyn Wilson's splendidly satisfying food (they share the cooking). Local beef and free-range chickens are a good start for the likes of beef in stout (£4.20), beef and bacon lasagne (£4.20) and chicken cooked in burgundy with smoked ham. There are always a couple of vegetarian dishes such as cheesy aubergine bake (£3.50) and vegetable curry (£3.60). For a snack try the sandwiches (all at £1.80): Club Meavy – with hot herb sausage and batter-fried onions; Oak special – with honey-glazed ham and mature Cheddar – and Rock Rooster – with chicken – all made with their own home-baked granary bed that also appears as some of the best garlic bread (£1) you've ever had. If you can save room for afters, go for some boozy bread pudding (£2) or an apple and blackberry pie (£2) that tastes as if the berries were fresh-picked that morning – and they probably were. *Bar Food & Meals 12-2, 7-9. Vegetarian dishes. Children's portions. Free House. Beer Boddingtons, Bass, Marston's Pedigree. Terrace, outdoor eating. No credit cards.*

Medmenham   Olde Dog & Badger

| Tel 0491 571362 |

Henley Road Medmenham Buckinghamshire SL7 2HE

Map 17 D3

Quaint white-painted 16th-century cottage pub with glorious hanging baskets in summer. Indoors is much modernised, but retains low beams and an open fire. Generally bustling. *Beer Whitbreads.*

Melksham   King's Arms

| Tel 0225 707272   Fax 0225 702085 | **B&B** |

Market Place Melksham Wiltshire SN12 6EX

Map 14 B3

A cobbled courtyard lit by coaching lamps brighten up the front of a traditional inn built from Bath stone, situated in the town's market square. Heavy carved-oak furniture and a beamed ceiling decorate the residents' lounge and a lounge bar is warmed by an open fire. Bedrooms are bright, pleasant and simply furnished; four singles share two bathrooms. Children up to 12 stay free in parents' room. *Beer Wadworth 6X. Patio/terrace. Accommodation 14 rooms, 10 en suite, £55 (single £45). Children welcome overnight, additional beds and cots available. Check-in all day. Access, Amex, Diners, Visa.*

Mellor   Millstone Hotel

| Tel 0254 813333   Fax 0254 812628 | **B&B** |

Church Lane Mellor nr Blackburn Lancashire BB2 7JR

Map 6 B1

10 minutes from junction 31 of the M6, in a quiet village off the A59, this small, friendly hotel effectively mixes modern conveniences with a traditional roadside inn. One of the two bars also acts as the village local. The well-designed bedrooms are better than one might expect from an inn and furnished in soft contemporary colours; some have neat, carpeted bathrooms, while ten have shower/WC only. Children up to the age of 14 are free in parents' room. Shire Inns. *Beer*

Thwaites. Family room. **Accommodation** *20 rooms, £84, £66 single. Extra beds and cots provided. Access, Amex, Diners, Visa.*

Melmerby   Shepherds Inn

Tel 0768 881217	**FOOD**
Melmerby nr Penrith Cumbria CA10 1HF	Map 4 C3

A lovely Lakeland building in a pretty village set in the picturesque Eden Valley. The bar is one long area with a pool table and games machine at one end and, at the other, an open fireplace. The Inn recently became a free house. A wide choice of home-prepared food is on offer from a menu illustrated with local places of interest – Cumberland sausage hot pot (£6.20), Ullswater trout (£5.70), roghan gosht (£6.20), steak and kidney pie (£5.40), mixed vegetable crumble (£5.10). The Inn prides itself on its selection of 26 cheeses (10 North Country) together with a range of local pickles and their home-made puddings of which toffee and banana pie (£1.95) is the most popular. Traditional roast Sunday lunch (£4.50 main course). **Bar Food** *10.30 for coffee, 11-3 (Sun 12-3), 6-11 (Sun 7-10.30). Vegetarian dishes. Children's portions. Free House.* **Beer** *Jennings Cumberland Ale, Jennings Snecklifter, Marston's Pedigree, guest beers – Hook Norton Ale, Fullers London Pride. Access, Amex, Visa.*

Meltham   Will's O' Nat's

Tel 0484 850078	
Blackmoorfoot Rd Meltham nr Huddersfield West Yorkshire HD7 3PS	Map 6 C2

Busy moorland pub with enthusiastic management, lovely views, a large garden and an intriguing selection of malt whiskies. **Beer** *Tetley. Garden. Children's play area.*

Mere   Old Ship Hotel

Tel 0747 860258	**B&B**
Castle Street Mere Wiltshire BA12 6JE	Map 14 B3

Until 1682 the home of Sir John Coventry, MP, whose banishment from court led to the expression "sent to Coventry", this sturdy coaching inn exudes old-world charm. Winter log fires warm the beamed bar and there is a snug, peaceful residents' lounge. Annexe bedrooms have practical units and modern bathrooms, while those in the main building are more traditional in style, one boasting a four-poster bed. All offer the usual little comforts. **Beer** *Hall & Woodhouse.* **Accommodation** *24 bedrooms, 16 en suite, £52 (single £39). Children welcome overnight, beds and cots available. Check-in all day. Access, Visa.*

Metal Bridge   Metal Bridge Inn

Tel 0228 74206	**B&B**
Floriston Metal Bridge Cumbria CA6 4HG	Map 4 C2

Picturesque bed and breakfasting hostelry in a picturesque village setting on the Esk estuary. The interior of what was formerly a fisherman's house is decorated with beamed bars, nets and rods. Bedrooms are agreeably rustic with pine furniture and nice views, and all have TVs. **Beer** *Scotch Bitter. Riverside garden. Family room.* **Accommodation** *4 bedrooms, 2 en suite, £45 (single £32). Children welcome overnight, additional beds, cots supplied. Check-in all day. Access, Amex, Diners, Visa.*

Mickleham   King William IV

Tel 0372 372590

Byttom Hill Mickleham Surrey RH5 6EL   **Map 17 F4**

Late 18th-century alehouse, built originally for Lord Beaverbrook's
estate staff; the large terraced beer garden has splendid views across the
Mole valley. *Free House. Garden.*

Middleham   Black Swan

Tel 0969 22221   **B&B**

Market Place Middleham North Yorkshire DL8 4NP   **Map 5 D4**

The stones that built this town-centre inn came from Middleham
Castle at the time when Cromwell was punishing it for being on the
Royalist side in the civil war. Today Middleham is a rather more
peaceful and quite pretty little market town; the smallest in Yorkshire
apparently. The comfortable bar comes complete with old beams and
cushioned high-backed settles but it is the recently refurbished
bedroom accommodation that we recommend here. The four rooms
at the front are the most characterful (and the largest) with exposed
ceiling beams but all are equally prettily decorated in co-ordinating,
floral fabrics and wall coverings and most have French-style,
sometimes fitted, furniture. All have neat carpeted bathrooms (the
small single with shower and WC only) with showers over tubs; all
rooms have TV, direct-dial phones and tea and coffee-making kits.
The resident ghosts are reputedly quite friendly. *Bar Food 12-2,
6.30-9. Vegetarian dishes. Children's menu/portions. Free House. Beer
John Smith, Theakston. Cider Scrumpy Jack. Garden, outdoor eating.
Family room. Accommodation 7 bedrooms, all en suite, £36 (single £23).
Children welcome overnight, additional beds, cot available (£5). Check-in
by arrangement. Access, Visa.*

Middleton   Olde Boars Head

Tel 061-643 3520

Long Street Middleton Greater Manchester   **Map 6 B2**

Handsomely renovated early medieval inn, with Elizabethan
refurbishments. Rambling and individually styled rooms are full of
ancient character and the cosy parlour atmosphere of the 19th century.
Piped pop. *Beer Lees. Patio/terrace.*

Middleton Stoney   Jersey Arms

Tel 086989 234   **B&B**

Middleton Stoney nr Bicester Oxfordshire OX6 8SE   **Map 16 C1**

Small, family-owned and managed 17th-century Cotswold-stone inn,
now a hotel and restaurant, well placed for Woodstock, Blenheim
Palace and Oxford (even Silverstone race circuit). Unpretentious and
cosy bars have a traditional feel. Bedrooms are divided between the
main house (where wooden beams and creaking floors abound) and
the courtyard, where they are a little more up to date. They're
equipped with colour teletext TVs, direct-dial telephones and
hairdryers; room service is also offered. One bedroom has a four-
poster and two have seating areas. *Free House. Beer Youngers Scotch
and IPA. Children allowed in bar to eat. Garden, outdoor eating.
Accommodation 16 bedrooms, all en suite, £65 (single £55). Children
welcome overnight, additional beds (children under 15 free), cots supplied.
Check-in all day. No dogs. Access, Amex, Diners, Visa.*

Middlezoy   George Inn

Tel 0823 69215

42 Main Road Middlezoy Somerset TA7 0NN   Map 13 E2

Handsome old inn that once housed the militia in the Battle of
Sedgemoor, the last to be fought on English soil. Flagstoned, beamy
public bar, and inglenook fireplaces both here and in the lounge,
which is overrun by diners at peak feeding times. *Garden. Children's
play area.*

Mildenhall   Bell Hotel

Tel 0638 717272   Fax 0638 717057   **B&B**

High Street Mildenhall Suffolk IP28 7EA   Map 10 B2

Family-run inn-hotel with a splendid interior of fire-blackened beams,
uneven surfaces and old panelling. Rooms are unfussy, neat and
comfortable, all furnished with telephones, television, tea/coffee-
making facilities and hairdryers; a laundry service is provided. *Free
House.* **Beer** *Bass IPA, Greene King IPA. Patio. Family room.*
Accommodation *20 bedrooms, all en suite, £55 (single £40). Children
welcome overnight, additional beds (£15 if over 14 yrs), cots supplied.
Check-in all day. Access, Amex, Diners, Visa.*

Mill Green   Viper

Tel 0277 352010

Highwood Road Mill Green Essex   Map 11 B4

Very popular, idyllically set little country pub, best enjoyed after a
wander through the surrounding woods – but beware the mosquitoes.
Food is secondary to the charm of the environment (lovely gardens
and traditional interior), and secondary to the life of the pub. **Beer**
Truman. Garden.

Milton   Jolly Brewers

Tel 0223 860585

5 Fen Road Milton Cambridgeshire CB4 6AD   Map 10 B2

Appealingly unpretentious, with low-beamed ceilings, pine and
darkwood tables, and jugs of fresh flowers. **Beer** *Cameron, Courage.
Garden.*

Milton Abbas   Hambro Arms

Tel 0258 880233

Milton Abbas nr Blandford Forum Dorset DT11 0BP   Map 14 B4

Thatched 18th-century inn in picturesque village street. Open fires in
winter. No children in the bar. **Beer** *Devenish. Children's play area.*

Milton Combe   Who'd Have Thought It

Tel 0822 853313   **FOOD**

Milton Combe near Yelverton Devon PL20 6HP   Map 13 D3

A 16th-century pebbledash pub in a tiny village romantically located
in a steeply wooded hollow. Lots of period touches in the main bar,
including ancient settles, foxes heads, and exposed stone. A fairly
routine printed menu is supplemented daily by a blackboard list of
around five starters including Stilton and broccoli soup (£2.25) and
calamares (£3.25); 10-15 main course specials may include chili
(£3.25), curry (£4.25) and pies. No children indoors. **Bar Food** *12-2*

(12-1.45 Sun), 7-9.30. Vegetarian dishes. Children's portions. Free House.
Beer *Bass, Blackawton Headstrong, Eldridge Pope Royal Oak, Exmoor Ale,*
Wadworth 6X. Riverside garden, outdoor eating. No credit cards.

Minster Lovell   Old Swan

Tel 0993 774441   Fax 0993 702002

Minster Lovell nr Witney Oxfordshire OX8 5RN

FOOD
B&B
Map 16 B2

The original half-timbered Cotswold inn close to the Windrush river
retains many traditional features of the pub it once was. There are
three lounges with polished flagstone floors and open log fires, and a
fine beamed restaurant opening on to a picturesque rear garden.
Sixteen superior bedrooms and excellent hotel services (graded at 67%
in our 1993 *Hotel & Restaurant Guide*) make this a truly comfortable
and relaxed place to stay. Beams feature in many bedrooms, some of
which have four-posters. The adjacent Minster Lovell Mill conference
centre is now in the same hands, making available its recreational
facilities to Old Swan guests. Its smaller bedrooms are offered at a
lower rate when not in use by resident delegates, though scrupulous
management ensures that individuals' privacy is not impinged upon.
The restaurant and private dining room are available for parties of no
more than ten. Diners can relax, therefore, in a comfortable, candle-lit
setting to enjoy some fine, robust cooking. Table d'hote may be
noodles with squid and scallops, beef fillet with creamed leeks and
potatoes, and strawberry yoghurt mousse. The seasonal à la carte adds
choices of duck confit in filo pastry on a plum sauce, grey mullet
baked with ratatouille, and banana brulée with hot rum and almond
butter sauce. Weekday lunches are in a lighter vein, as is the Gallery
Bistro which opens at night on the weekends. *Garden.* **Restaurant
Meals** *12-2, 7-10. Set L £9.50 Set D £19.50.* **Accommodation**
57 bedrooms, all en suite, £70. No dogs. Access, Amex, Diners, Visa.

Mithian   Miners Arms

Tel 0872 552375

St Agnes Mithian Cornwall TR5 0QZ
Map 12 B3

Characterful old pub extended by the addition of what was the village
shop. Low ceilings, wonky walls, a woodblock floor and attractive bits
of bric-a-brac, as well as a fascinating wall painting of Elizabeth I. **Beer**
Devonish. Garden. Children's play area. Family room.

Mobberley   Bird in Hand

Tel 0565 873149

Mobberley Cheshire WA16 7BN

FOOD
Map 6 B2

Owned by Samuel Smith's brewery and capably managed for some
years now by Andrew Towers, the "Bird" stands alongside the busy
B5085. A typical village inn, it sports picnic tables on the colourful
front patio, though parents of really young ones should be mindful of
the road. Indeed there's plenty of space for children inside among the
several panelled rooms, which include a separate stone-clad non-
smoking dining room. Drink and food orders are taken at a central
bar servery: a lengthy menu, encompassing sandwiches and salads
through to full bar meals, is supplemented by a daily blackboard
featuring perhaps king prawns in garlic butter (£5.50), spare ribs with
salad (£4.25) and turkey biryani (£5.50). Speciality of the house are
the giant Yorkshire dinghies filled with spicy sausage or steak and
onions (£5.25), or a smaller fruit-filled version with cream and syrup

(£1.95). Sunday is a big day here, starting with full English breakfast (and Sunday papers!) from 10am, a groaning plate of hot roast lunch (£5.50) added to the board and a single seasonal hot supper dish (£3.50) (chili perhaps in summer, hot pot in winter) the only fare regularly available at night. There's a fair selection of wines prominently displayed, house wines available by litre or glass and some well-kept Old Brewery Bitter and Museum ale on the hand-pumps. *Bar Food & Restaurant Meals 12-2 (2.30 Sun), 7-9.30 (not Sun eve). Vegetarian dishes. Children's portions. Beer Sam Smiths Old Brewery Bitter, Museum Ale. Cider Sam Smiths Medium. Patio/terrace, Outdoor eating. Family room. Access, Visa.*

Molesworth   Cross Keys

| Tel 080 14 283 | **B&B** |

Molesworth nr Huntingdon Cambridgeshire PE18 0QF   Map 7 E4

Skittles, darts and pool are all enjoyed by the locals at their unpretentious, 200-year-old pub which has a relaxed and friendly atmosphere. The bedrooms are warm, quiet and comfortable. All rooms offer en-suite bathrooms, TVs and tea-makers. *Free House. Beer Adnams Bitter, Scottish & Newcastle Export, Tartan, Flowers Best Bitter. Garden. Accommodation 9 bedrooms, all en suite, £35 (single 25). Children welcome overnight, cots available. Check-in all day. Visa.*

Monksilver   Notley Arms   ★

| Tel 0984 56217 | **FOOD** |

Monksilver Taunton Somerset TA4 4JB   Map 13 E1

The experienced Sarah and Alistair Cade have brought inimitable flair to the white-painted roadside Notley Arms and in just a few short years built up a formidably good reputation at this previously distinctly indistinctive village pub. The interior is charmingly simple: an L-shaped bar with plain wooden furniture, black and white timbered walls, candles at night, and twin wood-burning stoves; a small but bright and cheery family room leads off, and there's a stream at the bottom of the trim, cottagey garden. The big attraction here, though, is the bar food, which roughly divides into three categories – the traditional, the Eastern or exotic, and the vegetarian – all given equal thought, the finest fresh ingredients, and cooked with sure-handed skill. Old favourites and four or five daily hot specials are chalked up on the blackboard: start with an excellent home-made soup (£1.50), like a well-balanced tasty lentil and vegetable, or subtle potato and dill (served with French-flour bread). For a light but satisfying lunch, choose one of the delicious pitta bread sandwiches with garlic butter, tender meats and good crispy salad. Our own favourite, Chinese red roast pork (£5.25), features well-marinated cubes of meat in a soy, five spice and hoi sin sauce, with stir-fried pimento and courgette: delicious. The cod pie in filo pastry (£3.95), Somerset pork in cream, cider and shallots (£5.25), wild mushroom and pasta bake (£4.25) and braised beef with green peppercorn sauce (£5.75) are equally fine, as are puddings, with light pastry and good local cream. Try the lemon and cottage cheese cheesecake (£2.50), sticky toffee pudding (£2.50), or a locally made ice cream. A few more restaurant dishes like steaks and trout are added to the evening menu. Despite the crowds at peak times, all runs effortlessly smoothly and with good humour. *Bar Food and Restaurant Meals 12-2 (12-1.45 Sun), 7-9.30 (7-9 Sun). Vegetarian dishes. Children's portions. Beer Ruddles County, Theakstons Best, Ushers Best, Wadworth 6X. Cider*

Local scrumpy in summer. Riverside garden, outdoor eating, children's play area. Family room. No credit cards.

Montacute   King's Arms Inn

Tel 0935 822513

B&B

Montacute Somerset TA15 6UU

Map 13 F2

A 16th-century hamstone inn that was once an ale-house owned by the abbey situated in a very picturesque and unspoilt village about 30 minutes from the sea. Today's comfortable little inn offers characterful accommodation in 11 en-suite rooms, one with a four-poster bed. The Windsor Room is a relaxing lounge; the Pickwick Bar remains the centre of village life. Follow a peaceful night with a decent buffet-style breakfast. All rooms have TV, radio/alarm, tea and coffee-making facilities, drinks tray and telephone. *Free House.* **Beer** *Bass, Worthington, Toby, guest beer. Patio.* **Accommodation** *11 bedrooms, all en suite, £64 (single (£46). Children welcome overnight, additional beds (£7), cots supplied. Check-in all day. No dogs. Access, Amex, Diners, Visa.*

Moreton-in-Marsh   Redesdale Arms

Tel 0608 50308   Fax 0608 51843

B&B

High Street Moreton-in-Marsh Gloucestershire GL56 0AW

Map 16 A1

Once a stopping point on the Lincoln-Bath coach run, the Redesdale retains some period touches, including flagstones and Queen Anne panelling. Relaxation is easy in the bar and in the cane-furnished conservatory lounge. Bedrooms come in various shapes and sizes; six are in an annexe and three have patios and kitchenettes. *Garden.* **Accommodation** *17 bedrooms, £50. Access, Visa.*

Moretonhampstead   White Hart Hotel

Tel 0647 40406   Fax 0647 40565

B&B

The Square Moretonhampstead Devon TQ13 8NF

Map 13 D3

A fine traditional inn, one of the friendliest in the area, and formerly a Georgian posting house. This is due largely to likeable landlord Peter Morgan, who is very proud of his inn's 300-year history of hospitality. The beamed bar, where an open fire adds its cheery glow, houses all sorts of bric-a-brac, and there is a comfortable lounge. TVs, radios and phones are provided in the spotless bedrooms, all of which have private facilities including power showers included. *Free House.* **Beer** *Dartmoor Best Bitter, Bass Triangle.* **Cider** *Luscombe Local. Family room.* **Accommodation** *20 bedrooms, all en suite, £63 (single £43). No children under ten. Check-in all day. Access, Amex, Diners, Visa.*

Morval   Snooty Fox Hotel

Tel 05034 233

B&B

Morval nr Looe Cornwall PL13 1PR

Map 12 C3

In a valley north-west of Looe on the A387, the Snooty Fox consists of a charming original pub and an extension which houses the public bar. The bedrooms are reached via a spiral staircase and are named after months of the year. All have en suite facilities, TVs and tea-makers. A good base for exploring the lovely Cornish countryside. *Free House.* **Beer** *Flowers, Abbott Ale, Pedigree, monthly guest Bitter.* **Cider** *Scrumpy Jack. Garden, children's play area.* **Accommodation** *5 bedrooms, all en suite, £40 (single £30). Children welcome overnight, additional beds available. Check-in all day. Access, Visa.*

Morwenstow   **Bush**

Tel 028 883 242

Morwenstow nr Crosstown Cornwall   Map 12 C2

After a romantic walk along the cliffs, where the eccentric 19th-century local vicar, the Reverend Hawker, built a little shack from which to contemplate the sea and the greater questions (and now the smallest building in National Trust hands), the simple, traditional Bush, a genuinely ancient pub with a Celtic piscina set into one wall, makes the perfect resting place. No children. *Free House. Patio/terrace.*

Moulton   **Black Bull Inn**

Tel 0325 377289   **FOOD**

Moulton nr Richmond North Yorkshire DL10 6QJ   Map 5 E3

A stone's throw from Scotch Corner, this usually very busy retreat from the A1 is as popular as ever for its bar food. The lunchtime meals venue is the characterful, relaxing bar, warmed by a roaring fire in winter. Light meals include Welsh rarebit (£4.25), sandwiches (£2.25), home-made soup (£1.75), seafood pancake (£3.75) and spare ribs (£4.25). The side room has become an informal seafood bar – shellfish from the west coast of Scotland and seafood from the east coast of England. There's also an attractive conservatory and converted Pullman car for the evening trade, when the pub becomes a fish and seafood restaurant proper – Dublin Bay prawns (£12), lobster (£16.50) and salmon with asparagus (£13.50). No children in the bars. *Bar Food 12-2 (except Sun). Restaurant Meals 12-2 (except Sat/Sun), 6.45-10.15 (except Sun). Free House. Beer Theakston Best, Tetley Best. Patio/terrace, outdoor eating. Access, Amex, Visa.*

Mousehole   **Ship Inn**

Tel 0736 731234

Mousehole nr Penzance Cornwall TR19 6QX   Map 12 A4

Delightfully unassuming little fishing pub in a beautiful coastal village, friendly, simply furnished, uncarpeted, and with an open fire. *Beer St Austell. Family room.*

Much Wenlock   **Talbot Inn**   **FOOD**

Tel 0952 727077   **B&B**

High Street Much Wenlock Shropshire TH13 6AA   Map 6 B4

On the evening menu at the Talbot, there are dishes like sautéed lamb kidneys (£6.95), grilled lemon sole (£8.75), mushroom and Stilton gratin (£6.95) and a choice of puddings that includes their famous bread-and-butter pudding (£2.25), or chocolate pancakes in orange and pernod sauce (£2.95). Interesting varieties of ploughman-style picnic lunches at under £5 on the lunchtime list. A 3-course traditional Sunday roast lunch costs £7.95. The civilised interior of this ancient inn (originally a 14th-century abbot's hall) mixes original beams with plush-covered banquette seating; good open fires and nice touches like fresh flowers. There are also seats in the old courtyard (dating back to 1391). Bedrooms are divided between the inn and recent malthouse conversion with its own breakfast room; rooms are simple, pristine and modern with white cotton duvet covers. *Bar Food and Restaurant Meals 12-2, 7-9.30 (7-8.30 Sun). Vegetarian dishes. Beer Ruddles Best, Websters Yorkshire Bitter. Patio, outdoor eating. Accommodation 6 bedrooms, all en suite, £90 includes dinner for two (single £40). Children welcome overnight (minimum age 12). Check-in all day. No dogs. Access, Visa.*

Mundesley   Royal Hotel
Tel 0263 720096

30 Paston Road Mundesley Norfolk NR11 8BN   Map 10 D1

Little coastal town with good beach; the hotel is on the clifftop, overlooking the sea. Much modernised, but pleasant bar. *Beer Adnams, Greene King. Family room.*

Munslow   Crown
Tel 058 476 205

Munslow nr Craven Arms Shropshire SY7 9ET   Map 6 B4

Traditional country pub with stone walls and floors, and lots of period features in its opened-out, split-level lounge. *Beer Bass, Marston. Garden. Children's play area. Family room.*

Murcott   Nut Tree
Tel 086 733 253

Murcott nr Kidlington Oxfordshire OX5 2RE   Map 16 C2

Quaint white, thatched pub with a duckpond. *Free House. Garden.*

Nassington   Black Horse Inn
Tel 0780 782324   **FOOD**

2 Fotheringhay Road Nassington Northamptonshire PE8 6QB   Map 7 E4

The white-painted Black Horse is a pub with an emphasis on food; there are a couple of dining rooms, one with pine ceilings, but drinkers can sit on stools at the bar counter (constructed from old oak doors reclaimed from Rufford Abbey). The pink-plush, beamed lounge area has an old stone fireplace that may once have warmed Mary Queen of Scots as it was originally part of nearby Fotheringhay Castle. One can eat in any part of the pub from any part of the extensive menu that covers snacks: steak sandwich (£4.65), ploughman's salad (£4.25), cooked-to-order steak and kidney pies (£6.45); appetisers: Greek salad (£3.35), Arbroath smokies (£2.85); house specialities: magret of duck Montmorency (£9.95), chicken zingara (£8.95), fish dishes: poached lemon sole (£8.55); vegetarian dishes: vegetable and cream cheese crumble (£5.65), aubergine margarita (£5.95); steaks from the grill and puds like chocolate cups (£2.60) and a delicious blackcurrant and lemon pudding (£2.60). Despite the large menu (supplemented by a blackboard of dishes of the day) – everything is home-cooked by hard-working chef Darrell Belliveaux, who must look forward to Sunday lunchtimes when the menu is limited to a traditional roast lunch at £9.95. There's a very pretty walled garden for summer eating and drinking. Now under the same ownership (Margaret and Ron Orchard) as *The White Swan* at Woodnewton. *Bar Food 12-2, 7-10 (not Sun eve). Vegetarian dishes. Children's menu/portions. Free House. Beer Benskins, Burton Ale. Garden, outdoor eating. Access, Visa.*

Naunton   Black Horse

Tel 0451 850378

Naunton nr Cheltenham Gloucs GL5 4AD

Map 16 A1

The setting is a typical Cotswold village sunk deep in beautiful countryside. Flagstones, beams and simple furniture exude rural charm in the main bar while the lounge offers a smaller, snugger retreat. Plain, popular bar snacks start with half a pint of whole smoked prawns (£3.50), ploughman's (£2.50) or home-made soup (£1.50). A wider choice of main dishes include fresh salmon & broccoli fishcakes (£5), double English lamb chops (£6.50), home-cooked cold ham (£5) and a fine selection of home-made puddings (treacle and walnut tart £2). Vegetarians can ruminate on spring vegetables au gratin (£4) or vegetable lasagne (£4). Unfussy, modestly furnished bedrooms provide comfortable accommodation. The rooms have washbasins and tea and coffee-making facilities. *Bar Food 12-1.30 (Sun 12-1.15), 7-9.30 (Sun 7-9). Vegetarian dishes. Beer Donnington SBA and BB. Accommodation 2 bedrooms with shared bathroom, £30 (single £15). No children overnight. Check-in by arrangement. No dogs. No credit cards.*

Neasham   Newbus Arms

Tel 0325 721071

Neasham Road Neasham Darlington Durham DL2 1PE

Map 5 E3

A stunning white building, in part dating from 1610 but more reminiscent of a high Edwardian country house, complete with crenellated top at the rear. Lovely grounds. The bar is nicely pubby, with distinguished old counter fittings. *Beer Camerons, Strongarm. Garden. Children's play area.*

Nettlebed   White Hart

Tel 0491 641245

Nettlebed nr Henley-on-Thames Oxfordshire RG9 5DD

Map 17 D3

The Worsdells have done a splendid job over the last 18 months in reviving this 16th-century working inn on the A423. The redbrick exterior belies its size but once inside old timbers, low beams and the creaking floorboards of the bedrooms tell its history. In more recent times the White Hart was unofficial 'mess' for nearby RAF Benson with Douglas Bader a frequent visitor, and scenes from the film of his wartime exploits, 'Reach for the Sky', were filmed here. Today, food is a major attraction with a blackboard list of bar meals including steak and kidney pudding (£6.50) and vegetarian stuffed peppers (£6.25) plus sandwiches at lunchtime. The more sophisticated restaurant menu features the likes of green lentil, chive and quail's egg salad (£3.95), trout and scallop roulade (£6.55), roast goose breast with port sauce (£15.75) and an excellent summer pudding. Afternoon teas (£4.25) come with home-made scones and a beautifully moist fruit cake. Six cheerful bedrooms offer good cotton bedding, feather pillows and carpeted en-suite bathrooms with large, soft bath-sheets. All have remote-control TV and direct-dial phones and extras like fresh fruit and a welcoming glass of sherry. Five of the six rooms face the road so some traffic noise is unavoidable despite the secondary glazing. A neat garden and patio at the rear make a good spot for summer drinking and eating. *Bar Food & Restaurant Meals 12-2, 6.30-10 (7-9.30 Sun). Afternoon Tea 2-6. Vegetarian dishes. Children's menu (£1.95 per dish). Beer Brakspears Pale Ale and Special Bitter. Garden, Outdoor eating.*

Family room. **Accommodation** *6 bedrooms, all en suite, £59.50 (single £49.50). Children welcome overnight, additional beds (charge – by prior arrangement). Check-in all day. No dogs. Access, Visa.*

Nettleton   Nettleton Arms

Tel 0249 782783	**B&B**
Nettleton nr Chippenham Wiltshire SN14 7NP	Map 14 B2

There is a new landlord at the Nettleton Arms, where ancient timbers and a minstrel's gallery testify to the inn's considerable age – but there has also been a good deal of refurbishment and general updating. A medieval barn was recently converted into four comfortable, well-laid out bedrooms, the two upstairs keeping some old rafters. Plaster walls, floral curtains and practical modern furnishings are standard, and all rooms have TVs, direct-dial phones and good en-suite bathrooms with tubs and showers. *Free House.* **Beer** *Wadworth Henry Original, Wadworth 6X, Bass, Boddingtons, Nettles & Stinger. Garden, Children's play area.* **Accommodation** *4 bedrooms, all en-suite, £43.50 (single £30). Children welcome overnight, additional beds and cots available. Check-in all day. Access, Amex, Visa.*

New York   Shiremoor House Farm

Tel 091-257 6302	**FOOD**
Middle Engine Lane New York Tyne & Wear NE29 8DZ	Map 5 E2

This imaginative conversion of derelict farm buildings stands in open ground at the edge of a small industrial estate in a new town suburb five minutes from the Tyne tunnel. Courage and vision in unlikely circumstances have paid off, and the pub has luckily won many friends. Lunchtimes bring local trade from the industrial estate, while in the evening it's more of a drive-out-from-Newcastle crowd. Inside this mellow stone building, a large open-plan bar (its counter under the original gin gang) is subtly lit, with stripped walls. Flagstones support a mix of tables and chairs, wicker, upholstered, wing, country and banquette-style. The only modern intruder in an otherwise jukebox and fruit machine-free zone is the computerised till. Blackboard-listed dishes feature mostly fresh produce, like a tasty pork casserole in a Dijon mustard-flavoured cream sauce (£3.50), accompanied by a generous array of fresh, crisp vegetables. Old favourites from the English tavern repertoire, like liver and bacon casserole (£3.85), and steak and kidney pie (£3.85), appear alongside re-interpreted classics: poached haddock in a prawn and dill sauce (£3.95), or chicken with mushrooms and sweetcorn (£3.55). The evening à la carte menu in the restaurant offers rump steak in Provençal sauce (£5.95) or darne of salmon in véronique sauce (£5.95). It's honest, capable cooking at very competitive prices. **Bar Food** *12-2.30, 6-9.* **Restaurant Meals** *12-1.45, 7-8.30. Free House.* **Beer** *Bass, Stones Best Bitter, Theakston Best Bitter and Old Peculier, Courage Directors. Patio, outdoor eating. Access, Amex, Visa.*

Newcastle   Crown

Tel 058 84 271	
Newcastle nr Craven Arms Shropshire SY7 8QL	Map 6 A4

Pleasant 17th-century inn in the Clun Valley, formerly a drovers' inn serving the route from mid-Wales to the industrial Midlands. **Beer** *Bass, Whitbread. Garden. Children's play area. Family room.*

Newcastle-upon-Tyne   Cooperage

Tel 091-232 8286

32 The Close Quayside Newcastle-upon-Tyne Tyne & Wear NE1 3RF   Map 5 E2

A handsome former barrel-making shop dating from Tudor times, a city landmark and a popular meeting place. Inside is comfortable, rather than distinctively furnished or styled; modern machines and a juke box. *Free House.*

Newnham   George Inn

Tel 0795 890237

FOOD

44 The Street Newnham Kent ME9 0LL

Map 11 C5

Fine rugs on polished wood floors, exposed beams, open fires, evening candlelight, pretty flowers and a piano are a sample of the civilised ingredients at this lovely 16th-century tile-hung pub, its large garden backing on to sheep pastures. The food is always imaginative and varied, and takes over the whole interior at mealtimes, as there's no separate dining or restaurant area. There is always game, venison or rabbit according to season, with regular dishes such as garlic mussels (£3.50), smoked chicken and basil tartlet (£3.90) and fillet steak with port and cream sauce (£11.25) appearing on the menu along with a couple of vegetarian main courses. Pot-roast half shoulder of lamb with wine and redcurrant sauce (£9) is a popular dish. *Bar Food 12-2 (1.30 Sun), 7.30-10 (no food Sun eve, nor all day Mon). Vegetarian meals. Beer Shepherd Neame. Children allowed in bar to eat. Garden, outdoor play area, outdoor eating. No credit cards.*

Newton   Queens Head

Tel 0223 870436

A

Newton Cambridgeshire CB2 5PG

Map 15 F1

For thirty years now the Short family have owned and operated their tiny village pub which to this day resists change. Simple home-made soup served in earthenware mugs (many of them chipped!) and sandwiches filled and cut to order in the tiny bar servery have achieved over the years near cult status, while the Adnams Southwold bitter, served direct from cask, is flat yet flavourful. Village tradition, preserved by skittles table and dilapidated dart board, is echoed by pine settles, rickety chairs and old school benches which typify the pub's interior furnishings. *Free House. Beer Adnams. Outdoor eating.*

Newton   Red Lion

Tel 05297 256

FOOD

Newton nr Sleaford Lincolnshire

Map 7 E3

☺

In a quiet hamlet tucked away off the A52, this is a civilised, neatly kept pub with shaded rear garden and play area. Popular unchanging formula is the cold buffet of salmon and prawns, and carefully cooked cold meats, from pink beef ribs on the bone to Lincolnshire sausages. Price depends on the number of meats chosen: help yourself from a dozen or more accompanying salads. Limited choice of starters (soup, paté, rollmops £1.90) and ever-changing, similarly priced, array of home-made desserts. Children's prices and eating areas; informal, easygoing atmosphere. *Bar Food 12-2, 7-10 (9.30 Sun). Children's portions. Free House. Beer Bass, Batemans XXXB. Garden, outdoor eating, Children's play area. Family room. No credit cards.*

Newtown   Travellers Rest

Tel 0329 833263

Church Road Newtown Hampshire   Map 15 D3

A mid 18th-century cottage with two simply furnished old bars and a pretty garden. Occasional live folk music. *Beer Tibbs Mew. Garden.*

Nibley   Swan

Tel 0454 312290

Badminton Road Nibley Avon BS17 5JF   Map 13 F1

Lively, pleasant one-bar pub with an exciting garden for children, which features not only climbing frames, a trampoline and rabbits, but also a pair of genuine two-berth cruisers, dry-docked as ingenious play equipment. There's also a punch and judy show and barbecue on clement summer Sunday evenings. Indoors, children are only allowed in the dining area. *Beer Benskins, Courage. Garden. Children's play area.*

North Bovey   Ring of Bells

Tel 0647 40375

North Bovey Devon TQ13 8RB   Map 13 D3

Thatched 13th-century pub in a delightful village. The main bar is carpeted and opened up, with lots of heavy beams and a splendid inglenook fireplace. Fruit machine and piped music. *Free House. Garden. Children's play area. Family room.*

North Cerney   Bathurst Arms

Tel 0285 831281   **FOOD**

North Cerney nr Cirencester Gloucestershire GL7 7BZ   Map 14 C2

17th-century coaching inn alongside the A435, not far from Cotswold Water Park. In the rustic, flagstoned bar, good reliable food is served from an ever-changing blackboard selection, which includes dressed crab (£4.95), deep-fried whitebait (£3.20), salmon with fennel and Pernod (£6.50), coronation chicken (£4) and goat's cheese made in North Cerney. *Bar Food and Restaurant Meals 12-2.15 (12-2 Sun), 6.30-9.15 (7-9.15 Sun). Vegetarian Dishes. Children's portions. Free House. Beer Archers Best Bitter, Boddingtons, Courage Best, Hook Norton, Tetley, Wadworth, guest beers. Walled riverside garden, outdoor eating. Access, Visa.*

North Creake   Jolly Farmers

Tel 0328 738185

1 Burnham Road North Creake Norfolk NR21 9JW   Map 10 C1

Small local village pub, with an open log fire in the lounge. *Beer Courage, Flowers. Garden. Children's play area. Family room.*

North Dalton   Star Inn

Tel 0377 217688   **B&B**

Warter Road North Dalton Humberside YO25 9UX   Map 7 E1

A stopping-off point on the old Minster Way, the Georgian Star sits right next to the village pond, where the coach horses were watered. Inside, it has largely been remodelled in recent years with rough white plaster walls and exposed brick features in the cosy, welcoming bar and the creation of seven smart, comfortable bedrooms. All are of a good standard but vary a little; a couple have pine-boarded ceilings, one a splendid old brass bedstead; all have good solid wood furniture, neat, fully-tiled bathrooms – one with shower and WC only – direct-dial phone, remote-control TV and tea/coffee-making kit. *Free House. Beer John Smith. Garden.* **Accommodation** *7 bedrooms, all en suite, £39.50 (single £29.50). Check-in all day. Access, Visa.*

North Marston   Bell

Tel 029 667 635

25 The High Street North Marston Buckinghamshire MK18 3PD   Map 17 D1

Split-level, comfortable pub with original fireplace and lots of timber. *Beer Bass, ABC Best. Garden. Children's play area.*

North Newnton   Woodbridge Inn   ★   FOOD

B&B

Tel & Fax 0980 630266

North Newnton nr Pewsey Wiltshire SN9 6SZ   Map 16 A4

Here's a roadside inn, Wadworth-owned, which less than three years ago was closed and near-derelict: today it's akin to a 20th-century staging post, with a warm welcome to every weary traveller extended all day, every day by the new tenants, Lou and Terry Vertessy. As well as their abundant enthusiasm which has contributed so much to the pub's rejuvenation, is the commitment and imagination which has brought to these parts some truly unusual pub food. Hungarian Lou ensures a generous helping of paprika is added to the mushrooms paprikash (£3.50) and chicken Hongroise (£7.75), while Terry's world-wide experience in the kitchen leans towards the American Deep South for her blazin' redfish with creole sauce (£3.45) and traditional style Cajun blackened pork (£7.65). Mexican has become a hot favourite, represented by chimichangas (£5.55) with spiced fried beans and vegetarian or meat burritos (£5.50) topped with salsa and cheese: from the Far East comes Szechuan stir-fried lamb and prawns (£8.25). Wadworth supply the beers and many of the wines (over a dozen sold by the glass). The Vertessys have converted two bedrooms for guests' use, of which one has a private bathroom. Situated on the A345 bridge over the Avon, one and a half miles north of Upavon, it has a huge, colourful riverside garden ideal for all the family. It's open all day but more serious restaurant food begins around 7pm, and prospective diners at weekends are advised to book: a self-contained back room is available for parties of up to ten who may be disposed to that little extra merry-making. **Bar Food & Restaurant Meals** *11-10.30 (12-2.30, 7-10 Sun). Vegetarian dishes. Children's menu (£1.50-2.25 per dish)/portions. Beer Wadworth Henry's IPA, 6X and Farmer's Glory. Garden, Outdoor eating, Children's play area. Family room.* **Accommodation** *2 bedrooms, 1 en suite, £35 (single £30). Additional beds (£10), cots supplied. Check-in all day. No dogs. Access, Amex, Visa.*

North Shields   Chain Locker

Tel 091-258 0147

Dyke Street Ferry Landing North Shields Tyne & Wear NE29 6LQ   Map 5 E2

A useful stopping-off point for those using the ferry. The decor is low key and nautical, with pictures, maps and charts. *Riverside patio/terrace.*

North Wootton   Three Elms

Tel 0935 812881

North Wootton Dorset DT9 5JW

Map 13 F2

Simple old-fashioned local with a country coffee shop feel in one bar, more pubby in the other. A collection of around 900 model cars provides a focal point. *Beer Fullers, Greene King. Garden. Children's play area.*

North Wootton   Crossways Inn

Tel 0749 890237

B&B

North Wootton nr Shepton Mallet Somerset BA4 4EU

Map 13 F1

The Crossways Inn overlooks Glastonbury Tor across the historic Vale of Avalon. It is an 18th-century cider house enjoying a peaceful setting amidst lovely unspoilt countryside. Well-kept bedrooms are pleasantly decorated with floral fabrics and all have good thick carpets and duvets as well as hairdryers, trouser-presses, TVs and tea-makers. Compact modern en-suite facilities throughout. There is a homely little lounge for residents' use. *Free House. Beer Wadworth 6X, Bass, Smiles. Cider Mendip Magic. Garden. Family room. Accommodation 17 bedrooms, all en suite, £38 (single £28). No children under three. No dogs. Check-in all day. Access, Visa.*

Northleach   Wheatsheaf Hotel

Tel 0451 60244

West End Northleach Gloucestershire GL54 3EZ

Map 16 A2

Old roadside coaching inn, fairly quietly situated in an old Cotswold wool town that's famous for its 15th-century church. *Beer Theakston, Wadworth. Garden. Children's play area.*

Norton   Hundred House Hotel

Tel 0952 71353   Fax 0952 71355

FOOD

B&B

Norton nr Shifnal Shropshire TF11 9EE

Map 6 B4

A 14th-century half-timbered, thatch-roofed listed building signals the approach to the Phillips family's historic pub, in the old Hundred of Brimstree, beside what later turned into the A442. Henry, Sylvia and elder son David run the front of house and have recently been joined by younger son, Stuart, in the kitchen. The original inn dates from medieval times. This barn, for barn it be, for centuries housed the local court, and remains of the old stocks and whipping post can still be seen in the yard. The present building is largely 18th century, with quarry-tiled floors, exposed brickwork, beamed ceilings and oak panelling. The original rafters, cast-iron fire surrounds and blackened kitchen implements are all embellished by the hand-dried flowers which hang everywhere, and a persistent fragrance stems from the freshly picked mint and tarragon secreted among the table arrangements: diners are invited to pick them for garnish and to visit their hosts' extensive flower and herb gardens. Similar enthusiasm for freshness and quality pervades. Menu starters are generous enough to double as a bar snack: perhaps griddled black pud with apple sauce (£2.95), courgette and leek pancake with sage (£3.95), or garlic mushrooms with parsley and chives (£3.50). The new chef has introduced some of his own specialities to a menu which varies according to market and seasonal availability: trout packets (£4.50), bruschetta – grilled garlic bread with tomatoes, tapénade and basil

(£5.25), rabbit terrine (£4.50), spinach and mushroom roulade with onion sauce (£6.95), sirloin with tomatoes and mushrooms (£11.50) or boiled ham with parsley sauce are on a typical summer menu, with a similarly diverse list of puddings. There's a 3-course traditional Sunday roast lunch menu for £10.95. The bedrooms are equally classy, returning to the garden for their inspirational names and colour schemes. Brass bedsteads and rocking chairs abound, and extra child beds in the larger rooms are provided free of charge. There are even padded swing seats hanging from the rafters to keep the little people amused. Bathrooms are fully en suite, housekeeping throughout little short of immaculate, and fresh flowers and pot-pourris make thoughtful extras. *Bar Food and Restaurant Meals* 12-2.30, 6-10 (7-9 Sun). *Vegetarian dishes. Children's menu (£2.25 per dish). Free House.* *Beer Phillips Heritage Ale, Ailrics Old Ale, Flowers Bitter, Brains Dark Mild. Garden, outdoor eating.* *Accommodation* 9 bedrooms, all en suite, £69 (single £59). Children welcome overnight, additional beds and cots available. Check-in all day. Access, Visa.

Norton St Philip   George Inn
| Tel 0373 834224 | **A** |
| Norton St Philip nr Bath Somerset BA3 6LH | Map 13 F1 |

Certainly one of the oldest licensed premises in the land, the George has been around since before liquor licences were introduced! A Carthusian guest house since its first building in the 13th century, it has retained its present architectural features for 700 years now. Surviving to this day are the massive Gothic doorway, sloping cobbled courtyard and unique timbered galleries. On 12th June 1668, Samuel Pepys and party dined here, and watered their horses, for the sum of 10 shillings, while in June 1685 the Duke of Monmouth didn't pay at all when he and his army occupied the whole village for a week prior to their defeat at Sedgemoor. In this unique atmosphere, wonderfully steeped in history, landlord Michael Moore has been dispensing quality Wadworth ales for a mere quarter of a century. You'll get not even half a pint for ten shillings these days: but neither will it cost you a king's ransom. *Beer Wadworth's IPA and 6X, Draught Bass. Garden.*

Norwich   Adam & Eve
| Tel 0603 667423 | |
| Bishopgate Norwich Norfolk | Map 10 C1 |

The oldest pub in the city, part 13th-century, and traditionally furnished with ancient carved settles and benches, part-panelled walls, handsome parquet or tiled floors. *Patio/terrace.*

Norwich   Reindeer
| Tel 0603 666821 | |
| 10 Dereham Road Norwich Norfolk NR2 4AY | Map 10 C1 |

Popular home-brew pub – a window allows a view of the little brewhouse operation – with traditional, no-frills alehouse atmosphere; young and trendy in the evenings. Live folk music. *Beer (Own brews) Bill's Bevy, Red Nose, Sanity Clause at Christmas. Patio/terrace.*

Nottingham Lincolnshire Poacher

Tel 0602 411584

161-163 Mansfield Road Nottingham Nottinghamshire

Map 7 D3

Another of the Tynemill Group of 'green'-minded pubs, transformed from the former Old Grey Nags Head. Rather arty within, all bare boards, pine tables, banquette pews and low stools; also a tiny rear conservatory; there are picnic tables in the large rear yard. *Beer Batemans, Marston. Garden.*

Nottingham Trip to Jerusalem

Tel 0602 473171

A

Brewhouse Yard Castle Road Nottingham Nottinghamshire NG1 6AD

Map 7 D3

Originally a brewhouse for Nottingham Castle, and built into the caves at the foot of its wall, the Trip to Jerusalem (known as the Pilgrim in the 18th century) has been a pub for 800 years, "the oldest inn in England", a habitual resting place for crusading knights on their way to bash the heathen overseas. The present building is mainly 17th century; the unique rock-face walls are most apparent in the spooky upstairs bar, which is opened only when the pub is busy. Downstairs has panelled walls, built-in cushioned settles, barrel tables and exposed-rock alcoves; visitors' banknotes and coins litter the beams. In fine weather there are patios to the side and back, and extra seating in the cobbled yard opposite. There is also a souvenir shop. *Beer Hardys & Hansons, Kimberley Classic, Best, Mild, Pedigree Bitter, Marston. Patio/terrace.*

Nuffield Crown

Tel 0491 641335

Nuffield nr Henley-on-Thames Oxfordshire RG9 5SJ

Map 17 D3

Pleasantly refurbished pub with beams and inglenook. No children in the evenings. *Beer Brakspear. Garden. Family room.*

Nunney George Inn

Tel 0373 836458

B&B

11 Church Street Nunney Somerset BA11 4LW

Map 13 F1

White-painted, street-fronting coaching inn, its sign stretched right over the road, opposite the castle ruin. Real fire, no music. All the recently refurbished bedrooms have tea/coffee making facilities, colour TV with home movie channel, direct-dial telephones and hairdryers on demand. *Free House. Beer Bass, Butcombe, Wadworth 6X, Landlords Choice. Garden, outdoor eating. Family room. Accommodation 9 bedrooms, all en suite, £52 (single £42). Children welcome overnight, additional beds (from £5), cots supplied (£2.50). Check-in from 12.30. No dogs. Access, Visa.*

Nunton Radnor Arms

Tel 0722 329722

FOOD

Nunton nr Salisbury Wiltshire SP5 4HS

Map 14 C3

Unpretentious little ivy-clad pub with honest, hearty home-made food on offer. The same food can be eaten throughout the pub (in bar or dining room). Although there is no restaurant, there is a separate evening meal menu with a large selection of à la carte dishes. Some ideas might be broccoli and spring onion soup (£1.90) or sliced smoked trout to start, with devilled kidney beans (£4.25), smoked chicken and mushroom tagliatelle (£5.50), American style rib-eye steak (£7.25) or a choice of fresh fish (from Poole or Grimsby) – skate wings with caper sauce (£5.75) – to follow. Treacle tart and lemon crunch flan are popular puddings (£2). *Bar Food* 12-2, 7-9.30. *Vegetarian dishes. Children's menu (£2 per dish)/portions. Beer Hall & Woodhouse Tanglefoot, Badger Best, Hard Tackle, Charles Wells IPA. Garden, outdoor eating, children's play area. No credit cards.*

Oakerthorpe   Anchor Inn

Tel 0773 833575
Chesterfield Road Oakerthorpe Derbyshire DE5 7LP

Map 7 D3

Pleasant roadside pub with exposed stone, real fires, red turkey carpeting and large bow windows providing lots of light. *Garden. Children's play area.*

Odell   Bell

Tel 0234 720254	**FOOD**
Horesfair Lane Odell Bedfordshire MK43 7AG	Map 15 E1

There's great virtue in being content with serving the very simplest of pub food when the circumstances demand it, and at the tiny Bell Inn they've got it just about right. From the front, it's a mellow stone thatched house, and the original two front rooms, connected by a single bar servery, can still be clearly seen. Round the back, a brick extension has brought a succession of little rooms at varying levels, their low tables and stools adding to the almost miniature feel of the place. Old beams and original mantels, framing a cast iron range at one end, are hung with a collection of old brass beer taps; less traditional but rather more hygienic stainless steel engines are in active service now. Doreen Scott's stock-in-trade, in circumstances where the pub never appears less than full, is her single-dish flans of bacon or vegetables, pissaladière (£3.25) and pizza (£3), omelettes (from £3.25) and vegetable pie (£3.50), which come with salad or chips or both, and appear designed to be eaten with fork only, in a confined space. Which they are. Otherwise, there are cold platters, toasties and sandwiches (with commendable hand-sliced bread) (from £1.50) and a ploughman's (£2.45) which comes with a crock of home-made pickle. Added to these is a section honestly labelled "deep-fried" for lovers of scampi and other such things, and a routine dessert list with boozy chocolate moussse, rhubarb fool and yokel pie (all £1.60). But this is not all. A blackboard menu also materialises, offering turkey and mushroom pie (£4.60), ham, courgette and pasta bake (£4) or mango chicken (£5.10) – positively prodigious output from space so confined. It gets extremely busy, overflowing on summer days into the garden under trees down on the banks of the river Great Ouse. *Bar Food* 12-2 (12-1.30 Sun – restricted menu), 7-9.30 (except Sun). *Vegetarian dishes. Children's menu (£1.45-£2.25 per dish). Beer Greene King IPA, Rayment Bitter, Abbot Ale. Garden, outdoor eating. Family room. No credit cards.*

Odiham   George Hotel

Tel 0256 702081 Fax 0256 704213	**B&B**
High Street Odiham Hampshire RG25 1LP	Map 17 D4

The choice of accommodation at this historic inn includes characterful main-building bedrooms with their low beams and antique furnishings (including two four-posters), and rooms in the converted

coach house and former barn. Accessories throughout are thoroughly modern, and all rooms have private facilities. Farming artefacts decorate the flagstoned bar, while the residents' lounge features exposed stonework. One mile from the M3 (J5). *Beer Courage Best Bitter, Directors, Wadworth 6X.* **Cider** *Red Rock. Garden.*
Accommodation *18 bedrooms, all en suite, £68 (single £57.50). Children welcome overnight, additional beds £15, cots available £3. Check-in all day. Access, Amex, Diners, Visa.*

Old Dalby   Crown Inn

Tel 0664 823134	**FOOD**
Debdale Hill Old Dalby nr Melton Mowbray Leicestershire LE14 3LF	**Map 7 D3**

Tucked away down a lane in the village centre, this 300-year-old converted farmhouse is today the home of some enjoyable, often ambitious cooking. Cosy, antique furnished bars provide the setting, while the choice in both bar and restaurant embraces such home-made dishes as black pudding with fried apple in cream of mustard sauce (£7.50), crusty seafood pie (£7.50), duck breast with lemon, lime and champagne sauce (£9.95), soft-shell crab with anchovy butter and delicate shrimp sauce (£6.50), or stuffed aubergine and ratatouille with crusty herb topping (£6.50). Local Colston Bassett Stilton features amongst a good choice of cheeses. There is a constantly changing selection of draught bitters (approximately 15) always available. A large, pleasant and secluded garden provides a haven for children and offers a terraced area for outdoor eating from which guests can watch regular games of pétanque organised by local enthusiasts – some of whom play for England! *Bar Food 12-2, 6-9.45 (except Sun eve)* **Restaurant Meals** *12-2, 6-9.15 (except Sun eve). Vegetarian dishes. Children's portions. Free House.* **Beer** *Adnams Bitter, Broadside, Marston's Pedigree, Marston's Owd Rodger, Abbott Ale. Garden, outdoor eating. Family room.*

Old Heathfield   Star Inn

Tel 0435 863570	**FOOD**
Church Street Old Heathfield East Sussex TN21 8AH	**Map 11 B6**

Not the easiest pub to find, but head for the village church and the Star, built for pilgrims in the 14th century, is right next door. The outside has gained a few creepers over the centuries and the inside has mellowed nicely with its low beamed ceilings and large inglenook fireplace surrounded by burnished copper and brass ornaments. A major attraction is the peaceful, award-winning garden inhabited by peacocks, rabbits, doves and the bantam cocks that strut about amongst the tables showing off their fine plumage. An extensive menu covers just about everything (except sandwiches) from ploughman's (£3.75), egg mayonnaise (£2.35) and lasagne to cold turkey and home-cooked ham with bubble and squeak (a speciality), Yorkshire pudding with steak cooked in ale (£5.95) and whole lobster salad (£9.95). On weekday lunchtimes there is also a set lunch at £3.95. A daily-changing specials board might include pigeon breasts wrapped in bacon with wine sauce (£6.95) and half a roast duck with all the trimmings (£7.95) and, along with steaks and fish dishes, they also form part of the first-floor restaurant menu which has a strong military theme with lots of old uniforms on display. The restaurant opens for dinner on Thursday, Friday and Saturday and lunch on Sunday (and at other times on demand). The special £5.95 roast lamb Sunday lunch is always a sell-out. *Bar Food 12-2.15, 7-9.30.*

Restaurant Meals 12-2, 7-10 *(except Sun eve). Vegetarian dishes. Children's portions.* **Beer** *Harvey, Ruddles Best, Master Brew, Wadworth 6X. Garden, Outdoor eating, Children's play area. Access, Visa.*

Oldbury-on-Severn   Anchor Inn

| Tel 0454 413331 | **FOOD** |
| Church Road Oldbury-on-Severn Avon BS12 1QA | Map 13 F1 |

The hamlet of Oldbury lies deep in the flatlands of the Severn estuary two miles west of Thornbury and just half a mile from the water's edge. Michael Dowdeswell's old pub has a flower-decked stone frontage, a brick-lined pine furnished rear dining room and extensive streamside garden where a game of boules in the orchard is known locally as "Petanchors". An extensive bar food menu, typed up each day, relies on fresh local produce and regular favourites include grilled Gloucestershire "snorkers" sausages (£4.75), an Oldbury "Flat 'At" filled with roast beef and onion gravy (£4.90), and Oldbury mud pie of coffee mousse with fudge topping (£2.05). The same menu serves in all locations with orders taken at the bar: note here the Bass and Theakstons Old Peculier drawn from cask as well as the traditional hand-pulled ales. Severn salmon baked with white wine sauce or cold with salad (£7.75) leads the more substantial main meals alongside chargrilled sirloin and spiced chicken breasts (£6.25), and there are both vegetarian (£5.35) and meat curries. Plenty of wines by bottle and glass: book for the dining room. **Bar Food** *11.30-2, 6.30-11 (6-11 Sat).* **Restaurant Meals** *12-1.30, 7-9. Vegetarian dishes. Children's portions. Free House.* **Beer** *Draught Bass, Butcombe Bitter, Marston Pedigree, Theakston XB. Garden, outdoor eating. Access, Visa.*

Ollerton   Dun Cow

| Tel 0565 633093 | **FOOD** |
| Chelford Road Ollerton Cheshire WA16 8RH | Map 6 B2 |

Set four-square on to the A537, two miles from Knutsford, the solid-looking Dun Cow enjoys a reputation just as squarely built around its food. There are few surprises: bar snacks from a half-pint of prawns to a quarter-pound minute steak are supplemented by specials posted on the blackboard. Typical daily fare might include tomato and chili soup (£1.25), cottage pie (£3.25) and chicken, mushroom and sweetcorn pancakes (£3.95), with the likes of lemon lush or mandarin gateau (£1.95) to follow. More noteworthy, perhaps, are the junior menu (£2.95), several vegetarian dishes (e.g. Gruyère and broccoli Pithiviers or biryani with mung beans at £4.25) and an evening à la carte served at pink-clothed tables in a cottagey side room. Scampi thermidor (£6.95), duck à l'orange (£8.50) and char-grilled steaks set the tone here on Wednesday to Saturday evenings; tables are bookable, also for Sunday lunch (£7.50). Locals mostly use a traditional tap room, families can enjoy the roadside garden in fine weather and senior citizens much enjoy the bonus of a fixed-price, mid-week, three-course lunch. **Bar Food** *12-2, 6.30-9.30 (except Sun, Mon & Tues eve).* **Restaurant Meals** *12.30-2 Sun only, 7-9 (except Sun, Mon, Tues). Vegetarian dishes. Children's menu (£2.95 per dish).* **Beer** *Greenall Whitley. Garden. Outdoor eating. Family room. Access, Visa.*

Ombersley   King's Arms

Tel 0905 620315

FOOD

Ombersley Nr Droitwich Hereford & Worcester WR9 0EW

Map 14 B1

A wonderfully crooked-looking black and white timbered inn set in a quiet village just off the A449. Equally appealing within, it sports thick blackened oak beams hung with agricultural implements, gleaming brasses and polished copper pans which reflect the huge open fires in winter. The Charles II and Devonshire lounges are predominantly designated for eating, with prompt service to your chosen table from a well-organised and recently revamped kitchen. From a single menu, the choice is wide, though more tried and trusted than bristling with novelty: home-made soups (£1.95) and patés; grilled green back (£4.25), mussels and sardines; steak and kidney pie (£4.75), Mexican chicken (£6.50) and sirloin steaks; vegetarian options – mixed bean and vegetable chili (£5.50) – and a reasonable line of home-made puddings. Owing to its size and popularity, restrictions on children are strictly observed: no under-8s inside and 8s to 16s admitted for full meals only. There is, however, a sheltered rear patio to accommodate the unsuspecting and the hardy. *Bar Food & Restaurant Meals 12.15-2.15 (12-10 Sun), 6-10. Vegetarian dishes. Children's portions. Free House.* **Beer** *M & B Mild, Stones Bitter, Boddingtons Bitter, Bass Bitter. Terrace, outdoor eating. Access, Visa.*

Onecote   Jervis Arms

Tel 0538 304206

Onecote nr Leek Staffordshire ST13 7RU

Map 6 C3

17th-century Peak District pub in a riverside spot, a little wooden bridge connecting car park to garden. *Free House. Riverside garden. Children's play area. Family room.*

Orford   Jolly Sailor

Tel 0394 450243

Quay Street Orford Suffolk

Map 10 D3

Unspoilt quayside inn, made of old ship's timbers, with various rooms leading off an old-fashioned hatch servery; unusual staircase, uncommon collectables. *Beer Adnams.*

Orford   King's Head Inn

Tel 0394 450271

B&B

Front Street Orford Suffolk IP12 2LW

Map 10 D3

Pleasantly modernised, very old inn with surviving Tudor details and a welcoming real fire. Recently refurbishment has meant new seating in the bar, new carpets and landscaping of the garden. There are six bedrooms sharing two bathrooms. *Beer Adnams Bitter, plus regularly changing guest bitters. Garden, outdoor eating. Family room (in school holidays). Accommodation 6 bedrooms, sharing 2 bathrooms, £38 (single £23). Children welcome overnight (minimum age 5). Check-in by arrangement. Diners.*

Osmotherley   Three Tuns

Tel 0609 83301

FOOD

Osmotherley nr Northallerton North Yorkshire DL6 3BN

Map 5 E3

The Three Tuns sits amongst a row of solid stone cottages in the centre of the village, just two minutes drive from the A19. Its frontage is greatly enhanced by some colourful hanging baskets and flower displays. Inside, three connecting rooms are served by a central bar, simply yet effectively furnished with solid bench-style seating softened by comfortable padded upholstery, and simple wooden tables. The walls are hung with sporting prints and, in the top bar, a display of framed deeds to the building, dating back to the 1700s. Plants and dried flower displays also feature. But it's the food that makes the Three Tuns stand out; the cooking is in the joint hands of licensees Hugh and Juliet Dyson, who create some extremely innovative and enjoyable dishes, and pride themselves on only using fresh produce, as much of it local as possible. Fish is especially strong, coming from Whitby, with fresh lobsters every day (£13.25). A printed menu is supplemented by a regularly changing specials board: perhaps scallops wrapped in bacon with spinach (£9.95), a parcel of salmon and plaice with crab sauce (£8.95), or fried goujons of Whitby sole (£5.40). Meat dishes, too, show an imaginative touch, like Juliet's chicken Valdostana – York ham-stuffed, topped with cheese, tomato and basil sauce (£7.75). Each meal is accompanied by a breadboard bearing a generous hunk of good quality granary bread, and a selection of fresh vegetables is competently handled. Desserts (£2.25) are good – plum and apple crumble and bread-and-butter pudding make decisive choices difficult. The main dining area is at the top of the pub, where neatly clothed tables provide a more formal setting. It is wise to be early: once tables there are all taken, diners eat in the bar areas, but when the pub is busy (which is fairly often) a hold might be put on meals served in this area. As everything is cooked to order, a short delay can occur between courses. Prices are deliberately kept down and are really very reasonable; a competitively priced Sunday lunch (4 courses £8.50) is proving very popular indeed. Two local cheeses are supplied by a farmer with a Jersey herd. To the rear, a small garden has rustic furniture and, at the front, a couple of benches make an ideal venue for watching village life go by. *Bar Food and Restaurant Meals 12-2.30 (12-2 Sun), 7-9.30 (except Sun). Vegetarian dishes. Children's portions. Free House. Beer Younger Scotch, Theakston Best and Old Peculier. Garden, outdoor eating. Family room. No credit cards.*

Over Haddon   Lathkil Hotel

FOOD

B&B

Tel 0629 812501

Over Haddon nr Bakewell Derbyshire DE45 1JE

Map 6 C2

Signposted from the B5055 White Peak scenic route, just two miles from Bakewell, the Lathkil scores with residents and visitors alike with its unparalleled views of the Peak National Park and spectacular Lathkil Dale several hundred feet below. It's been a pub since 1813 or earlier and extensions in the 1930s created a Victorian-style bar whose use of miniature-sized tables and chairs gives an illusion of space; there's also a post-war dining room extension with huge picture windows for making the most of the view. Local landscape photographer Ray Kenning has contributed a stunning set of portraits of Derbyshire's great houses, Haddon, Chatsworth, Hardwick and Kedleston among them. Lunch is served buffet-style from a hot and cold counter to the rear with standard bar food including soup, paté, steak and kidney pie, beef and mushroom casserole, lasagne and quiche. Dinner à la carte, and Sunday lunch (reservations only) produce melon with prawns and Marie Rose sauce (£2.95), soup (£2), crayfish with garlic mayonnaise (£3.40), goujons of plaice with tartare sauce (£3), chicken supreme with asparagus (£8.50) or beef casserole with prunes and hazelnuts (£8.75). Puddings are home made and frequently change at peak times, cheesecake, walnut flan and treacle tart giving way to fruit crumble, Bakewell pudding or lemon meringue pie. Four bedrooms, converted to include bathrooms some five years ago (one a single with shower only), may be limited in space, but are comprehensive in facilities: all have colour television, clock radios, telephone and a personal bar and fridge. The best two, at the front, look across the dale to Youlgrave and the original village of Nether Haddon, now part of the Haddon estate. From the rear rooms, there are less edifying views, of fellow-patrons' wheel-hubs in the car park! **Bar Food** 12-2. **Restaurant Meals** 7-9 (not Sun). Vegetarian dishes. Children's menu (from £2.25 per dish). Patio, outdoor eating. Family room (lunchtimes only) **Accommodation** 4 bedrooms, all en suite, £60 (single £32.50). Children welcome overnight. Check-in all day. Access, Diners, Visa.

Over Peover	The Dog	FOOD
Tel 0625 861421		B&B
Well Bank Lane Over Peover nr Knutsford Cheshire WA16 0QD		Map 6 B2

Proprietors Frances and Jim Cunningham promote their business as a pub serving food, and so popular has it proved that these days table reservations are the norm. A well-tried formula invites choice of starters and main courses from the daily-updated blackboard, offering a range of soups (£2), melon with prawns, black pudding with mustard and smoked sprats with salad (all at £3.65) ahead of an equally wide range of main courses. Substantial dishes with vegetables and choice of potatoes are all under £6: liver, bacon and onions, smoked haddock and prawn au gratin, duck breast in plum sauce and rack of lamb with apricot and ginger exemplify the range. Desserts (£2.50) are selected from a groaning sideboard and cold cabinet replete with fruit pies, chocolate foods and assorted boozy gateaux. The Dog's identity as village local is retained in the Tap Room, while there's plenty of space for casual drinking on the front patio or in a rear garden where more limited snack service operates. In terms of its food, the pub could write North-Western appetites into folklore, the term "volume" being applicable equally to the portions as to the numbers who tuck into them. The individually decorated bedrooms are equally popular, their cottage appeal enhanced by the practical addition of spacious, carpeted bathrooms, colour TVs, trouser presses and beverage trays, thus attracting a clientele quite capable of providing their own telephones. **Bar Food** 12-2 (bookings essential Sun), 6.30-9.30 (Mon-Sat). Vegetarian dishes. Children's portions. Free House. **Beer** Boddington Bitter, Castle Eden, Flowers IPA, Marstons Pedigree, Ruddles Best. Garden, Outdoor eating. **Accommodation** 3 bedrooms, all en suite, £55 (single £30). Children welcome overnight, additional beds. Check-in by arrangement. No credit cards.

Over Stratton   Royal Oak   ★

FOOD

Tel 0460 40906

Over Stratton nr South Petherton Somerset TA13 5LQ

Map 13 F2

Although now a pub, this row of three 400-year-old thatched cottages still merges with its neighbours in the main street of the village and, but for the pub sign, it would be easy to miss altogether. At the South Petherton roundabout (A303) take the old Ilminster town-centre road. Cottage atmosphere is still the secret of an interior with a real sense of style. Original features like old beams, hamstone and flag floors (as well as a couple of stone pillars that look to have been there for ever but were actually salvaged from the cellars of a nearby house a couple of years ago) blend successfully with dark rag-rolled walls, scrubbed wooden tables, a polished granite bar counter and extensive displays of dried flowers, hops and strings of garlic. The latter seem to work as there is never a vampire to be seen. A globe-trotting menu takes its inspiration from you name where: croissants from France, Hawaiian pineapple and prawns (£4.95), Polynesian lamb kebabs (£5.65), steak and kidney pie (£5.95) from Blighty and much else besides. Perhaps surprisingly, given its impressive scope, everything is genuinely home-cooked. Non-fans of McDonalds should give the Royal Oak's own home-made char-grilled burger (£5.75) a try; this is as good as a burger can be. Fat, moist, succulent and laced with onions, it comes with a piquant barbecue sauce, a generous amount of varied salad and crisp, plump, golden chips. Landlady Lyn Holland is not only charming but also full of good ideas, like the Booty Box (£2.75) on the children's menu, full of goodies including a wholemeal sandwich, cheese, fruit, crisps and a crunchy bar in a special box children can take away with them. The adult equivalent is a barbecue pack (£8.50) containing a pair of lamb cutlets, sausage, gammon steak and a chicken drumstick (along with salad and jacket potato) that, weather permitting, is cooked on the grill outdoors. Other choices include squid platter (£4.95), baked avocado with crab (£5.95), veal escalope in Calvados (£11.95) and garlic fried chicken (£7.95). Beyond the barbecue, there are swings, a junior assault course and no less than three trampolines to keep the kids amused. *Bar Food and Restaurant Meals 12-1.45, 7-10 (7-9.30 Sun). Vegetarian dishes. Children's portions. Children allowed to eat in restaurant. Beer Hall & Woodhouse Tanglefoot, Badger Best, Hard Tackle. Garden, outdoor eating, children's play area. Access, Visa.*

Ovington   Bush Inn

Tel 0962 732764

Ovington Hampshire SO24 0RE

Map 15 D3

Lost down a winding, wooded lane (off A31) in the Itchen valley, this rose-covered cottage has rustically furnished, softly lit bars, often crammed with people. Nice riverside walks. Children are allowed in the dining room. *Beer Gales, Wadworth, Whitbread. Patio/terrace, outdoor eating.*

Oxen Park   Manor House

Tel 0229 861345

Oxen Park Cumbria LA12 8HG

Map 4 C4

Roadside inn set in a small hamlet on the edge of Grizedale Forest; spick and span, original beams, nice open fire. *Beer Hartley XB, Robinsons. Children's play area.*

Oxford   The Bear

Tel 0865 721783

A

Alfred Street Oxford Oxfordshire OX1 4FH

Map 16 C2

The oldest pub in Oxford – over 750 years old. In four low-ceilinged and partly panelled rooms, over 8,000 club ties arranged around the walls and in glass cases. Very popular with students in term time and can get very crowded. *Beer Tetley, Wychwood Best, Burton. Garden. Family room.*

Oxford   Kings Arms

Tel 0865 242369

Holywell Street Oxford Oxfordshire OX1 3SP

Map 16 C2

Part of the very bricks and mortar of Wadham College. The bar areas have been opened up to give an open-plan effect with wooden floors. On the left there is a food area and behind the main bar area is a smaller, cosier bar called the Don's Bar. *Beer Youngs, three guest beers. Family room.*

Oxford   Queens Arms

Tel 0865 204060

FOOD

1 Park End Street Oxford Oxfordshire OX1 1HH

Map 16 C2

Paul Dailey, also landlord of the *Blue Boar* at Longworth (qv), upgraded and refurbished the Queens Arms with Morrells last year. Now it has two rooms, with views of Oxford Castle Tower, left to the old marmalade factory and the railway tracks beyond; sliding windows at one end of the airy lounge overlook the Castle mill stream, complete with ducks and swans. Framed Spy cartoons grace the lounge walls, while the tap room is more spartan with a log-burning stove and a piano. Straightforward cooking ranges from seafood lasagne (£4.90), chicken and mushroom pie (£4.75) and stuffed smoked chicken breast (£5.25) to avocado and spinach salad for vegetarians. *Bar Food 11.30-2.15, 6-10.15. Vegetarian dishes. Beers Morrells, Bass.*

Padstow   London Inn

Tel 0841 532554

Lanadwell Street Padstow Cornwall PL28 8AN

Map 12 B3

Three old fisherman's cottages, merged into a pub in 1802, the London is plainly decorated and furnished, full of nautical atmosphere, and often busy, with a thriving local trade. An old fashioned pub "for mature drinkers", they say; children are only allowed in the restaurant. *Beer St Austell.*

Painswick   Royal Oak

Tel 0452 813129

St Mary's Street Painswick Gloucestershire GL6 6QG

Map 14 B2

Busy, friendly pub in the centre of this quaint and affluent little town, The modernised lounge, partitioned by an enormous open fireplace, has exposed stone and a beautiful old oak door; there's a second bar and little sun lounge room too. *Beer Flowers Original, Boddingtons, West Country P.A. Garden.*

Paulton   Somerset Inn

Tel 0761 412828

Bath Road Paulton Avon BS18 5PS

FOOD

Map 13 F1

Described by landlord Ian MacFarlane as "buried alive in the country near Midsummer Norton", the Somerset is an inn which quietly and quickly grows on you. Maybe it's the Mozart and Scarlatti tapes which ease the mood. Just as likely it's the pub's surprising lack of space, which necessarily and immediately instills a kind of pleasant intimacy between its customers. At the bar are half a dozen stools, and in front of it a similar number of smallish bar tables sharing the warmth of an open fire, while tucked away around the corner is a single larger dining table. Failing pre-booked use of this particular table, families with young children must fear relegation to the garden. Five years ago, this was a male-orientated darts-and-dominoes pub; today it's South Avon's honeypot for the food-minded. Yvonne's dedication to her food is total, and from nearby Radford Mill Farm come free-range eggs, organic vegetables, garlic and herbs, plus meats, when available, from its organically reared herd. The only thing you'll find fried from her menu is an egg on top of the ever-popular Somerset breakfast. The blackboard menu exhibits a much wider range of skills and eclectic influences, for instance, Spanish pork (£6.75), Zorba's surprise (roast beef in a chili-tomato sauce served with pitta bread (£6.75) and a Greek salad, Portuguese cod casserole (£6.95) or chicken and prawn creole (£6.95). Vegetarians are equally well cared for: perhaps tortellini di ricotta (£6.50) served with generous heaps of salad. These are all substantial meals for one; alternatively, the baked trout cooked in white wine and served with prawns (£13.50) is plattered up with fresh vegetables and offered as a meal for two. Sandwiches, too, arrive doorstep size (£1.75-3.25), with wonderful local fresh bread and generous fillings of tuna, cooked meats or cheese, perfectly accompanied by a glass of Ian's particularly well-kept Courage Best. To follow, rhubarb and ginger crumble (£2.50) with rhubarb from the garden, while the sweeter "pudding pie" (£2.50) is made from apples soaked in Somerset cider, with walnuts and sultanas. The laid-back, unhurried atmosphere continues to draw its fair share of local trade – fishermen and farmers – while Wednesday evening's acoustic guitar session encourages (cajoles, even) regulars into turning up with their own guitars and compositions. Children are encouraged to share parents' portions. *Bar Food 12-2, 7-9. Vegetarian dishes. Beer Usher Founder's Ale and Best, Courage Best. Garden, outdoor eating, children's play area. No credit cards.*

Pelynt   Jubilee Inn

Tel 0503 220312   Fax 0503 220290

Pelynt nr Looe Cornwall PL13 3JZ

B&B

Map 12 C3

Originally the Axe Inn, this friendly, pink-painted pub patriotically changed its name in 1887 to commemorate Queen Victoria's Jubilee. A collection of Victorian china decorates the characterful lounge bar, and there is a simpler, flagstone-floored public bar. Good-sized bedrooms are pleasantly furnished in period style and all offer neat private bathrooms, direct-dial telephones and TVs. A homely lounge is available for residents' use. *Free House. Beer Jubilee Original, Tetley. Garden, children's play area. Accommodation 12 bedrooms, all en suite, from £48 (single £25). Children welcome overnight, additional beds, cots available. Check-in all day. Access, Visa.*

Pembridge   New Inn

Tel 05447 427

FOOD
B&B

Market Square Pembridge Hereford & Worcester HR6 9DZ

Map 14 A1

A favourite for its modest but enjoyable, good value bed and
breakfast, this atmospheric 14th-century inn overlooking the tiny
covered village market has bulging wall, heavy beams, sloping floors
and lots of rustic character. Bar food avoids the usual with-chips
cliché, and goes for deep-fried brie, and chicken in cider (£3.50)
instead. The nicest bedroom is the big one at the front, with its own
en suite shower. *Bar Food* lunchtime and evening. *Vegetarian dishes. Free
House. Beer Ruddles Best, Wadworth 6X, Directors. Children allowed in
bar to eat. Patio/terrace, outdoor eating. **Accommodation** 6 bedrooms, 1 en
suite, £32 (single £16). Children welcome overnight, cot available.
Check-in by arrangement. No credit cards.*

Penistone   Cubley Hall

Tel 0226 766086

Mortimer Road Penistone South Yorkshire S30 6AW

Map 6 C2

Converted from a rather grand Edwardian villa in 1983, and lots of
Edwardian style survives the transformation, despite the fruit machines
and piped music. 4 acres of gardens and grounds. 3 car parks. *Free
House. Beer Tetley Bitter, Burton Ale, Marston Pedigree. Garden and
patio, children's play area. Two family rooms.*

Penkhull   Greyhound

Tel 0782 48978

Manor Court Street Penkhull Staffordshire ST4 5DW

Map 6 B3

Originally the local manor courthouse, with cells in what are now the
pub cellars, but little of the 16th-century original remains, though
some materials were used in the 1936 rebuilding: one bar is smartly
traditional, another distinctly post-war in style. *Beer Marston Pedigree,
Tetley Bitter, Burton Ale. Garden. Family room.*

Penn Street   Hit or Miss

Tel 0494 713109

Penn Street Buckinghamshire HP7 0PX

Map 17 D3

Cricket-mad pub with its own team and ground, and lots of
memorabilia in the comfortably modernised low-beamed bar. Real
fire; no music. *Beer Boddingtons, Marston Pedigree, Flowers Original,
guest beer. Garden. Family room.*

Pensax   Bell Inn

Tel 0299 896677

FOOD

Pensax nr Abberley Hereford & Worcester WR6 6AE

Map 14 B1

Very much a country roadside pub, the Bell's attempts to be most
things to all comers succeeds primarily because of what might be
called, in marketing-speak, consistency of product. John Stroulger's
enthusiasm for his cellar brings a continually varying selection of real
ales and guest beers: Hook Norton, Woods Special and Pendle
Witches Brew among them. Christine's approach to the food is pure
dedication, involving early starts and also invariably late finishes, just
to keep up with the demand for her beef in Guinness, steak and
kidney (secret recipe), lasagnes (including vegetarian), bolognese and
chili. Plainer palates are equally catered for on a menu of some two

dozen main dishes, as well as bar snacks of sausage, egg and chips, ploughman's various, and steak or sausage sandwiches, which are always on offer. Additional blackboards proclaim the guest beers on offer as well as listing the kitchen special, perhaps lamb and apricot pie (£5.75), soy sauce chicken (£5.95) and fresh fish specials starting at £7.25. All puddings are home-made, including the hot walnut fudge with caramel sauce (£2.10). The Bell isn't instantly appealing, and needs tidying up outside, but its interior has recently been decorated by the staff of the Bell. There are bare boards and pews in the bar, odd refectory and Britannia tables and captains' chairs in the dining room – which has a fine view of the rolling Herefordshire countryside – and a fenestrated snug which once housed the old bar. But it is the licensees who make the place, highly personable people with an enthusiasm that is infectious. *Bar Food & Restaurant Meals 12-2, 6.30-10 (9.30 Sun). Vegetarian dishes. Children's menu. Free House. Beer Hook Norton, Jolly Roger, Moorhouse Pendle Witches Brew, Old Hooky, Wood Special. Garden, patio/terrace, outdoor eating. Family room. No credit cards.*

Penzance Turks Head Inn
Tel 0736 63093
Chapel Street Penzance Cornwall TR18 4AF   Map 12 A4

Popular terraced side-street local, a lot older than it looks; the present main bar at the front was originally the medieval inn's courtyard. The old cellar is now the dining room, where the old smugglers' tunnel to the harbour, later used as secret access to first floor priest holes, can still be seen. Usually busy, popular for lunches, and lively with young locals in the evening. Piped music. *Beer Marston Pedigree, Boddingtons, Cornish Original. Garden. Family room.*

Perranuthnoe Victoria Inn
Tel 0736 710309
Perranuthnoe nr Penzance Cornwall TR20 9NP   Map 12 A4

Village pub just off the A394, with lots of maritime memorabilia in the bar. *Beer Courage Directors, Ushers Best, John Smith. Garden. Family room.*

Peter Tavy Peter Tavy Inn
Tel 0822 810348   **FOOD**
Peter Tavy Devon PL19 9NN   Map 12 C3

Off A386, atmospheric, popular old pub, once a home for masons, now very popular for its food. Marvellous in winter, with its series of heavy-beamed, snug little bars, and roaring fire. Dishes emerging from the kitchen include butter bean, leek, sweetcorn and mushroom pie (£1.80), crunchy nut pasta (£3.50), lasagne (£4.55) and seafood pasta (£3.50). Restaurant food is also available: typically, scallops wrapped in bacon (£4.45) or Hungarian salmon (£10.15). *Bar Food & Restaurant Meals 12-2.15, 7-9.30 (10 restaurant). Vegetarian dishes. Free House. Beer Adnams, Butcombe, Eldridge Pope, Flowers Original, Palmers, Royal Oak, guest beer. Cider Inch's Stonehouse. Garden, outdoor eating. Family room. Access, Visa.*

Petersfield   Good Intent

Tel 0730 263838

40-45 College Street Petersfield Hampshire GU31 4AF   Map 15 D3

16th-century free house with a beamy single bar and a small patio.
Beer Bass, London Pride, Ringwood, guest beer.

Petworth   Angel

Tel 079 84 2153   Fax 079 84 4355   **B&B**

Angel Street Petworth West Sussex GU28 0BG   Map 11 A6

This inn dates from the 13th century and bowed walls, exposed
beams, headcracking doorways and wildly sloping floors all testify to
its antiquity. The jumble of centuries is particularly apparent in the
bedrooms, which the new owners have extended and upgraded. All
rooms have either bath or shower facilities and TVs, tea-makers,
hairdryers and trouser presses. Decorated in blue, they have co-
ordinated floral bed linen and oak furnishings. In the bar, tapestry-
covered stools and benches, Windsor chairs and horse brasses create a
fairly standard old-world look. *Free House. Garden. Beer Badger,
Bateman, Gales, Ballards, Tanglefoot. Cider Scrumpy Jack.
Accommodation 8 bedrooms, all en suite, £50 (single £40). Children
welcome overnight, additional beds available. Check-in all day.*
Access, Amex, Visa.

Petworth   Welldiggers Arms

Tel 0798 42287   **FOOD**

Pulborough Road Petworth West Sussex GU28 0GH   Map 11 A6

Very much a dining pub, usually very busy in both bar and snug. One
can gaze at the lovely view to the South Downs from the closed-in
patio. Popular with enthusiasts of racing (Goodwood), shooting and
polo (Cowdray Park). Excellent seafood – crab soup (£3.50), lobsters
(£14.50 whole, £10.50 half), seafood platter (£10.50), seafood royale
(£18) – and properly hung steaks: T-bone (£14.50), sirloin (£11.50)
and mixed grill (£8.50). Alternatives are home-cooked ham, egg and
chips (£4.95), chili (£3.50), roast duck with apple sauce (£8.50) or
courgette cheese bake (£4.50). Home-made puddings include treacle
tart and lemon meringue pie (both £3.50). *Bar Food 12-2, 6-10
(7-10 Sun in summer, closed in winter). Vegetarian dishes. Children's
menu (£3.50). Free House. Beer Directors, Youngs, Ruddles. Pub closed
on Sunday evenings in winter.* Access, Amex, Diners, Visa.

Philleigh   Roseland Inn

Tel 0872 580254   **FOOD**

Philleigh nr Truro Cornwall TR2 5NB   Map 12 B3

17th-century cob-built Cornish treasure, run with enthusiastic panache
and never less than spotless. The front terrace is delightfully floral, and
indoors there are old-fashioned seats, a lovely old settle, worn slate
floors, fresh flowers, low beams and a welcoming fire. The menu
covers a range from Cornish pasty (£1.50) and creamy garlic
mushrooms with bacon and toast (£2.95) to crab salad (£6.95) and
ratatouille au gratin (£3.25). In the evening, pan-fried sirloin steak
chasseur (£8.75), grilled local lemon sole (£8.25) and vegetable curry
with saffron rice (£6.50) are offered in addition. Roast Sunday lunch.
*Bar Food 12-2, 6.30-9 (no food Sun, Mon, Tue & eves in winter). Beer
Cornish Original, Whitbread Flowers IPA. Patio/terrace, outdoor eating.
No credit cards.*

Pickhill   Nags Head

FOOD
B&B
Map 5 E4

Tel 0845 567391   Fax 0845 567212

Pickhill nr Thirsk North Yorkshire YO7 4JT

Both the village of Pickhill and the Nags Head are posted off the A1. In the centre of the village, just up from the village green, this former coaching inn, much extended and improved over the years, has been owned and run by brothers Raymond and Edward Boynton since 1972. Outside the cream-painted, part creeper-clad building, is the Boyntons' Infallible Weather Stone, basically a large stone on a chain with humorous explanations as to how it predicts the weather. The flagstoned porchway is also the inn's reception area, while a narrow corridor leads into the very lively public bar (recently refurbished), which is extremely popular with locals and always a hive of noise and conversation. There are beamed ceilings, flagged floors, walls covered with photos of aircraft from local and visiting RAF stations, aerial photos of the pub, and a huge collection of ties hung around the whole bar and from the ceiling – it's as if every male visitor to the pub had his tie pinched, so beware! The adjoining lounge bar is dimly lit, with banquette seating in dark green, beamed ceilings and a central fireplace. Walls are hung with a number of framed pictures, many of which are offered for sale. Two blackboards are in each bar, showing the day's choice of bar food (described as "informal eating"). It's an interesting selection, with dishes like smoked pork chop with sauerkraut (£7.25), salmon and halibut fishcakes with prawn and lobster sauce (£6.25), rainbow trout filled with crab deep-fried in beer batter (£7.25), and game pie (£7.50). A longer restaurant menu has a more varied choice, with dishes priced a pound or two higher than in the bar, e.g. Hare & Hounds fillet steak (£10.50), pork fillet stuffed with ham and Stilton (£8.75). The restaurant itself is decorated in tones of green and salmon pink, with clothed tables and a more contemporary style. Bedrooms are split between the main building, the next-door house and a cottage, which can also be let in its entirety. Main-building rooms have darker shades of decor, pine furniture and matching duvets. The house next door is more modern, with pastel pink walls, contrasting green borders and co-ordinated fabrics. En-suite bathrooms (3 with shower only) are all carpeted, and those with baths also have good showers fitted over them. *Bar Food* 12-2, 6-10 *(7-9.30 Sun)*. *Restaurant Meals* 7-9.30 *(except Sun)*. *Vegetarian dishes. Children's portions. Free House.* *Beer* *Theakston XB, Best and Old Peculier, Hambleton Best, Younger Scotch. Garden, outdoor eating, children's play area.* *Accommodation* *15 bedrooms, all en suite, £42 (single £30). Children welcome overnight, additional beds (from £5) and cots (from £5). Check-in all day. Access, Visa.*

Picklescott   Bottle & Glass

Map 6 A4

Tel 0694 751345

Picklescott nr Church Stretton Shropshire SY6 6NR

17th-century inn near Long Mynd, with an attractive garden for summer eating, and fine bordered front seating area. Two refurbished, carpeted bars, with oak beams and open fires. *Free House.* *Beer* *Bass, Worthington. Garden, patio, outdoor eating.*

Piddlehinton   Thimble Inn

Tel 03004 270

Piddlehinton nr Dorchester Dorset DT2 7UE   Map 13 F2

Creeper-covered, picturesque thatched old pub with intimate, cosy interior, nice wooden furnishings and a thimble collection. *Free House. Beer Hall & Woodhouse, Eldridge Pope, Ringwood. Riverside garden, children's play area. Family room.*

Piercebridge   George

Tel 0325 374576

Piercebridge Co Durham DL2 3SW   Map 5 D3

Handsome white 16th-century roadside coaching inn in the heart of the North-East tourist area. Three civilised and comfortble bars have at least five open fires between them, old wooden furniture, and in the lounge, overlooking the river Tees, chesterfield sofas. Two brothers who died at the George, and their grandfather clock which stopped at the same moment, prompted an 1850s American lyricist to pen a well-known song. The clock is still here. Fishing is free to overnight residents. *Free House. Beer John Smiths Magnet, Websters. Riverside garden. Family room.*

Pin Mill   Butt & Oyster

Tel 0473 780764

Pin Mill nr Chelmondiston Suffolk CB8 9PP   Map 10 C3

Classic riverside pub, chock-full of tourists when not with locals, all enjoying the simple charm of its old settles, tiled flooors and fine views: be early for a waterside window seat, or one of the sturdy wooden outdoor ones on the bank. Traditional pub games are popular when the crowds have gone home. *Beer Tolly Mild, Bitter and Original, Tetley Bitter. Riverside patio. Family room.*

Pitton   Silver Plough

Tel 0722 72266   **FOOD**

Pitton nr Salisbury Wiltshire SP5 1DZ   Map 14 C3

The Silver Plough was a farmhouse until after the Second World War. Everything about it is neat and well-kept: the lawns at the front, full of white plastic tables and chairs for summer drinking, and the main bar with its dust-free jugs, bottles and curios hanging from the ceiling timbers. It's very much an eating pub and part of this bar has some clothed tables, spilling over from the restaurant in the next room. There's also a snug, with old settles and an extraordinary thatched roof over its bar counter, off which is a little skittles alley, available to the casual player when not booked by a private party. At lunchtime the menu is set out on various blackboards, backed by an additional printed menu. There is a choice of two table d'hote menus – one off the blackboard (2-course £10.95, 3-course £12.95) and the other from the printed menu (2-course £12.95, 3-course £15.95). The choice of food is wide and the cookery adventurous: poached chicken wrapped in olive bread (£3.95), locally smoked trout fillets with Stilton mayonnaise (£3.95) or steamed chicken breast with mustard and herb gratin (£8.50) typify the style. Even the ploughman's, lunchtime only, offers a choice of seven different cheeses from surrounding counties. The selection of drinks is equally wide. There are real ales, of course, but also more exotic brews from

Czechoslovakia and Thailand, no less than ten wines offered by the glass, from an excellent, wide-ranging list of bottles, and a whole raft of country wines, from elderberry and damson to ginger and parsnip. Although not setting out to attract children especially, they are happy to produce smaller portions of suitable dishes and can always come up with a plateful of chips for philistine toddler tastes. *Bar Food 12-2, 7-10 (7-9.30 Sun). Vegetarian dishes. Children's portions. Beer Wadworth 6X and IPA, Courage Best, Bass, Bunce Old Smokey. Garden, outdoor eating. Family room. Access, Amex, Diners, Visa.*

Pluckley   Dering Arms

Tel 0233 840371

Station Road Pluckley nr Ashford Kent TN27 0RR   Map 11 C5

Impressive manorial building, once the Dering Estate hunting lodge, with curving Dutch gables, rounded triple lancet 'Dering' windows, and a rather spooky grandeur. *Free House. Beer Goacher: Real Mild, Maidstone Ale, Dering Ale, Old Ale; Shepherd Neame's Spitfire, Young's Special. Garden. Family room.*

Plush   Brace of Pheasants

Tel 03004 357

Plush Dorset DT2 7RQ   Map 13 F2

Characterful converted row of village cottages in a pretty rural spot. The bar is lovely in winter, with its stove at one end, log fire at the other. *Free House. Beer Greene King Abbot, Wadworth IPA, Exmoor Stag. 2 gardens, children's play area. Family room.*

Plymouth   The China House

Tel 0752 260930   **FOOD**

Marrowbone Slip Sutton Harbour Plymouth Devon PL4 0DW   Map 12 C3

The China House has had many uses since being built as a quayside warehouse in the mid-1600s, King's bakehouse, hospital for seamen, porcelain factory (from which period it takes its name) and prison, amongst others. Now cleverly rebuilt inside to reflect its warehouse days with great bulks of timber, cast-iron pillars and nets of mock cargo, it makes a most unusual hostelry with the added attraction of some good bar food. The lunch menu is not large: about half-a-dozen hot dishes like jacket potatoes with tuna and onion (£2.95), chicken and broccoli pie (£4.95) and spaghetti carbonara (£4.35) plus open 'doorsteps' sandwiches from £2.15, with beef, prawn, local crab or ham on great wedges of good granary bread. Puds (all at £2.50) include fruit pies and various ice creams (£1.95). At night the sandwiches disappear but there are a couple of starters and a few more main dishes: rack of lamb with garlic and mint (£8.95), barbecued spare ribs (£5.95) and fresh fish according to the market (£8.95). There is a no-smoking area and a narrow verandah (no tables) jutting out over the waters of the harbour. *Bar Food & Restaurant Meals 12-2.30, 6-10. Vegetarian dishes. Children's portions. Beer Ansells, Dartmoor Best and Strong. Terrace, outdoor eating. Access, Amex, Visa.*

Pocklington   Feathers Hotel

Tel 0759 303155

56 Market Place Pocklington Humberside YO4 2AH

B&B

Map 7 D1

Popular with the locals, who enjoy a drink in the spacious, welcoming bar, this pebbledash pub on the market place also has decent overnight accommodation. The six main-house bedrooms of varying sizes have a traditional appeal (one boasts a half-tester), while the remaining six, across the car park, are in chalet style. All offer hairdryers, trouser presses, tea-makers and smart private facilities. Residents have use of a homely TV lounge. *Beer* Youngers Scotch, Theakston. *Accommodation 12 bedrooms, all en suite, £48 (single £34). Children welcome overnight, additional beds and cots available. Check-in all day. No dogs. Access, Amex, Diners, Visa.*

Polperro   Blue Peter

No telephone

The Quay Polperro Cornwall

Map 12 C3

Unspoilt little fishing pub in a very touristy village; it's a good ten minute walk down from the public car park at the top to the quaint little harbour and its popular little pub. Head for the main bar, and be early: it's traditional, authentically seafaring in mood, with nice old furnishings, and soothing views – but there are also modern games machines and piped music. Families can use the less atmospheric family room upstairs. *Free House.*

Polperro   Three Pilchards

Tel 0503 72233

The Quay Polperro Cornwall PL13 2QZ

Map 12 C3

Polperro's oldest pub, plain and simple, popular with fisherman and walkers. *Beer* Ushers Best and Founders. *Roof garden, outdoor eating.*

Pontefract   Parkside Inn

Tel 0977 709911   Fax 0977 701602

Park Road Pontefract West Yorkshire WF8 4QD

B&B

Map 7 D1

If you enjoy attending race meetings, this is the place for you, as it is directly opposite the racecourse, near juntion 32 of the M62. The spacious bar has a conservatory, oak beams and old-fashioned bar counter. The bedrooms are neat, compact, modern and attractively decorated with matching fabrics. TVs, telephones, mini-bars and tea-makers are standard, as are excellent en-suite bathrooms. *Free House. Beer* John Smith Magnet, Stones. *Cider* Scrumpy Jack, Addlestones. *Garden, children's play area. Accommodation 28 bedrooms, all en suite, £55 (single £47.50). Children welcome overnight, additional beds and cots available. Check-in all day. Access, Visa.*

Port Gaverne   Port Gaverne Hotel

Tel 0208 880244

Port Gaverne nr Port Isaac Cornwall PL29 3SQ

B&B

Map 12 B3

Set in a sheltered cove 50 yards from the beach is a charming 17th-century inn which has been run for 25 years by Freddie and Midge Ross. The best of the cheerful en suite rooms have dormer windows and sea views. A Club Bar and balconied lounge are available for residents' use and there are two cosy, popular pub bars. Self-catering cottages are also offered. *Free House. Beer* Flowers IPA, St Austell

HSD. Garden. Family Room. **Accommodation** *19 bedrooms, all en suite, £76 (single £38); 7 self-catering cottages, from £182 per week. Children welcome overnight, additional beds (priced by age), cots supplied. Check-in all day. Closed January. Access, Amex, Diners, Visa.*

Porthleven   Ship Inn

Tel 0326 572841

Porthleven nr Helston Cornwall TR13 9JS   Map 12 A4

Small harbourside pub, romantically set in the cliffside and reached by a flight of stone stairs. Superb sea views from the window seats, and good log fires in winter, in the year-round upstairs bar; the family room is to the rear of this, while the ground floor 'cellar bar' is used only in summer. **Beer** *Courage Best and Directors, Ushers Best and Founders. Garden. Family room.*

Powerstock   Three Horseshoes Inn   **FOOD**

Tel 0308 85328   **B&B**

Powerstock nr Bridport Dorset DT6 3TF   Map 13 F2

Reliable old favourite, rebuilt in 1906 after a devastating fire, but solidly old-fashioned in style, with its stone and thatch, simple country furnishings, open fires and a delightful garden. But people come here for chef/licensee's food; not cheap, certainly, but fresh and delicious, specialising in fish, for instance fresh crab with melon (£4.50), grilled sardines with garlic butter (£3.50), John Dory deauvillaise (£9.50) or fillet of sea bass on a julienne of vegetables with garlic sauce (£12.50). The blackboard menu can also include anything from grilled lobster to fish pie, bourride and sea bass cooked in a paper bag. Meat and game dishes, too: garlic-studded rack of lamb, kidneys turbigo, venison pie. Desserts include summer pudding, sticky toffee pudding and sunken chocolate soufflé (£2.50-£3.50). Must book for busy Sunday lunches in winter. Tables in the garden for summer eating. Bedrooms are large and traditionally styled with central heating, en-suite bathrooms and lovely views. Delightful garden. Families with children are welcome. **Bar Food & Restaurant Meals** *12-2, 7-10. Vegetarian dishes. Children's portions.* **Beer** *Palmers Bridport Bitter, IPA. Children allowed in bar to eat. Garden, outdoor eating, children's play area.* **Accommodation** *2 bedrooms, both en suite, £50 (single £25). Children welcome overnight, additional beds, cots supplied. Check-in all day. Access, Amex, Visa.*

Preston   Fox & Hounds

Tel 057285 492

2 Cross Lane Preston Leicestershire LE15 9NQ   Map 7 E4

16th-century pub in what estate agents describe as a "most sought-after village". Lots of beamy character remains. **Beer** *Adnams. Garden, children's play area.*

Priddy   New Inn

Tel 0749 676465

Priddy nr Wells Somerset BA5 3BB   Map 13 F1

15th-century farmhouse, unchanged until the 1970s, when bars and more bedrooms were added. In the heart of the Mendips, this is the highest pub in Somerset. *Free House.* **Beer** *Pedigree 6X, Hardy Country Bitter, Webster's Yorkshire Bitter, Eldridge Pope Best Bitter, Crystal Malt Bitter. Garden, children's play area. Family room.*

Priors Dean   White Horse

Tel 0420 58387

FOOD

Priors Dean nr Petersfield Hampshire GU32 1DA

Map 15 D3

Also called the Pub with No Name; there is no sign. Fiendish to get to: leave Petersfield on the A272 Winchester-bound, turn right towards Steep, then after about 5 miles, take the East Titsted road at the crossroads, then immediate right down the second gravel track. It's worth the effort, for this is a quite wonderful 17th-century farmhouse pub of utterly simple (uncomfortable, some would say) charm and genuinely unspoilt by modernity; in fact, the pub's present state is so popular that it hasn't been redecorated for 30 years! The bar menu includes various dishes like chicken, gammon and mushroom pie (£4.95), moussaka (£4.05), fisherman's pie (£4.50) and beef and ale pie (£5.75). At Sunday lunchtime, only sandwiches are served together with home-made soup in winter (thick country soup £2.95). First World War poet Edward Thomas wrote his first published work, *Up in the Wind*, about the pub; it's 750 feet up on the top of the Downs, with peaceful views on every side. There are 26 country wines. No children indoors. *Bar Food 11.30-2, 7.30-9.30 (Wed, Thur & Fri only). Vegetarian dishes. Free House. Beer Ballard's Best Bitter, Broadwood, Courage Best and Directors, Eldridge, No Name Bitter, Ringwood Fortyniner. Garden, outdoor eating, children's play area. No credit cards.*

Puckeridge   White Hart

Tel 0920 821309

High Street Puckeridge Hertfordshire SG11 1RR

Map 15 F1

Small family-run business with a nice, animal-laden garden for children. *Beer McMullens Country Bitter and AK Mild, Courage Directors. Patio, garden, children's play area.*

Pyrton   Plough

Tel 0491 612003

Pyrton nr Watlington Oxfordshire OX9 5AP

Map 17 D2

17th-century thatched village pub with large open log fires. No children indoors. *Free House. Beer Adnams, Fuller's. Garden.*

Radwell   Swan Inn

Tel 0234 781351

Felmersham Road Radwell Bedfordshire MK43 7HS

Map 17 E1

Quiet 17th-century thatched country pub with rustic charm and real fire, in delightful village. *Beer Charles Wells Eagle Bitter, guest beer. Garden, children's play area. Family room.*

Rainow   Highwayman

Tel 0625 573245

Rainow nr Macclesfield Cheshire SK10 5UU

Map 6 C2

A characterful pub and a very popular one, with tremendous views across the Cheshire Plain and an old-fashioned interior with various little rooms warmed by a real fire. The beer's reliably good too. Get here early for a seat. *Beer Thwaites Bitter. Terrace. Family room.*

Ramsbury   Bell at Ramsbury

| Tel 0672 20230 | **FOOD** |

Market Square Ramsbury nr Marlborough Wiltshire SN8 2PE   Map 16 A3

A very low-key pub with a laid-back atmosphere at the heart of a
sleepy Wiltshire village. The Bell's stock-in-trade remains the
provision of good quality, carefully prepared bar food at affordable
prices. Sensibly short and to the point, the menu gives equal billing to
home-made soups and patés and single-course snacks such as tagliatelle
carbonara (£4.95) or chicken jambalaya (£5.75), while fresh fish
(halibut, perhaps with parsley sauce) and steaks, sauced or plain, are
accompanied by plainly cooked fresh vegetables. To follow are plenty
of traditional nursery puddings from spotted dick to gooseberry
crumble and home-made ices and sorbets. To the rear of a glassed-in
screen, the restaurant, with ten or so well-spaced, polished tables,
comes in to its own in the evenings – and on Sunday lunch – with a
number of additions on a carefully restricted à la carte: perhaps
avocado mousse or deep-fried whitebait for starters, main dishes
including lamb steak with rosemary butter and stir-fried pork and
vegetables, and treacle tart or a summer pudding to close. This is not
the "Bell" of old but it is still worth a visit. *Bar Food & Restaurant
Meals 12-2.30, 6.30-9.30. Children's portions. Free house. Beer
Wadworth Henry's IPA, Wadworth 6X, Fullers London Pride. Garden,
outdoor eating, children's play area. Access, Amex, Visa.*

Ramshaw Rocks   Winking Man

| Tel 0538 300361 | |

Ramshaw Rocks nr Blackshaw Moor Staffordshire ST13 8UH   Map 6 C2

Named after a local rock formation, at the heart of the Peak District.
Three discos a week in the function room. *Free House. Beer Bass.*

Rattery   Church House Inn

| Tel 0364 42220 | **FOOD** |

Rattery South Brent Devon TQ10 9LD   Map 13 D3

Originally an 11th-century monastic resting house and hostel for the
masons working on the nearby church; the list of vicars since 1199 is
displayed in the bar. Though opened up into an elongated lounge, the
massive oak screen and beams, great open fireplaces and spiral stone
staircase remain. Friday evenings are candlelit. Bar food includes rabbit
and ham pie (£5.25), fisherman's pie (£5.30) and Orlando beef
(£5.95) with home-made puddings such as chocolate hazelnut
cheesecake and pear Bakewell tart (both £2.25). *Bar Food 12-2, 7-10.
Vegetarian dishes. Children's menu (from £2.50). Free House. Beer Ind
Coope Burton Ale, Dartmoor Best, Tetley Bitter. Patio, outdoor eating.
Family room. Access, Visa.*

Ravenstonedale   Black Swan Inn

| Tel 05396 23204 | **B&B** |

Ravenstonedale nr Kirkby Stephen Cumbria CA17 4NG   Map 5 D3

A turn-of-the-century, Lakeland-stone inn, six minutes from the M6
(junction 38) and a mere half an hour from Ullswater, useful as a base
for walking and fishing. Main bedrooms in traditional style are
supplemented by more modern additions in the old stables, where
ramps and wide doorways offer good access for disabled guests. *Free
House. Beer Hartleys, Theakston, Younger, Robinsons. Garden, lake and*

river fishing, tennis. **Accommodation** *16 bedrooms, £57 (single £41).*
Children welcome overnight (under-6s free in parents' room), cots supplied.
Access, Amex, Diners, Visa.

Rede   Plough

`Tel 028489 208`

Rede Suffolk IP29 4BE   Map 10 C3

Early 17th-century pub in a peaceful and lovely spot by the village
pond. Beams aplenty and a fine collection of teapots. Children allowed
in bar to eat. **Beer** *Greene King IPA and Abbot. Garden.*

Redmile   Peacock Inn

`Tel 0949 42554`   **FOOD**

Church Corner Redmile Nottinghamshire NG13 0GA   Map 7 D3

Right on the Notts/Leicestershire border: turn off the A52 at the signs
to Belvoir Castle to find Redmile deep in the flatlands. Its pub, the
Peacock, was rescued from dereliction some six years ago. The interior
is a tribute to the skills of landlord Colin Crawford whose restoration
of its old fireplaces and former ships' timbers is commendable. His
most recent work has enclosed the rear flagstoned patio to create a
skylit Garden Room replete with wrought-iron tables and fanciful
murals. Jean Louis supervises a busy kitchen: from the daily changing
blackboard wild mushrooms in puff pastry (£3.50) and scallops
provençale (£3.50) could precede such main courses as grilled cod
with saffron sauce (£6.45) or lamb's kidneys with a brandy cream
sauce (£5.50) with a fromage frais cheesecake or lemon and pancake
terrine (£2.25) to follow. A la carte dishes – a typical meal of seafood
brochette (£4.50) rack of lamb in puff pastry (£10.25) and iced
blackcurrant mousse with vanilla sauce (£3.50) – come in less than
authentic French translations. The atmosphere, however, remains one
of the Crawfords' village local, for they were brought up here: their
"locals" in turn have much to be grateful for. Within the last 18
months they have converted and opened their second outlet at the
Blue Ball in Braunston, Leicestershire (*qv*): the Peacock formula is
surely strutting its stuff. **Bar Food** *12-2.30, 6.30-10* **Restaurant Meals**
12.30-2, 7-9.30. Vegetarian dishes. Children's portions. Free House. **Beer**
Abbot Ale, Bass, Tetley, Marston Pedigree. Garden, outdoor eating. Family
room. Access, Visa.

Reedham   Reedham Ferry Inn

`Tel 0493 700429`

Reedham nr Norwich Norfolk NR30 5TX   Map 10 D2

Traditional back bar and less inspiring front bar in a little riverside
pub popular with Norfolk Broad holidaymakers. Well-kept and
thoughtfully run. *Free House.* **Beer** *Adnams, Wherry. Riverside terrace,*
outdoor eating. Family room.

We do not necessarily recommend food in pubs that do not carry the FOOD symbol against their
entry.

We always welcome new recommendations from readers. Please use the form provided at the back
of this Guide.

We do not accept free meals or hospitality – our inspectors pay their own bills and never book in
the name of Egon Ronay's Guides.

Other Egon Ronay's Guides available:

Egon Ronay's Cellnet Guide 1993 Hotels & Restaurants £13.99
Egon Ronay's Just a Bite Guide 1993 £8.99 (published Mar '93)
Egon Ronay's Guide 1993 ...and Baby Comes Too £8.99 (published Mar '93)

Rennington   Masons Arms

Tel 0665 577275

Rennington nr Alnwick Northumberland NE66 3RX

Map 5 D1

Large 18th-century coaching inn on the old Great North Road.
Free House. Beer McEwan. Patio/terrace. Family room.

Richmond   The Orange Tree

Tel 081-940 0944

45 Kew Road Richmond Surrey TW9 2NQ

FOOD

Map 17 F3

Named after the first orange tree planted in Kew Gardens, it has been
around since 1870. Today it is under new management with a freshly
opened wine bar/restaurant downstairs. The pub is large and airy,
with an attractive darkwood and red velvet ambience. There is a
theatre upstairs. The back is used as a dining room for bar meals
served all day. The menu offers a selection of the usual steak and ale
pie (£3.95), lasagne or chili, but the daily blackboard has different
alternatives like cream of leek with lentils and tarragon, curried beef
Madras (£3.75), chicken satay and a vegetarian dish. Everything is
made in house with fresh ingredients. Espresso and cappuccino coffee
are available. *Bar Food 11-10.30. Vegetarian dishes. Children allowed in
wine bar only. Beer Youngs Bitter, Special. Patio, outdoor eating.
Access, Amex, Diners, Visa.*

Richmond   The Racing Page

Tel 081-940 4067

2 Duke Street Richmond Surrey TW9 1HP

Map 17 F3

Situated between the High Street and the Green and, as its name
would suggest, decorated with horse pictures and models, it is popular
with business clientele, office workers, shoppers, local residents and
due to the proximity of the Richmond Theatre, actors, technicians and
theatregoers. Inexpensive bar food. Popular live jazz on Sunday
evenings. In the same group as *The Front Page* and *The Sporting Page*
(see entries under London section).
Beer Webster, Ruddles County, Boddingtons.

Richmond   White Swan

Tel 081-940 0959

25/26 Old Palace Lane Richmond Surrey

FOOD

Map 17 F3

Not far away from the Thames and Twickenham Bridge the White
Swan is secluded in a quiet cul de sac. A charming pub, it combines an
old-fashioned intimate low-ceilinged bar with a modern conservatory
at the back. There is also a flowery paved garden. A large selection of
hot and cold food is piled up on the cramped counter all prepared in
house and of a reasonable standard. Salads and sandwiches only in the
evenings. *Bar Food 12-2.30. Beer Courage. Garden. Family room.*

Rickinghall   Hamblyn House

Tel 0379 898292

The Street Rickinghall Suffolk IP22 1BN

Map 10 C2

Originally the home of one of James Hamblyn, one of the founding
fathers of the city of Chicago, and a fine building with strong Dutch
architectural. Traditional bars, and a splendid staircase sweeping up to
the bedrooms. *Free House. Beer Adnams, Greene King. Garden,
children's play area. Family room.*

Rickling Green & Quendon   Cricketers' Arms

Tel 079988 322   Fax 079988 512

Rickling Green & Quendon Essex CB11 3YE   Map 10 B3

Mellow redbrick pub, nicely set by the village green, though not very special inside, except for its enormously hospitable hosts. *Free House.* *Beer Tetley, Bateman Dark Mild, guest beer. Patio/terrace. Family room.*

Ringstead   Gin Trap Inn

Tel 048525 264

High Street Ringstead Norfolk   Map 10 B1

Opened-up split level bar, clean and comfortable with attractive touches be early for a window seat, and lots of bric-a-brac, including the notorious traps themselves. Pétanque played in the garden. Children allowed in bar to eat. *Free House.* **Beer** *Adnams, Gin Trap, Greene King Abbot, Bass, Woodforde's Norfolk Nog. Garden.*

Ripley   Seven Stars

Tel 0483 225128

Newark Lane Ripley Surrey GU23 6DL   Map 17 E4

Pleasant pebbledash pub on the B367, just north of Ripley. *Beer Ringwood Best Bitter, Banks's & Taylor Summer Ale, Wadworth Best Bitter, regularly changing guest beers. Garden. Family room.*

Ripponden   Old Bridge Inn

Tel 0422 822595

Priest Lane Ripponden West Yorkshire HX6 4DF   Map 6 C1

Ancient pub with medieval character, enormously thick stone walls and some nice old furniture in its three connecting bars. Probably originally a 14th-century monastic guest house. The modern world intrudes little into the finished interior; no machines, music, pool table, and pump clips are only tolerated for guest beers. There isn't even an inn sign. *Free House.* **Beer** *Taylor Best Bitter and Golden Best, Samuel Smith Old Brewery Bitter, Thwaites Bitter.*

Rochester   Redesdale Arms

FOOD
B&B

Tel 0830 20668

Rochester nr Otterburn Northumberland NE19 1TA   Map 5 D2

Standing alongside the A68 12 miles from the Scottish border, this mellow, stone-built coaching inn is part of the Northumbrian National Park and makes a good base for visitors exploring the region. Tapestry-style banquettes, wheelback chairs and copper-topped tables help make the bar an inviting spot in which to enjoy home-made snacks like warming lentil soup (£1.40) or well filled 'stottie' sandwiches (£1.75). Open from 7.30 am to 11 pm, this family-run hotel offers home-made biscuits, cakes and scones at breakfast and tea times. The bar and restaurant menu changes daily – beef and kidney pie (£5.50), vegetable pie with walnut pastry (£5.65), roast pork with cider and apples (£6.25), chicken en croute (£7) and home-made puddings including old-fashioned jam roly-poly (£1.95). Traditionally furnished bedrooms (three with four-posters) range from fairly simple with white-painted walls to larger, prettier rooms featuring attractive wallpapers. All offer duvets, tea-makers, telephones and TVs, and four have en-suite facilities; the rest share two public bathrooms. ***Bar Food and Restaurant Meals*** 11.30-3, 7-9 (Sat 7-10).

Vegetarian dishes. Children's menu (£2.50-£3.50 per dish). Free House.
Beer *Newcastle Bitter, McEwans Best Scotch. Garden, outdoor eating.
Family room.* **Accommodation** *12 bedrooms (4 en suite), £41.50 (single
£16.50). Children welcome overnight, additional beds (£10.50-£11.50),
cots supplied. Check-in all day. Access, Diners, Visa.*

Roke   Home Sweet Home Inn

Tel 0491 38249

Roke nr Benson Oxfordshire OX9 6JD   Map 16 C2

Handsome 16th-century dining pub with a cosy, characterful double-
roomed main bar, carpeted sitting room and log fires. **Beer** *Brakspear
Special and Ordinary. Garden. Family room.*

Romaldkirk   Kirk Inn

Tel 0833 50260

Romaldkirk nr Barnard Castle Co Durham DL12 9ED   Map 5 D3

On the village green, also the local post office for two hours each
morning, this is a real community local. *Free House.* **Beer** *Boddingtons,
Castle Eden, Butterknolle Brewery, guest ale. Garden, outdoor eating.
Family room.*

Romaldkirk   Rose & Crown   ★   FOOD
B&B

Tel 0833 50213   Fax 0833 50828

Romaldkirk Co Durham DL12 9EB   Map 5 D3

In an area of pretty villages, Romaldkirk must be one of the most
picturesque, with its attractive cottages and open greens. The Rose &
Crown, an imposing 18th-century coaching inn, stands alongside the
ancient village church, together effectively dominating the village
centre. The main bar has a fine stone fireplace, lots of wood panelling,
old black and white photos of the village, a grandfather clock and
some alarming-looking traps. Wrought iron- legged tables are
surrounded by roundback chairs or bench seating, and on the dining
side of the room there are exposed stone walls, beams and old farm
implements. A part-panelled restaurant has elegantly clothed tables and
a civilised air, and the residents' lounge, heavily endowed with more
stripped stone and beams, features wing chairs and period furniture,
books, magazines and board games. Everywhere there are local
watercolours. Regularly changing bar menus (which differ lunch and
evening) are supplemented by a specials blackboard. Fresh produce is
combined to good effect in interesting and imaginative dishes like
locally smoked chicken with a fresh herb sauce (£4.65) or fresh pasta
tossed in cream with peppers and mushrooms (£3.65). At lunch,
sandwiches and a ploughman's prepared with 'real' local cheeses are
also available. Fish comes from the East coast – the deep-fried Whitby
scampi (£5.65) are not the usual run of the mill, and puddings are all
home made except for the delicious lemon cheesecake which comes
from a Cumbrian farm with a Jersey pedigree herd. Service is friendly
and smiling. Meanwhile, in the restaurant, the £20 fixed-price dinner
also has a local produce bias, using game and black puddings, fowl and
cheeses.This is artistically presented food, carefully prepared with
obvious knowledge and enthusiasm. Creaking floorboards, beams,
stripped stone walls, well-chosen antique furniture and contemporary
fabrics feature in the refurbished and improved bedrooms, and duvets
can be swapped for sheets and blankets. Front views overlook the
village green. Five further rooms, in an outside annexe, are more

uniform in size and design, with modern furniture and fittings. *Bar Food* 12-1.30, 6.30-9.30 (7-9 Sun). *Restaurant Meals* 12-1.30, 7.30-9 (except Sun). *Vegetarian dishes. Children's portions. Free House. Beer Scottish & Newcastle Scotch, Theakston Best, Old Peculier. Children allowed in bar to eat. Patio, outdoor eating. Accommodation 13 bedrooms, all en suite, £70 (single £48). Children welcome overnight, additional bed (£12), cots available (£12). Check-in all day. Access, Visa.*

Rosedale Abbey   Milburn Arms

FOOD
B&B

Tel & Fax 07515 312

Rosedale Abbey nr Pickering North Yorkshire YO18 8RA

Map 5 E3

A hotel really, largely built in the mid-1700s though some bits are older and some newer, but, as their brochure puts it 'we're also the village pub'. Indeed, the spacious bar with its low beams does have a pubby atmosphere and comes complete with dart board and a couple of games machines but it's the extensive range of bar meals that is the big attraction; tiger tail prawns in garlic (£2.95), lasagne (£3.95), vegetarian tartlet (£3.95), pork and cider casserole (£5.45) rabbit and vegetable pie (£5.45), steaks (from £8.95) and an excellent summer pudding (£1.95) demonstrate the range. There is also an interesting set-price dinner (£16.50) on offer in the smart, split-level Priory Restaurant. Bedrooms are individually decorated in a variety of styles – rich reds and blues, pale pink and yellow, pastel seersucker fabric – and furnished with a mixture of pine, freestanding darkwood and hotel unit-style furniture. All have good bathrooms (with showers over tubs) plus TV, direct-dial phone and beverage kit. A good spot in summer is the peaceful garden, opposite the village green, with tables set out under a splendid 150-year-old cedar. *Bar Food* 12-2.15, 7-10 (9.30 in winter). *Restaurant Meals* 12-2.30 (Sun only), 7-9. *Vegetarian dishes. Children's menu/portions. Free House. Beer Bass, Stones, Theakston. Garden, outdoor eating. Accommodation 11 bedrooms, all en suite, £64 (single £39.50). Children welcome overnight, additional beds, cot available. Check-in all day. Access, Diners, Visa.*

Rosedale Abbey   White Horse Farm Hotel

FOOD
B&B

Tel 07515 239

Rosedale Abbey nr Pickering North Yorkshire YO18 8SE

Map 5 E3

The White Horse was a farm when Rosedale Abbey was a thriving mining village with a population ten times greater than it is now. As was then the practice, one end of the farmhouse was turned into a 'taps room' for the miners and its transformation into today's hotel had begun. The bar is full of interest with a couple of rough-hewn tree trunks acting as poles holding up the ceiling beams, stuffed birds, a fish in a glass case, horse harness and much besides decorating the walls, some of which are of rough exposed stone. Yorkshire fare features strongly on the bar menu: Yorkshire pudding either with onion gravy – although the chef sometimes forgets the onions (£1.95) or with a filling like mince and vegetables (£4.10), Cropton Stoggies (casseroled wood pigeon £6.95), Yorkshire rarebit made with Theakstons Bitter (£3.50), Whitby haddock pots (£3.99); along with a few dishes from further afield like Frikadella – spicy Danish burgers (£3.99), Bar-B-Q spare ribs (£5.60) and vegetable curry (£3.25). There are also various sandwiches and a short list of puds. Bedrooms, including two de luxe rooms with separate sitting areas, are prettily decorated with matching floral bedcovers (no duvets here), curtains and dado band around the woodchip walls. Even the en-suite bathrooms, half with showers and half with tubs, co-ordinate with their respective bedrooms. All rooms have TV and tea and coffee-making equipment and some have wonderful views across Rosedale. *Bar Food* 12-2, 6.30-9.30 (till 10 Fri). *Restaurant Meals* 12-1.30 (Sun only), 7-8.45. *Vegetarian dishes. Children's menu.* **Beer** *Tetley, Theakston XB, Best Bitter.* **Cider** *Scrumpy Jack. Garden, outdoor eating. Family room.* **Accommodation** *15 bedrooms, all en suite, £60 (single £35). Children welcome overnight, additional bed and cot available. Check-in all day. Access, Amex, Diners, Visa.*

Rotherwick   Coach & Horses

| Tel 025 676 2542 | **FOOD** |

The Street Rotherwick Hampshire RG27 89BG   Map 17 D4

Winter fires, beamed ceilings and a motley collection of furniture in two little rooms leading off the separate hatch servery in this creeper-covered part 16th-century village dining pub, very popular with locals for lunch. Reliably good food ranges from the simple and snackish to steaks and fish; carvery on Sundays. A huge range of real ales. *Bar Food* 12-2, 7-10 (9.45 Sun). Free House. **Beer** *Ansells, Bunces, Eldridge Pope, Palmers. Children allowed in bar to eat. Patio/terrace. No credit cards.*

Rothwell   Red Lion Hotel

| Tel 0536 710409 |

Market Hill Rothwell Northamptonshire NN14 2BW   Map 7 D4

Imposing Edwardian market place hotel, with four bars and a comfortable atmosphere. Live music Saturdays. Morning coffee. **Beer** *Charles Wells Eagle and Bombardier.*

Rowde   George & Dragon   ★

| Tel 0380 723053 | **FOOD** |

High Street Rowde nr Devizes Somerset   Map 14 C3

Here's an object lesson in what true commitment, some imagination and simple, inventive cooking can achieve in otherwise humble surroundings. Helen and Tim Withers' village pub, on lease from Wadworth's Brewery, contains a single bar with half a dozen Britannia tables and two dozen assorted bentwood chairs in the dining room set at plain unclothed tables. Everywhere are blackboards proclaiming what's on offer. Look especially for the Cornish fish, grey mullet served with leeks, scallops with spiced lentil and coriander sauce and lobster in season. Attendant menus offer choices from cheese soufflé and fishy hors d'oeuvre through to pork loin with tapénade and rumpsteak with herb and onion relish. There's a daily £10 lunch (increased to £12.50 on Sundays) offering, perhaps, a ham mousse with cucumber pickle, Andalusian-style leg of lamb and summer pudding. In addition to Wadworth's IPA and 6X on hand-pumps, the pub's 'English-only' policy is extended to the mineral water (Abbey Well and Malvern) and cheeses, of which Stilton, Allerdale, Sharpham and Cotherstone are a typical selection. Of over 40 wines, any may be ordered by the glass, so look, too, for some bargains on the bar representing previous diners' unconsumed favourites. Unsurprisingly, booking is always advised, probably as much as ten days ahead for a table at weekends. *Bar Food* 12-2, 7-10. *Vegetarian dishes.* **Beer** *Wadworth. Access, Visa.*

Rowhook   Chequers Inn

Tel 0403 790480

Rowhook nr Horsham West Sussex RH12 3PY   Map 11 A6

Agreeable 15th-century pub, much modernised, but least so in the
Flagstone Bar. A pretty garden has play equipment, animals and a
pétanque pitch. **Beer** *Marston, Whitbread. Garden, outdoor play area.
Family room. Access, Visa.*

Ruckhall Common   Ancient Camp Inn   **FOOD**

Tel 0981 250449		**B&B**

Ruckhall Common nr Eaton Bishop Hereford & Worcester HR2 9QX   Map 14 A1

The route from the A465 at Belmont Abbey to Ruckhall turns into a
twist of narrow lanes. Once there, look carefully for signs to the
Ancient Camp, so named because the site was once an Iron Age fort.
Certainly, it must have been impregnable from the northern side, as
the pub stands atop an escarpment overlooking a wide bend in the
river Wye. In fair weather, there's a fine view across the fertile river
valley from a front patio bordered by roses, the backdrop of the inn
fronted by window boxes and hanging baskets. The interior decor of
the pub retains the original stonework and flagstone floors, which
results in an intimate atmosphere to which dried flowers and huge log
fires add a special glow in winter. Doyenne of the kitchen is Nova
Hague, and her production is prodigious. Bar meals and some
sandwiches are available at lunchtime (except Monday), and though
bar food remains available in the evenings and may be booked in
advance, much greater emphasis is placed on her evening restaurant
menu. Start with home-made soup, or pears in roquefort and
watercress salad, followed perhaps by seafood provençale (£10.50) or
stuffed chicken breast wrapped in bacon and orange sauce (£9.75).
Tempting home-made puddings include chocolate roulade and iced
coffee soufflé (both £2.45). It's not only the food that shines at the
Ancient Camp: the inn's five-bedroomed accommodation is also quite
special. At the rear are three neat bedrooms with en-suite showers; to
the front, two superb bedrooms, one with a private sitting room, the
other's en-suite bath elevated to maximise its river view. All are fully
centrally heated, with telephone, television and bedside clock radio.
Bar Food *12-2 (not Mon in Summer), 7-9.30 (except Sun eve & all
Mon).* **Restaurant Meals** *7-9 Tue-Sat. Vegetarian dishes. Free House.*
Beer *Bentleys Yorkshire, Whitbread WCPA, Woods Parish Bitter.
Garden, riverside garden, outdoor eating. Family room.* **Accommodation**
*5 bedrooms, all en suite, from £48 (single £35). Children welcome
overnight (minimum age 8). Check-in all day. No dogs. Access, Visa.*

Running Waters   Three Horse Shoes   **B&B**

Tel 091 373 0286

Sherburn House Running Waters Nr Durham Co Durham DH1 2SR   Map 5 E3

Standing alongside the A181 a few miles south-east of Durham, this
friendly pub, with new owners, is surrounded by beautiful
countryside. The two popular bars are comfortably rustic. Prettily
decorated bedrooms with simple modern furnishings have duvets,
TVs, tea-makers and radio alarms. Original rooms offer shower
cubicles only and share a smart carpeted bathroom, while the four
newer rooms have their own up-to-date en-suite facilities. *Free House.*
Beer *John Smith, Ruddles Best, Dryborough Scotch. Garden, children's
play area.* **Accommodation** *6 bedrooms, 4 en suite, £46 (single £30).*

Children welcome overnight, additional beds and cots available. Check-in all day. Access, Amex, Diners, Visa.

Rusholme   Rampant Lion

Tel 061 224 1916

17 Anson Road Rusholme Greater Manchester M14 5BZ   Map 6 B2

Formerly a private club with showbizzy members; a pub since 1984. Just five minutes from Manchester city centre, with extensive grounds and parking. Function room. *Free House.* **Beer** *Cains Bitter, Tetley Bitter, Burton Bitter, Boddingtons Bitter. Garden, children's play area. Family room.*

Russells Water   Beehive Inn

Tel 0491 641306

Russells Water nr Henley-on-Thames Oxfordshire RG9 6ER   Map 17 D3

Immortalised on celluloid in *Chitty Chitty Bang Bang*: the car drove through the duck pond at the front of this 17th-century pub converted from a pair of little cottages; original fireplaces and their bread ovens remain. Situated on an enormous common. *Free House.* **Beer** *Brakspear, Wadworth 6X. Garden. Family room.*

Rusthall   Red Lion

Tel 0892 20086   **FOOD**

82 Lower Green Road Rusthall Kent TN4 8TW   Map 11 B5

Licensed since 1415, with a characterful beamed bar and plush carpeted lounge. Very simple, good home cooking; less choice in the evening. **Bar Food** *12.30-2, 7-10 (no food Sun). Children's portions.* **Beer** *Marston Pedigree, Wadworth 6X, Whitbread Fremlins Bitter. Children allowed in bar to eat. Garden, outdoor eating. No credit cards.*

Saffron Walden   Eight Bells

Tel 0799 522790   **FOOD**

18 Bridge Street Saffron Walden Essex CB10 1BU   Map 10 B3

Solidly traditional bar, partitioned by ancient wall timbers into two smaller rooms, complete with old furniture, mellow cream walls, exposed timbers and brick. The bar and restaurant menus offer reliably good food. **Bar Food** *12-2.30, 6.30-9.30 (6-10 Sat/7-9.30 Sun).* **Beer** *Adnams Bitter, Burton, Greene King IPA, Tetley, Wadworth 6X. Children allowed in bar to eat. Garden, outdoor eating. Family room.*

Saffron Walden   Saffron Hotel

Tel 0799 522676   Fax 0799 513979   **FOOD**
                                                 B&B
High Street Saffron Walden Essex CB10 1AY   Map 10 B3

With origins in the 16th century and having been a coaching inn in its day, the Saffron Hotel is more hotel than pub today but the green plush bar still welcomes all and offers both real ales and good food. The printed bar menu includes steak, kidney and Guinness pie (£5.50), home-cooked ham and eggs (£5.25) and jacket potatoes with various fillings while the daily-changing blackboard menu ranges from baked cod with cheese and tomato topping (£4.50) and pork steak with rice and sweet and sour sauce (£4.75) to liver and bacon with gravy (£4.50) and chocolate mousse (£1.95). There are no sandwiches or ploughman's available. The more formal restaurant (recommended in our Hotel and Restaurant Guide) has a table d'hote menu at £16.50 for three courses, plus à la carte. Bedrooms come in all shapes and sizes, some with head-threatening beams. The best and largest have been recently refurbished with stylish fabrics and smart new veneered furniture, the worst are cramped singles that share a shower room. All have telephone and TV. *Bar Food* 12-2.30, 6.45-9.15 *(except Sun)*. *Restaurant Meals* 12-2.30, 7-9.30 *(except Sun)*. *Children's portions. Free House. Beer Greene King IPA, Batemans, Boddingtons. Accommodation 21 bedrooms, 18 en suite, £68, (single £49). Additional beds and cots supplied. Check-in all day. Access, Amex, Diners, Visa.*

St Agnes   Driftwood Spars Hotel

Tel 087 255 2428

Trevaunance Cove St Agnes Cornwall TR5 0RT   Map 12 B3

Tempting oasis of a place, on the edge of one of Cornwall's best beaches. Built in the 17th century, of local stone and slate, it used enormous ship's timbers and spars – hence the name. *Beer Bass, Ind Coope. Family room.*

St Albans   Garibaldi

Tel 0727 55046

61 Albert Street St Albans Hertfordshire AL1 1RT   Map 17 F2

Pleasant old pub with unexpected hidey-holes around its small island bar, and a piney, dining café-style conservatory room leading off. *Bar Food 12-2, 6.30-9 (except Sun eve). Vegetarian dishes. Children's portions. Beer Fullers. Patio/terrace, outdoor eating. Family room. No credit cards.*

St Albans   Rose & Crown

Tel 0727 51903

St Michael's Street St Albans Hertfordshire AL3 4SG   Map 17 F2

This is a pleasingly simple, woody and traditional old pub down in St Michaels, near Verulamium Park; a little off the office-trade patch, so often a quiet gem at lunchtimes. *Beer Benskins. Outdoor eating.*

St Austell   White Hart Hotel

Tel 0726 72100   **B&B**

Church Street St Austell Cornwall PL25 4AT   Map 12 B3

A convenient place to stay in the centre of St Austell (though parking isn't easy), the White Hart offers attractive, comfortable accommodation. There is no separate residents' lounge as such; the public area includes a saloon bar with bright red velour banquettes and a polished-wood bar counter. The bedrooms all have smart darkwood furniture, pink and plum decor, brass light fittings, TVs, telephones, hairdryers, tea-makers and modern carpeted bathrooms. *Beer St Austell Tinners Ale, Duchy, Wreckers, Bosuns, HFD. Family room. Accommodation 18 bedrooms, all en suite, £59.50 (single £38). Children welcome overnight, additional beds and cots available, under-threes no charge. Check-in all day. Access, Amex, Diners, Visa.*

St Briavels   George
Tel 0594 530228

High Street St Briavels Gloucestershire   Map 14 B2

Three connecting rooms with nice furnishings, beams and a big open fire, popular with all comers and often very busy. Piped music; garden chess. *Free House. Garden, outdoor* eating.

St Cleer   Stag Inn
Tel 0579 42305

St Cleer nr Liskeard Cornwall PL14 5DA   Map 12 C3

Traditional village local with a cosy atmosphere, on the edge of Bodmin Moor. *Beer St Austell, Whitbread. Outdoor eating.*

St Margarets-at-Cliffe   Cliffe Tavern
Tel 0304 852749   **B&B**

High Street St Margarets-at-Cliffe Kent CT15 6AT   Map 11 D5

Long a favourite for its particular charm, the Cliffe Tavern is a series of 17th-century Kentish clapboard buildings with a pretty walled garden, at the heart of the village. It's well liked for bed and breakfast particularly – most rooms are across the yard in cottages. An excellent stop-over on the way to Channel ferries. *Free House. Beer Benskins, Burton, Tetley. Garden. Family room. **Accommodation** 12 bedrooms, all en suite, £49.50 (single £39.50). Children welcome overnight, cot available. Check-in all day. Access, Amex, Visa.*

St Mawes   Rising Sun
Tel 0326 270233   **B&B**

The Square St Mawes Truro Cornwall TR2 5DJ   Map 12 B4

Popular and lively hotel, with a harbour-view terrace that attracts the crowds when the sun shines. The small cane-furnished conservatory frontage houses a lounge bar, and there's a public bar that's a favourite with the locals. Residents can retreat to their own little lounge at the back (six seats, with TV). Bedrooms are smart and simple, with pine furniture and neat, practical bathrooms; three rooms are not en suite. Now owned by the St Austell brewery. *Accommodation 12 bedrooms, £58. Access, Amex, Visa.*

St Neots   Chequers Inn
Tel 0480 472116   **FOOD**

St Mary's Street Eynesbury nr St Neots Cambridgeshire PE19 2TA   Map 15 F1

A lovely old English country pub, where you can sit in the main bar with its roaring winter fires and highly polished dark furniture or at tables with white tablecloths for bar food, or in the dining area for a more substantial meal. The changing blackboard bar menu offers home cooking by landlord David James: ham, soups (£1.65), chicken and mushroom pie (£5.25), a substantial ploughman's (£3.45), crispy cauliflower with provençale sauce (£3.95), pasta with chicken (£4.25). The restaurant proposes a selection of prawn dishes, pork tenderloin in garlic cream sauce (£7.25), steak fillet in white wine sauce (£14.95) and a 3-course traditional Sunday lunch is £11. *Bar Food 12-2, 7-10. Restaurant Meals 12-1.30, 7-9.30 (Sun 7-9). Vegetarian dishes. Children's portions. Free House. Beer Webster, Bateman XB, Sam Smith. Garden, outdoor eating, children's play area. Access, Amex, Diners, Visa.*

St Neots   Eaton Oak

Tel 048 021 9555   Fax 048 040 7520   **B&B**

Crosshall Road Eaton Ford St Neots Cambridgeshire PE19 4AG   **Map 15 F1**

Formerly the Rocket, the Eaton Oak has been taken over by the
Childswell Group and completely renovated. Located at the junction
of the A1 and A45, the Eaton Oak's bedrooms are happily undisturbed
by traffic, and you can expect a comfortable overnight stay. The
rooms in the motel extension are large and warm, with fitted units,
colour TVs, tea-makers, direct-dial telephones and well-fitted
bathrooms. In the main building (once a farmhouse) the bar has been
extended along with the restaurant and a conservatory added which
leads on to the garden. *Beer Eagle, Bombardier, guest ale.*
*Accommodation 9 bedrooms, all en suite, £40 (single £35). Children
welcome overnight. Check-in all day. Access, Amex, Visa.*

Salisbury   Haunch of Venison

Tel 0722 322024   **A**

1 Minster Street Salisbury Wiltshire SP1 1TB   **Map 14 C3**

A pub of great antiquity and genuinely unspoilt character, and
consequently very popular with tourists, who crowd into the tiny bar
and chop house above. Carved oak benches jut out of blackened stone
walls, alongside beer-barrel tables; watch out for the very low beams
upstairs. *Beer Courage, Ringwood.*

Salisbury   King's Arms

Tel 072 232 7629   **B&B**

9 St John Street Salisbury Wiltshire SP1 2SB   **Map 14 C3**

You could have taken a room here when the place was 90 years old
and still watched them start to build the cathedral. That makes the
wattle-and-daub facade added in the early 1600s relatively modern. Its
beamed, panelled and sloping-floored, and one is grateful for a bar to
hold on to and an open fire to warm by. Varying sized bedrooms,
including two four-poster rooms, are all en suite and share a high
standard of comfort which the new owners are keen to maintain. *Free
House. Beer Flowers, Castleden, Whitbread, guest beers. Courtyard.*
*Accommodation 15 bedrooms, all en suite, £68 (single £45). Check-in
all day. Access, Amex, Diners, Visa.*

Sandford Orcas   Mitre

Tel 096 322 271

Sandford Orcas Dorset   **Map 13 F2**

Lots of animals, old flagstones, an open fire, wall benches and a
separate dining room in this white-painted old village pub.
Free House. Garden.

Sandgate   Ship

Tel 0303 48525

65 High Street Sandgate Kent CT20 3AH   **Map 11 C5**

Attractive street-corner gabled local which looks as if it might be
about to put to sea. Unchanged within since the early 1950s.
Outdoor eating.

Satwell   Lamb

Tel 049 17 482

Satwell Oxfordshire   Map 17 D3

Classic cottage pub, low-beamed and quaint, with a real fire in the
inglenook. *Beer Breakspears. Garden.*

Saunderton   Rose & Crown

Tel 084 44 5299   Fax 084 44 3140   **B&B**

Wycombe Road nr Princes Risborough Buckinghamshire HP17 9NP   Map 17 D2

A grand square pianoforte dating back to 1840 is an unusual feature of
the spacious, oak-furnished bar at this large pub on the A4010.
Brightly decorated bedrooms (including one reached by an outside
staircase) with built-in units and two easy chairs apiece all have
compact en-suite bathrooms, as well as TVs, tea-makers, telephones
and radio alarms. *Free House. Beer Morlands, Morrell Varsity, Brakspear
PA. Garden. Family room. Accommodation 17 bedrooms (14 en suite),
£55 (single £49.50). No children under 8. Check-in all day. No dogs.
Closed Christmas week. Access, Amex, Diners, Visa.*

Sawley   Sawley Arms

Tel 0765 620642

Sawley nr Fountains Abbey North Yorkshire HG4 3EQ   Map 6 C1

A carpeted ramble of little rooms is pleasantly simple in style, with a
mix of modern and old-fashioned furnishings and real fires. There's
also a plain white-walled dining area. No children indoors.
Free House. Garden.

Scales   White Horse

Tel 07687 79241   **FOOD**

Scales nr Threlkeld Cumbria CA12 4SY   Map 4 C3

Set back from the A66 between Keswick and Penrith and 1000 feet
above sea level, the whitewashed White Horse is surrounded by
stunning Cumbrian countryside and is within easy reach of splendid
walking country. Immaculately kept, the interior has a strong hunting
and sporting theme, its uneven whitewashed walls covered with
horsey prints, photographs of local meets, and caricatures, while a
large hanging backs up the white horse theme. The low beamed
ceiling, slate fireplace (customers put coins between the gaps, later
collected for charity), well-polished copper pans, stuffed birds and
animals, and lots of plants all add to the rustic atmosphere. Local
produce features strongly on the short lunchtime bar menu which
includes their delicious Cumberland sausages served with apple sauce,
mushrooms and port jelly (£7.75). There might also be cottage pie
(£3.95) or a fresh nectarine filled with herb cream cheese paté. Sticky
toffee and ginger pudding (£2.40) to finish. Evenings bring
candlelight and a more restaurant menu; booking is essential, as it
gets extremely busy. Melon with strawberry sorbet (£2.50), local
lamb cutlets with Cumberland sauce (£8.95) and steak served with
herb and garlic or blue Stilton savoury butter (£9.75) testify to first-
rate fresh produce. Prices are fair: expect to spend in the region of
£30 for two for a three-course meal with coffee. *Bar Food 12-2,
7-8.45. Vegetarian dishes. Children's portions. Children allowed in bar to
eat. Free House. Beer Jennings Castle, Marstons Pedigree. Patio, outdoor
eating. Family room. Access, Visa.*

Scole   Crossways

FOOD
Tel 0379 740638
B&B

Ipswich Road Scole Norfolk IP21 4DP

Map 10 C2

The Crossways' location at the crossing of the A140 with the A143
would be ideal were it not for incessant traffic hold-ups on the corner.
Double-glazing for the bedrooms works well enough, but the pub's
exterior is not self-cleaning, and simply crossing the road is at times
plain treacherous. This is not to detract in any way from Peter Black's
unusual and idiosyncratic pub, which plays host to a good mix of
generations and tastes with its admirably varied choice, first of food
from pizzas and curries through to seafood or steaks, and second, of
locations in which to relax and enjoy it. Central to the issue is the pub
bar itself, which manages to capture all the trappings and atmosphere
of a good local without resorting to darts and a pool table.
Prominently displayed menu boards offer a variety of different dishes.
Evenings add a weekly changing table d'hote at around £10 for three
courses, as well as a varied à la carte menu. Eat either in an airy
conservatory-style bistro or in the more formal dining-room, where
French windows open out on to a rear patio and large, enclosed
garden. There's a strong showing of fresh fish from Lowestoft, and the
first-class steaks from come from the locally-farmed herds. Scallops of
pork with apple and cider sauce (£6.95), Dover sole (£14.95) and
sirloin steak King Charles (£9.95) are typical favourites from a much
wider selection. Puddings include sherry trifle, treacle tart and pavlova
(all £2.95). In addition to a well-kept range of beers, amongst which
the prize-winning Adnams is the star, the bar's new vacu-vin allows
up to thirty wines to be served by the glass from an even more
extensive list whose many bargains can also be purchased wholesale.
The building is reputed to be 16th-century and was still a private
house until conversion in the 1960s, when original floorboards from
the upper storey were used to panel the walls of what is now the pub
lounge. Upstairs, the bedrooms have been carefully designed and
neatly kitted out. Three have full en-suite facilities, the remaining two
sharing a bathroom. *Bar Meals 11.30-2.15 (12-2 Sun), 6-10
(7-10 Sun). Restaurant 12-2, 7-10. Vegetarian dishes. Children's menu.
Free House. Beer Adnams, Fullers London Pride, Wallington Best. Cider
Burnards. Garden, outdoor eating, summer barbecue. Family room.
Accommodation 5 bedrooms, 3 en suite, £40 (single £25). Children
welcome overnight, cot available. Check-in all day.
Access, Amex, Diners, Visa.*

Scole   Scole Inn

Tel 0379 740481 Fax 0379 740762	**B&B**

Norwich Road Scole Norfolk IP21 4DR

Map 10 C2

Built in 1655 by a wool merchant, this red-brick inn is Grade I listed
for its architectural interest. Splendid brick gables front and rear show
a Dutch influence. Bedrooms in the Georgian stable block are quieter
than those in the main building, which face a busy lorry route. These
rooms, though, are full of character, many having carved oak doors,
old timbers and fireplaces plus four-poster or half-tester beds. The bar
also has plenty of atmosphere. *Accommodation 23 bedrooms, £62.
Garden. Access, Amex, Diners, Visa.*

Scorrier   Fox & Hounds

Tel 0209 820205

Scorrier nr Redruth Cornwall TR16 5BS

Map 12 B3

One long bar is broken up by partitions; seating is modern red plush, tables coppertopped, and walls adorned with foxhunting prints; good log fires in winter; a small front extension is reserved for non-smokers. **Beer** Devonish (Whitbreads). Garden.

Scottow   Three Horseshoes

Tel 069 269 243

Scottow Norfolk

Map 10 C1

Keen real ale pub with a good, constantly changing range and August mini beer festival. Garden.

Seahouses   Olde Ship

Tel 0665 720200   Fax 0665 721383

B&B

9 Main Street Seahouses Northumberland NE68 7RD

Map 5 D1

Perched above the small harbour with splendid sea views out to the Farne Islands, the Olde Ship began life as a farmhouse in 1745 and was first licensed in 1812. It has been in present licensees Alan and Jean Glen's family since 1910, each generation, beginning with Alan's grandparents, introducing its own improvements. Behind the grey stone exterior there lies a real treasure trove of nautical paraphernalia collected over 80 years; the saloon bar is quite something and must be a nightmare to clean! The whole room is full of objects hanging from ceiling, walls and bar; a ship's figurehead, oars, diving helmet, brass lamps, ship's wheel, baskets, model boats, pictures, barrels, fishing gear and more besides. The smaller cabin bar has panelling, royal blue upholstered seating and even more collectibles, while a small area to the rear (where children can sit) features stuffed seabirds in cases. Upstairs the nautical theme continues, with a fine collection of large model boats in one of the first-floor hallways. The bedrooms, including three in outside annexes, are clean, neat and unfussy, with plain painted walls and cottagey bedspreads; furniture varies from modern fitted units to more traditional freestanding pieces; two rooms have four-poster beds. Direct-dial telephone, television (with satellite) and mineral water (local of course) are standard, and every room is en suite, though half have shower only, and some are on the small side. The pub also has its own lawn and summerhouse overlooking the harbour and enjoying fabulous views. In the evenings, the bars fill with the locals and fishermen who mix well with outsiders. Free House. **Beer** Theakston Best, XB, Longston. Garden, putting, outdoor play area. Family room. **Accommodation** 15 bedrooms, all en suite, £62 (single £31). Children welcome overnight (minimum age 10). Check-in after 2pm. No dogs. Access, Visa.

Seathwaite   Newfield Inn

Tel 0229 716208

Duddon Valley Seathwaite nr Broughton-in-Furness Cumbria LA20 6ED

Map 4 C3

Sensitively modernised, genuine unspoilt old country inn in good walking area which sidesteps the main tourist routes. Wordsworth wrote 34 sonnets about the Duddon Valley. 16th-century bar with oak beams and original slate floors. **Beer** McEwans, Theakston. Garden, Children's play area. Family room.

Seaview   Seaview Hotel   FOOD

Tel 0983 612711   Fax 0983 613729   B&B

High Street Seaview Isle of Wight PO34 5EX   Map 15 D4

A small early Victorian seaside hotel, whose pubby bars are at the
very heart of town life and whose bar meals are too good to miss. Just
yards from the seafront with its pebble beach and pretty assortment of
sailing dinghies bobbing in the Solent, the hotel has enormous charm,
starting with the small front patio complete with flagpole, and the
little rear courtyard which literally heaves in season with youngsters.
Both bars have a nautical theme, one with a myriad of photos of old
ships and small round tables, the other more rustic in style with bare
floorboards, dado pine panelling and, more unusually, part of an old
ship's mast. Eat in the cosy, smoke-free restaurant under table lamps set
on crisply-clothed tables (two sittings in high season), or choose from
the bar menu served both both inside and outside on the terrace;
either way there is usually good seafood on offer: perhaps rich, hot
crab ramekin (£3.80), cold escalope of salmon (£4.95) or local
lobster; local Island smoked garlic is put to good use in a herby dish of
garlic chicken with mushrooms and mixed salad leaves (£3.95); crab
sandwiches are also always popular. Pretty, individually decorated
bedrooms – blues and yellows are the favoured colours – are most
appealing, with lots of pictures, books and objets d'art. The best, and
largest, rooms feature antique furniture; others have simple white-
painted built-in units. Two of the rooms have small patios
(overlooking the small rear car park) and on the top floor there's also
a suite, its two bedrooms separated by a sitting room. Bathrooms are
as spick and span as the bedrooms; toiletries come in little wicker
'swan' baskets, and towels are large and soft. Two cosy lounges are
reserved for residents and restaurant diners. *Bar Food 12-2,
7-9.30 Restaurant Meals 12.30-2, 7.30-10 (not Sun eve). Vegetarian
dishes. Children's menu. Free House. Beer Whitbread Flowers IPA,
Original. Children allowed in bar to eat. Patio/terrace, outdoor eating.
Accommodation 16 bedrooms, all en suite, £69 (single £48.50). Children
welcome overnight, cots available. Check-in all day. Access, Visa.*

Sedbergh   Dalesman

Tel 053 96 21183

Main Street Sedbergh Cumbria LA10 5BN   Map 5 D4

Well-kept old market town inn with spartan public bar no juke box,
popular buttery, and pavement tables. *Free House. Outdoor eating.
Family room.*

Sedgefield   Dun Cow Inn   B&B

Tel 0740 20894

43 Font Street Sedgefield Co Durham TS21 3AT   Map 5 E3

An appealing old town-centre inn where standards of accommodation
have been high under the care of landlord Geoff Rayner. Six
immaculate bedrooms in mock rustic style with smart darkwood
furniture and tapestry-weave fabrics all offer TVs, telephones, tea-
makers and fresh fruit. They share three splendid bath/shower rooms,
generously equipped and spotlessly kept. Downstairs the spacious bar
has comfortable red banquettes. *Free House. Beer Theakston XB & Best
Bitter, weekly guest beers. Accommodation 6 bedrooms, not en suite, £45
(single £36.50). Children welcome overnight, additional beds and cots
available. Check-in all day. Access, Amex, Diners, Visa.*

Sellack   Loughpool Inn

Tel 098 987 236

Sellack nr Ross-on-Wye Hereford & Worcester HR9 6LX   Map 14 B1

Pretty Marches cottage pub with a genuinely unspoilt interior: beams, stone flags, nice old furnishings and two log fires in the main bar, with other attractive rooms leading off. Children are only allowed in the dining room. *Free House. Garden, outdoor eating.*

Semley   Benett Arms

FOOD
B&B

Tel 0747 830221

Semley nr Shaftesbury Wiltshire SP7 9AS   Map 14 B3

An agreeable, old-fashioned pub set in rolling countryside, with a genial landlord and a warm, welcoming atmosphere in the rustic bars. Down-to-earth bar food covers a good range and caters for varying appetites. Fresh fish from Poole is delivered on Tuesdays and Thursdays and is consumed as quickly as it arrives! Bar food includes such dishes as bouillabaisse (£5.95), grilled sardines (£3.95), braised squid (£5.95) served in earthenware pots, steak and kidney pie (£4.75), leek and nut bake (£4.65), and fresh halibut (£6.95). Popular with French visitors, who choose rack of lamb (£8.95) from the varied restaurant menu (herrings in Madeira £3.50, gammon in cider and apples £7.95); all puddings are home-made (treacle and walnut tart £2.50). On Sunday a traditional roast lunch is served (2-course £7.95, 3-course £8.95). Bedrooms, all kept in good order, are traditionally furnished in the main building, much more modern in the annexe. TVs, direct-dial phones and tea-making facilities are standard. *Bar Food and Restaurant Meals 12-2, 7-10. Vegetarian dishes. Children's portions. Beer Bishops Tipple, Salisbury Best Bitter. Garden, outdoor eating. Family room. Accommodation 5 bedrooms, all en suite, £40 (single £26). Children welcome overnight, additional beds (£4). Check-in all day. Access, Amex, Diners, Visa.*

Sennen Cove   Old Success Inn

B&B

Tel 0736 871232   Fax 0736 788354

Sennen Cove by Whitesands Bay Cornwall   Map 12 A4

Located off the A30, next to a huge beach just a mile north of Land's End, this 17th-century inn has been refurbished in smart modern country hotel style with lots of plain white plaster, pine panelling and old photographs. The location is glorious, with tremendous views. Comfortable en-suite bedrooms, all have solid pine furnishings (one four-poster bed), attractive fabrics and all the usual facilities. The residents' lounge is spacious and stylish. *Free House. Beer Bass. Garden. Family room. Accommodation 12 bedrooms, 10 en suite, £50 (single £25). Children welcome overnight, additional beds, cots supplied. Check-in all day. Access, Visa.*

Shaldon   Ness House Hotel

B&B

Tel 062 687 3480   Fax 062 687 3486

Marine Drive Shaldon Devon TQ14 0HP   Map 13 D3

Built in 1810 and overlooking the Teign estuary and the town of Shaldon, the inn has retained its Regency exterior. The new landlord has recently upgraded the accommodation to offer en-suite facilities, TVs, telephones and tea-makers. There is a spacious open-plan bar and, at the back, a small, simple lounge. *Beer Royal Oak, Palmers, Hardy*

Country. Garden. Family room. **Accommodation** *12 bedrooms, all en suite, £68 (single £35). Children welcome overnight, additional beds (£15), cots supplied. Check-in all day. Access, Amex, Visa.*

Shamley Green   Red Lion

Tel 0483 892202	**FOOD**
	B&B
Shamley Green Surrey GU5 0UB	Map 17 E4

Listed 300-year-old building on village green with three open fireplaces, and beer barrels on display behind the bar. Reliably good, homely food in the bar – garlicky stuffed mushrooms (£3.55), seafood pancake (£4.95), chicken Indienne (£6.45) and popular puddings such as treacle tart or sticky toffee pudding (both £2.45). In the restaurant, the starters are the same as the bar but main courses are more substantial – fillet steak au poivre (£12.45), lamb cutlets (£7.95) or lemon sole (£8.65). Fresh, chintzy, antique-furnished bedrooms upstairs have relatively new en-suite facilities. *Bar Food 11.30-2.30 (Sun 12-2.30), 6-10 (Sun 7-9.30). Vegetarian dishes. Children's portions.* *Beer Fullers London Pride, Benskins. Garden, outdoor eating.* **Accommodation** *4 bedrooms, all en suite, £35 (single £30). Children welcome overnight, additional beds (from £5). Check-in all day. No dogs. Access, Amex, Diners, Visa.*

Shardlow   Malt Shovel Inn

Tel 0332 792392	
The Wharf Shardlow Derbyshire	Map 7 D3

Trent and Mersey Canal-side pub, dating from the 18th century and originally a busy maltings; the conversion is successful, spacious and pubby; be early for a window seat. *Beer Marstons.*

Shave Cross   Shave Cross Inn

Tel 0308 68358	**A**
Marshwood Vale Shave Cross Dorset DT6 6HW	Map 13 E2

Charming cob and flint old inn in beautiful Marshwood Vale, once a busy resting place for pilgrims on their way to Whitchurch, as well as monastic visitors, who frequently had their tonsures trimmed while staying, hence the name. Stone floor, inglenook fireplace, beamed ceiling, rustic furnishings, and a delightful suntrap garden. Popular with the local caravan site on wet summer days. *Free House. Beer Bass, Eldridge Pope Royal Oak, Hall & Woodhouse Badger Best. Cider Taunton Traditional. Garden, children's play area. Family room. Closed Mondays, except Bank Holidays.*

Shelf   Duke of York

Tel 0422 202056	
West Street Stone Chair Shelf West Yorkshire HX3 7LN	Map 6 C1

The Calderdale Way passes the front door of a pub whose cosy bar houses a vast array of bric-a-brac. *Beer Marston, Whitbread.* *Outdoor eating.*

Shelley   Three Acres Inn   ★

FOOD
B&B

Tel 0484 602606   Fax 0484 608411

Shelley Roydhouse nr Huddersfield West Yorkshire HD8 8LR   Map 6 C1

The Emley Moor television mast, red-lit at night, makes a useful guide when heading towards this unassuming greystone roadside inn, set high in the Pennines above Huddersfield – it's just a couple of fields away and towers over Roydhouse. Inside, the bar is civilised rather than characterful, plain and modernised, but with lots of darkwood panelling around the bar counter, and in the ceiling beams. An attractive dining area, linen-laid, leads off at one end, and there's a separate restaurant proper. Bar food is worth a detour here, for its quality, simplicity and presentation. The menu suits both large and small appetites with a range of some 15 sandwiches (£2.50-£3), 2-3 warm salads (the star of these features chicken livers, smoked bacon and croutons dressed with nutmeg cream on a generous base of fresh French leaves £5.50), Cumberland sausage and mash with onion gravy (£4.95), deep-fried fresh fillet of Whitby haddock with chipped potatoes and mushy peas (£5.95) and several home-made puddings. The 3-course table d'hote traditional Sunday lunch menu (£8.95) has a choice of six main dishes. On the evening à la carte, the choice is even wider: puff pastry case filled with lamb's kidneys and venison sausage in a Cumberland and juniper sauce (£4.50) or savoury baked custard of smoked salmon and scallops in lemon and dill sauce, followed by grilled fillet of red mullet with roast fennel and salsa (£8.95) or fillet of Yorkshire beef with caramelised shallots in red wine sauce (£10.95). Puddings tend to be wickedly rich: look out for our favourite, a chocolate and rum mousse (£2.25). All is clean and professionally run (in the same hands for 23 years); its inn-meets-small-hotel style emphasised by the eleven extra bedrooms which were developed in adjacent cottages in 1989. Bedrooms are light, nicely furnished and immaculately kept, those in the newer wing styled similarly to the originals. Old beams and occasional open fireplaces add age and characterto otherwise smartly modern decor, with pretty pastels, good carpets, pine furniture and beds, comfortable chairs or sofas, well-placed mirrors, and contemporary fabrics. Some of the neat, cream-carpeted en-suite bathrooms have showers only. Prices are lower at weekends. **Bar Food and Restaurant Meals** 12-1.45, 7-9.45. *Vegetarian dishes. Children's portions. Free House.* **Beer** *Timothy Taylor, Tetley, Theakston. Patio/terrace, outdoor eating.* **Accommodation** *20 bedrooms, 18 en suite, £57.50 (single £47.50). Children welcome overnight, additional beds and cots available. Check-in all day. No dogs. Access, Amex, Visa.*

Shenington   Bell

Tel 0295 87274

Shenington nr Banbury Oxfordshire OX15 6NQ   Map 16 B1

Delightful old golden-stone cottage in a pretty terrace. Heavy beams, wall and window seats, and three simply modernised rooms. Tables at the front of the building overlook the attractive green. *Free House.*

Shepperton   Anchor Hotel

Tel 0932 221618   Fax 0932 252235

Church Square Shepperton Middlesex TW17 9JZ

B&B

Map 17 F4

Sympathetically restored after fire damage, the Anchor is a sturdy old inn overlooking a tiny square. It has occupied its Thames-side position for over 400 years. There is no residents' lounge, but the friendly bar with its authentic-looking linenfold panelling has ample charm and character. Attractive bedrooms on the first floor are double-glazed and cosy and all offer TVs, telephones and tea-makers, as well as compact shower rooms (one also has a bath). *Free House. Beer Hardys, Royal Oak.* **Accommodation** *29 bedrooms, all en suite, £72 (single £56). Children welcome overnight, additional beds and cots available. Check-in all day. Access, Amex, Diners, Visa.*

Shepperton   Warren Lodge

Tel 0932 242972   Fax 0932 253883

Church Square Shepperton Middlesex TW17 0JZ

B&B

Map 17 F4

In the corner of a pretty village square, this 18th-century inn offers clean, basic accommodation in a picturesque setting. There are views of the river not only from the wood-beamed bar but also from six rooms in a new wing which lead on to a courtyard, motel-style. Modestly decorated bedrooms are kept in good order. A handsome old walnut tree dominates the cool and shady garden that leads down to the banks of the Thames. **Accommodation** *52 bedrooms, all en suite, £82 (single £57). Children welcome overnight. Access, Amex, Diners, Visa.*

Shepton Mallet   Kings Arms

Tel 0749 343781

Leg Square Shepton Mallet Somerset BA4 5LN

B&B

Map 13 F1

Check directions when booking at this 1660 stonebuilt pub, as it is set in a quiet corner of town. Locally known as the 'dusthole' from the days when it was a haunt of quarry workers, it contains low beamed bars with open stone walls and some photographs of the area past and present. The bar and restaurant area were recently refurbished, and the bedrooms are now all en-suite and offer TVs and tea-makers. *Beer Burton, Ansells.* **Cider** *Addlestones. Family room.* **Accommodation** *3 bedrooms, all en suite, £33 (single £25), additional beds £7. Check-in by arrangement. Access, Visa.*

Sherston   Rattlebone Inn

Tel 0666 840871

Church Street Sherston Wiltshire SN16 0LR

Map 14 B2

Busy old Cotswold-stone pub with its original stone roof intact, and lots more exposed stone inside, oak beams and open fires. No music. Boules pitch in the garden. *Beer Butcombe, Moorhouse. Garden, outdoor eating.*

Shifnal   Oddfellows

Tel 0952 461517

Market Place Shifnal Shropshire TF11 9AU

FOOD

B&B

Map 6 B4

A mixture of pub, wine bar and eatery in an idiosyncratic conversion of the former Star Hotel, hard by Shifnal station and railway viaduct. This provides an unusual view from the new conservatory and rear terrace, which provide some refuge from the frenetic activity around the bar. Diners can also sit inside at a dozen or so well-spaced pine tables and choose from blackboard menus of adventurous complexity. Single-course nursery food plays its part at lunchtime, while in the evening cottage pie and variously sauced pasta gives way to the likes of chicken satay with spiced peanut dip (£3.25), monkfish with chives and tarragon (£6.75) and lamb noisettes with a dip of redcurrant and ginger (£6.25). Liquid choices include four cask-conditioned ales (look for the Theakstons XB and Timothy Taylors Landlord) and a fair selection of wines. Four bedrooms with en-suite bathrooms are upstairs in the old Star. They're just a little rough and ready, which is curiously not at odds with Oddfellows below. *Bar Food & Restaurant Meals 12-2.30, 7-10. Vegetarian dishes. Children's portions. Free House. Beer Boddingtons, Old Hooky, Theakston XB, Timothy Taylors Landlord. Terrace, outdoor eating. Accommodation 4 bedrooms, all en-suite, £45 (single £30). No children overnight. Check-in by arrangement. Access, Visa.*

Shifnal   White Hart

Tel 0952 461161
4 High Street Shifnal Shropshire TF11 8BH   Map 6 B4

Tastefully refurbished 16th-century coaching inn with exposed beams taken from old ships. *Beer Ansells, Bass. Garden.*

Shiplake   Baskerville Arms

Tel 0734 40 3332   **B&B**
Station Road Shiplake nr Henley Oxfordshire RG9 3NY   Map 17 D3

A fine weeping willow dominates the patio garden of this red-brick pub near the Thames, making it a pleasant spot on sunny days for enjoying a traditional pint. Inside, the single bar is large and simply furnished, and a family room is available. For overnight guests, the four neat bedrooms redecorated in 1991 have co-ordinated bed linen and curtains, TVs, and tea-making facilities; they share a carpeted bathroom with separate shower unit. *Beer Wethered SPA, Flowers Original, Brakspear Special, Murphys Stout. Cider Scrumpy Jack. Garden. Family Room. Accommodation 4 bedrooms, not en suite, £35 (single £20). Children welcome overnight, additional beds (£5), cots supplied. Check-in by arrangement. Access, Visa.*

Shipston-on-Stour   White Bear Hotel

FOOD
Tel 0608 661558   **B&B**
High Street Shipston-on-Stour Warwickshire CV36 4AJ   Map 16 A1

A fine old coaching inn, partly 16th-century, overlooking the market place. The public bar has a large fireplace, log-burning stove, solid wood furniture and the obligatory fruit machine, while in the narrower and more characterful lounge there's a part red-tiled, part carpeted floor, fine stripped wood tables, round-back chairs, massive settles and some original beams. Rag-rolled walls are covered with a variety of pictures, including cartoons referring to regulars, old photographs of Shipston as it was in times past, and the daily newspapers are left out for customers to browse through, always a thoughtful touch. There's also a restaurant, to the rear of the bar, a more spartan room enlivened with large, colourful prints. A typical bar food meal off the blackboard menu could start with pan-fried garlic mushrooms (£3.50), with a pork chop with plum sauce

(£5.10) or lamb's kidneys cooked in red wine (£4.50) to follow. There's a good fresh selection of vegetables and potatoes, and to round things off perhaps a traditional and delicious apple and apricot crumble (£2.50). It gets very busy, especially at lunchtimes. The whole pub has a lively and relaxed atmosphere in which locals mix easily with the business and holiday traffic. Meanwhile, up the narrow staircase, the White Bear continues to provide comfortable accommodation in its ten individually styled, though by no means large, bedrooms. There's a mixture of period, pine and stripped wood furnishings, duvets and televisions in each room, and all are en suite, seven having compact shower cubicles, the rest baths. *Bar Food* 12-2, *6.30-9.30. Vegetarian dishes, children's portions.* **Beer** *Bass. Patio/terrace.* **Accommodation** *9 bedrooms, all en suite, £47 (single £35). Children welcome overnight, additional beds and cots available. Check-in after midday. Access, Visa.*

Shipton-under-Wychwood	Lamb Inn	**FOOD**
Tel 0993 830465		**B&B**
High Street Shipton-under-Wychwood Oxfordshire OX7 6DQ		Map 16 B2

Tucked away down a quiet side road, the Lamb is a typical 17th-century Cotswold building, complete with honey-coloured stone walls and stone tiled roof, and its neat little patio with parasol-shaded tables makes an ideal spot in summer. Inside, all is equally immaculate. The beamed bar has a polished woodblock floor and mostly antique furniture: a settle here, a pew there, and attractive old oak tables. At lunchtimes, the cold buffet displayed in the bar offers cold cuts like fresh salmon, ham and beef, a vegetarian tart and hot dish of the day. In the evening an extensive blackboard menu offers the choice of a full three-course meal or perhaps just a light snack. Main dishes like guinea fowl or whole pan-fried Cornish plaice come in generous portions with good simply-cooked fresh vegetables; as a bonus, someone in the kitchen has the cool, light hand needed to produce a melt-in-the-mouth pastry for the home-made fruit pies. For more formal dining there is a cosy low-beamed restaurant. The owner's interest in wine is evident from a well-chosen wine list, four or five of which are available by the glass. The Lamb's eight bedrooms are all as neat as a new pin, with cream-coloured melamine furniture and spotless modern bathrooms. Two of the rooms boast some old beams and these help lend a little extra character. Televisions, radio-alarms and tea and coffee making kit are standard, with mineral water and bowls of fruit as welcoming extras. The convivial hubbub from the bar below is quite audible in some rooms, which might be a problem if you want an early night. Good hearty cooked breakfasts are worth getting up for. *Bar Food* 12-2, 7-10. *Restaurant Meals* 7-9.30. *Vegetarian dishes. Children's portions.* **Beer** *Hook Norton, Wadworth.* **Cider** *Bland. Patio/terrace, outdoor eating.* **Accommodation** *8 bedrooms, all en suite, £68 (single £48). Check-in all day. Access, Amex, Visa.*

Shipton-under-Wychwood	Shaven Crown Hotel	**FOOD**
Tel 0993 830330		**B&B**
High Street Shipton-under-Wychwood Oxfordshire OX7 6BA		Map 16 B2

Originally a 14th-century hospice to Bruern Abbey, hence the monastic-sounding name (which doesn't really do this charming building any favours). A delightful courtyard garden, where you can eat in good weather, is the most unspoilt spot; residents' lounge in the old medieval hall, and more down to earth Buttery Bar. Bar food choices begin with home-made soup (£2.50), crispy duck (£9.50), Cotswold pie (£6.50) and end with summer pudding (£2.50) or cheesecake (£2.50). A traditional Sunday roast (3 courses £13.50) is served in the restaurant. The restaurant table d'hote menu (3 courses £17.50) might offer smoked trout, melon and Parma ham, poached salmon steak or fillet of beef medallion, among other dishes. Bedrooms vary in size, some smaller than you might expect for the price. *Bar Food* (except Mon) 12-2, 7-9.30 (Sun 7-9). *Restaurant Meals* (except Mon) 12-2 (Sun only), 7-9.30. *Vegetarian dishes. Children's portions. Children allowed in bar to eat.* *Beer* Hook Norton Best Bitter, Wadworth. *Cider* Bland. *Garden, outdoor eating.* *Accommodation* 5 bedrooms, all en suite, £55 (single £48). Children welcome overnight (over 14 years). Check-in by arrangement. No dogs. Access, Amex, Visa.

Shirley   Saracens Head Hotel

Tel 021 733 3888 Fax 021 733 2762	**B&B**
Stratford Road Shirley nr Solihull West Midlands B90 3AG	Map 6 C4

A few minutes from junction 4 of the M42 on the A34 Birmingham to Stratford road, is a substantial purpose-built hotel recently taken over by Ansell Hotels. All the bedrooms are very comfortable and well equipped. Pastel colour schemes, brass lamps, prints and lightwood units combine with en-suite facilities, direct-dial telephones, tea-makers and effective double-glazing to provide above-average accommodation. There are two bars, one with a lively atmosphere and music which attracts a younger crowd, and a cocktail/lounge bar which is more peaceful. *Beer* Ansells, Tetley, Burton. *Accommodation 34 bedrooms, all en suite, £43 (single £38). Children welcome overnight, cots available. Check-in all day. No dogs. Access, Amex, Diners, Visa.*

Shobdon   Bateman Arms

Tel 056 881 374	
Shobdon nr Leominster Hereford & Worcester HR6 9LX	Map 14 A1

Imposing 15th-century black and white pub, whose attractive interior sports open fires, antique and country charm. *Beer* Woods Parish Bitter. *Garden, children's play area.*

Shroton   Cricketers

Tel 0258 860421	
Shroton Dorset DT11 8QD	Map 14 B4

Secluded village pub beneath Hambledon Hill, popular with walkers and HQ for the local cricket team. *Beer* Courage Best, Green King. *Garden, Outdoor eating, Children's play area.*

Sibford Gower   Wykham Arms

Tel 029 578 351	
Colony Lane Sibford Gower Oxfordshire OX15 5RX	Map 16 B1

Thatched pub whose low-beamed lounge contains an old well (now glassed over). *Beer* Hook Norton, Fremkins. *Garden, Children's play area. Family room.*

Siddington   Greyhound

Tel 0285 653573

Ashton Road Siddington Gloucestershire   Map 14 C2

Interesting furnishings of eclectic taste, lots of brass and copperware,
beams, two open fires and a woodburning stove in this successfully
extended old village pub; no music in the lounge. Very popular
locally, usually busy and friendly to strangers. No children indoors,
though. **Beer** *Wadworths. Garden.*

Silk Willoughby   Horseshoes

Tel 0529 303153   **FOOD**

Silk Willoughby Nr Sleaford Lincolnshire HG34 8NZ   Map 7 E3

A redbrick pub standing near the A15 bypass at the heart of an
otherwise quiet village. The large bar, divided up into distinct sitting
areas, is homely and unpretentious in decor and furnishings: bottle
green banquettes, solid, simple wooden tables with little vases of
flowers, plants on windowsills and indoor hanging baskets, twin brick
fireplaces, and an eclectic mix of pictures, prints and splendid old
photographs on the walls. Large windows admit lots of natural light
in the daytime; it's rather gloomy in the evening. The bar food,
which is ever popular, features paté (£2.75), fisherman's pie (£3.95)
and the old standards of the lasagne or steak and kidney pie type.
There's also a 30-seat restaurant, smartly turned out, its tables
spaciously arranged, with a predominantly seafood menu with typical
dishes of lobster Napoleon (£11) and grilled Dover sole fillets in herb
butter (£9.50). **Bar Food & Restaurant Meals** *12-2, 7-10. Vegetarian
dishes. Children's portions.* **Beer** *Riding, Old Bailey. Children allowed in
bar to eat. Garden, outdoor play area, outdoor eating. Family room. Access,
Visa.*

Silverton   Three Tuns

Tel 0392 860352

14 Exeter Road Silverton Devon EX5 4HX   Map 13 E3

Pleasantly upgraded 15th-century thatched inn in a large village-cum-
small town, popular with locals and tourists. Window seats and log
fire. **Beer** *Courage Directors, John Smith.*

Skidby   Half Moon Inn

Tel 0482 843403   **FOOD**

16 Main Street Skidby Humberside HU16 5TG   Map 7 E1

Chips with everything is not the stuff of the Half Moon; its speciality
is home-made Yorkshire puddings – eight different combinations
(£2.20-£4.15) including one with vegetarian gravy. They are almost
big enough to obscure the waitress. The half-acre garden has its own
'Sproggies Bar' for children together with the only huge suspended
spiral climbing frame in the country. Open from 11am to 11pm
(Mon-Sat), the pub itself is not without idiosyncrasies, having four
little bars and wooden pillar supports. More home-made pies (£3.60),
soups (£1.25), chilis, curries (£3.35) and burgers are also available.
Bar Food *12-10 (Sun 12-2.30, 7-10). Children's portions. Garden,
outdoor eating, children's play area. Access, Visa.*

Skirmett   Old Crown

Tel 049 163 435

High Street Skirmett Buckinghamshire   **Map 17 D3**

Characterful old pub whose two linked rooms have dining tables,
beamed ceilings and open fires; there's also a real old-fashioned tap
room, and all available space is cluttered with a vast collection of bric-
a-brac. Children under ten aren't even allowed in the garden. *Beer
Brakspears. Garden, outdoor eating.*

Slaidburn   Hark to Bounty

Tel 02006 246   **B&B**

Slaidburn nr Clitheroe Lancashire BB7 3EP   **Map 6 B1**

Just off the B6478, inspiring countryside, seemingly untouched by   ☺
progress, surrounds the picturesque village of Slaidburn, a solidly rural
village full of stone buildings and narrow streets. Just off the main
road, the Hark to Bounty dates back to the 13th century, built from
the same sombre local stone. Its most interesting feature is an original
first-floor courtroom, for many years the main court between
Lancaster and York, and still in use until 1937. Nowadays it's used as a
function room, which can cater for up to 140 people, complete with
old jury benches and witness box, now a bar counter. The main bar is,
oddly, rather lacking in character. One long room, with rough-painted
walls and rustic wooden tables and chairs, it's rather spartan in style,
but has an open fireplace adorned with polished brass and copperware,
and a few heavy beams across the ceiling. Upstairs, eight en-suite
bedrooms (one with shower only) are cottagey in style, with floral
curtains and bedspreads, creaking floorboards, exposed beams, and
furniture which varies from modern fitted units to period pieces. One
room is a family room with a double bed and two single beds.
Bathrooms are carpeted, but rather dimly lit; many baths also have
showers. To the rear of the inn, a sheltered garden, with wooden
tables and bench seating, leads down to the pretty little river. *Beer
Theakston. Riverside garden. **Accommodation** 8 bedrooms, all en suite,
£45 (single £20). Children welcome overnight, cots available. Check-in all
day. Access, Amex, Visa.*

Sledmere   Triton Inn

Tel 0377 86644

Sledmere Humberside YO25 0XG   **Map 7 E1**

Characterful old roadside inn on an ancient East Yorkshire estate. *Beer
Tetleys, Youngers. Outdoor eating. Family room.*

Sleights   Salmon Leap

Tel 0947 810233   **B&B**

Coach Road Sleights nr Whitby North Yorks YO22 5AA   **Map 5 F3**

A homely pub close to the river Esk. The ten compact bedrooms have
been individually decorated and all offer bedside cabinets and tea-
makers. Two rooms are suitable for families and there are four small,
shared bathrooms with showers. Residents have the use of a first-floor
lounge and there are three simple bars, where fishermen and the
moorland walkers often pause for refreshment. *Free House. **Beer**
Cameron Traditional, Tetley Imperial. Garden. Family Room.
Accommodation 10 bedrooms, not en suite, £30 (single £15). Children
welcome overnight, additional beds and cots available. No dogs. Check-in all
day. No credit cards.*

Smallburgh   Crown

Tel 0692 536314

Smallburgh Hill Smallburgh Norfolk NR12 9AD   Map 10 D1

Thatched, beamed 15th-century building with barrel furniture and a large open fire. *Free House. Garden, Children's play area.*

Smarden   Bell

FOOD
B&B

Tel 0233 770283

Bell Lane Smarden Kent TN26 8PW   Map 11 C5

Tiled and rose-covered medieval Kentish inn in peaceful countryside (take the road between the church and Chequers pub, then left at the junction). The usually very busy, rustic interior has hop-festooned oak beams and inglenook fireplaces in three flagstoned bars; candlelight in the evenings. Bar food is reliable with home-made soup (£1.50), paté (£2.20) and scampi (£4.75). A narrow outside spiral staircase leads to four cottagey bedrooms furnished in solid period style. Continental breakfasts only, served in rooms. *Bar Food 12-2, 6.30-10. Vegetarian dishes. Children's portions. Free House. Beer Ringwoods Old Thumper. Garden, outdoor play area, outdoor eating. Family room. Accommodation 4 bedrooms, sharing 2 bathrooms, £32 (single £20). Children welcome overnight. Check-in by arrangement. Access, Visa.*

Smarden   Chequers Inn

FOOD
B&B

Tel 0233 770217

1 The Street Smarden Kent TN27 8QA   Map 11 C5

14th-century weatherboarded pub with real fires and ghosts, run for over 20 years by the Stevens family. Decent bar food runs from the simplest snack to things with chips and more restauranty dishes that might include home-made soup, fresh sardines (£3.50), lemon sole (£6.75), supreme of chicken (£5.95) or crispy roast duckling (£9.75). Fresh vegetables and real French bread are served. One of the rooms is a family room for 4. Good choice for breakfast. *Bar Food 12-2.30, 7-10. Vegetarian dishes. Children's portions. Free House. Beer Bass, Worthington IPA, Youngs Special. Children allowed in bar to eat. Garden, outdoor play area, outdoor eating, family room. Accommodation 6 bedrooms, sharing 2 bathrooms, £31 (single £19). Children welcome overnight, cots available. Check-in all day. Access, Visa.*

Snainton   Coachman Inn

B&B

Tel 0723 859231

Snainton nr Scarborough North Yorks YO13 9PL   Map 5 F4

The pub sign turn-off at the village entrance from Pickering leads you to a 200-year-old coaching inn flanked by paddocks and a verdant garden for summer drinking. The public and little lounge bars both have coal fires and sturdy wooden furniture. The bedrooms are spacious, plainly decorated in cream and white and simply furnished. All have en-suite facilities, TVs, tea-makers and extra heaters as standard. Cosy, old-fashioned residents' lounge. *Free House. Beer Cameron Traditional Bitter. Cider Scrumpy Jack. Garden. Accommodation 12 bedrooms, all en suite, £40 (single £25). Children welcome overnight, additional beds and cots available. Check-in all day. Access, Amex, Diners, Visa.*

Snape   Golden Key

Tel 072888 510

FOOD

Priory Road Snape Suffolk IP17 1SQ

Map 10 D3

Close to the Snape Maltings Concert Hall, a delightful and tasteful pub with a tiled old-fashioned public end and a carpeted lounge end, a real fire at each, plus pretty furnishings and pictures. The food is simple but reliably good – sausage, egg and onion pie (£4.95), steak and mushroom pie (£5.95), hot smoked haddock quiche (£4.95). Roast beef on Sundays. Children over 14 allowed indoors. *Bar Food 11-2.30, 6-9.30. Vegetarian dishes. Beer Adnams Best, Old Ale and Tally Ho (at Christmas). Patio, outdoor eating. No credit cards.*

Snettisham   Rose & Crown

Tel 0485 541382

A

Old Church Road Snettisham Norfolk PE31 7LX

Map 10 B1

Splendid white-painted 14th-century inn, with oak beams, old-fashioned stone-floored locals' public bar, traditional front bar with inglenook fireplace and airy modern extension. It can become very crowded when busy. Straightforward accommodation. *Free House. Beer Courage Directors, Greene King, IPA, Abbot Ale. Family room. Outdoor play area, garden. Accommodation 3 bedrooms, 1 en suite, £40 (single £25). Children welcome overnight, extra beds supplied £10. Check-in by arrangement. No dogs. Access, Visa.*

Soberton   White Lion

Tel 0489 877346

Soberton Hampshire SO3 1PF

Map 15 D3

Extremely lively 17th-century country pub, with two slightly worn looking bars and lots of theme events; as they cheerfully admit, "we'll celebrate anything, even Mexican Independence Day". *Beer Whitbreads. Garden, children's play area. Family room.*

Sonning   Bull

Tel 0734 693901

FOOD

B&B

High Street Sonning Berkshire RG4 0UP

Map 16 D3

Quintessentially southern English traditional pub, its ancient black and white exterior covered with plants and flowers – you can sit out here and admire them – while in its two linked rooms there are sturdy old beams, gleaming brass, quarry tiles, barrel chairs and an inglenook fireplace, alive with logs in winter, ablaze with flowers in summer. Very simple but decent lunchtime bar food centres on the cold buffet table (assorted meats and salad £4.80) and in winter a home-made soup and hot dish (steak and kidney pie £4.75, goulash £5.25) are added to the menu. In the evenings, a more varied menu is served in the restaurant – savoury pancake (£2.90), chicken in garlic butter (£7) or sirloin steak (£8.40). Bedrooms are stylishly old-fashioned, with white walls, beams and solid freestanding furniture; most overlook the church and courtyard. *Bar Food 12-2. Vegetarian dishes. Free House. Beer Wethered, Flowers, Brakspear special. Patio/terrace, outdoor eating. Accommodation 4 bedrooms, sharing bathroom, £63.45 (single £35.25). No children overnight. Check-in by arrangement. No credit cards.*

Sonning Eye   Flowing Spring

`Tel 0734 693207`

Henley Road Sonning Eye Oxfordshire RG4 9RB   Map 17 D3

A spring rises in the field next door to this cosy roadside pub which prides itself on a relaxing atmosphere. The huge garden is reached via a wrought-iron staircase. *Beer Fullers. Garden, outdoor eating.*

South Dalton   Pipe & Glass

`Tel 0430 810246`   **FOOD**

South Dalton nr Beverley Humberside HU17 7PN   Map 7 E1

A Wolds village pub with an attractive traditional interior, beamed bars, leather seats, settles and log fires. Reliable bar food is available from the daily-changing menu which includes crispy chicken wings (£2.65), Yorkshire pudding with gravy (£1.65) and grilled loin of pork (£4.50). In the conservatory restaurant a set carvery menu at £11.75 is one of the options. The garden is lovely in summer. *Bar Food (not Sun) 12-2, 7-10. Restaurant meals same times plus Sunday lunch. Vegetarian dishes. Children's menu. Free House. Beer Ruddles Best, John Smith, Whitbread Castle Eden Ale. Garden, outdoor eating, outdoor play area, family room. Pub closed Mondays. Access, Visa.*

South Harting   Ship Inn

`Tel 0730 825302`   **FOOD**

South Harting West Sussex GU31 5PZ   Map 15 D3

Colourful flower baskets adorn the outside of this white-painted mid-17th century inn in the centre of the village, and a wisteria is getting established. Mind you head once through the door, as the beams are rather low. The interior furnishings are a mixture of varnished rustic tables, banquettes and wheelback chairs with hunting prints on the walls. The main bar is largely given over to eating, with an extensive menu of mostly home-made dishes; soup is popular, perhaps mushroom or pumpkin (£2.25), and the steak and kidney pie combines chunks of lean beef with a crisp pastry lid (£4.95). Fresh seafood is a speciality and usually oysters or mussels can be eaten at weekends. Fish starters feature strongly on the menu – crevettes provençale (£4.90), marinated herrings (£3.75) or potted shrimps (£3.45) and the comprehensive list of main dishes offers plenty of variety: salmon en croute (£7.95), game pie (£6.35), dressed crab salad (£7.25), fillet steak with mushroom and tomato garnish (£9.30). Leave room for splendidly traditional puddings like treacle tart (£2.35) to round things off. It's usually wise to book for meals but at lunchtime snacks are also offered, like sandwiches (from £2.15) and jacket potatoes (from £3.25). Short, carefully chosen wine list. A small public bar has a dartboard and fruit machine. Children under 14 years are not allowed inside, but in fine weather are welcome in the small garden, which boasts an aviary with cockatiel and quail amongst other birds. *Bar Food 12-2.30, 7-9.30 (7-9 Sun, no food Sun eves from November to March). Vegetarian dishes. Free House. Beer Ruddles. Cider Scrumpy Jack. Garden, outdoor eating. Access, Visa*

South Harting   White Hart

Tel 0730 825355

High Street South Harting West Sussex GU31 5QB

FOOD

Map 15 D3

Pleasant village pub with three beamed bars, wooden tables, polished wood floors, log fires and a decent choice of good, fresh food. Known for their traditional country recipes, the licensees display their menu on a blackboard where three specials appear daily – gamekeeper's stew (£4.50), chicken and broccoli baked in pepper sauce (£4.50) are typical choices. On Thursday, Friday and Saturday evenings the restaurant, formerly an old scullery, with flagstone floors and open inglenook fireplace, features dishes such as stuffed local trout (£10.50), jugged venison (£12.50) or baked lamb with orange and ginger (£8.50); good vegetables are served with main-course dishes. Vegetarians may wish to try the corn and avocado bake (£4.50) or chestnut and red wine paté. Desserts are the old favourites: bread-and-butter, treacle tart or fresh fruit puddings (all £1.85). In fine weather, families may wish to venture into the beautiful garden overlooking the South Downs where children can safely play around the pond and waterfall. *Bar Food 11-2 (12-2 Sun), 7-10. Restaurant Meals 6.30-10.30. Vegetarian dishes. Children's menu/portions. Free House. Beer Tetley, HSB, Burton. Garden, outdoor eating, children's play area. Family room (with toy box). No credit cards.*

South Leigh   The Masons Arms

Tel 0993 702485

South Leigh nr Witney Oxfordshire

Map 16 B2

Large thatched pub in the centre of a small village. Flagstoned bar with a multitude of coppers and brasses. Families will enjoy the large garden with peacocks. Sowlye (the old name for South Leigh) is specially brewed for the pub. *Free House. Beer Hook Norton, Sowlye. Garden. Pub closed Mondays.*

South Pool   Millbrook Inn

Tel 0548 531581

South Pool Kingsbridge Devon TQ7 2RW

FOOD

Map 13 D3

Opening hours at this white-painted, 400-year-old pub vary somewhat according to the state of the tide in the creek that extends into the heart of the pretty village and brings a number of the Millbrook's customers by boat. Inside it is small and cosy with tapestry cushions on the wheelback chairs and ceiling beams decorated with old clay pipes, horse brasses, old bank-notes and hundreds of visiting cards. To the rear a tiny terrace overlooks a small stream which is home to a family of ducks. The menu includes something to suit most tastes from filled jacket potatoes, quiche lorraine (£3.50) and smoked mackerel to steaks, cottage pie, fisherman's pie (£4.15), Devon pastry (£2) and cheesy leek and potato bake (£3.35). Puds such as Devon apple cider cake (£1.45) and treacle tart provide a sweet conclusion. *Bar Food 12-2, 6.30-9. Vegetarian dishes. Free House. Beer Bass, John Smith. Patio/terrace, outdoor eating. Family room. No credit cards.*

South Rauceby   Bustard Inn

Tel 0529 8250

Main Street South Rauceby Lincolnshire   **Map 7 E3**

Modernised, listed stone pub in an idyllic village setting. In winter, a good log fire; in summer, a lovely garden. *Beer Ruddles Best. Outdoor eating, children's play area.*

South Zeal   Oxenham Arms

Tel 0837 840244   **B&B**

South Zeal Devon EX20 2JT   **Map 13 D2**

Ancient village-centre inn, romantically fronted and creeper-covered. Genuinely unspoilt inside too, with worn flag floors, vast open fires, original beams, rough plaster walls, spooky passageways, solidly traditional drinking areas, and a relaxing clubbish lounge. Nice, old-fashioned bedrooms offer discreet modern comforts; a delightful place to stay. *Free House. Beer Bass, St Austell Tinner's. Garden, children's play area. Family room. Accommodation 8 bedrooms, 7 en suite, £50 (single £40). Children welcome overnight, additional beds, cots supplied. Check-in all day. Access, Amex, Diners, Visa.*

Southwold   Crown   ★

Tel 0502 722275   **FOOD**
                                                             B&B

High Street Southwold Suffolk IP18 6DP   **Map 10 D2**

Local brewers, Adnams, take the credit for the stylish restoration of Southwold's central Georgian inn. While not without fault in attempting to be most things to all comers, the Crown is to be applauded for its success in bringing straightforward food, prime-condition beers and excellent wines to the average spender. As the brewery's head offices happen to be housed upstairs, the nautically themed rear bar is naturally a showcase for their Mild, Bitter and Broadside ales; complete with binnacle and navigation lamps, the bar's curved and glassed-in rear panel gives the entirely fitting impression of being the flagship's bridge. To the front, facing the High Street, the Parlour serves as half lounge and coffee shop, while the front bar and attendant restaurant, decked out with green-grained panelling and Georgian style brass lamps, has a refined air, yet is totally without pretension or stuffiness. 20 wines by the glass, from a list selected monthly by Simon Loftus, are kept in peak condition by the Cruover machine, and the choice is second to none from 300 available wines. Menus are produced daily, with an accent on fresh fish. The selection from the keenly-priced bar meals list or fixed-price restaurant menu (£16.25 for two courses, £18.50 for three) is peerless. In the bar: grilled sardines (£3.85), steamed black pudding with sweet onion sauce (£3.95), baked catfish with herb crust and Basquaise sauce (£6.85), steamed fillet of brill à la portugaise (£8.50), orange fritters (£2.74), lemon meringue pie (£2.75). On the set menus, start with cream of tomato soup with croutons or medley of smoked fish with dill mayonnaise, and proceed to a duo of halibut and salmon with Chablis and sorrel sauce, cushion of sea bass filled with a light fish mousse, beef strogonoff or avocado filled with cream cheese and walnuts baked in filo, and finish with Poire William cheesecake with coffee sauce or baked apples with a nutty caramel sauce. A simple old-fashioned roast beef and Yorkshire pudding (£6.85) is served on Sundays. The dozen well-equipped bedrooms are similarly tasteful and all have private bathrooms, though three are not strictly en suite.

Freestanding furniture is antique or decent-quality reproduction, and both fabrics and furnishings are conducive to a restful stay. Pleasant staff take care of the rest, by offering a warm welcome, good but informal service, and a light breakfast promptly served in one's bedroom along with the morning paper. *Bar Food 12.30-1.45, 7.30-9.45. Restaurant Meals 12.30-1.30, 7.30-9.30. Vegetarian dishes. Children's portions. Children allowed to eat in bar. Beer Adnams. Patio, outdoor eating. Accommodation 12 bedrooms, 9 en suite, £58.50 (single £38.50). Children welcome overnight, additional beds (£7.50), cots supplied. Check-in from 1pm. No dogs. Access, Amex, Visa.*

Sowerby Bridge   Moorings

Tel 0422 833940

No. 1 Warehouse Canal Basin Sowerby Bridge W Yorkshire HX6 2AG   Map 6 C1

Converted 1790 canalside warehouse, refitted in light modern, if rather functional, style with lots of exposed stone and pine. Large windows overlook canal basin; good, balconied family room plus waterside patio. Appetising range of about 100 bottled beers, including many fine Belgians. *Free House. Children's play area. Family room.*

Sparsholt   Plough

Tel 096 272 353

Main Road Sparsholt Hampshire SO21 2NW   Map 15 D3

Originally a Whitbread pub and now in the Wadworth stable, it has two acres of lawns. *Beer Flowers. Garden, outdoor eating. Family room.*

Speldhurst Hill   George & Dragon

Tel 089 286 3125

Speldhurst Hill nr Tunbridge Wells Kent TN3 0NN   Map 11 B5

A well-loved ancient timbered landmark. *Free House. Garden, outdoor eating. Family room.*

Springthorpe   New Inn

Tel 042 783 254

16 Hill Road Springthorpe Lincolnshire DN21 5PY   Map 7 E2

Country pub in charming village, with a garden and a green for sunny days. *Beer Batemans, Ruddles. Garden.*

Sproughton   Beagle

Tel 0473 730455   **FOOD**

Old Hadleigh Road Sproughton Suffolk IP8 3AR   Map 10 C3

Tucked away, about half a mile out of the main village on the Old Hadleigh Road going towards the A12, the Beagle is an old wooden-beamed establishment converted from four farm cottages. More recently, a conservatory was built on the side of the lounge bar overlooking the herbaceous borders in the splendid sheltered garden. There is reliably good food from the daily changing blackboard menu – liver and bacon casserole (£4), cheesy chicken fricassee (£3.50), steak and kidney pie (£4.90), topside of beef ploughman's (£4), rum, raisin and walnut flan (£1.75), lemon meringue pie (£1.75). *Free House. Bar Food 12-2 (not Sun). Children's portions. Beer Adnams, Greene King. Garden, outdoor eating. Family room (minimum age 5). Access, Visa.*

Stalybridge   Hare & Hounds

`Tel 061-338 4614`

Mottram Road Stalybridge Greater Manchester SK15 2RF   Map 6 C2

Country pub-style city pub. **Beer** Bass. Garden, Children's play area.
Family room.

Stamford   Bull & Swan

`Tel 0780 63558`   **B&B**

71 High Street St Martins Stamford Lincolnshire PE9 2LJ   Map 7 E3

Opposite the former house of Lady Wingfield, who in 1643 persuaded
Cromwell not to raze the town, today's Bull & Swan is wonderfully
preserved; its inheritors should be truly grateful to their erstwhile
neighbour for its survival! Its creeper-hung stone facade and mullion
windows house an intimate pub within, its two-tiered timbered bar
hung with horse-brasses and old brass beer taps. Bedroom
accommodation, though modest, echoes the sense of history: while
five of the bedrooms sport only en-suite showers (and one has a bath)
they obtain their charm from bright duvets and curtains and their
character from the 15th-century sloping floors and angled ceilings.
Beer Burton Ale, Marston Pedigree, Tetley. Patio, outdoor eating. Family
room. **Accommodation** 7 bedrooms, 5 en suite, £45 (single £28).
Children welcome overnight, additional bed and cots available.
Check-in by arrangement. Access, Visa.

Stamford   The George of Stamford

`Tel 0780 55171`   **FOOD**
                                                                            B&B

71 St Martins Stamford Lincolnshire PE9 2LB   Map 7 E3

Arguably the finest and grandest of England's old coaching inns, the
George is a fully modernised hotel (graded at 72% in our 1993 *Hotel &
Restaurant Guide*) that retains some wonderful period atmosphere. It's
believed that there's been a hostelry of sorts here since the Norman
period, originally as a stopping place for pilgrims on their way to the
Holy Land, and a crypt under what's now the cocktail bar is certainly
medieval, while much of the present building, which dates from 1597,
remains in the veritable warren of rooms which makes up the public
areas. Facing the High Street, the oak-panelled London Suite and York
Bar were once waiting rooms for the "twenty up and twenty down"
stages which passed this way, but for the modern pub-goer this bar is
probably the least attractive, being solidly masculine in its appearance
– and the guest beer has (like some of the wayfarers of old) been
known to hang around longer than is good for it. The Garden
Lounge, however, which is exotically bedecked in orchids, palms and
orange trees, provides a fine setting for informal eating throughout the
day: lunch including a fine cold buffet augmented by home-made pies,
with which, incidentally, up to 20 wines are offered by the glass. Next
door, and by far the most picturesque spot, is the enclosed courtyard.
Surrounded by the ivy-covered hotel buildings, hung with vast
flowering baskets and illuminated by old street lamps, it makes an
ideal venue for morning coffee and afternoon tea, as well as barbecues
on mid-summer evenings. Restaurant dining, in an elegant,
chandeliered hall sporting silver urns, duck presses, and carving
trolleys still in daily use, runs along more classical – and
comparatively pricey – lines. Plenty of modern touches shine through
in the food, though: spring onions and stem ginger with a ravioli of
crab, perhaps; or a duet of contrasting sauces, one of sweet onions, one

of port wine, partnering a generous tasty beef fillet. Accommodation at the George is strictly hotel, which is fine if you're prepared to pay. A liveried porter shows you to the room and there's a full, cosseting night service; not too many pubs today recall this part of our heritage! But the comfort of plushly draped bedrooms, close-carpeted through to the bathrooms fitted out with bespoke toiletries, generous towels and rather wonky telephone showers is all quintessentially British and not to be sneered at. A morning tray of tea appears at the appointed time with folded daily paper, and a traditional English breakfast down in the Garden Lounge sets well-rested residents up for the day. *Bar Food* all day. Restaurant 12.30-2.30, 7.15-10.30. *Vegetarian meals, children's portions.* **Beer** *Adnams Bitter, Ruddles Best.* **Accommodation** *47 bedrooms, all en suite, £97.50 (single £66). Children welcome overnight, cots available. Check in all day.* *Access, Amex, Diners, Visa.*

Stanford Dingley   Bull Country Inn

FOOD

Tel 0734 744409

B&B

Stanford Dingley nr Reading Berkshire RG7 6LS

Map 16 C3

A tranquil village and a 15th-century redbrick pub, one bar staunchly traditional with its quarry tiling, barrel seats, window settle and big black beams, the other a more modern, plainer saloon with plush banquettes. Reliably good home cooking is a feature of the Bull – Stilton soup (£2.25), smoked salmon rollmop (£3.40), leek, cheese and potato pie (£4.10) or savoury pancake with salmon and shrimp (£4.50). Puddings are £1.90 and vary from toffee pudding to raspberry pavlova. *Bar Food* 12-2.30, 7.30-10. *Vegetarian dishes. Free House.* **Beer** *Bass, Charrington IPA. Garden, outdoor eating. Family room (until 8.30). No credit cards.*

Stanford Dingley   Old Boot

Tel 0734 744292

FOOD

Stanford Dingley nr Bradfield Berkshire RG7 6LS

Map 16 C3

White brick building with black woodwork and hanging baskets of flowers. Two large bars with church pews as seats and assorted country pictures on the walls. Blackboard menus offer (in the bar) sweet and sour pork (£4.95), chicken Alsace (£5.75), curried lamb (£5.75) and halibut (£6.95) while the restaurant opens in the evening and offers the likes of smoked haddock with tomato coulis (£3.95), or scampi (£2.15), followed by pan-fried calf's liver (£7.95) or duck with cassis (£9.55) and hot treacle tart (£2.55) or strawberry crepes (£2.55) to finish. The wine list is comprehensive with the house wine at £5.90. The new owners are redecorating everywhere and upgrading (new inside loos). There are also plans for a conservatory and an enlarged car park. *Bar Food* 12-2, 6-10. *Restaurant Meals* 6.15-10. *Vegetarian dishes. Children's portions. Garden, outdoor eating.* *Access, Visa.*

Stannersburn   Pheasant Inn

Tel 0434 240382

Stannersburn nr Falstone Northumberland NE48 1DD

Map 5 D2

Old stone country inn a mile from Kielder Water. Beamed ceilings and open fires. **Beer** *Theakston Best. Children's play area.*

Stanton St John   Star Inn

Tel 086735 277   **FOOD**

Stanton St John nr Oxford Oxfordshire OX9 1EX   **Map 16 C2**

A former 18th-century butcher's shop and abattoir with lots of period
feel in the two original little bars, both low-beamed, one brick-
floored, the other carpeted and furniture-crammed. An answer to
extreme popularity has been found in a successful extension. Families
can now eat in a separate no smoking room and children can use the
outside play area. Reliably good food is offered on a simple menu –
soup (£1.80), cheesy seafood bake (£4.55), lamb and apricots (£4.55),
fisherman's platter (£7.25) and such puddings (all £2.05) as Bakewell
tart or bread-and-butter pudding served with clotted cream. A
separate vegetarian menu with a choice of six dishes is always
available. *Bar Food 12-2, 7-10 (7-9.30 Sun). Vegetarian dishes.
Children's menu.* **Beer** *Wadworth Old Timer (in winter) and Farmers
Glory (summer), 6X and IPA, Hall and Woodhouse Tanglefoot. Garden,
outdoor eating, children's play area. No credit cards.*

Stanton Wick   Carpenters Arms

Tel 0761 490202   **FOOD**
                                                                                       B&B
Stanton Wick Pensford Bristol Avon BS18 4BX   **Map 13 F1**

Converted from a row of 17th-century miners' cottages in the tiny
hamlet of Stanton Wick, which overlooks the Chew valley, the
Carpenters Arms is all one would expect of a country inn, complete
with roses clambering up the walls and tubs of colourful flowers.
Inside, there are low oak beams, natural stone walls and warming log
fires; at one end of the building is a restaurant for formal eating, at the
other, the less formal Coopers Parlour. The printed menu here
includes grills (T-bone steak £10.95), pies (chunky chicken and bacon
£5.95) and a good choice of vegetarian dishes (spinach and cheese en
croute £4.55) on a varied menu ranging from salade niçoise to Welsh
rarebit. There are also daily specials on the short blackboard menu.
The restaurant menu has a more elaborate choice: Mendip snails
(£3.75), liver and cognac paté with cranberry coulis (£2.95), poached
darne of salmon with dill and cucumber sauce (£12.50), escalope of
veal champignon (£12.75). Traditional sweets include bread and
butter and summer puddings, and the ice cream is home made (all
£2.35). There are some ten wines available by the glass from a good
realistically-priced wine list and a handful of real ales to wash down
the eats. Immaculate bedrooms are appropriately cottagey in style,
with pine furniture and pretty co-ordinating fabrics and wall
coverings. Modern conveniences are not forgotten and there are smart,
modern carpeted bathrooms. *Bar Food 12-2, 7-10.* **Restaurant** *12-2
(except Mon), 7-10 (except Sun). Vegetarian dishes. Children's portions.
Free House.* **Beer** *Bass, Butcombe Bitter, Wadworth 6X. Terrace, outdoor
eating.* **Accommodation** *12 bedrooms, all en suite, £49.50 (single
£42.50). Children welcome overnight (minimum age 10), additional beds
available. No dogs. Check-in all day. Access, Visa.*

Staple Fitzpaine   Greyhound Inn

Tel 0823 480227   °   **FOOD**

Staple Fitzpaine nr Taunton Somerset TA3 5SP   **Map 13 E2**

Built as a hunting lodge by the local lord of the manor in 1640, the
Greyhound has since been extended a number of times. The result is a
series of connecting rooms, some with flagstone floors, some with old

timbers or natural stone walls and stools made out of old barrels. The latest additions, just a couple of years old, has been aged with dark-stained board panelling and a high plate shelf above, helping it to blend happily with the older parts of the inn. This is now the restaurant area, with ready-laid tables, red paper napkins and waitress service; start, perhaps, with baked fresh dates stuffed with Stilton (£2.85) or crusty mushrooms with a garlic dip (£2.75); good chargrills may follow: gammon (£6.45), mixed meat kebab (£6.95), trout (£6.75). The other rooms, also much used for dining, have good eating-height solid wooden tables sporting little posies of flowers and candles in bottles. A blackboard menu combines standard pub stuff such as chili, sandwiches or ploughman's lunch (here called a woodcutter's lunch), with more out-of-the-way offerings like chilled watermelon, avocado with cottage cheese and elderberries, plus several pasta dishes. Audrey Watts, who owns the pub with her son Steven, takes personal charge of the puddings, and her plum and melon pie is a particularly successful, and unusual, combination, while the hot treacle tart with clotted cream is so popular that customers will not allow its removal from the menu. Children are welcomed with smaller portions at smaller prices, and a play area outside has a splendid rustic climbing frame and slide to keep them amused. A skittle alley with its own bar is set in a former cow shed and is available to groups: booking required. *Free House.* **Bar Food** *12-2, 7-10* **Restaurant Meals** *7-10. Vegetarian dishes. Children's portions.* **Beer** *Exmoor Ale, Marston Pedigree, Boddingtons Bitter, Flowers Original.* **Cider** *Lanes Farmhouse. Family room, patio, outdoor eating. Access, Visa.*

Starbotton	**Fox & Hounds** ★	**FOOD**
Tel 0756 760269		**B&B**
Starbotton North Yorkshire BD23 5HY		Map 5 D4

A typical stone-built, white-painted Yorkshire pub dating back about 400 years. Inside it is quite unspoilt with flagstone floors, a few plates on the wall for decoration and a motley collection of jugs, pots and mugs hanging from the ceiling beams, plus a real fire in the stone fireplace in winter. In summer there are a few tables outside. What is untypical about the Fox & Hounds is Hilary McFadyen's excellent cooking with an ever-changing blackboard menu offering the likes of chicken and leek crumble (£5.25), Moroccan-style lamb with apricots, prunes and almonds (£5.50), crispy-topped cauliflower cheese (£4.25), sausage and apple pie (£4.50), bacon and mushroom quiche (£3.95) and wine and nut loaf (£4.25). Lunchtimes there is also a ploughman's that comes with an apple and Hilary's own home-baked granary bread (£3.50), Yorkshire pudding with various fillings (from £3.50) and crusty French stick sandwiches. Two single, charming bedrooms with en-suite shower rooms offer comfortable overnight accommodation with TV and tea and coffee-making kit. **Bar Food** *12-2, 7-9. Vegetarian dishes. Children's menu/portions. Free House.* **Beer** *Theakstons Best, Youngers No. 3. Patio, outdoor eating. Family room.* **Accommodation** *2 bedrooms, both en suite, £40 (single £20). Children welcome overnight. Check-in by arrangement. No credit cards.*

Staverton   Sea Trout Inn

Tel 080 426 274   Fax 080 426 506

Staverton nr Totnes Devon TQ9 6PA

B&B

Map 13 D3

A warm welcome heralds a pleasant stay at the Sea Trout, a country
inn that is a particular favourite of fishermen. The fishing theme runs
through the pub, some specimens mounted in showcases, others
depicted in paintings or on plates. A recent addition to the
conservatory leading from the restaurant to the garden. All rooms
have TVs, telephones, tea-makers and are decorated in a cottagey style.
Free House. **Beer** *Dartmoor Best, Wadworth 6X, Bass, Ruddles.* **Cider**
Luscombe. Garden. **Accommodation** *10 bedrooms, all en suite, £45 (single
£37.50). Children welcome overnight, additional beds (£8) and cots
available. Check-in all day. Access, Amex, Visa.*

Steep   Harrow Inn

Tel 0730 262685

Steep Hampshire GU32 2DA

FOOD

Map 15 D3

Somewhere between 400 and 500 years old, the Harrow is a modest
little pub tucked down a sleepy country lane that dwindles into a
footpath by a little stream. The tenancy has been in the same family
since 1929 and in recent years, the landlord has been engaged in
constant battles with the brewery, who wanted to modernise. Edward
McCutcheon finally won the war in 1992, when he managed to buy
the inn; he can now keep it very much as it must have been in the last
century (earlier, even). Two small rooms have boarded walls, an old
brick inglenook fireplace, scrubbed wooden tables and a hatch-like
bar, behind which barrels ofbeer sit on racks, with bundles of drying
flowers hanging above. There's a small cottagey garden to one side,
and some old sloping rustic benches and tables out at the front. Toilets
are in a separate brick building on the other side of the lane. The food
is limited to a few wholesome snacks, a split pea and ham-based soup
(£2.10) full of fresh vegetables served with great chunks of bread; a
few salads and ploughman's of beef, cheese or home-cooked ham
(£5.50) – Ellen cooks about 20 gammons a week; home-made Scotch
eggs (£1.20), most of the eggs coming from their own hens, and
perhaps, meat loaf or marrow filled with mince and topped with
cheese (£4.75). Apart from the beers, there's a good selection of fruit
wines. **Bar Food** *12-2, 6.30-10 (7-10 Sun). Vegetarian dishes. Free
House.* **Beer** *Flowers, Boddingtons. Garden, outdoor eating. No credit cards.*

Steeple Aston   Red Lion

Tel 0869 40225

Steeple Aston Oxfordshire OX5 3RY

FOOD

Map 16 C1

Colin and Margaret Mead run this pretty 330-year-old village pub,
just off the main Oxford-Banbury A4260. A small flower-filled
terrace leads into a comfortable beamed bar to the left and a small
dining room to the right. Very well kept beer, a multitude of malt
whiskies and an extensive wine list all complement Margaret's
cooking. Home-made hot-pot in winter (from £4.50), rare roast beef
sandwiches (£1.60) and ploughman's (£3) made with local cheeses are
specialities in the bar, while a more creative and imaginative small
menu (3-course meal with coffee is priced according to main dish –
stuffed breast of goose £19.25, fillets of brill £17.80) is offered in the
dining room at night, making use of game in season and local
produce. Home-made puddings include Craigellachie cream (Scottish

syllabub made with syrup of marmalade and malt whisky). *Bar food 12-2 (except Sun)*. *Restaurant Meals 7.30-9.15 (except Sun and Mon)*. *Vegetarian dishes. Free House. Beer Tanglefoot, Hook Norton, Wadworth. Garden, outdoor eating. Access, Visa.*

Steppingley   French Horn

Tel 0525 712051

5 Church Road Steppingley Bedfordshire MK45 5AU   Map 17 E1

Old and attractive inn, family-run, and now divided into a pool-table dominated public bar, L-shaped lounge with exposed 17th-century timbers, and popular restaurant. Real fire, no music. *Beer Bass, Tetley. Garden, Outdoor eating.*

Stiffords Bridge   Red Lion

Tel 0886 880318

Stiffords Bridge nr Malvern Hereford & Worcester WR13 5NN   Map 14 B1

Old oak-beamed inn with log fires in both lounges and fairly low-key piped music, but no juke box or pool. *Beer Banks's, Ind Coope. Riverside Garden, Children's play area.*

Stilton   Bell Inn

Tel 0733 241066

Great North Road Stilton nr Peterborough Cambridgeshire PE7 3RA   Map 7 E4

FOOD
B&B

Reputedly the oldest coaching inn on the Great North Road, the Bell boasts a Roman well in its courtyard and an impressive 15th-century stone frontage. 1990 additions include hotel reception glassed-in under the original archway. Discreetly concealed from the road are two wings of en-suite bedrooms whose 20th-century trappings include telephones, satellite television and whirlpool baths, while tokens of the past are confined to the odd four-poster bed. This is a pity, as the rest of the building is simply splendid. The village bar retains its stone-flagged floor and cosy alcoves huddled round the great log fire; this is where the original Stilton cheese was sold to travellers in the 1720s. Today it's served on its own with plum bread (£3.95), or with a hazlenut paté (£3.25), or in a celery soup (£3.50). For the less single-minded, there's ham and mushroom tartlet (£4.50), trio of tiger prawns (£5.50) or vegetable bake (£7.95). More serious food is on offer in the galleried restaurant, where linen-covered tables are widely spaced in two sections under gnarled oak beams and a vaulted ceiling with original exposed rafters. Here, one can eat from either the weekly table d'hote menu (3 courses £14.50) which offers perhaps the best value: Italian seafood salad or baked avocado preceeding beef forestière, chicken Dijon or pork provençale, or from the extensive à la carte: Marlborough duck (£14.25), plaice paupiette (£9.95) or seafood ragout (£11.75). The "After Thoughts" menu offers baked pear Alaska, sticky toffee pudding or warm cheesecake (fruit cheesecake, baked and layered on a fruit coulis) (all £3.95). *Bar Food 12-2 (12.-1.45), 6-9.30 (7-9 Sun) Restaurant Meals 12-2 (Sun only), 7-9.30 (7-9 Sun). Vegetarian dishes. Free House. Beer Marston, Ruddles County, Tetley. Garden, outdoor eating. Accommodation 19 bedrooms, all en suite, £62 (single £57). Children welcome overnight, extra beds available (£10), cots supplied. Check-in all day. No dogs. Access, Amex, Diners, Visa.*

Stock   Hoop

Tel 0277 841137

21 High Street Stock Essex CM4 9BD   Map 11 B4

Unspoilt, simple, cosy beer-lovers' favourite in an equally unspoilt
Essex village. May Day weekend features a 100 brand-name beer
festival. *Free House. Garden, Children's play area.*

Stockbridge   White Hart Inn

Tel 0264 810475   Fax 0264 810268   **B&B**

High Street Stockbridge Hampshire SO20 6HF   Map 14 C3

On the Test Way (a popular walk), this ancient inn is unusual in
appearance, the first-floor overhang creating a covered area for
enjoying a drink outside (there is also a garden). Low beams, brick
pillars and timber-laced walls give the bar the look of cosy old age, a
charm that extends to main-house bedrooms. The stable block area
provides alternative accommodation in simple motel style. All
bedrooms offer TVs and tea-making facilities. Staff are courteous, and
plenty of printed local information is available in reception. *Free
House.* **Beer** *Wadworth 6X, Bass, guest beers. Garden.* **Accommodation**
*16 bedrooms, 10 en suite, £57.50 (single £35). Children welcome
overnight, additional beds (under-14 £5, over-14 £8), cots supplied.
Check-in all day. No dogs. Access, Visa.*

Stockland   King's Arms

Tel 040 488 361

Stockland Devon EX14 9BS   Map 13 E2

A tremendous range of island malt whiskies is just one of the lures at
the King's Arms; the last exciseman at Lagavulin distillery was also
the landlord's father! An inn since the early 18th century at least, it's
grade II listed, though considerably renovated and extended a few
years ago. A marvellously unspoilt interior, both in the dining lounge
and flagstoned stone-walled bar. *Free House. Children's play area.
Family room.*

Stockport   Red Bull

Tel 061 480 2087   **FOOD**

14 Middle Hillgate Stockport Greater Manchester SK3 4YL   Map 6 B2

Modest little pub with good home cooking – pea and bacon soup
(£1.40), large open sandwiches (£2.50), gammon and egg (£3.70),
fish and chips (£3), treacle sponge and custard (£1.30). *Bar Meals
12-2.15. Vegetarian dishes. Children's portions. Children allowed in bar to
eat at lunchtime.* **Beer** *Robinson's Mild and Bitter. No credit cards.*

Stoke Abbot   New Inn

Tel 0308 68333

Stoke Abbot Beaminster Dorset DT8 3JW   Map 13 F2

As the name doesn't suggest, the New Inn is very old, thatched and
cobbled without, simply modernised within. A huge collection of
horse brasses, and pictures of birds spotted in the garden. Children are
allowed in the separate dining room. *Beer Palmers. Garden, children's
play area.*

Stoke Row   Crooked Billet

Tel 0491 681048

Newlands Lane Stoke Row Oxfordshire   Map 16 C3

Traditionally furnished, pleasingly rustic interior with three little rooms, real fires, and a three-acre garden merging into Chiltern woods. One of the few remaining pubs without a bar counter: beer is drawn directly from barrels in a little cellar. *Beer Brakspears. Garden.*

Stoke St Gregory   Rose & Crown

Tel 0823 490296

Woodhill Stoke St Gregory Somerset TA3 6EW

FOOD
B&B

Map 13 E2

In the hamlet of Woodhill, the Rose & Crown is a 17th-century cottage pub with a delightful patio and, indoors, a fairly subtle horsey theme, lots of nooks and crannies, timbers and brasses aplenty. Readers are still travelling miles for the famous scrumpy chicken (£5.25) and cherry cheesecake (£1.95), just two of their good home-made dishes. Other popular dishes include grilled skate (£4.95) (fresh fish from Brixham harbour), or on the fixed-price menu (£11): California salad, hot peppered mackerel or grilled trout with almonds, and a choice of home-made ice cream specialities. There is a 3-course traditional Sunday roast lunch (£7). Bedrooms are modest with modern fittings; as we went to press one of the three bedrooms was being altered to have a bathroom en suite. *Bar Food and Restaurant Meals 12-2.30, 7-11 (7-10.30 Sun). Vegetarian dishes. Children's portions. Beer Eldridge Pope, Exmoor Ale. Garden, outdoor eating. Family room. Accommodation 3 bedrooms, sharing a bathroom, £40 (single £36). Children welcome overnight, additional beds available. Check-in all day. No dogs. Access, Visa.*

Stoke-by-Nayland   Angel Inn

Tel 0206 263245   Fax 0206 37386

Stoke-by-Nayland nr Colchester Suffolk CO6 4SA

FOOD
B&B

Map 10 C3

Soft lamplight glows in the windows of this solid, beautifully restored old inn. Inside, the bar divides into two: a comfortable lounge bar with a brick fireplace, log-burning stove, exposed timbers and wooden furnishings, and a real sitting room with deep sofas, wing chairs and a grandfather clock. Fresh fish features prominently on the menu, simply cooked under the grill: plaice (£7.50), hake (£7.75), halibut (£7.95) are some examples all served with salad and French fries. A fish platter costs £8.50, lobster £17.95 and when available more unusual fish, such as red bream or New Zealand sand sole are on offer. Non fish-eaters may prefer beef en croute (£14.75), escalope of guinea fowl (£7.50), or rack of lamb (£8.95). All puddings are home-made. A 3-course traditional Sunday lunch costs £11.50. Of the bedrooms, three original-house rooms are reached via a small gallery above the restaurant, the others are housed in an annexe, but all decent-sized and furnished with a strong sense of style. No children in the bar, no under-tens overnight. *Bar Food and Restaurant Meals 12-2 (12-2.30 Sun), 6.30-9 (7-9 Sun). Vegetarian dishes. Beer Adnams, Greene King, Nethergate. Patio, outdoor eating. Accommodation 6 bedrooms, all en suite, £55 (single £42). No dogs. Check-in all day. Access, Amex, Diners, Visa.*

Stokesby   Ferry Inn

Tel 0493 751096

Stokesby nr Great Yarmouth Norfolk NR29 3EX   Map 10 D1

Plain, traditional waterside pub of spartan character. Busy with river
folk in summer (free moorings). *Beer Adnams, Flowers. Riverside
Garden, children's play area. Family room.*

Stony Stratford   Bull Hotel

Tel 0908 567104   Fax 0908 563765   **B&B**

64 High Street Stony Stratford Buckinghamshire MK11 1AQ   Map 17 D1

A massive wrought-iron pub sign landmarks this former coaching inn,
which with its neighbour, the Cock, coined the 'cock and bull' story.
A lounge bar doubles as reception, and refurbishment has taken place
in the Vaults Bar which attracts a younger crowd with live music at
weekends. The Mexican Bar is a recent addition. Accommodation is
adequate for over-nighters. Colourful curtains brighten smallish rooms
with TVs, tea-makers, direct-dial phones and en-suite bathrooms. *Free
House. Beer ABC, Bass, Wadworth 6X, Caines, Worthington, Eldridge
Pope Royal Oak, Hook Norton, Fullers, Youngers IPA. Accommodation
14 bedrooms, all en suite, £55 (single £39). Children welcome overnight,
additional beds £15, cots available. Check-in all day. Access, Amex,
Diners, Visa.*

Stony Stratford   The Cock Hotel

Tel 0908 567733   Fax 0908 562109   **B&B**

64 High Street Stony Stratford Buckinghamshire MK11 1AQ   Map 17 D1

New landlord Chris Hellier is enthusiastically restoring the Cock to its
past glory. This former coaching inn dates from 1300 and was
rebuilt after a fire in 1750. '*Ride a cock horse to Banbury Cross*' – the
horse was apparently from the Cock Hotel stables and with its
neighbour the Bull, gave rise to the phrase 'cock and bull' story. The
accommodation has recently been extended and now has 30 well-
equipped bedrooms. There is a comfortable bar and walled garden.
*Beer Speckled Hen, Hook Norton. Accommodation 30 bedrooms, all en
suite. Children welcome overnight, additional beds and cots available.
Check-in all day. Access, Amex, Diners, Visa.*

Stopham Bridge   White Hart

Tel 0798 873321   **FOOD**

Stopham Bridge nr Pulborough West Sussex RH20 1DS   Map 11 A6

Neat, simple roadside stone-built pub, opposite the River Arun and
not far from Stopham Bridge. It has a rambling assortment of bright,
attractive carpeted bars with a dining area leading off down some
steps: the resulting style is modern but relaxingly cottagey. Good hot
bar meals come in the form of soup (£1.50), jacket potatoes (from
£2.60), or home-made fish pie (£4.25). The restaurant menu is
wider-ranging with dishes such as cheesy Arbroathsmokie (£3.50),
seafood melée (£4.95), red snapper Cantonese-style (£10.50) or 10oz
sirloin steak (£11.95). They make their own ice cream (£1.75),
lemon meringue pie (£1.75) and crème brulée (£3.50). *Bar Food
12-2.30, 7-9.30. Restaurant Meals 12-2.15, 7-9.30. Vegetarian dishes.
Children's menu/portions. Beer Flowers, Whitbread. Riverside garden,
outdoor eating, children's play area. Access, Visa.*

Stow Bardolph   Hare Arms   ★

Tel 0366 382229

FOOD

Stow Bardolph nr Kings Lynn Norfolk PE34 3HT

Map 10 B2

A picturesque country pub in a delightful Norfolk village nine miles
south of Kings Lynn. Inside is pleasantly refurbished and immaculately
run, with a cosy bar, elegant restaurant, popular conservatory
extension (also the family room) and an intriguing coach house in the
garden for children. The pub gets its name, not from the animal, but
from a prominent local family, still found in these parts; venture into
the church, and a wax effigy of one Sarah Hare is posted as a warning
to others not to transgress the Sabbath – the unfortunate Sarah pricked
her finger whilst sewing on a Sunday and died of blood poisoning.
Cast such morbidity aside, and head straight for the cheery welcome
and excellent food at the Hare, where a fairly ordinary printed menu
of home-made curries, lasagne and grills is thrown into the shade by
quite exceptional daily specials. But be early, because this is by no
means a secret. The star of the specials board is the freshest local fish,
perhaps a Dover sole with fresh vegetables (£14.50), prawn and
spinach-stuffed plaice in a cream and white wine sauce (£13.50) or a
salmon fillet coated in creamy prawn and lobster sauce (£12.50). But
meat-eaters are by no means neglected; chicken breast stuffed with
paté, wrapped in bacon and served with Madeira sauce (£12.25) or
grilled fillet steak with mushroom and tomato (£13.50) are typical of
the daily specials. Winter brings game casseroles. It's not really a pub
for vegetarians, though one or two dishes are offered. Nice wines by
the glass and a serious list of bottles. *Bar Food 12-2, 7-10. Children's
portions.* *Beer Greene King, IPA, Abbot Ale, Rayments Bitter. Children
allowed in bar to eat (minimum age 10). Garden, outdoor eating. Family
room (conservatory). No credit cards.*

Stratfield Turgis   Wellington Arms

Tel 0256 882214   Fax 0256 882934

B&B

Stratfield Turgis nr Basingstoke Hampshire RG27 0AS

Map 17 D4

First a farmhouse and later a coaching inn, the Wellington Arms
provides a high standard of overnight accommodation under the new
manager. Behind a handsome Georgian facade a lot of care has gone
into preserving character by way of flagstones and fine woodwork,
open fires and inviting armchairs. A new extension was recently
finished which has resulted in many more bedrooms, well equipped
(one with four-poster and jacuzzi and two suites). *Beer Badger Best,
Malthouse.* *Accommodation 35 bedrooms, all en suite, £77.50 (single
£67.50). Children welcome overnight, additional beds available. Check-in
all day. Access, Amex, Diners, Visa.*

Stratford-upon-Avon   Slug & Lettuce

Tel 0789 299700

FOOD

38 Guild Street Stratford-upon-Avon Warwickshire CV37 6QY

Map 14 C1

Occupying a corner site adjacent to the Birmingham road, close to the
town centre, the Slug & Lettuce is one of Stratford's places to be seen.
With more than a hint of wine bar/bistro atmosphere, the pub is a
particular haven for the young and trendy; it's lively and informal,
and usually packed to the gunnels at weekends. Large blackboards
display the day's choice of imaginative and well-handled dishes.
Starters and light meals include black pudding topped with Stilton
(£4.75), Cumberland sausages in Dijon mustard (£4.75) or Mexican-

style spare ribs (£4.95) and more substantial main meals are chicken breast stuffed with avocado (£8.75) or grilled fresh shark steak (£9.75). All main dishes come with a side dish of crisp vegetables. Puddings are nice, there's a good choice of coffees too. Drinks are chosen from a blackboard wine list, real ale handpumps, or from a range of the designer lagers presently so fashionable. Staff are young and cheerful. Outside, a small paved patio, floodlit at night, is a pleasant spot for a summer drink. **Bar Food** *(Sun/Mon/Tue/Wed) 12-2.30, 5.30-10, (Thu/Fri/Sat) 12-9. Vegetarian dishes.* **Beer** *Ansells, Ind Coope Burton Ale, Tetley, Slug. Patio/terrace, outdoor eating. Access, Visa.*

Stutton   Hare & Hounds

Tel 0937 833164

Manor Road Stutton North Yorkshire SL24 9BS   Map 6 D1

The low-ceilinged lounge interior is decorated in good taste in that style known as Olde Worlde, with lots of beams, pictures, brass, fresh flowers, small windows and a general air of being very well cared for. *Garden, children's play area.*

Sudbury   Waggon & Horses

Tel 0787 312147

Acton Square Church Walk Sudbury Suffolk CO10 6HG   Map 10 C3

Revitalised turn-of-the-century-pub in a town-centre back street, popular with local families and tourists. Public bar, games room, snug and dining room, in an architecturally diverse, attractive building reached through a courtyard. **Beer** *Greene King. Children's play area. Family room.*

Surbiton   Fox & Hounds

Tel 081-390 3408   **FOOD**

60 Portsmouth Road Surbiton Surrey KT6 4HS   Map 17 F4

No chips, and none of the exotic dishes that are so common in pubs these days: there's just a short blackboard menu of simple home-cooked dishes that attract a host of regular customers here at lunchtime. There's always a soup (£1.95) and a daily-changing selection of hot dishes – turkey and mushroom pie (£3.25) made with an excellent short-crust pastry, lasagne (£3.95), pasta bake (£2.95) – plus ploughman's with Dijon mustard-baked ham, cheese or cheese-filled potatoes (all at £2.95 or served as salads at £3.95). A couple of traditional puds like bread-and-butter pudding and treacle tart (£1.25) provide the finale. The atmosphere is that of a friendly 'local' and the smart decor has something of a Victorian feel. There are a few tables outside on a roadside terrace. **Bar Food** *12-2.30. Vegetarian dishes. Children's portions. Outdoor eating. No credit cards.*

Sutton   Anne Arms

Tel 0302 700500   **FOOD**

Suttonfield Road Sutton South Yorkshire DN6 9JK   Map 7 D2

The village of Sutton is signposted off the A19 about five miles north
of Doncaster. At its heart is the ever-popular Anne Arms, a mellow stone building covered in creepers and colourful flower boxes. Its garden, which leads from an attractive conservatory (fitted with white cast-iron furniture and featuring caged budgies and other birds) is full of children's play equipment and picnic tables. The interior of the

main pub is bursting with character: in the main bar area, old wooden beams and panelling and polished wooden tables surrounded by floral upholstered chairs and bench seating. Glass display cabinets placed around the room hold a splendid collection of porcelain figurines and glassware. The ceiling, bar counter and window sills are adorned with a large collection of colourful Toby jugs as well as some Bavarian drinking steins. A small snug with bench seating and copper-topped tables has a number of stuffed birds, and the final lounge area has lace-clothed tables and a host of highly polished brass and copperware. The pub appears to be especially popular with the retired community, who flock here in droves. The queue to the food servery starts forming at about 11.50am, and often stretches right back through the bar. The menu features a short selection of dishes like rabbit pie (£3.25), braised steak with Yorkshire pudding (£3.25), cod in broccoli sauce (£3.25), or stuffed breast of chicken (£3.25). They cook the food in bulk (such is the turnover), then display and serve it quickly from a hot cabinet servery. Portions and prices are very fair, but the quality can obviously decline the later you arrive; no doubt that's why it's so busy as soon as it opens. You may find it difficult to find a table anywhere after 12! Don't expect wonders, but for good, cheap, honest home-made food, the Anne Arms is well worth a visit. Children are welcome in the conservatory or snug. *Bar Food 12-2 (except Sun), 7-9. Children's portions. Beer Courage, John Smith. Family Room (over 5 years). Garden, outdoor eating, children's play area. No credit cards.*

Sutton Courtenay   Fish

Tel 0235 848242

Appleford Road Sutton Courtenay Oxfordshire OX14 4NQ   Map 16 C2

Unassuming-looking late 19th-century roadside pub. *Beer Morlands.*

Sutton Gault   Anchor Inn

Tel 0353 778537   **FOOD**

Bury Lane Sutton Gault Cambridgeshire CB6 2BD   Map 10 B2

Deep in Fen country, just off the A142 at Sutton village, the Anchor is protected from 'hundred foot drain' (part of the Bedford river) by a veritable rampart of earthworks. Descend, then pass a new riverside patio into the low, brick-built pub to discover an Aladdin's cave of improbability, a low-beamed bar servery, its beer jugs hanging from hooks, racked Tolly Cobbold Original served direct from cask and landlord Robin Moore's preference for light classical music which seems entirely apposite to the setting. A long menu which relies heavily on fresh produce indicates careful daily shopping. Single-course meals and snacks start with soup and chilled melon with raspberry sorbet and progress through green-lip mussels in garlic butter or smoked duck-breast with tzatziki salad to baked stuffed aubergine or steak, kidney and Guinness pie. Seafood may include salmon or red Australian prawns, and the more substantial main courses perhaps wild hare with port and redcurrant sauce or fillet steak with green peppercorns. Year round the Anchor is a busy pub; those with children or particularly favouring the non-smoking Inglenook Room are well advised to book; it's virtually essential at weekends. In addition to the beer and a 60-plus wine list from Lay and Wheeler, other beverage choices include freshly squeezed orange juice and cups of cappuccino, chocolate or speciality teas. *Bar Food 12-2, 6.30-9.30 (Fri & Sat to 10, Sun 7-9). Vegetarian dishes. Children's portions. Free House. Beer Tolly Cobbold Original. Garden, outdoor eating. Family room. Access, Visa.*

Sutton Howgrave   White Dog

Tel 0765 640404	**FOOD**

Sutton Howgrave nr Bedale North Yorkshire DL8 2NS

Map 5 E4

Quaint converted village cottage by the delightful green, with simply furnished, cosy interior featuring working kitchen range. Lovely in summer when the clematis and window boxes bloom, though you can't eat out of doors. Bar food is served at lunchtime only – Stilton and apple soup (£2.20), smoked duck breast and melon (£4.25), mariner's hot pot (£4.25) – and on Friday and Saturday evenings the small restaurant (4 tables) is open for reservations only. All the starters are served with freshly baked bread. Main courses include giant prawns in garlic butter (£5.85), venison pie (£9.95), Mexican chicken (£9.40) and half a roast duck (£10.50). Children not allowed in the pub. Vegetarians catered for 'by request' in the restaurant (cracked wheat casserole £8.50). **Bar Food** 12-2.15. **Restaurant Meals** 7-10 (Fri/Sat only). *Vegetarian dishes. Free House.* **Beer** *Webster Pennine. Garden. No credit cards.*

Sutton Poyntz   Springhead

Tel 0305 832117	**FOOD**

Sutton Poyntz Dorset DT3 6LWD

Map 13 F3

The pub takes its name from the nearby spring and waterworks, which actually incorporates one of the funnels from Brunel's steamship, the *Great Eastern*. Owned by Devenish, the inn has an interior that's largely the work of brewery designers, with its high shelves of contrivedly casual piles of old books and bottles, and various framed displays of clay pipes, brass plates and shotgun cartridges, but managers Jim and Julie White have successfully individualised things with the help of a bar billiards table, magazines, and the daily papers to read, and their own relaxed friendliness. The food side is down to Julie, who cooks everything herself. The recently redecorated restaurant serves a wide variety of dishes including beef and almond curry (£5.25), chicken in ginger with green and red chilis (£5.65) and puddings include banana and cream profiteroles with butterscotch sauce (£2) or a spicy apple meringue pie. There are also plenty of sandwiches (good ham) and French sticks (£2.50), ploughman's (£2.50), jacket potatoes (£2.50) and salads; for the children there are fish-shaped fish cakes or jumbo sausages, and they will always boil an egg. They're looked after in the garden, too, where an extensive play area has rustic swings, a slide and a climbing frame, as well as splendid views of the Dorset Downs and the huge chalk-cut figure of a mounted George III. One of the pub's outbuildings has been turned into a shop where genuinely locally made craft goods and pictures by local artists are on sale throughout the summer and at weekends in winter. **Bar Food & Restaurant Meals** 12-2, 7-9.30. *Vegetarian dishes. Children's portions. Free House.* **Beer** *Eldridge Pope, Hardy, Wadworth. Riverside garden, outdoor eating, children's play area, summer barbecue. Access, Visa.*

Swalcliffe   Stags Head

`Tel 0295 78232`

Swalcliffe nr Banbury Oxfordshire OX15 5EJ   Map 16 B1

Thatched Cotswold stone inn in picturesque village. Oak settles and
stools. **Beer** *Adnams, Hook Norton. Garden, children's play area.*

Swanton Morley   Darby's

`Tel 0362 637647`

Swanton Morley nr Dereham Norfolk NR20 4JT   Map 10 C1

Converted from two cottages in 1986 by the licensee, a local farmer,
after the local mega-brewery closed the village's last traditional pub.
Beer *Adnams, Greene King. Garden, children's play area. Family room.*

Swavesey   Trinity Foot

`Tel 0353 778537`

Huntingdon Road Swavesey Cambridgeshire CB4 5PD   Map 15 F1

Fairly modern pub, named after Trinity College's hunt, or rather,
specifically, its horse-less followers. **Beer** *Whitbread. Children's play
area.*

Talkin Village   Hare & Hounds Inn

FOOD
B&B

`Tel 06977 3456`

Talkin Village nr Brampton Cumbria CA8 1LE   Map 4 C2

Once used by monks as a resting place on the way from Armathwaite
to Lanercost Priory, this homely 200-year-old village inn is now run
by John Goddard. Popular snacks are served in the traditional bars;
these range from filled jacket potatoes ('Talkin tatties' – from £1.30)
and generously layered sandwiches to pizzas, steaks (£8.05), venison in
red wine (£6.15) and grilled rainbow trout (£4.50). Different daily
specials at lunch and dinner like chicken breast in honey and lemon
(£4.95) or pork fillet kebabs (£4.45) ring the changes, and calorie-
rich puddings include death by chocolate (£1.50), sticky toffee
pudding (£1.60) and apple pie (£1.30). Children have their own
menu of amusingly named dishes (from £1.05). There are four
bedrooms – one en-suite twin family room, one en-suite double with
four-poster and a twin and double that share bathroom facilities. **Bar
Food** *12-2.30, 7-9.30. Vegetarian dishes. Children's menu. Free House.*
Beer *Boddingtons, Jennings Cumberland Ale, Theakston Best and XB.
Garden, outdoor eating, children's play area.* **Accommodation** *4 bedrooms,
all en suite, £35 (single £25). Children welcome overnight, additional beds
(from £7), cots supplied. Check-in all day. No credit cards.*

Tangley   Fox Inn

FOOD

`Tel 026470 276`

Tangley nr Andover Hampshire SP11 0RU   Map 16 D4

Remote, smartish country pub off the A343 with a welcoming
atmosphere in its tiny bars. Reliably good food from the landlady
cook. Try the fresh Poole crab salad (£6.50) or chicken tarragon on
rice (£3.25) in the bar and from the restaurant menu in the evenings,
try the deep-fried Camembert with cranberry sauce (£2.50), fresh
trout with bacon and mushrooms (£7.50) or slices of beef in spiced
tomato and mushroom sauce (£7.50). The landlord, John Troke, has a
comprehensive wine list, eight of which are available by the glass. **Bar
Food and Restaurant Meals** *12-2, 6.30-10 (except Sun eve). Vegetarian*

dishes. *Free House. **Beer** Bass, Courage Best, Eldridge Pope Royal Oak. Patio/terrace, outdoor eating. No credit cards.*

Tarporley   Rising Sun

Tel 0829 732423

High Street Tarporley Cheshire CW6 0DX   Map 6 B2

Another fine Cheshire village pub of such unspoilt charm. Various low-ceilinged, quaint little rooms ramble about, warmed by a trio of fires, and with ancient settles among its nice decorative touches like a series of old Worthington brewery mirrors. It gets incredibly busy at weekends, especially when the local cricketers move in. *Beer Robinson's.*

Tattenhill   Horseshoe Inn

Tel 0283 64913

Main Street Tattenhill Staffordshire DE13 9SD   Map 6 C3

Pleasant cream-painted roadside village inn dating back to 1680. *Beer Marston's. Garden, children's play area. Family room.*

Temple Grafton   Blue Boar Inn

Tel 0789 750010   **FOOD**

Temple Grafton nr Alcester Warwickshire B49 6NR   Map 14 C1

The oldest part of the Blue Boar dates back to the 17th century and includes a well (now glassed over and illuminated) that is set into a flagstoned floor and is home to some goldfish – the water reaches to within a few feet of floor level. Elsewhere, its furnishings are in typical pub style with red carpet, tapestry upholstery and Britannia tables set with red paper napkins in the restaurant area. The menu, hand-written in a copperplate hand indicating that it doesn't often change, covers all the standard items like steak and kidney pie (£4.75), gammon steak (£4.95), pint of prawns (£4.75), jacket potatoes, ploughman's and sandwiches plus devilled roes (deep-fried herring roes with tartare sauce (£2.75), a couple of pasta dishes and several vegetarian options – vegetable curry (£4.75), mushroom stroganoff (£4.75). The restaurant menu (from which one can also eat at the bar) is in similar vein and includes steaks and salads. *Bar Food 12-2, 6.30-10 (7-9.30 Sat/Sun). Vegetarian dishes. **Beer** Flowers Original, IPA. Outdoor eating. Access, Amex, Visa.*

Testcombe   Mayfly

Tel 0264 860283   **FOOD**

Testcombe Stockbridge Hampshire SO20 6AZ   Map 14 C3

Located opposite the River Test, the Mayfly (dated 1808) is a beamed old farmhouse with a quaintly traditional bar and bright conservatory, and a riverside beer garden for sunnier weather. Simple home-cooked bar food (soup of the day £1.75, River Test trout £3.30, hot chicken tandoori £3.40) and a delicious variety of British and Continental cheeses. *Bar Food 12-2, 7-9. Vegetarian dishes. Free House. **Beer** Whitbread. Garden, outdoor eating. Family room. Access, Visa.*

Tetford   White Hart

Tel 0507 533255

Tetford nr Horncastle Lincolnshire ON9 6QQ

Map 7 F2

Original, simple village pub bar, with a tiled floor, wood tables, cushioned settles, and inglenook; also functional modern dining extension, and non-smoking snug. In a good walking area. *Free House.*

Tewin   Plume of Feathers

Tel 043871 7265

57 Upper Green Tewin Hertfordshire AL6 0LX

FOOD

Map 17 F2

A prominent sign, which also doubles as a bus stop, is the first clue to the location of the Plume of Feathers, which is hidden behind tall bushes well back from the main road. Its white painted exterior is made pretty by splendid plant boxes and flower displays. The Plume's interior is not large, but the bar has tremendous character, with low ceilings, intimate corner, exposed beams, uneven walls, old wooden and copper-top tables, period settles and a variety of roundback and spindle chairs. Pictures of horses and other rural scenes litter the walls, along with a cheerful clutter of horse brasses, stuffed fish and game birds and other rural paraphernalia, while a collection of ties hang over the bar counter, and vases of fresh flowers add a cheery, personal note. The second room is lighter and smaller, with less bric-a-brac, and less atmosphere. It's the food most people are drawn to, either in the bar or more expensive restaurant. Head for the main bar, but get there early. The daily changing menu, written up on blackboards, ranges from the comfortingly traditional to the daringly nouvelle. Champagne and cauliflower soup (£2.50), deep-fried whitebait (£2.75), fresh darne of salmon (£5.75), chicken Cordon Bleu (£4.95), and daily-changing home-made puddings (£2.50) – jam roly poly, treacle pudding. There are also toasted sandwiches. The cooking is better than competent, showing real respect for the produce and for flavour, and fair pricing won't break the bank. In contrast, the restaurant, with its more formal settings and service can see an average bill for two hit £50. Service is friendly and relaxed, by and large. This is a lovely village pub, popular with a wide range of people, including locals like Dame Barbara Cartland, and the standard of food on offer makes it all well worth a detour. **Bar Food and Restaurant Meals** *12-2.30, 7-9.30 (except Sun eve). Vegetarian dishes. Children's portions. Free House.* **Beer** *Weekly changing traditional ales. Garden, outdoor eating. Access, Visa.*

Thame   Abingdon Arms

Tel 0844 260116

21 Cornmarket Thame Oxfordshire OX9 2BL

Map 17 D2

Friendly, imaginatively run little pub with an unspoilt interior; newspapers and magazines provided for lazing with. *Garden, children's play area.*

Thaxted   Farmhouse Inn

Tel 0371 830864

Monk Street Thaxted Essex CM6 2NR

Map 10 B3

Popular ex-farmhouse hotel. **Beer** *Adnams, Greene King, IPA. Garden, children's play area.*

Thelbridge   **Thelbridge Cross Inn**

Tel 0884 860316

Thelbridge nr Witheridge Devon EX17 4SQ   Map 13 D2

Attractive old inn, recently extended. Views across to Dartmoor and good local walks. Owner-managed, with a cosy bar, and simple pretty bedrooms. No live music, juke box or pool table. 'Lorna Doone' stagecoach brings extra Sunday lunch trade. *Beer Fuller's London Pride, Marston, Whitbread Flowers. Garden, children's play area. Family room.*

Thornborough   **Lone Tree**

Tel 0280 812334

Buckingham Road Thornborough Buckinghamshire MK18 2DZ   Map 17 D1

Popular thatched pub on the A421, about four miles east of Buckingham – note the working Victorian post box in the wall. *Garden, children's play area.*

Thornham   **Lifeboat Inn**

FOOD

B&B

Tel 048526 236

Ship Lane Thornham Norfolk PE36 6LT   Map 10 B1

A perennial classic: the Lifeboat is a charming whitewashed 16th-century ex-farmhouse, ideally set for weekend escapes on the edge of an expanse of salt flats: wake to the sound of the sea, or of doves cooing in the cote. Even casual visitors can enjoy the characterful ramble of old rooms, low-ceilinged, small-doored, four open fire-places, rustically furnished and decorated. Food is good: hearty winter hot dishes, summer al fresco, autumn seafood, and a splendid restaurant which serves the likes of Parmesan chicken livers, crab thermidor and beef kebabs Oriental on a set menu at £17.50. A new dining room with a dance floor seats an extra 70 customers. *Bar Meals 12-3 7-10 (all day summer). Children's menu/portions. Free House. Beer Adnams, Greene King. Garden, outdoor eating, children's play area, summer barbecue. Family room. Accommodation 13 bedrooms, all en suite, from £60 (single £35). Children welcome overnight, cots available. Check-in all day. Access, Diners, Visa.*

Thornton   **Ring O'Bells**

Tel 0274 832296

Hill Top Road Thornton West Yorkshire BD13 3QL   Map 6 C1

Converted chapel with modern extension, in a windy spot above Thornton. *Beer Old Mill, Ruddles, Webster's. Children's play area.*

Thornton Hough   **Seven Stars**

Tel 051-336 4574

Church Road Thornton Hough Greater Manchester   Map 6 A2

Cleanly refurbished, purposeful dining pub. Attractive terrace and garden area for fine weather. *Garden.*

Thornton Watlass   **Buck Inn**

Tel 0677 422461

Thornton Watlass nr Bedale North Yorkshire HG4 4AH   Map 5 E4

Next to the village green cricket pitch – it's a four if the ball hits the pub wall, a six if it clears the roof – this is refurbished but traditional, well-run, friendly village institution. Fly fishing on the Urr; quoits in the garden on Wednesday evenings. *Beer Tetley's, Theakston. Garden, children's play area. Family room.*

Thorpe Mandeville   Three Conies
Tel 0295 711025

Thorpe Mandeville Northamptonshire OX17 2EX   Map 16 C1

17th-century stone-built village pub. Attractively modernised low-beamed lounge; pool table-dominated public bar; nice garden. The family homes of George Washington and John Dryden are close by. *Beer Hook Norton. Garden. Family room.*

Threshfield   Old Hall Inn
Tel 0756 752441

Grassington Road Threshfield nr Grassington North Yorkshire
BD23 5HB   Map 6 C1

Attractively simple, very popular pub, the rear room of which is Tudor, hence the name. *Beer Timothy Taylor, Theakston, Younger. Garden, children's play area. Family room.*

Thursley   Three Horseshoes
Tel 0252 703268

Dye House Road Thursley nr Elstead Surrey GU8 6QU   Map 17 E4

One minute off the A3 between Milford and Hindhead, a characterful, 300-year-old beamed local. *Free House. Beer Gale's HSB and BBB. Cider Scrumpy Jack. Garden.*

Tichborne   Tichborne Arms
Tel 0962 733760   **FOOD**

Tichborne Hampshire SO24 0NA   Map 15 D3

Despite its quiet location, in an Itchen Valley hamlet, this is a pub much driven out to for lunch and supper. It was burnt down twice and last rebuilt in 1940 retaining the charm of a small, redbrick thatched pub. Very much the centre of village life where the Hunt meets, beaters eat and the village carol service and harvest supper take place. It has an unspoilt panelled room on the right, and a larger, noisier room on the left with fruit machine et al. The reliably good cooking includes Stilton and celery soup (£1.75), pork in cider casserole (£4.95) and poacher's pot (pigeon, pheasant and rabbit £4.95) with especially tempting puddings – golden syrup sponge, fudge and walnut flan and bread-and-butter pudding. No children under 14 indoors. *Bar Food 12-1.45, 6.30-9.45 (7-9.30 Sun). Vegetarian dishes. Free House. Beer Courage Best and Directors, Wadworth 6X. No credit cards.*

Tideswell   George
Tel 0298 871382

Commercial Road Tideswell Derbyshire   Map 6 C2

18th-century market town coaching inn. Small snug, traditional locals' noisy tap room, dining lounge and dining room proper. *Beer Hardy, Hansons.*

Tillingham   Cap & Feathers

Tel 0621 779212

8 South Street Tillingham nr Southminster Essex   Map 11 C4

Delightfully unspoilt, imaginatively preserved and run, classic
weather-boarded Essex village inn, in a sleepy village. Warm, woody
interior with eclectic mix of traditional furnishings, board floors, real
fire; several distinct areas ramble about; ancient bar billiards table still
operates on shillings. *Garden. Family room.* **Beer** *Crouch Vale ales.*

Tivetshall St Mary   Old Ram

Tel 0379 608228 (tables)/676794 (accommodation)

FOOD

B&B

Ipswich Road (A140) Tivetshall St Mary Norfolk NR15 2DE   Map 10 C2

Five 'luxury' en-suite rooms are on offer at this popular roadside
family dining pub, and in one of the larger rooms there are two bunk
beds for family use (children are charged at £10 per night). On the
eating side, try the daily seafood specials like crab, lobster or jumbo
cod in batter (£6.50). Good traditional features and a warming fire in
the main bar, which has other nice rooms leading off, plus a dining
room proper. **Bar Meals** *7.30-10. Vegetarian dishes. Children's portions.
Free House.* **Beer** *Adnams, Greene King, Ruddles. Garden, outdoor eating.
Family room (coachhouse).* **Accommodation** *5 bedrooms, all en suite, £54
(single £39). Children welcome overnight. Check-in all day. No dogs.
Access, Visa.*

Tockington   Swan Inn

Tel 0454 614800

Tockington Green Tockington Avon BS12 4NJ   Map 13 F1

Pleasant, spacious pub in sleepy village. **Beer** *Courage Best. Garden.*

Toot Hill   Green Man

Tel 0992 522255

Toot Hill nr Ongar Essex CM5 9SD   Map 11 B4

Many years an award winner for its floral courtyard. No children
under ten inside. **Beer** *Adnams, Ruddles, Webster's. Garden, children's
play area.*

Torcross   Start Bay Inn

Tel 0548 580553

Torcross nr Kingsbridge Devon TQ7 2TQ   Map 13 D3

Busy thatched dining pub by Slapton Ley lake. **Beer** *Marston,
Whitbread. Patio overlooking beach. Family room.*

Tormarton   Compass Inn

Tel 0454 218242

Tormarton nr Badminton Avon GL9 IJB   Map 13 F1

Busy creeper-clad former coaching inn one minute off the M4.
Pleasant conservatory (ideal for families). Good-sized bedrooms in two
modern extensions. **Beer** *Archers Village Bitter, Draught Bass, Smiles.
Garden, children's play area. Family room.*

Towcester   **Plough**
Tel 0327 50738

Market Square Towcester Northamptonshire

Map 15 D1

Pleasant two-roomed pub by the market place. Real fire; no music. **Beer** *Adnams, Charles Wells.*

Towersey   **Three Horseshoes**
Tel 084421 2322

Towersey nr Thame Oxfordshire OX9 3QY

Map 5 D2

Redbrick, part 13th-century pub, with a covered 12th-century barn, now popular for functions. Roaring log fire in winter. **Beer** *Guest ales. Garden.*

Tregadillet   **Eliot Arms**
Tel 0566 772051

Tregadillet nr Launceston Cornwall PL15 7EU

Map 12 C3

Also known as the Square and Compass, the pretty, creeper-covered Eliot Arms was built in 1626, modernised in 1840, and contains a collection of some 66 clocks, as well as a host of other memorabilia, littered across every square inch of wall. Lots of little rooms ramble about, and nice old furniture is freely and successfully mixed with modern seating. **Beer** *Cornish Best, Whitbread. Garden, children's play area. Family room.*

Treleigh   **Inn For All Seasons**
Tel 0209 219511

FOOD

Treleigh Redruth Cornwall TR16 4AP

Map 12 B3

Now run full-time by the people who used to be at the *Rising Sun* at St Mawes. The bar is large and attractively decorated, and much used for dining; service is friendly and welcoming. **Beer** *Wadworth.*

Trent   **Rose & Crown**
Tel 0935 850776

FOOD

Trent nr Sherborne Dorset DT9 4SL

Map 13 F2

Initially two separate thatched cottages, the Rose & Crown is refreshingly unpretentious within, simply furnished, with a rug-strewn stone floor and roaring log fires in winter. No pub games, fruit machines or music. A great emphasis on good fresh food, though, making good use of local gardens and farms. The 40-seat conservatory restaurant serves dishes such as smoked pigeon breast with kiwi and lime sauce (£2.50) and half a roast duck with apricot and ginger sauce (£7.95). Regular bar food is also all home-made. Sustaining snacks could include a cheese and sirloin steak sandwich (£4.95) or prawn and garlic pizza (£4.25). Excellent local cheeses. **Bar Food & Restaurant Meals** *12-2, 7-9.30 (10 Sat/Sun). Vegetarian dishes. Children's menu/portions.* **Beer** *Boddingtons, Fuller's London Pride, Hook Norton.* **Cider** *Sanfords, local farmhouse. Garden, outdoor eating. Family room. Access, Visa.*

Troutbeck   Mortal Man Hotel

FOOD

Tel 05394 33193   Fax 05394 31261

B&B

Troutbeck Cumbria LA23 1PL

Map 4 C3

A hotchpotch of antique seating, gleaming copper-topped tables, beams, horse brasses, pewter tankards, hunting horns and views of a gentle green valley through the windows give the bars at the Mortal Man plenty of rustic charm. One is kept mainly for residents, but it provides an overspill when the public bar is full. There is a plentiful supply of food on offer such as home-cooked ham, lovely fresh summer salads (£4), home-made soup (£1.40), Cumberland sausage, smoked trout, whilst the restaurant offers a set menu dinner (5 courses £17.50) of more substantial dishes – halibut with poached pears and anchovy fillets, smoked ham with redcurrant jelly. Roast Aberdeen Angus beef features for Sunday lunch (5-course menu £11). The bedrooms are clean and comfortable, with attractive, homely decor in coordinated colours and well-cared-for furniture. All have smart, clean, en-suite bathrooms, TVs and entrancing views. Housekeeping is excellent. Half-board terms only. Garden. **Bar Food** 12-1.45, 6-9 (*except Monday*). **Restaurant Meals** 7.30-8.30. *Vegetarian dishes. Free House.* **Beer** *Theakston, Scotch Bitter.* **Accommodation** *12 bedrooms, all en suite, half-board £104. Check-in all day. Pub closed Jan-mid Feb, accommodation closed mid Nov-mid Feb. No credit cards.*

Trudoxhill   White Hart

Tel 0373 836324

Trudoxhill nr Frome Somerset BA11 5DP

Map 13 F1

The home of the splendid Ash Vine Brewery, which alone makes it worth a visit, but it's also a nice, relaxing pub, with a long, opened-out bar and two real fires. **Beer** *Bass, Ash Vine Bitter. Garden.*

Tuckenhay   Maltsters Arms

Tel 0803 732350

FOOD

Tuckenhay Devon TQ9 7EQ

Map 13 D3

TV chef Keith Floyd has lavished much time and hard cash carefully un-modernising the Maltsters, and it's now stylishly simple, with various individually decorated rooms, the best of which is the riverside restaurant, flooded with light at lunchtime through large picture windows. Cheap it ain't, but everything's home-made and carefully prepared, the menu displaying a typically Floydian range – from cockles to caviar, superbly fresh seafood and wonderful bar snacks. **Bar Food** 11-2.30, 6-10. *Children's portions. Free House.* **Beer** *Dartmoor Ale, Bass, Blackawton, Exmoor Ale. Garden, summer barbecue. Access, Amex, Visa.*

Turvey   Three Cranes

Tel 023064 305

High Street Loop Road Turvey Bedfordshire MK43 8EP

Map 15 E1

300-year-old stone pub renovated by the Victorians, in a pretty stone-built village, with an interesting church and abbey. **Beer** *Adnams, Fuller's. Garden, children's play area.*

Turville   **Bull & Butcher**

Tel 049163 283

Turville Buckinghamshire RG9 6QU

FOOD

Map 17 D3

Back in the 1700s some workmen on the local church went on strike for want of a village pub, prompting an enterprising cottager to turn his home into one; thus the Bull & Butcher was born. Inside the black and white timbered building there are dried hops and fairy lights over the bar, lots of horse brasses, William Morris curtains and some white rustic furniture. The Hanson family (parents and son) came here direct from running a beach-bar in Spain, something of a culture shock, but their brand of home-cooked food and friendliness was an immediate hit. They all share in the cooking (doing their own special dishes) along with some local ladies who help out in the kitchen and others who provide dishes, perhaps just a dessert, from their own homes – don't miss the chocolate and raspberry roulade. Typical choices might be Stilton and walnut paté (£2.50), chicken Benedictine (£4.95), Brakspears pie – made with beef and old ale topped with shortcrust pastry (£4.95) and Aunt Mary's treacle tart (£2.25). On Monday and Thursday evenings there is a special deal which gives a choice of any main course and any dessert plus a bottle of the George Duboeuf house wine for just £15 per couple. Christmas day is the only one without food and Boxing Day brings a free buffet. *Bar Food 12-2, 6.45-9.45 (7.30-9.30 Sun). Vegetarian dishes. Beer Brakspears Ordinary, Special and Old. Garden, outdoor eating. No credit cards.*

Tushingham   **Blue Bell Inn**

Tel 0948 2172

Bell o' the Hill Tushingham nr Whitchurch Cheshire SY13 4RS

Map 6 B3

Probably the only pub in this guide haunted by a ghost duck; the full story is explained on the bar wall. A remarkable old building, opposite a farm, just off the A41, the Blue Bell has massive oak doors, an original multi-roomed layout, heavy beams and old-fashioned hatch serveries, but also modern plush wall seating. *Beer Greenalls. Garden, children's play area. Family room.*

Tutbury   **Ye Olde Dog & Partridge**

Tel 0283 813030   Fax 0283 813178

High Street Tutbury Staffordshire DE13 9LS

FOOD

B&B

Map 6 C3

There's a 500-year tradition of hospitality at the Dog & Partridge, and much of the original 15th-century building is still happily intact. Its half-timbered frontage with diamond-leaded windows is classic picture-postcard material, bedecked with flower tubs and hanging baskets in summer. In 1568, Mary Queen of Scots was detained in nearby Tutbury Castle at which time the inn was already a celebrated haunt of the aristocracy. The building was further extended in the 18th and 19th centuries to cope with its new-found fame as a coaching inn on the main Liverpool/London route, and over the last ten years has been painstakingly renovated to achieve the levels of comfort expected in the 1990s. Hotel reception apart, the entire ground floor has now been made over to dining. A series of rooms with alcoves and old world partitions manages to give the impression of a collection of intimate spaces, despite the presence, when full, of upwards of 150 diners; yet there's still room for the pianist, one of whose jobs it is to trot out Happy Birthday, virtually on call, several times a night. All sections, however, lead to the buffet and carvery, which is what they all come for. It's a catering operation of quality-numbing complexity, and you'll work hard to find – and be served – the quality bits (described as à la carte) when all around are single-mindedly set on quantity, amassing groaning plates of roasts and potatoes piled high with self-serve vegetables. (Cold table: help-yourself roasts and salads £5.25-7.25; hot roast: £6.75-6.95). There are à la carte dishes (Owd Rodger pie £5.50) and local ice-creams (£2.65-£2.95). Three original bedrooms remain in the main building, whose black and white panelling and creaking, uneven floors provide the kind of romance craved by honeymooners and Americans. The remainder, however, are housed in an adjacent Georgian property which contains a fascinating central spiral staircase, ascending to an ornate glass-domed roof. Individually decorated, these bedrooms offer comprehensive 20th century comforts from private bathrooms to satellite television and mini-bars. *Bar Food* 12-2 (*not Sun*). *Restaurant Meals* 12-2, 6.30-10 (9.30 Sun, 6.15-10.30 Sat). *Vegetarian dishes. Children's portions.* **Beer** *Marston Pedigree. Garden, outdoor eating.* *Accommodation 17 bedrooms, all en suite, £69.50 (single £49.50). Children welcome overnight, additional beds available. Check-in all day. Access, Amex, Visa.*

Twywell   Old Friar

Tel 0832 732625

Lower Street Twywell Northamptonshire NN14 3AH   Map 7 E4

Dining pub with plain wood furnishings; beams and brick fireplaces have firar motifs. Good outdoor play area for children, with tree swings. **Beer** *Ruddles, Webster's Yorkshire. Garden, children's play area.*

Ufford   Ye Olde White Hart

Tel 0780 740250

Main Street Ufford nr Stamford Cambridgeshire PE9 3BH   Map 7 E4

17th-century farm, a pub since 1800. Open fires, four acres of garden and goat-filled paddock. A sunken patio, which seats 100, is used for Sunday morning jazz. **Beer** *Theakston. Garden, children's play area. Family room.*

Ulcombe   Pepper Box

Tel 0622 842558   **FOOD**

Fairbourne Heath Ulcombe Kent ME17 1LP   Map 11 C5

The Pepper Box is a cottagey pub with low eaves and white-painted stone walls, surrounded by fields of corn. Dating back to the 15th century, it was once the haunt of smugglers and takes its name (apparently unique) from their favourite weapon, the Pepper Box pistol. A three-piece suite takes pride of place in front of an inglenook fireplace in the beamed bar, and old pewter mugs – some belonging to regular customers – hang above the bar counter along with decorative hopbines. A Shepherd Neame-owned house, the tenancy has been in the same family since 1958 with Sarah and Geoff Pemble currently providing the hospitable welcome. Fresh fish is one of the highlights of a bar menu that includes Mediterranean seafood salad (£3), smoked salmon and mushroom tagliatelle (£6), duck with black cherry (£8) and steak and kidney pudding (£5.80). The same menu is also available in the small dining room, with its oak tables and wood-burning Aga, by prior reservation. Children are not allowed inside the pub, but they are welcome in the large, pretty garden, which has swings and a tree house. There's a short but varied list of wines, and the Shepherd Neame ales are drawn direct from barrels behind the bar. *Bar Food 12-2, 7-9.45 (no food Sun). Vegetarian dishes. Children's portions. Beer Shepherd Neame. Garden, children's play area, garden, outdoor eating. No credit cards.*

Ulverston   Bay Horse Inn & Bistro

FOOD
B&B

Tel 0229 53972

Canal Foot Ulverston Cumbria LA12 9EL

Map 4 C4

1½ miles from Ulverston, an old pub with sympathetic conversion that includes an intimate conservatory restaurant with picturesque views over the Leven estuary. Chef Robert Lyons gives full rein to his wide-ranging repertoire; once the protegé of co-owner John Tovey at Miller Howe, he's equally at home with a deceptively simple salad or a balanced soup of courgette and fennel (£1.95), as with elaborate dishes typified by a dish of medallions of pork fillet with apple, chestnuts, shallots, cream and Calvados (£11.95). Complimentary coffee is served in the lounge. Lunch offers a limited choice of two dishes per course plus a few more sweets. There's a feature wine list with a fine selection of New World (mainly Antipodean) wines, with little over £20. No children under 12. No smoking. Of the six bedrooms, five open out on to a small terrace with a view of the Leven estuary. Light afternoon tea is also served. *Bar Food 12-2 (except Mon). Restaurant Meals 12-1.30 (except Sun), 7.30-8. Beer Mitchells. Riverside terrace. Accommodation 6 rooms, all en suite, £130+10% service (single £75) for dinner, bed and breakfast. Access, Visa.*

Umberleigh   Rising Sun Inn

B&B

Tel 0769 60447   Fax 0769 60764

Umberleigh Devon EX37 9DU

Map 13 D2

After a day fishing the Taw, salmon and trout anglers will find racks for rods and drying cabinets in this 17th-century roadside inn. The public bar is a welcome spot in which to exchange fishing stories with the locals. Six charming bedrooms have cottagey pine furniture; bathrooms with hand-shower sets are simple and neat. A new extension built last year houses two new bedrooms, plus a new restaurant and kitchen. Children up to three stay free in parents' room. Fishing should be reserved at time of booking. *Accommodation 8 bedrooms, £55 (single £30). Children welcome overnight. Garden. Access, Visa.*

Uploders   Crown Inn

Tel 030885 356

Uploders Dorset DT6 4NU

Map 13 E2

Enthusiastic young licensees have extended the Crown into the adjoining stable and furnished it attractively in a winning country style. *Beer Palmers Bridport. Garden, children's play area. Family room.*

Upper Benefield   Wheatsheaf Hotel

Tel 08325 254

Upper Benefield nr Peterborough Northamptonshire PE8 5AN

Map 7 E4

Well-heeled pub hotel. *Beer Adnams, Courage Best. Garden, children's play area.*

Upper Oddington   Horse & Groom

Tel 0451 30584   **B&B**

Moreton-in-Marsh Upper Oddington Gloucestershire GL56 0XH   **Map 16 A1**

Golden-stone village inn with two delightfully rustic bars, lots of
exposed stone, a cheering open fire, solid old furnishings, and
flagstoned floors. A separate cosy dining room has less charm, but the
garden is huge and full of features, a stream, fishpond, little bridge,
and aviary amongst them. Bedrooms are simple and modernised, with
white walls and modern fabrics and fittings. *Free House. Beer Hook
Norton, Wadworth 6X, guest beer. Garden, outdoor eating, children's play
area. Family room. **Accommodation** 8 bedrooms, all en suite, from £42
(single £29). Children welcome overnight, additional beds (from £4), cots
supplied. Check-in by arrangement. Access, Visa.*

Uppermill   Cross Keys

Tel 0457 874626

Running Hill Gate Uppermill Greater Manchester   **Map 6 C2**

A bustling, lively 18th-century local and magnet for visitors. Its
rambling interior has flagstone floors, low beams and ancient settles
among the more modern seats; open fire; no music. It's the HQ of the
Oldham Mountain Rescue Team. There's folk music on Wednesday.
Beer Lee.

Upton   French Horn

Tel 0636 812394

Main Street Upton Nottinghamshire   **Map 7 D3**

Opened-out, refurbished dining pub with the most crowded pub car
park in Upton: the interior's simple with cushioned leather chairs,
banquettes and wooden tables, and there's a large sloping rear garden
with picnic tables to the rear. *Beer Courage.*

Upton Cheyney   Upton Inn

Tel 0272 324489

Brewery Hill Upton Cheyney Avon BS15 6LY   **Map 13 F1**

Village pub with creeper-clad exterior, elegant interior with wall-
hangings, and separate restaurant. No children under 14.

Upton Grey   Hoddington Arms

Tel 0256 862371   **FOOD**

Upton Grey nr Basingstoke Hampshire RG25 2RL   **Map 17 D4**

Warm and welcoming local dating back to the 18th century. The
licensees, Ian and Irene Fisher, are also the cooks; the daily-changing
blackboard menu recently offered a fresh crab salad alongside a crab
stick salad, although one was not warned of the difference when
ordering. Other typical dishes might include pasta with chili and
tomato sauce (£3.50), moules marinière (£3.75) or salmon and prawn
mousse (£3.50), roast guinea fowl in rich port sauce (£7.75), and
summer pudding with raspberry purée. On a fine day you can eat on
the small rear patio or on benches in the long, pleasant garden, at the
top of which is a children's swing. *Bar Food 12-2, 7.30-9.30.*
*Restaurant 7.30-9.30 (except Sun eve). Vegetarian dishes. Children's
menu/portions. Beer Morland Old Speckled Hen and Original, guest beer.
Garden, outdoor eating, children's play area. Family room. Access, Visa.*

Uttoxeter   White Hart

Tel & Fax 0889 562437	**B&B**
Carter Street Uttoxeter Staffordshire ST14 8EU	Map 6 C3

An old town-centre coaching inn owned by Ansells Brewery. Adequate overnight accommodation; 15 of the bedrooms have en-suite facilities. Children under 16 stay free in parents' room. *Accommodation 26 bedrooms, £54. Children welcome overnight. Access, Amex, Diners, Visa.*

Ventnor   Spyglass Inn

	FOOD
Tel 0983 855338	**B&B**
The Esplanade Ventnor Isle of Wight PO38 1JX	Map 15 D4

Stephanie and Neil Gibbs are both native islanders (or Calk Heads, in the vernacular) who have done a marvellous job of totally rebuilding the Spyglass Inn after the disastrous fire of just a few years ago. Wandering around the several interconnecting rooms, which include two reserved for non-smokers and several where children are welcome, it is difficult to believe that the pub is not hundreds of years old. The bar counter is built of old pews and the whole place is full of old seafaring prints and photographs, as well as numerous nautical antiques, ranging from a brass binnacle and ship's wheel to old oars and model ships in glass cases. The setting could not be better, at one end of the seafront with a front terraced area stretching right to the edge of the sea wall. In winter, the waves break right over the wall and more than one customer has been known to get a soaking by mis-timing their exit from the pub. In summer, there's an outside bar and kiosk selling shellfish and ice cream. The menu features casseroles such as chicken and white wine with mushrooms and garlic (£4.95) or steak and ale (£4.95); the thing to look out for is the local seafood: crab served out of its shell in generous bowlfuls with salad (£5.95), and locally caught lobsters (£11.50). In winter, there are home-made soups (£1.95) from a blackboard menu, and on Saturday nights a candlelit dinner, for which booking is advisable, complete with pianist. In the season, there is entertainment nightly (less frequently in winter), which might be live piano, a jazz trio or a skiffle group. One neat little flatlet with upholstered rattan furniture and a sea-facing balcony offers accommodation for up to two adults and two children. A public car park is just 50 yards away, but check your brakes before venturing down here – the road to the seafront has hairpin bends and a gradient of 1 in 4. *Bar Food 12-2.15, 7-9.30 (7-9 Sun). Vegetarian dishes. Children's menu. Free House. Beer Burton Real Ale, Spyglass King Rock Ale. Garden, riverside patio/terrace, outdoor eating. Family room. Accommodation 1 en-suite flatlet, sleeps 4, £45. Children welcome overnight, cot available. Check-in after midday.*

Vernham Dean   Boot Inn

Tel 0264 87213	
Vernham Dean Littledown nr Andover Hampshire SP11 0EF	Map 16 B4

A charming old thatched pub, built in the 15th century with a 16th century extension. Originally the premises of a cobbler who doubled as an ale-maker. The tiny white-panelled bar is still fetchingly homely; there's also a conservatory and family room, but it's nicest out of doors on sunny days in the two acres of grounds. *Beer Hall & Woodhouse. Garden, children's play area. Family room.*

Walkern   White Lion

Tel 0438 861251	**FOOD**
High Street Walkern Hertfordshire SG2 7PA	Map 17 F1

Pleasant old pub with alcoves and inglenook furniture, warm and welcoming. Sound home cooking includes various soups (£1.90), steak and kidney pie (£5.95), steaks (from £7.95) and fresh fish (from £5.50). Home-made puddings include ginger and rhubarb crumble (£1.95). *Bar Food 12-2, 7-9.30. Vegetarian dishes. Children's portions. Beer Greene King IPA, Abbot Ale. Garden, outdoor eating, children's play area. Access, Visa.*

Wall   Hadrian

Tel 043481 232	**B&B**
Wall nr Hexham Northumberland NE46 4EE	Map 5 D2

Warm and inviting foyer and lounge with deep luxurious armchairs, in handsome 16th-century house with Jacobean features; a nice place to stay. Though only three of the bedrooms are fully en suite, the others have clean, functional shower units. *Beer Vaux Samson, Lorimers Best Scotch. Accommodation 9 bedrooms, 3 en suite, £45. Access, Visa.*

Wallsend   Rose Inn

Tel 091-263 4545	
Rosehill Bank Willington Quay Wallsend Tyne & Wear NE28 6TR	Map 5 E2

A large Victorian roadside pub with a busy local bar meal and restaurant trade. No music.

Waltham-on-the-Wold   Royal Horseshoes

Tel 066478 289	**B&B**
Melton Road Waltham-on-the-Wold nr Melton Mowbray Leicestershire LE14 4AJ	Map 7 D3

This thatched old village pub has a new owner to take over the polishing of the brass and oak within the single bar. Bedrooms have recently been refurbished and offer en-suite facilities, TVs and tea-makers and good light-wood furniture. *Free House. Beer Pedigree, John Smith, Courage. Patio. Accommodation 4 bedrooms, all en suite, £40 (single £25). Children welcome overnight. Check-in all day. No credit cards.*

Warbleton   Warbill-in-Tun Inn

Tel 0435 830636	**FOOD**
Warbleton nr Heathfield East Sussex TN21 9BD	Map 11 B6

Attractive and well-kept old roadside dining pub about which many stories are told: tales of contraband, priest's holes, sudden death and, of course, ghosts. The licensees care about good food using fresh produce (husband is a master butcher); tables in the carpeted, pleasantly modernised low beamed bar areas are often at a premium. All the food is home-made: soup (£1.40), fish paté (£2.05), Cyprus chicken (£6.10), cottage pie (£4.75), poached salmon (£8.95), fillet steak (£11.25). Vegetarians are offered a separate menu with a choice of eight dishes. Friendly service. *Bar Food and Restaurant Meals 12-2.30, 7-9.30. Vegetarian dishes. Children's portions. Free House. Beer Harvey, guest beers. Garden, outdoor eating. Access, Visa.*

Wardlow   Bull's Head

Tel 0298 871431

Wardlow nr Tideswell Derbyshire SK17 8RP   Map 6 C2

Unassuming-looking but very popular village dining pub. *Beer Mansfield. Garden, children's play area. Family room.*

Warenford   Warenford Lodge   ★

Tel 0668 213453   **FOOD**

Warenford nr Belford Northumberland NE70 7HY   Map 5 D1

There's a wonderfully eclectic range of good bar food on offer at Warenford Lodge, a solid stone building on the village loop road off the A1. Inside, it's a handsome old place, with exposed thickset stone and a smartly modern air which blends well with the atmosphere of an old-fashioned private house. There are little mullion windows, polished light pine tables and cushioned benches in the split level bar, a big stone fireplace in the lower part, and a woodburning stove in the upper area, which has armchairs and sofas just made for relaxing. Menus change here twice yearly, in spring and autumn, reflecting seasonal produce and appetite, but a random selection of favourites might well feature Northumbrian fish soup (£6.90) or English wood pigeon casserole, perfectly seasoned and partnered by a great wedge of brown bread. Equally unmissable are the grilled herby mussels, plump and tender with a light breadcrumb, parsley and garlic topping. Herbs are particularly skilfully used here, in a subtle leek and lovage soup, say, or the unusual and delicious blackcurrant and mint pie. The unifying factor behind it all, exotic or homely, is the instinctive, hearty cooking of Mrs Matthewman, at work in the kitchen while Ray tends to the bar. Owing to the popularity of the Warenford you need to book for weekend evenings (or any time in summer). *Bar Food 12-1.30 (Winter Sat & Sun only), 7-9.30 (all year). Restaurant Meals 7-9.30. Vegetarian dishes. Children's portions. Garden. Pub closed Mondays. Access, Diners, Visa.*

Wargrave   Bull Hotel

Tel 0734 403120   **FOOD**
                                                              B&B

High Street Wargrave nr Reading RG10 8DD   Map 17 D3

Situated on the corner of the main crossroads in the centre of Wargrave; parking is a problem but not a deterrent. The white-painted, black-timbered Bull is decorated with hanging baskets and rose-filled tubs. The bar has three separate areas, one for drinking only, one for drinking and eating and a restaurant. At lunchtime, the bar offers simple dishes such as soup (£2.25), steak and kidney pie (£4.75) or fresh plaice (£5.25). The restaurant is painted cream with low beams and has copper ornaments, china animals and plates decorating the walls; tables have fresh flowers and candles, the seating is comfortable, there's no background music and the traffic from the busy crossroads cannot be heard. In the evenings, the restaurant menu is also served in the bar area: spare ribs (£3.25), brie Amandine (£3), poached salmon (£6.95), duck with apple (£7.25), rack of lamb (£6.95), chocolate roulade, fresh raspberries and cream or meringue nest of strawberries (both £2.25). There are three simple bedrooms (one double and two singles) with basins, sharing bathroom facilities. *Bar Food 12-2. Restaurant Meals 6.45-9.30. Vegetarian dishes. Beer Brakspear PA and Special. Garden, outdoor eating. Accommodation 3 bedrooms, sharing bathroom facilities, £35 (single £20). No children overnight. Check-in by arrangement. No dogs. No credit cards.*

Warmington   Wobbly Wheel

Tel 029589 214   Fax 029589 384

Warwick Road Warmington Warwickshire OX17 1JJ

Map 14 C1

Attractive pub with welcoming atmosphere located on the A41
towards Shotteswell. **Beer** Bass Traditional, guest beer. Garden.

Warminster   Old Bell Hotel

FOOD

B&B

Tel 0985 216611

42 Market Place Warminster Wiltshire BA12 9AN

Map 14 B3

Old town-centre coaching inn which dominates the market place.
Outdoor eating in the handsome inner courtyard, or indoors in the
Chimes Bar, a dining room where you'll find deep-fried Camembert
(£2.75), seafood mornay (£3.95), Dover sole (£12.50), rack of lamb
(£7.95) and a sweet trolley with all dishes at £2.45. A new bistro
dining area offers the likes of filled potato skins (£1.95), Mexican
fajitas (£6.95) and lemon cream pavlova (£1.95); children are
welcome to eat here. Sunday lunch is £8.50. There's also a pubbier
drinkers' bar. Bedrooms are neat and simply furnished, functional
rather than luxurious in style; front rooms have double-glazing. **Bar
Food** 12-2 (2.30 restaurant), 6-10.30. Vegetarian dishes. **Beer** Bass,
Wadworth. Patio, outdoor eating. **Accommodation** 20 bedrooms, 14 en
suite, £58 (single £46). Children welcome overnight, extra beds and cots
available. Check-in all day. Access, Amex, Visa.

Warren Street   Harrow Inn

FOOD

B&B

Tel 0622 858727   Fax 0622 850026

Warren Street Lenham nr Maidstone Kent ME17 2ED

Map 11 C5

Once a rest house for Canterbury pilgrims, now a converted and
refurbished downland inn not far from the M2 motorway. Simple
cushioned chairs and stools around little tables in the lounge bar, much
used for dining, plus a separate restaurant overlooking the garden.

Food is reliably good in the bar, with ravioli filled with crab and
prawns (£1.95), guinea fowl with sherry sauce (£9.25); while in the
restaurant dishes such as frog's legs provençale (£3.95) or trellis of
salmon and cod poached in white wine (£9.95) are offered. Good bed
and breakfast, too, some of the rooms being especially large and
cluttered with comforts. All are now en suite, and 4 of them are
'family rooms'. **Bar Food & Restaurant Meals** 12-2, 7-10. Vegetarian
dishes. Children's menu. Free House. **Beer** Ruddles County, Shepherd
Neame. Children allowed in bar to eat. Garden, outdoor eating, children's
play area. **Accommodation** 15 bedrooms, all en suite, £45 (single £35).
Children welcome overnight, cots available. Check-in all day. Access, Amex,
Visa.

Warslow   Greyhound

Tel 0298 84249

Warslow nr Buxton Derbyshire SK17 0JM

Map 6 C2

Relaxing, nicely furnished old pub, with beams, quality furnishings,
including one or two antique settles, and an open fire. Close to the
Manifold Valley. **Beer** Marston's Pedigree, Tetley. Garden.

Warwick-on-Eden   Queen's Arms Inn

Tel 0228 560699	**B&B**
Warwick-on-Eden nr Carlisle Cumbria CA4 8PA	Map 4 C2

Close to junction 43 of the M6, this pleasant 18th-century inn makes a convenient stopover. A traditional village pub, painted cream with hanging flower baskets in a quiet location. Neatly kept bedrooms (including three in a separate cottage) feature attractive floral fabrics and all offer TVs, radio-alarms, tea-makers and compact bathrooms (most with shower only). A sofa bed and good-sized work area are useful extras. Pictures of the area and a display of china add a homely note in the panelled bar and there's a children's playground and garden. *Free House.* **Beer** *Tetley, Theakston, Burton Ale. Family room.* **Accommodation** *7 bedrooms, all en suite, £42 (single £32). Children welcome overnight, additional beds (£13), cots supplied. Check-in by arrangement. Access, Visa.*

Wasdale Head   Wasdale Head Inn

	FOOD
Tel 09467 26229 Fax 09467 26334	**B&B**
Wasdale Head Gosforth Cumbria CA20 1EX	Map 4 C3

Famous walkers' and climbers' pub in splendid isolation with steep fells by way of backdrop, a setting of romantic grandeur. Ritson's Bar, named after its first landlord (the world's biggest liar) has high ceilings, a polished slate floor, wood panelling, and cushioned old settles. Food is largely traditional: vegetable soup (£1.50), garlic mushrooms (£2.75), Cumberland sausage (£5.75), Cumberland tatie pot (£5.95), hedgerow crumble (£2.50). There's a residents' bar and relaxing lounge. Bedrooms are comfortable and unfussy with tea and coffee kits provided. **Bar Food** *11-3, 6.30-10.* **Restaurant Meals** *7.15 for 7.30. Vegetarian dishes. Children allowed in bar to eat (min age 8).* **Beer** *Jennings, Theakston, Old Peculier, Yates and guest beer. Riverside garden, outdoor eating. Family room.* **Accommodation** *10 bedrooms, all en suite, £106 (single £55) dinner included. Children welcome overnight, additional beds (£15), cots available. Access, Visa.*

Wass   Wombwell Arms   ★

	FOOD
Tel 03476 280	**B&B**
Wass North Yorkshire YO6 4BE	Map 5 E4

This whitewashed village inn dates from the 18th century and sits in the shadow of the Hambleton hills, just a couple of miles from the A170, east of Thirsk. The interior consists of four connecting rooms with stylish fabrics and furnishings. The first room to the left of the entrance has lightwood floorboards, stripped pine tables and chairs, and half-panelling. This room is especially good for families. The bar and its adjoining dining area have a mix of flagstone and red-tiled flooring, some exposed stone walls, more panelling and original beams. Some walls have attractive Laura Ashley wallpapers, while farmhouse kitchen style tables are covered with colourful cloths. The final room is similarly appointed. Throughout the pub, there are splendid fresh and dried flower displays, watercolours of chickens, foxes and other country subjects, magazines and books. Over the bar is an original drawing of TV's Captain Pugwash, drawn for the landlord by its creator John Ryan, an old boy of nearby Ampleforth College. A huge blackboard displays the day's choice of interesting bar food. Rather bistro in style, this is the preserve of Lynda Evans, who is a more than competent cook. Only fresh, mostly local produce is used, and the choice is extensive and varied: perhaps carrot and orange soup (£1.75), Dijon beef (£6.95), seafood chicken stuffed with prawns and Wensleydale cheese in a lobster bisque sauce (£7.95), wild pigeon in a vermouth and mushroom sauce (£8.95). There are good vegetarian dishes too, like cauliflower and three-cheese quiche, or brandy creamed mushrooms. Desserts are well up to standard, with a fine summer pudding, orange mousse or a hot cherry sundae. There's also a selection of lighter lunch dishes. The three bedrooms are equally impressive. Two doubles and a twin are kitted out in colourful Laura Ashley wallpapers, with matching curtains and duvet covers, and stripped pine furniture. They're impeccably kept and offer a selection of magazines as well as televisions and radio alarms. Each room is en suite, one with a shower, two with baths. To immaculate housekeeping is added a sense of fun: plastic ducks are provided. Alan Evans looks after the bar and is an extremely jovial host. A quite exceptional country pub, well worth a detour. *Bar Food* 12-2, 7-10. *Vegetarian dishes. Children's portions. Free House.* *Beer* Cameron Traditional, Everards. *Accommodation 3 bedrooms, all en suite, £43 (single £21.50). Children welcome overnight (minimum age 8), additional beds available. No dogs. Check-in by arrangement. Access, Visa.*

Waterley Bottom   New Inn   **FOOD**

| Tel 0453 543659 | **B&B** |

Waterley Bottom North Nibley nr Dursley Gloucestershire GL11 6EF   Map 13 F1

Large, friendly, modernised pub at the end of a winding country lane to the east of North Nibley, in a pretty and secluded valley in a good touring area. The beamed lounge, mercifully devoid of canned music, and warmed by an open fire, has old settles, Windsor chairs, and picture windows with views across the garden. It's a keen real ale pub littered with breweriana. The food is routine bar meal stuff – home-made soup (£1.50), steak and onion pie (£3.70), lasagne (£3.80), chili (£3.50). This is a decent, popular and inexpensive place to stay, with attractive accommodation in co-ordinated bedrooms with TVs and tea/coffee making facilities provided. *Bar Food* 12-2 (12-1.30 Sun), 7-9.30. *Vegetarian dishes. Free house.* *Beer* Cotleigh Tawny Bitter, Greene King Abbot Ale, Smiles Exhibition, Theakston Old Peculier, guest beer. *Cider* Inch's. *Garden, outdoor eating, children's play area. Accommodation 2 bedrooms, sharing a bathroom, £35 (single £20). Children welcome overnight, additional beds (half-price if under 12 yrs), cot supplied. Check-in by arrangement. No dogs. No credit cards.*

Wath-in-Nidderdale   Sportsman's Arms   **FOOD**

| Tel 0423 711306 | **B&B** |

Pateley Bridge Wath-in-Nidderdale nr Harrogate North Yorkshire HG3 5PP   Map 6 C1

Follow the signs for Wath from the centre of Pateley Bridge and after a couple of miles you'll see a sign to the pub itself. Once over a narrow bridge crossing the River Nidd, you'll see the mellow-stone 17th-century Sportman's Arms, just back from the river bank in its own grounds, in beautiful moorland surroundings. Just up the road (quarter of a mile) is Gouthwaite Reservoir, a favourite spot with ornithologists. The Sportsman's has two cosy lounges, used by residents and diners alike. Each has a good assortment of armchairs and well-used couches, as well as antique furniture and a lot of parlour plants. The bar to the rear of the building is rather plush and comfortably decorated in soft tones of salmon pink with blue upholstered banquette seating. Food, served in the bar every lunchtime, is interesting, fresh and skilfully produced under the watchful eye of owner Ray Carter. A printed menu is supplemented by a blackboard which offers an array of super seafood, exceptionally fresh and carefully handled: monkfish with garlic, spinach, spring onion sauce (£6.90), grilled whole lemon sole (£7.20), turbot on saffron pasta with chive sauce (£6.90). Meat-eaters aren't neglected: Ray Carter is constantly striving to find the best meat in the area for dishes like Nidderdale lamb with garlic, tomatoes and asparagus or venison sautéed in wild mushroom and juniper berry sauce which can be found on the table d'hote menu (£18.50 inc ½ bottle wine) in the restaurant. In the evenings (and Sunday lunchtimes) the attractive restaurant comes into its own. The menus, both à la carte and fixed-price, are more extensive and allow more scope for ambition. Expect to pay about £50 for two, though the fixed price menu works out cheaper. It's worth it: cooking here is of a notably high standard and shows real flair. There is a separate cheese menu. The seven bedrooms (five double, two twin) are light, airy and neatly maintained. All have smart lightwood furniture, contemporary style wallcoverings in soft colours and bright, soft furnishings. Two rooms have their own en-suite shower rooms and toilet; the remainder share two good-sized bathrooms and two separate toilets. Front-facing rooms have fine country views. This is a hotel constantly undergoing improvements and serving first-rate food in a lovely peaceful spot. It also boasts fishing rights on the River Nidd, rich in trout. *Bar Food 12-2, 7-9.30. Restaurant Meals 7-10. Vegetarian dishes. Children's portions. Free House. Beer Younger, Scotch, McEwan Export. Garden, outdoor eating. Accommodation 7 bedrooms, 2 en suite, £50 (single £30). Children welcome overnight, additional beds and cots available. Check-in all day. Access, Visa.*

Watlington   Chequers

| Tel 049161 2874 |
Love Lane Watlington Oxfordshire OX9 5RA   Map 17 D2

A useful stop, less than two and a half miles from junction 6 of the M40. It's a characterful, rambling old pub with a lovely summer garden. *Beer Brakspears. Garden.*

Watton-at-Stone   George & Dragon

| Tel 0920 830285 | **FOOD**
High Street Watton-at-Stone Hertfordshire SG14 3TA   Map 15 F1

The George & Dragon is popular with everyone, from OAPs to business class, and its well-balanced bar menu and separate table d'hote 3-course restaurant menu (£18.50 inc service), attracts a fair number of locals. On any one day, the bar food menu could offer Australian royal prawns and squid rings cooked in Provençal sauce (£4.75), fillet pork goulash (£5.50), vol-au-vents with diced chicken and ham in cream and mushroom sauce (£5) or fillet pork goulash (£5.50). Puddings such as summer pudding start at £2. The set price menu in the restaurant has six starters, six main courses and several puddings to choose from: mussels cooked in white wine, garlic and cream, paupiettes of lemon sole filled with salmon mousse, roast breast of duck served in red wine sauce. Reasonable house wines are available by the carafe. The bars are usually bustling with diners, some of whom travel some distance to eat here. The public bar is a locals' spot, though, with keen cribbage players, black and white photographs of the pub and village in days gone by, and furnishings similar to the main bar, in the oldest part of the building, which has a wonderfully homely atmosphere enhanced by jovial management and welcome touches like fresh flowers and the day's newspapers. There are also exposed beams, open fireplaces, yellow stained walls hung with a mixture of framed oil and watercolour paintings, and two large bay windows admitting lots of natural light. Furnishings are a mixture of blue upholstered bench seating and simple wood chairs around oak tables topped with candles. There are a couple of modern regulations though: no credit cards are taken for bills under £10, and singlet tops are prohibited in the bars. This is a difficult pub to miss, as it dominates the centre of the village, and is of pink-painted pebbledash. There's a small flower-filled garden and patio for kinder weather. *Bar Food* 12-2, 7.15-10 (except Sun eve). *Restaurant Meals* (except Sun/Mon) 12-2, 7.15-9.30. Vegetarian dishes. Children's portions. *Beer Greene King IPA, Abbot Ale. Garden, patio/terrace, outdoor eating. Access, Amex, Diners, Visa.*

Weald   Chequer Tree
Tel 0732 463386

Scabharbour Road Weald Kent TN14 6WL   Map 11 B5

Roomy, modernised, tidy country pub with a lovely and varied garden. *Beer Ruddles, Webster's. Garden, children's play area.*

Weaverthorpe   Star Inn
Tel 09443 273

Weaverthorpe nr Malton North Yorkshire YO17 8EY   Map 5 F4

Well-run, well-kept, two-bar Wolds village pub with a pleasing philosophy geared towards regional foods and recipes all year round. Overnight accommodation is cheap and unassuming. *Beer Taylor, Tetley, Webster's. Family room.*

Well   Chequers
Tel 0256 862605

Well nr Odiham Hampshire RG25 1TL   Map 17 D4

Low-ceilinged, panelled, beamed, old-fashioned pub whose vine-covered patio is lovely in summer. *Beer Wadworth 6X, Whitbread Boddingtons. Garden, children's play area. Family room.*

Wellow   Olde Red Lion
Tel 0623 861000

Eakring Road Wellow Nottinghamshire   Map 7 D2

Several small cosy bars in this popular old pub; refurbished, well-run and often swamped with hungry locals at peak feeding times; good value food in generous portions. Sunday lunch is particularly busy. *Beer Marston, Ruddles, Whitbread. Garden, children's play area.*

Wells-next-the-Sea   Crown Hotel

FOOD
B&B

Tel 0328 710209

The Buttlands Wells-next-the-Sea Norfolk NR23 1EX   Map 10 C1

Outward appearances are sometimes deceptive, the facade of the Crown being a case in point. It stands at the foot of a tree-lined village green, the Buttlands, where medieval marksmen once practised their archery. Compared to the elegant Georgian terraced houses which surround the green, the Crown's black and white painted exterior (genuinely Tudor, as it turns out) has the rather care-worn look of a modest town pub. But what a jewel it is inside! The bar progresses on three levels from front to back, where a family-friendly conservatory of high-backed settles opens on to the rear patio and stableyard. Within, there's an open log fire, high bar stools and low copper-topped, barrel-shaped tables, the walls throughout covered with portraits and memorabilia of Horatio Nelson – born in a nearby village and whose sister reputedly lived on the Buttlands. The beer's good and the bar menu is extensive. Single-course meals of pasta dishes and omelettes come in generous portions at under £5, and grills from a mini 'steakwich' through to a full mixed grill at £11.50. Plenty of salads, sandwiches, and sausage-burger-fishfinger combinations for the children complete the picture. The adjoining restaurant, continuing the interior's Victorian theme, is neatly decked out with pink cloths and fresh vased pinks, and offers more adventurous dining. Lunch is available daily (booking essential on Sunday), and there is an evening choice of table d'hote or à la carte, on which locally landed fish and shellfish feature prominently. Local mussels in filo with Provençal sauce and wild salmon hollandaise are prettily presented and reveal much skill in their saucing, without the pretence of haute cuisine nor the pretension of 'moderne'. Gressingham duck breast (£11.50), tournedos Rossini and wiener schnitzel are equally appealing, without taking any undue risks, and the cream-heavy desserts carefully made. To describe the bedrooms as modest is not to decry them: they are simply but adequately furnished and even the smallest offers a view of the charming old town, across the Lion Yard where the London mail coach once pulled in, and over pantiled roofs to the sturdy Norman church below. The seal is set on an enjoyable stay by a tranquil night's rest in these evocative surroundings, a hearty and enjoyable English breakfast, and the friendly service and warm hospitality of the Foyers family and their youthful staff. *Bar Meals 12-2, 6.30 (7 restaurant)-9.30 (9 Sun and winter). Vegetarian dishes. Children's menu/portions. Free House.* **Beer** *Adnams, Marston Pedigree, Tetley. Patio/terrace, outdoor eating. Family room.* **Accommodation** *15 Bedrooms, 10 en suite £62 (single £34). Children welcome overnight (under-10s £10, 10-15s £15), cots available (£3). Check-in all day. Access, Amex, Diners, Visa.*

Wendron New Inn

Tel 0326 572683	B&B
Wendron nr Helston Cornwall TR13 0EA	Map 12 B4

Outside, the inn sign and harvest gold walls act as a colourful backdrop to hanging baskets, and within plush red carpets and varnished pine panelling combine well. The public bar retains a more traditional look. The two modest bedrooms have TVs and kettles, and share a bathroom. **Beer** *Newquay Steam, Cornish Original, guest beers. Garden.* **Accommodation** *2 bedrooms, not en suite, £40 (single £18). No children under 14. Check-in by arrangement. Access, Visa.*

Wenlock Wenlock Edge Inn

Tel 074636 403	FOOD
	B&B
Hill Top Wenlock Shropshire TF3 6DJ	Map 6 B4

It's well worth the drive some four miles up the B4371 from Much Wenlock just to enjoy the view from Wenlock Edge. Leave the car park opposite the pub and cross a sheep pasture to find Ippikin's Rock, from where you can admire the three and a half miles of wooded escarpment which forms the National Trust park. The pub is owned by the Warings and run very much as a family affair. The menu, like the landlord, is on the chatty side: if there's no wedgie pie (£6.50) available, you can always ask if they're doing oink and apple instead. In addition to hand-written menus describing the delights of beef and mushroom pie (£4.60) (guaranteed no kidney), prawn salad and plaice, the latter served with fresh vegetables and boiled potatoes but absolutely never with chips, there are daily specials listed on illuminated boards in each of the two bars. Garlic mushrooms (£2.75), whole breast of chicken in creole sauce (£6.40), tomato and celery pasta bake (£4.90), and chicken and apricot flan (£4.60) are typical offerings. But leave room, too, for the good home-made puddings (all £2.10), of which "the famous lemon pudding" (their description) and summer fruit crumble are typical. The building itself is decidedly quirky, original stone at the front, but with brick extensions tacked on higgledy-piggledy at the sides and rear, and access to a dilapidated farmyard. The far from spacious interior features pews and cushioned window seats, an odd assortment of tables, and a tiny extension which serves in the evenings as a restaurant-cum-parlour. As fellow diners may almost be rubbing shoulders, Stephen Waring plays host from the bar, breaking the ice between strangers with animated conversations. There are three bedrooms in the inn and a fourth in the little cottage to the rear, all with en-suite bathrooms. **Bar Food** (except Mon) 12-2, 7-9. Vegetarian dishes. Children's portions. Free House. **Beer** Robinson, Ruddles, Webster's. Garden, outdoor eating. **Accommodation** 4 bedrooms, all en suite, £48 (single £30). Children welcome overnight, additional beds (from £2), cots supplied. No credit cards.

Weobley   Olde Salutation Inn

Tel 0544 318443

Market Pitch Weobley Hereford & Worcester HR4 8SJ   Map 14 A1

Nice pub in picturesque village. Pleasantly modernised lounge has a real fire, with restaurant leading off; also public bar with machines and juke box. **Beer** Hook Norton, Whitbread, Boddingtons. Family room.

West Bexington   Manor Hotel

FOOD
B&B

Tel 0308 897785   Fax 0308 897035

Beech Road West Bexington nr Bridport Dorset DT2 9DF   Map 13 F2

Old manor house just a short walk from Chesil Bank, with stone-walled cellar bar, leafy conservatory and residents' lounge. Books, magazines and dried flower arrangements add a homely, welcoming touch to simply furnished but well-equipped bedrooms, which come complete with tea and coffee kits, TVs, direct-dial phones, sherry, elderflower water and goodnight chocolates. They offer a £10.95 set Sunday lunch, and a special £6.65 three-course children's menu. Food is typified by monkfish and scallop kebab (£10.95), chicken stuffed with garlic and parsley wrapped in filo (£8.25), fish thermidor (£10.95) and sticky toffee pudding (£2.50). **Bar Food** 12-2, 6.30-10 (7-10 Sun) **Restaurant Meals** 12-2, 7-9.30. Vegetarian dishes. Children's menu. Free House. **Beer** Eldridge Pope, Palmers Bridport, Royal Oak, Wadworth 6X. Garden, outdoor eating, children's play area. Family room. **Accommodation** 13 bedrooms, all en suite, £71 (single £45). Children welcome overnight, additional beds (£5), cots available (£3). Check-in all day. No dogs. Access, Amex, Diners, Visa.

West Bradford   Three Millstones

Tel 0200 23340

Waddington Road West Bradford Lancashire BB7 5SX   Map 6 B1

Old coaching inn close to the river Ribble, in a historic village.
There's a view of Pendle Hill from the beer garden. *Beer Theakston.
Garden, children's play area. Family room.*

West Bromwich   Manor House

Tel 021 588 2035

A

Hallgreen Road West Bromwich West Midlands   Map 6 C4

Water-moated medieval manor house (dating from 1275), carefully
restored, and making an unusually atmospheric pub. Shields with coats
of arms decorate the walls and there are three ghosts – a young girl in
the store room who fell into the inglenook fireplace, a lady in grey in
the chapel and Fred, the house ghost, who gets blamed for everything!
Free House. Beer Banks's. Garden.

West Huntspill   Crossways Inn

Tel 0278 783756

West Huntspill nr Highbridge Somerset TA9 3RA   Map 13 E1

Proprietor-run 17th-century inn with a simple old-fashioned interior
and a delightful covered patio at the rear. *Beer Batcombe, Whitbread
Flowers. Garden, children's play area. Family room.*

West Ilsley   Harrow Inn   ★

Tel 063528 260

FOOD

West Ilsley nr Newbury Berkshire RG16 0AR   Map 16 B3

The Harrow Inn remains as friendly and popular as ever. Antique
furniture and several country settles create a smartly rustic but simple
and old-fashioned atmosphere. Following refurbishment, there's now
more space in which to relax and enjoy an excellent pint of Morland
(who founded their brewery in this village in 1711, but are now based
in Abingdon), and a delicious lunch or supper. The food is as good as
always, and the consistency of approach and cooking is admirable. For
exceptional value for money, try the rabbit pie (£4.50) which wraps
tender pieces of fresh rabbit with lemon and herbs in a puff pastry
crust, accompanied by vegetables like cabbage, potatoes, and a savoury
side dish of leeks in a tomato sauce. The range of dishes, chosen from
the seasonally changing handwritten menu and daily changing specials
board (lamb with redcurrant sauce £8.25, chicken with cider and
apples £7.25, marmalade sponge with orange sauce £2.50), is wide
enough to suit all tastes and pockets, from a simple home-made
hamburger to a hearty three-course meal. Soups, salads, bread and
puddings are reliably good, the home-made puddings especially, and a
fine selection of constantly varying British cheeses puts the seal on a
splendid bill of fare. Portions are generous and decidedly non-nouvelle,
and vegetarians are thoughtfully catered for: all in all a properly
pubby combination of the imaginative and homely, which keeps
people coming back. There are other reasons to visit too, like the
village green setting, complete with lazy ducks on the pond, and a
good garden for children with playthings and animals. It's on the edge
of the Berkshire Downs, and just a mile from the Ridgeway footpath.
*Bar Food 12-2.15, 6-9.15. Vegetarian dishes. Children's portions. Beer
Morland Original, Old Master, Old Speckled Hen. Garden, outdoor eating,
children's play area. Access, Visa.*

West Leake   Star Inn

Tel 0509 852233

Melton Lane West Leake Nottinghamshire LE12 5RQ   Map 7 D3

Also known as the Pit House – cockfights were once popular here.
Warm and welcoming, traditionally furnished interior. *Beer Adnams.
Children's play area.*

West Lulworth   Castle Inn

Tel 092941 311   Fax 092941 415   **B&B**

Main Road West Lulworth Dorset BH20 5RN   Map 14 B4

Quaint 17th-century roadside pub with a heavy thatch and country-
style bars (mind your head on the hanging pewter tankards). Homely
bedrooms vary greatly in size, but all have thoughtful extras including
TVs and tea and coffee kits. Attractive terraced rose garden. *Beer
Cornish Royal Wessex, Flowers Original, Marston Pedigree, Whitbread
Best. Garden, outdoor play area. Family room. **Accommodation**
14 bedrooms, 10 en suite, £39 (single £26). Children welcome overnight,
additional beds, cots supplied. Check-in all day. Access, Amex, Diners, Visa.*

West Pennard   Red Lion

FOOD

Tel 0458 832941   **B&B**

Glastonbury Road West Pennard Somerset BA6 8NH   Map 13 F1

Great effort and not a little expense have been applied by new
proprietors to return the Lion to its former place at the heart of
village life. It exudes a comfortable informality in the central stone-
flagged and low-beamed bar, where some easy chairs have been added
around a huge inglenook that boasts a roaring log fire in winter.
Radiating off are the neatly-set dining room and a cosy parlour which
doubles as family and breakfast room. There's local praise for some
well-kept Oakhill and Ash Vine bitters, and for the revitalised pool
room and skittle alley. Menus run from burgers (£1.95) to steaks
(£9.50), with daily soup (from £1.75), specials such as chicken and
tarragon pie (£2.95) and the ever-popular farmer's pie (£4.95) of
beef, Guinness and Stilton added on the blackboard. A la carte are
garlic prawns (£3.50), lemon sole with crabmeat filling (£7.25), veal
à la creme (£9.95) and cashew nut paella (£6.95): a 3-course house
menu (£8.95) is popular with residents and the £5.50 Sunday lunch
(half price for children) a hit with families. Bright duvets and new
bed linen and towels have smartened up the bedrooms in the adjacent
former stable block. Bathrooms are neat, clean and carpeted, while
extras include colour TVs, dial-out phones and radio alarm clocks. *Bar
Food & Restaurant Meals 12-2 (Sun only), 7-9.30. Vegetarian dishes.
Children's menu/portions. Free House. **Beer** Hall & Woodhouse. **Cider**
Inch's Stonehouse, Wilkins Farmhouse. Garden, outdoor eating. Family
room. **Accommodation** 7 bedrooms, all en suite, £45 (single £30).
Children welcome overnight, additional beds. Check-in by arrangement. No
dogs. Access, Visa.*

West Stafford — Wise Man Inn

Tel 0305 263694

West Stafford Dorset DT2 8AG Map 13 F2

The nearest pub to Thomas Hardy's birthplace at Bockhampton; a poem hymning the virtues of ale, attributed to Hardy, appears on the front wall: "health lies in the equipoise", apparently. Thatched, pleasant two-bar pub, tidy and well run. *Beer Whitbread, Flowers. Garden, children's play area.*

West Witton — Wensleydale Heifer

Tel 0969 22322 **B&B**

West Witton nr Leyburn North Yorkshire DL8 4LS Map 5 D4

Well kept, pleasant 17th-century inn with chintzy furniture (perhaps more hotelly than strictly pubby in style), lounge and two further bars; good log fire in winter. Pretty recently refurbished bedrooms with new linens and curtains, half of them in adjacent cottages; three with four posters. On main A684 Leyburn-Hawes road, in attractive countryside. *Free House. Beer Theakston, Murphy.* **Accommodation** *19 bedrooms, all en suite, £65 (single £45). Children welcome overnight, additional beds (£5 if under 10 yrs), cots supplied. Check-in all day. Access, Diners, Visa.*

West Wycombe — George & Dragon

Tel 0494 464414   Fax 0494 462432 **FOOD** **B&B**

West Wycombe nr High Wycombe Buckinghamshire HP14 3AB Map 17 E2

A cobbled archway entrance is one of several original features at this Tudor coaching inn, which reputedly extend to the ghost of a 'White Lady'. Set in a National Trust village beside the A40, period appeal continues inside with large oak beams, settles and Windsor chairs by roaring fires. Friendly staff offer a promising menu ranging from potted Stilton (£3.10) and herby mushrooms (£3.45) to salmon in pastry (£6.95), chicken Copenhagen (stuffed with cream cheese, wrapped in bacon and breadcrumbs £5.65), beef Wellington (£7.25) and a spinach and blue cheese pancake (£4.45). Follow with a rich, gooey treacle tart or bread and butter pudding (both £1.95). There are nine bedrooms of all different shapes and sizes, two with four-posters. TVs, direct-dial telephones, radio alarms and tea/coffee facilities are provided. *Bar Food 12-2 (12-1.30 Sun), 6-9.30. Vegetarian dishes. Beer Courage Best and Directors, guest beer. Garden, outdoor eating, children's play area. Family room.* **Accommodation** *9 bedrooms, all en suite, £50 (single £40). Children welcome overnight, additional beds and cots available. Check-in all day. Access, Amex, Visa.*

Westmill — Sword in Hand

Tel 0736 71356

Westmill nr Buntingford Hertfordshire SG9 9LQ Map 15 F1

Attractive pub in a charming village just off the A10. Carpeted bar with good log fire and black and white timbering. *Beer Greene King, Ind Coope. Garden, children's play area.*

Weston   White Lion Inn
Tel 0270 500303

Main Road Weston nr Crewe Cheshire CW2 5NA   Map 6 B3

The orignal Tudor farmhouse pub, complete with appropriately
atmospheric beamed bar, now has a modern hotel with a businesslike
atmosphere and features grafted onto the back. Piped music, smartly
turned out staff and a conference trade. *Beer Ind Coope, Burton Ale.
Garden. Family room.*

Westwoodside   Park Drain Hotel
Tel 0427 752255

Westwoodside Isle of Axholme Humberside   Map 7 D2

Secluded, unusual Victorian pub, in Park Drain, about 400 yards off
the B1396. Spacious public bar, comfortable lounge and separate
restaurant. Homely in the bar, smarter in the restaurant, where
children are permitted. *Beer Courage.*

Wetheringsett   Cat & Mouse
Tel 0728 860765   **A**

Pages Green Wetheringsett Suffolk IP14 5QB   Map 10 C2

Roy and Ann Booth's Cat & Mouse is one of those rare pubs which
defies all conventions and threatens to survive against all odds, despite
breaking most of the usual rules. Here we have a staunchly traditional
pride of leonine publicans who truly believe that too much food can
only get in the way of the proper enjoyment of one's pint. When it
comes to real ale, read several pints, unalloyed – they hope – by
stodgy pies or soggy chips. The beer is the thing. Landlord Roy runs
off up to a dozen names in a single breath, each pulled straight from
the cask in full view, and greatly to his credit takes the fullest possible
pleasure in recommending which of the brews are in prime condition
that day. He and Ann bought this closed, non-trading and generally
written-off pub a few years ago from a national brewer. "Flying in the
face of all advice," says Ann, they set it up then and run it still as a
vehicle for serving only prime cask-conditioned ales. Geographically,
you'll find the pub at Pages Green, at a fork in the road no more than
a couple of miles from Wetheringsett. Without directions from those
with local knowledge, you may never find it. We should leave it that
way: for to do otherwise would only spoil the romance of it all. *No
Food. Free house. Beer Adnams, Brakspears, Marston, Mauldons,
Nethergate, Boddingtons, Bass, Worthington, Youngs, Robinsons, Old
Growler. Garden.*

Whatcote   Royal Oak
Tel 0295 680319   **A**

Whatcote nr Shipston-on-Stour Warwickshire CV36 5EF   Map 16 B1

Highly atmospheric ancient alehouse, with a romantic history: the
inglenook features rungs leading up to a secret chamber. Beams are
very low, furnishings various, and there's a miscellaneous array of
bric-a-brac. *Free House. Beer Marston's Pedigree, Castle Eden, Whitbread.
Garden. No credit cards.*

Whitchurch   White Swan

Tel 0296 641228

10 High Street Whitchurch Buckinghamshire HP22 4JT   Map 17 D1

Partly-thatched, 500-year-old building which has been an inn since the mid-17th century, and still has the unspoilt atmosphere of an old-fashioned country pub. There's piped music, but no nasty modern gaming machines. The two bars are named after the house dogs, Charlie and Sam. Nice old furnishings and fresh flowers. *Beer Fuller's, London Pride. Garden, children's play area. Family room.*

Whiteleaf   Red Lion

FOOD
B&B

Tel 08444 4476

Upper Uckfield Way Whiteleaf Buckinghamshire HP27 0LL   Map 17 D2

Cream and red-painted 17th-century village pub, set back from the road with a terrace out front. Inside, the spotless interior positively shines – highly polished furniture and gleaming brasses and copper pots decorate the two bar areas and small dining area. Bar and restaurant food is simple rather than elaborate: home-made lasagne (£4.75), steak and kidney pie (£4.75), basket meals, i.e. scampi (£2.50), chicken Cordon Bleu (£3.95), treacle pudding and custard (£1.95). There is no restaurant menu on Sunday though a traditional 3-course roast lunch (£8.95) is served. There are four bedrooms, all en suite. *Bar Food and Restaurant Meals 12-2.30, 6-9.30. Vegetarian dishes. Children's portions. Free House. Beer Morland, Hook Norton, Brakspear. Garden, outdoor eating. Accommodation 4 bedrooms, all en-suite, £39.50 (single £29.50). Children welcome overnight, additional beds (£10). Check-in by arrangement. Access, Visa.*

Whitewell   Inn at Whitewell

FOOD
B&B

Tel 02008 222

Whitewell Forest of Bowland Lancashire BB7 3AT   Map 6 B1

Well away from the hurly burly, the Whitewell Inn stands next to the village church, overlooking the river Hodder (and owns eight miles of fishing rights) in the beautiful, unspoilt countryside of the little-known Forest of Bowland. Back in the 14th century, the inn was home to the keeper of the King's deer, and the Queen still owns the building as part of the Duchy of Lancaster. Inside, it's wonderfully relaxed, laid-back, even mildly eccentric, with a haphazard arrangement of furnishings and bric-a-brac. In the main bar there are wooden tables, old settles, roundback chairs, a stone fireplace, log fire in cold weather, and heavy ceiling beams. An entrance hall has colourful rugs, more settles, even a piano, and a selection of magazines, papers and books for some serious loitering. A wide variety of pictures, dotted about the building, come from the Inn's own art gallery; there's also a small wine merchant business, as well as expensive sweaters and hunting gear in the shop. Food is served in both the bar and restaurant, which overlooks the river; the bar meal selection follows the tried and trusted from mostly fresh local produce, and is decently rather than excitingly cooked. More ambitious cooking is at work in the restaurant, where local ingredients include fish from this very river. The à la carte menu features dishes like potato and wild garlic soup (£1.50), rack of lamb (£12.50) and Loch Fyne smoked salmon (£9). Calorific puddings like sticky toffee pudding (£2.50); a good wine list. There are nine bedrooms, seven of them refurbished with antique furniture, peat fires and Victorian baths. Unusual extras include video recorders and superb Bang and Olufson stereo systems, as well as books, magazines, and a set of binoculars; the best and largest rooms overlook the river and the country beyond. Everything is immaculately clean. On sunny days the attractive rear lawn furnished with simple benches is an ideal spot to relax and soak in the view. *Bar Food 12-2, 7.15-9.30.* *Restaurant Meals 7.30-9.30.* *Vegetarian dishes. Children's portions.* *Beer Moorhouse's Premier Bitter, Pendle Witches Brew. Riverside garden, outdoor eating.* *Accommodation 9 bedrooms, all en suite, £57 (single £43) Children welcome overnight, cots available. Check-in all day. Access, Amex, Diners, Visa.*

Whitmore   Mainwaring Arms
Tel 0782 680851
Whitmore Staffordshire   Map 6 B3

Delightfully unspoilt old pub, with a maze of old-fashioned little rooms, lots of oak beams, several open fires, and a mix of ancient and modern furnishings. Lovely in summer, when barbecues are held on the cobbled rear terrace, or for its front seating area, with a classically English view of the quaint old church. *Beer Bass, Marston. Terrace.*

Whitney-on-Wye   Boat Inn
Tel 04973 223
Whitney-on-Wye Hereford & Worcester HR3 6EH   Map 14 A1

Roomy and always tidy riverbank pub, nicely furnished, with picture windows overlooking the water. *Beer Bass, Marston Pedigree. Riverside garden.*

Whitney-on-Wye   Rhydspence Inn   FOOD / B&B
Tel 04973 262
Whitney-on-Wye nr Hay-on-Wye Hereford & Worcester HR3 6EU   Map 14 A1

Well-loved, reliably entertaining old inn set in the heart of Kilvert country, on the A438 about a mile out of Whitney-on-Wye. Delightful timbered interior and two attractive bars, with real fires, old furniture and beams aplenty. Nice touches include magazines and newspapers, creating an atmosphere in keeping with the old library chairs. The charming dining room and restaurant overlook the garden. Five comfortable bedrooms have beams, sloping floors, plus an armchair at the least; some rooms are more romantic, others more modern in style; one has a four-poster. Bar food suggestions include spinach and mozzarella crunch (£4.95), braised liver and onion (£5.75), and seafood platter (£6.50). The longer restaurant menu is as varied: ricotta and spinach pancake (£4.85), bavarois of smoked salmon (£5.75), monkfish and salmon brochette (£12.95), fillet steak with Stilton (£13.50), plus an excellent choice of farmhouse cheeses. A 3-course traditional Sunday lunch is available in the restaurant (£10.95). *Bar Food & Restaurant Meals 11-2 (12-2 Sun lunch in restaurant), 7-9.30. Vegetarian dishes. Children's portions. Free House. Beer Bass, Robinson, Marston pedigree. Cider Dunkerton. Garden, outdoor eating. Family room. Accommodation 5 bedrooms, all en suite, £55 (single £27.50). Children welcome overnight, additional beds (£12.50). Check-in all day. No dogs. Access, Amex, Visa.*

Whitwell — Noel Arms

Tel 078086 334

Main Street Whitwell Leicestershire LE15 8BW

Map 7 E3

Get here early for a seat in the tiny twin rooms at the front, the original alehouse. The overflow spills into a spacious rear extension of much less charm. *Beer Tetley, Ruddles county, Burton. Garden. Children's play area.*

Wickham — Five Bells

Tel 048838 242

B&B

Wickham nr Newbury Berkshire RG16 8HH

Map 16 B3

On the Newbury-Lambourn road, the mellow thatched Five Bells boasts a large garden complete with children's paddling pool. Log fires warm the handsome beamed bar, where a good selection of ales and wines by the glass are served. An adjoining stable block houses four neat, bright bedrooms with simply painted walls and pretty curtains. They share a spacious bathroom and all have washbasins, TVs and tea-makers. *Beer Ushers Best, Webster's Yorkshire, Morland, Ruddles County. Garden. Family room. Accommodation 4 bedrooms, not en suite, £35 (single £25). Children welcome overnight, additional beds and cots available. Check-in all day. Access, Visa.*

Widecombe-in-the-Moor — Old Inn

Tel 03642 207

A

Widecombe-in-the-Moor Devon TQ13 7TA

Map 13 D3

14th-century Dartmoor inn, which sits beneath the 120ft tower of the St Pancras church, 'cathedral of the moors'. A devastating fire in the 1970s means much of the Old Inn is actually pretty new, though original stonework and fireplaces and two ghosts remain. *Free House. Beer Ushers Best Bitter, Widecombe Wallop. Cider Grays. Garden, outdoor eating, children's play area. Family room.*

Wigglesworth — Plough Inn

Tel 0729 840243

Wigglesworth nr Skipton North Yorkshire BD23 4RJ

Map 6 B1

A fine old country inn with a conservatory and landscaped garden. *Beer Tetley, Whitbread. Family room.*

Wilmcote — Masons Arms

Tel 0789 297416

FOOD

Wilmcote nr Stratford-upon-Avon Warwickshire CV37 9XX

Map 14 C1

A short drive from Stratford on the A34 and located next to Shakespeare's mother's house, the Masons is popular for its reliable bar food and smarter restaurant fare (children allowed here). Traditional simple food is served in the bar at reasonable prices (£4-£5): steak and kidney pie (made with local meat), lasagne, curries, salads. Popular restaurant main courses (priced between £6.50 and £10) include filet mignon with Madeira sauce (£9.90) or poached salmon in vermouth and prawn sauce (£7.30). There's a new conservatory extension. *Bar Food 12-2, 7-9.15. Restaurant Meals 7-9.15. Vegetarian dishes. Children's portions. Beer Hook Norton, Wadworth 6X, Boddingtons. Garden, outdoor eating. Access, Visa.*

Wilmcote   Swan House Hotel

FOOD
B&B

Tel 0789 267030   Fax 0789 204875

Wilmcote nr Stratford-upon-Avon Warwickshire CV37 9XJ

Map 14 C1

First-rate landlords Ian and Diana Sykes run their extremely friendly
pub in exemplary fashion. It's a tall, white-painted inn with a modern
extension housing a well-planned reception area. Open from 11am to
11pm (except Sunday), the bar is bright and cheerful, and serves
freshly prepared home-made dishes such as lasagne (£4.70), steak and
mushroom pie (£5.95), mixed grill (£7.50) and chili con carne
(£7.50). On a red-hot granite stone, guests are invited to cook their
own 'Steak on the Stone' (sirloin £9.95, fillet £10.95). The restaurant
dining area is only open at peak times though food is always available
in the bar. All the bedrooms have matching curtains and bedspreads
and white furniture which gives a cheerful look. All have en-suite
facilities, TVs, radio-alarms and tea-makers. One room sports a four-
poster. The outdoor children's play area has a Wendy house, see-saw
and trampoline. *Bar Food 12-2.30, 7-9.30 (Sun 7-9).* ***Restaurant***
Meals *7-9.30 (Sun 7-9). Vegetarian dishes. Children's menu (£2.25 per
dish). Free House. Beer Theakston XB, Hook Norton Best.* ***Cider***
Scrumpy Jack. Garden, outdoor eating, children's play area.
Accommodation *8 bedrooms, all en suite, £56 (single £36). Children
welcome overnight, additional beds (£5-10), cots supplied. Check-in all day.
No dogs. Accommodation closed four days January, three days Christmas.
Access, Amex, Visa.*

Wilmslow   Farmers Arms

Tel 0625 532443

Chapel Lane Wilmslow Cheshire SK9 5JH

Map 6 B2

This bustling town-centre local is attractively old-fashioned, with
various little rooms, lots of bric-a-brac, fine etched windows, and a
family room decked out with cartoons. Real fires; no music. *Beer
Boddingtons. Garden. Family room.*

Winchelsea   New Inn

Tel 0797 226252

German Street Winchelsea East Sussex TN36 4EN

Map 11 C6

A characterful, spacious 18th-century inn with three rambling lounge
rooms, nice old furniture, hopbines aplenty and good log fires. There's
also a separate public bar. *Beer Courage, King & Barnes. Garden,
children's play area. Family room.*

Winchester   Old Vine

Tel 0962 854616

8 Great Minster Street Winchester Hampshire SO23 9HA

Map 15 D3

Attractive cottage pub opposite the main cathedral gates whose
licensees who have brought a dining emphasis, besides a total
refurbishment. *Beer Courage, John Smith's. Family room.*

Winchester   Wykeham Arms   ★

FOOD
B&B

Tel 0962 853834   Fax 0962 854411

75 Kingsgate Street Winchester Hampshire SO23 9PE

Map 15 D3

Tucked away in the narrow back streets of Winchester, hard by the
Cathedral Close, Graeme and Anne Jameson have turned the mellow,
redbrick, 250-year-old 'Wyk' into one of the finest hostelries in the
land. The main bar, which is mostly for drinkers, has old-fashioned

schoolroom desks with integral seats, some authentically carved with
the initials of inattentive pupils from years gone by. Collections of
hats, mugs and fascinating old prints and cartoons adorn the bar and
no less than six other interconnecting rooms, all set up for eating, with
a special dining area for non-smokers. The old pine, candle-lit dining
tables each have a brass money slot to collect donations for the upkeep
of the cathedral; at present the pub is trying to raise £60,000
(£25,000 collected to date) to endow the "Wykeham Lay Clerkship"
which will support at least one Lay Clerk (paid chorister) in
perpetuity. Much patronised by the Dons from Winchester College,
and barristers attending the local courts (amongst many others), this is
probably the best place to eat in town, and booking is essential. A
blackboard menu at lunchtime changes daily, offering unusual, but
invariably successful, combinations of flavours like Stilton and
gooseberry paté (£3.50), 'Wyk' cottage pie served with crusty bread
(£5.25), lamb and rosemary casserole (£5.95). Main course
suggestions on the restaurant menu are grilled fillet of turbot topped
with spiced crumbs on a tomato and crab cream sauce (£10.25),
roasted duck breast with orange and onion confit and bitter orange
sauce (£10.85) and chicken breast stuffed with cashew nuts, gruyère
cheese and fennel (£9.25). A separate pudding menu offers mouth-
watering choices like carrot and ginger pudding with butterscotch
sauce and white chocolate and Drambuie mousse with bananas.
Twenty-two names on the well-chosen wine list are also available by
the glass, and for summer eating and drinking there is a neat walled
garden. Individually decorated bedrooms have stylish matching
bedcovers and curtains and mostly honeyed pine furniture. All have
mini-bars, television and telephone, plus homely extras like fresh
flowers, books, magazines and pot-pourri. Modern en-suite bathrooms,
all with showers over tubs, boast quality Woods of Windsor toiletries.
First-rate cooked breakfasts, with freshly squeezed orange juice, are
served in a charming period breakfast room on the first floor. *Bar
Food and Restaurant Meals* (*except Sun*) *12-2.30* (*sandwiches served till
6*), *6.30-8.45. Vegetarian dishes.* **Beer** *Eldridge Pope. Garden, outdoor
eating.* **Accommodation** *7 bedrooms, all en suite, £69.50 (single £59.50).
Children over 14 welcome overnight, additional beds (£10). Check-in all
day. Amex, Visa.*

Winforton   Sun Inn   ★

Tel 0544 327677

Winforton Hereford & Worcester HR3 6EA

FOOD

Map 14 A1

The Wye Valley road, otherwise known as the A438, winds out of
Wales past Hay-on-Wye, a popular tourist route to Hereford and
points north. By following the road some three miles into England,
Wendy and Brian Hibbard have become celebrated émigrés, and the
numbers are growing of those who follow to sample Wendy
Hibbard's inspirational cooking. A Jane Grigson fan, yet a fine
innovator in her own right, her inclination towards spicy, Eastern
flavours has brought many fans beating a path to the door with dishes
like Arabian lamb with apricots, red and green peppers, pine nuts and
couscous (£6.99). Lighter lunch treats might include tomato, lentil
and spinach soup (£1.75) and crab and coriander fishcakes (£3.15). In
addition to a flair for the cooking of foreign parts, good old
traditional English cooking is also well represented, often with a
characteristic Hibbard twist in the tail: her popular pies and celebrated

'Piggy in the Orchard' are always assured of a place on the menu. For more adventurous evening diners, bream on samphire (£6.99), breast of local chicken with fennel and tomatoes (£7.50) and roast leg of local wild boar in cinnamon and orange (£10.99), always accompanied by generous portions of crunchy, flavourful vegetables. A little bit of room should still be reserved for some unusual desserts (all £2.75), a 'nuts about nuts tart', or 'Kilimanjaro', an ice cream pudding topped with snowy meringue, or a sticky ginger pudding. Throughout the menu, food is beautifully designed as well as cooked: Wendy takes pride in presentation, a skill which has evolved apace following her success in national pub food competitions. Yet we are still talking pub here. Brian Hibbard sees to that, overseeing proceedings from the bar with an avuncular eye, while dispensing Brains, from Cardiff, and Woods, from Craven Arms; he's equally at home discussing the merits of a fine selection of cheeses for the ploughman's (£3.75) where Shropshire Blue, Orkney smoked and mature farmhouse Cheddar rub rinds with his native Merlin goat's cheese and a fine organic Pencarreg. Equally, the exposed stone walls studded with agricultural implements, wood-burning stoves and high settles, and the corner dart board (for occasional use), ensure that the surroundings remain essentially pubby, that the conversation is convivial and that the relaxed atmosphere remains conducive to the enjoyment of fine pub food. The Sun Inn was our 1992 British Meat Pub of the Year. *Bar Food and Restaurant Meals 12-2, 7-9.30 (except Tues eve)(7-9.45 weekends). Vegetarian dishes. Children's portions. Free House. Beer Brains, Whitbread Boddingtons, Flowers Original, Woods. Cider Weston. Garden, outdoor eating. No credit cards.*

Winfrith Newburgh   Red Lion

`Tel 0305 852814`

B&B

Winfrith Newburgh nr Dorchester Dorset DT2 8LE

Map 14 B4

This creeper-clad pub was rebuilt in 1965 after a fire destroyed the original 14th-century building. The new licensee has recently refurbished the bar but has kept its rustic character. Upstairs, there is a multi-purpose lounge and four neat, homely bedrooms with floral wallpaper, candlewick bedspreads and simple white furniture. All have TVs, tea-makers and a shared bathroom. *Beer Hall & Woodhouse Badger Best, Tanglefoot, BXB, Malt House. Garden, children's play area. Family room. Accommodation 4 bedrooms, not en-suite, £36 (single £24). Children welcome overnight, additional beds and cots available. Check-in all day. Access, Amex, Diners, Visa.*

Winkfield   Olde Hatchet

`Tel 0344 882303`

Hatchet Lane Winkfield Berkshire SL4 2EE

Map 17 E4

Charming black and white country pub with conifers and umbrella-topped tables at the front and a garden to the side. *Beer Bass. Garden.*

Winkton   Fisherman's Haunt Hotel

`Tel 0202 484071   Fax 0202 478883`

B&B

Salisbury Road Winkton Christchurch Dorset BH23 7AS

Map 14 C4

The river Avon runs alongside the grounds at an immaculately kept, wisteria-clad hotel. Stuffed fish and an old well with running spring water are unusual features of the characterful beamed bars, and there is an airy conservatory. Spotless bedrooms in the main 17th-century building, extended coach house and nearby cottage blend pretty fabrics with a mixture of modern and traditional furnishings. All offer TVs, telephones and tea-makers and two rooms also boast four-poster beds. *Free House.* **Beer** *John Smith's, Worthington, Ringwood Best Bitter. Garden. Family Room.* **Accommodation** *20 bedrooms, 16 en suite, £55 (single £35), additional beds £6.50, and cots available £5. Check-in by arrangement. Access, Amex, Diners, Visa.*

Winsford	Royal Oak Inn	FOOD
Tel 064385 455 Fax 064385 388		**B&B**
Winsford Exmoor National Park TA24 7JE		**Map 13 D2**

A hotel in a sleepy picture-postcard Exmoor village resistant to street lighting and noise. Despite the hotel status, this lovely 12th-century thatched inn is very much a village local. In a pleasantly refurbished, semi-smart and relaxing interior, a large selection of home-made food is available in the form of bar snacks and meals, a 3-course set-price lunch menu (£12.50), and for dinner, a 3-course table d'hote (£20) or à la carte menu. In the bar, suggestions include daily pasties (£2.95), jacket potatoes with various fillings (£2.95), sandwiches with ham or roast beef (£1.95). For a more substantial lunch in the restaurant, choose perhaps leek and potato soup, followed by a local fresh trout and finish with a sweet from the trolley. In the evening, the dinner menu may offer button mushrooms stuffed with Stilton paté or fresh crab and asparagus wrapped in filo pastry, followed by strips of fillet steak sautéed with mushrooms, granary mustard, wine and cream sauce or half a fresh, locally bred Gressingham duck with pear and orange sauce. Bedrooms (some in a modern annexe) are individually appointed, with pretty floral fabrics and freestanding furniture. Get up in time for breakfast – the poached haddock is marvellous. A family can be accommodated in a converted cowshed (sleeps two adults and three children). The inn's also notable for its unusually good vegetarian choice – an entire menu in the restaurant: stuffed red and green peppers, pancakes filled with vegetables with a gouda sauce. Children can eat in the back bar only. **Bar Food** *12-2, 6.30-9 (6.30-9.30 summer) (7-9 or 9.30 Sun).* **Restaurant Meals** *12.30-1.30 (Sun only), 7.30-9.30. Vegetarian dishes. Children's portions. Children allowed in bar to eat.* **Beer** *Whitbread Flowers Original, IPA. Riverside garden, outdoor eating.* **Accommodation** *14 bedrooms, all en suite, £89.50 (single £59.50). Children welcome overnight, additional beds (from £5), cots supplied. Check-in before 6pm. Access, Amex, Diners, Visa.*

Winslow	Bell Hotel	
Tel 029671 2741 Fax 029671 4805		**B&B**
Market Square Winslow Buckinghamshire MK18 3AB		**Map 17 D1**

Beer pumps that used to splatter the floorboards in coaching inn days are all still intact. Today the Georgian facade looks proudly over the market square. Heavy beams, oak and leather furniture and an inglenook fireplace complete the period picture. There are eighteen bedrooms, two designed for the disabled, all spacious, with traditional furnishings and extras like hairdryers and trouser presses. *Free House.* **Beer** *Pedigree, Old Hookey, Courage Best, Speckled Hen.* **Cider** *Scrumpy Jack. Garden.* **Accommodation** *18 bedrooms, all en suite, £50, (single £40). Children welcome overnight, additional beds and cots available. Check-in all day. Access, Amex, Diners, Visa.*

Winterton-on-Sea   Fisherman's Return

FOOD

Tel 0493 393305

B&B

The Lane Winterton-on-Sea Norfolk NR29 4BN

Map 10 D1

Small it maybe, but this prettily-kept row of former fishermen's
cottages is an ideal hang-out for locals and visitors alike, be they
fishermen or not. Built in traditional brick and flint, the buildings are
probably 16th-century, and unaltered over the last quarter century or
more. The public bar is lined in varnished tongue-and-groove
panelling and hung with sepia photographs and prints of Lowestoft
harbour, the Norfolk Broads and the pub itself. Some of these, movie
buffs will note, are not as old as they seem. Centrestage, the cast-iron
wood-burner opens up in winter to add a glow of warmth to an
already cheery atmosphere. A smaller and possibly older lounge, low-
ceilinged, with a copper-hooded fireplace and oak mantel, is carpeted
these days and ideal for a quick, if cramped, snack. Families will more
likely head to the "Tinho", a timbered rear extension of pool table and
games machines which leads mercifully quickly to a lovely enclosed
garden and adventure playground. The menu's pretty comprehensive.
Individual savouries and omelettes, generously garnished, are the
popular choices; there are pasta dishes at £4.75 and sea trout with
herb dip and new potatoes at £5.25. Overnighters, too, are in for a
treat. A tiny flint-lined spiral staircase leads up under the eaves to four
cosy bedrooms, which share the house television (propped up on a
seaman's trunk) and a pine-panelled bathroom. The largest, family
room also has a sitting area with its own television and fridge. Modest
comforts, maybe, but entirely adequate for a brief stay, a stone's throw
from the beach and long walks over the dunes. Visitors are made truly
welcome by John and Kate Findlay, and seen on their way with the
heartiest of seafarer's breakfasts. Unsurprisingly, not only fisherman
return. *Bar Meals 11-2, 6 (7 winter)-9.30. Vegetarian dishes. Children's
menu. Beer Adnams. Cider James White. Garden, outdoor eating, outdoor
play area. Family room. Accommodation 4 bedrooms, sharing a bathroom,
£40 (single £28). Children welcome overnight. Check-in by arrangement.
No credit cards.*

Wistanstow   Plough

Tel 0588 673251

FOOD

Wistanstow Craven Arms Shropshire SY7 8DG

Map 6 A4

Signed from the A489 by its junction with the A49 is The Wood
Brewery and its adjunct pub, The Plough. Naturally, the local beer is
Wood's (Parish, Special and Wonderful Bitters), but the pub is rather
more than a local. Simply furnished with closely-spaced polished tables
and a small front patio, the upper bar is a haven for foodies, with
salads and ploughman's (£3.50) at lunchtime, alongside home-made
steak and kidney pie (£4.75), chicken in cider (£4.75) and kidneys
créole (£3.95). The evening blackboard menu graduates to baked
John Dory with lime and cream sauce (£7.20), local pigeon in red
wine (£5.20) and rack of lamb with redcurrant and gooseberry sauce
(£6.50). Puddings such as hazelnut meringue and lemon syllabub are
displayed in a chilled counter; also prominently advertised, the wine
list, mostly from Tanners of Shrewsbury, offers up to a dozen
selections by the glass. *Bar Food & Restaurant Meals (except Sun eve
and all day Mon) 12-1.45, 7-8.30 (7-9 Fri/Sat). Children's portions. Beer
Woods Parish, Special and Wonderful Bitters. Cider Weston's Stowford
Press. Terrace, outdoor eating. No credit cards.*

Withypool   Royal Oak Inn

Tel 064383 506   Fax 064383 659

B&B

Withypool nr Minehead Somerset TA24 7QP

Map 13 D1

The convivial beamed bars of this 300-year-old Exmoor inn are extremely popular with the local farming population as well as walkers, who should sleep soundly in the eight characterful beamed bedrooms, all of which enjoy lovely rural views. Pretty fabrics, a light decor and fine period furnishings are used to excellent effect and most have smart modern bathrooms. Direct-dial telephones, TVs and tea-makers are standard throughout. *Free House. Beer Usher Best Bitter, guest beers. Cider Hancocks. Accommodation 8 bedrooms, 6 en suite, £64 (single £44). No children under 8, additional beds available. Check-in all day. Access, Amex, Diners, Visa.*

Woburn   Magpie

Tel 0525 290219

Bedford Street Woburn Bedfordshire MK17 9QB

Map 17 E1

Little lounge, larger, basic but pleasant public bar, and separate restaurant in this 16th-century former coaching inn near Woburn golf club. Licensee's dedication to fresh vegetables extends to growing his own in poly tunnels. *Beer Ruddles, Webster's. Garden.*

Wolsingham   Bay Horse

Tel 0388 527220

Upper Town Wolsingham Durham DU3 3EX

Map 5 D3

Neatly kept two-roomed inn on the edge of the town. Nice to children. *Beer Tetley, Whitbread.*

Wolverton   Red Lion

Tel 0373 830350

FOOD

Wolverton Somerset BA3 6QS

Map 14 B3

Fronted by neat lawns, and set back from the busy road, this smart pub has flagstone floors, exposed stone walls, and open fires, plus a pleasingly informal approach to good eating. Hearty portions of interesting salads (from £4), attractively presented, and unusually-filled baked potatoes, priced according to which of the twenty fillings you choose (£1.20-£3.95), dominate the bar menu. This winter, the Red Lion is planning to offer a wide range of Yorkshire puddings (from £3). The garden is lovely for a summer lunch. *Bar Food 12-2.30, 7-10. Vegetarian dishes. Beer Bass, Wadworth. Garden, outdoor eating. Family room. No credit cards.*

Wolverton Common   Hare & Hounds

Tel 0635 298361

FOOD

Wolverton Common nr Basingstoke Hampshire RG26 5RW

Map 16 C4

Busy 17th-century pub just off the A339, personably run with a homely style. Simple but good home cooking of the shepherd's pie sort is supplemented by imaginative offerings like aubergine and cauliflower moussaka cooked with nut oil (£4.95), honey-roasted duck with cinnamon and finished with Southern Comfort (£11.50), spinach, walnut and cheese pancake (£5.50), and steaks with a variety of sauces. Try the exotic Caribbean meringue or more homely hot treacle pudding for 'afters' (both £2.25). *Bar Food 11.30-2, 6-10 (12-2, 7-10 Sun). Vegetarian dishes. Children's portions. Free House. Beer*

Ruddles Best and County, Ushers. Garden, outdoor eating. Family room. Access, Visa.

Wooburn Common   Chequers Inn

FOOD
B&B

Tel 0628 529575   Fax 0628 850124

Wooburn Common nr Beaconsfield Buckinghamshire HP10 0JQ   Map 17 E3

The Chequers lies perched on the rolling Chiltern Hills, midway between the M4 and M40, and is a charming 17th-century inn which has been carefully and lovingly developed over the years by Peter Roehrig. Find him chatting to the locals in the convivial beamed bar, where quality wines by the glass are supplemented by simple but stylish lunchtime snacks. Choose from open sandwiches (£2.75), ploughman's, leek and potato soup (£2.25), tossed salad of avocado, smoked salmon and prawns with hazelnut dressing (£5.85) or mignons of pork fillets with a Dijon mustard and red wine sauce (£6.95). Two 3-course table d'hote menus (lunch £13.95 and dinner £16.95) are available in the restaurant as well as à la carte dishes. The evening menu offers four choices in each category – perhaps chicken liver and veal paté, then ragout of monkfish in a tomato and cream sauce with strips of smoked salmon, followed by summer pudding with fruit coulis. Home-made petits fours and good coffee to finish. The cottagey bedrooms all have en-suite facilities and are equipped with TVs (plus Sky), telephones, clock-radios, trouser presses, tea/coffee making facilities. One room has a four-poster. *Bar Food 12-2.30. Restaurant Meals 12-2.30, 7-9.30. Vegetarian dishes. Children's portions. Free House. Beer Eldridge Pope, Thomas Hardy. Garden, outdoor eating. Accommodation 17 bedrooms, all en suite, £77.50 (single £72.50). Children welcome overnight, additional beds available. Check-in all day. No dogs. Access, Visa.*

Woodchester   Ram Inn

Tel 0453 873329

Woodchester South Woodchester nr Stroud Gloucestershire GL5 5EL   Map 14 B2

An attractive blend of ancient and modern, plus three open fires in the L-shaped bar makes this a good spot for a winter visit, and in summer the terrace is equally delightful, with wonderful views across the valley. *Beer Archers, Boddingtons.*

Woodnewton   White Swan

Tel 0780 470381

FOOD

Main Street Woodnewton Northamptonshire PE8 5EB   Map 7 E4

Four miles from both the A1/A47 intersection and Oundle. When the White Swan was closed and bought by developers in 1988 the villagers thought they had lost their only pub, but after a vociferous campaign which involved busloads of residents lobbying council planning meetings, the White Swan was saved and reopened in 1990 after extensive renovations. One end of a single oblong room is the bar, focusing on a wood-burning stove, with the other end set up as a restaurant. A long menu of home-cooked dishes includes such items as ham and leek au gratin (£4.25), Woodnewton club sandwich (£3.35) and chili con carne (£3.95) as well as more substantial dishes ranging from swordfish steak with olive oil, garlic and oregano dressing (£6.95), drunken rabbit casserole (£6.40), game pie (£6.50) and steak au poivre (£9.95) to crispy cod bites and golden chicken nuggets (both at £1.75) for youngsters. Sunday brings a traditional roast lunch at £8.95 (£4.95 for children). Also under the same ownership of Margaret and Ron Orchard: *The Black Horse Inn* at Nassington. *Bar Food 12-2, 7-10. Vegetarian dishes. Children's menu/portions. Free house. Beer Bass, Benskins, Burton. Garden, outdoor eating. Access, Visa.*

Woodstock   The Punch Bowl

Tel 0993 811218   Fax 0993 811393

12 Oxford Street Woodstock Oxfordshire OX20 1TR   **Map 16 B2**

Family run 'olde-worlde' pub dating back to 1176 with exposed beams, fireplaces and ancient stonework. Convenient situation on the main A34 Oxford-Stratford road. *Free House. Beer Flowers, Wadworth. Garden. Access, Amex, Visa.*

Wookey   Burcott Inn

Tel 0749 673874

Wookey nr Wells Somerset BA5 1NJ   **Map 13 F1**

Popular roadside country pub, pleasingly simple in style, with lots of guest beers. Real fire. No music. *Beer Archers, Fuller's. Garden, children's play area. Family room.*

Woolhampton   Angel Inn

Tel 0734 713307

Bath Road Woolhampton Berkshire   **Map 16 C4**

Attractive ivy-covered pub near the Kennet and Avon canal. The interior is festooned with bric-a-brac of every kind, collected by the landlord; it's lovely to sit out by the pond with its little bridge in good weather. They have a popular skittle alley, and offer conference facilities. *Beer Brakspears, Marston. Garden.*

Woolhope   Butcher's Arms

FOOD
B&B

Tel 0432 860281

Woolhope Hereford & Worcester HR1 4RF   **Map 14 B1**

The infectious enthusiasm of family owners and their commendable reliance on local produce bring customers from far and wide to pub not easily found down narrow country lanes. A black and white timber frontage, copiously hung with flower baskets, and the neat, colourful streamside garden and patio induce an anticipation more than adequately fulfilled by the food. Smoked cod's roe paté (£2.35), leek and hazelnut terrine (£2.35) and Woolhope wild rabbit and cider pie (£4.95) head the bar menu, while on weekend evenings (bookings advised) the restaurant menu extends to wild Scottish salmon hollandaise (£9.75), Herefordshire beef fillet with peppered sauce (£11) and herb-crusted rack of lamb (£9.75). Plenty of home-made sweets – almond pudding (£1.75), fresh fruit pavlova (£2.25). Good cask-conditioned ales and house wines by the glass round out the experience. The three bedrooms are small and cosy: decor is in appropriate cottage style, and they share a bathroom. There's abundant peace and quiet in this hidden valley, and a substantial breakfast to look forward to come the morning. *Bar Food 11.30-2, 7-10. Restaurant Meals 7-10 (Fri/Sat only). Vegetarian dishes. Children's portions. Free House. Beer Hook Norton, Marston's Pedigree, Charles Wells Bombardier. Cider Westons Stowford Press. Garden, outdoor eating, children's play area. No credit cards.*

Woolley Moor   White Horse

FOOD

Tel 0246 590319

White Horse Lane Woolley Moor Derbyshire DE5 6FG

Map 6 C3

Approached from the A61 at Stretton, the Taylors' smart, friendly and very popular pub scarcely on the beaten track, being in a tiny hilltop hamlet above the river Amber at the point where it flows into Ogston reservoir. The large paddock and garden border the memorial sports field; a sandpit, swings, and small adventure playground help keep the youngsters happy. There are at least two dozen trestle tables outside; bag one for a summer lunch, but remember the number before going inside to order. Within there's restaurant seating for around 60 people, and it fills up quickly, so booking is recommended. This dining area, reached through a stone archway, was originally the pub lounge, a cottagey, carpeted area in two sections, with large picture windows and attractive lace-clothed tables. On the printed menu, dishes such as paté (£1.70), soup (£1.95), deep-fried Brie (£1.95), steak and kidney pie (£3.25) or a chicken special (£4.50) are offered. Desserts could include treacle and walnut tart (£1.50) and traditional bread-and-butter pudding (£1.50). It's substantial stuff, nicely cooked and presented and, above all, tasty. Meanwhile the Smoke Room still remains the village local, with is quarry-tiled floor, red leather banquettes, Britannia tables and prominent dartboard; Monday night dominoes are played in a seriously competitive spirit. This is where a good drop of ale comes in. In addition to draught Bass, a healthy rotation of guest beers is publicised well in advance, a good proportion of them from independent breweries. Piped music, when playing, is of the restful kind. This is a smart and impressive pub, professionally managed, and it runs like clockwork. *Bar Food & Restaurant Meals 11.30-2 (2.15 Sun), 6.45-9 (6.30-9.30 Fri/Sat) No food Sun eve. Vegetarian dishes. Children's menu. Free House. Beer Bass, Worthington, guest beers. Garden, outdoor eating, children's play area. Family room. No credit cards.*

Wootton Rivers   Royal Oak

Tel 0672 810322

Wootton Rivers nr Marlborough Wiltshire SN8 4NQ

Map 16 A4

Very much an eating pub, though there's also a noisy public bar, the thatched and charmingly rustic Royal Oak is often packed with diners; tables can be booked, and people seem to dress up in the evenings. *Beer Hall & Woodhouse.*

Worcester   Farriers Arms

Tel 0905 27569

9 Fish Street Worcester Hereford & Worcester WR1 2HN

Map 14 B1

Attractively modernised old city tavern, with a relaxing lounge and large public bar, as well as a summer terrace with its own hatch servery. No children indoors. *Beer Courage.*

Worcester   Slug & Lettuce

Tel 0905 28362

FOOD

12 The Cornmarket Worcester Hereford & Worcestershire WR1 2DF

Map 14 B1

A popular and atmospheric city-centre pub with a clever open-plan design that still retains some intimate corners. The choice of food (lunchtime only) is appetising and reasonably priced – garlic mushrooms (£3), filled baps (£2), baked Brie and cranberries (£3), skillet of Worcester sausage (£4.20), seafood lasagne (£4). Home-made rum and raisin cheesecake or apple pie makes a fine finale. **Bar Food** 12-3 (Sun 12-2.30). Vegetarian dishes. Children's portions. **Beer** Tetley, Bass, Slug & Lettuce. Garden, eating area. Access, Amex, Diners, Visa.

Worminghall   Clifden Arms

Tel 0844 339273

Worminghall Buckinghamshire HP18 9JR   Map 16 C2

Quaint timbered and thatched old pub on the edge of the village, with lots of beams and a big fireplace, where logs roar in the winter. Lots of old-fashioned, homely style in the main bar, also a lino-floored public and poor room, plus a restaurant, where families are permitted. A large, attractive garden has lots to interest children, including domestic birds and animals. A good pub for summer. The village is delightful, too. **Beer** Hook Norton, Tetley. Garden. Family room.

Worth   St Crispin Inn

Tel 0304 612081

The Street Worth Kent CT14 0DF   Map 11 D5

Refurbished village pub with heavy timbers, brick walls, a big log fire and a pleasant rear garden. A rear terrace has an all-weather retractable awning. **Beer** Gales HSB. Garden, children's play area.

Wybunbury   Swan

Tel 0270 841280

Wybunbury Cheshire   Map 6 B3

An attractive little two-roomed pub, which has lots of agricultural and other bric-a-brac and pretty decorative touches, as well as a cheering winter fire. **Beer** McEwan, Theakston. Garden, children's play area.

Wye   New Flying Horse Inn

Tel 023 381 2297   **B&B**

Upper Bridge Street Wye Kent TN25 5AN   Map 11 C5

With a 400-year history, this white-painted inn is characterised by low ceilings, black beams, open brickwork and a large open fireplace. The main bar has copper-topped tables and simple chairs, and an adjoining room provides easy chairs for more serious relaxtion. Rooms in the main building vary in size and are modestly furnished, but one has a four-poster and more traditional pieces. In the stable block the four rooms are uniform and are all en suite. The new manager has plans for an extra two bedrooms. **Beer** Master Brew, Spitfire. Garden. **Accommodation** 10 bedrooms, all en suite, £46 (single £36). Children welcome overnight, additional beds, cots available. Check-in all day. Access, Amex, Visa.

Wykeham   Downe Arms

Tel 0723 862471   Fax 0723 864329   **B&B**

Pickering Road Wykeham nr Scarborough YO13 9OB   Map 5 F4

Refurbishment has brightened the spacious and popular bar of a thoughfully extended roadside pub. A colourful aquarium provides a focal point of interest in the intimate little cocktail bar and there are numerous conference suites. Upstairs, good-sized bedrooms with

simple white furniture and attractive matching fabrics all have TVs
and tea-makers as well as carpeted en-suite bathrooms (some with
shower only). *Free House. **Beer** Theakston, Youngers Scotch & No 3.
Cider Scrumpy Jack. Garden. Family room. **Accommodation**
10 bedrooms, all en suite, £58 (single £35). Children welcome overnight,
additional beds and cots available. Check-in all day. Access, Amex, Diners,
Visa.*

Wymondham   Hunters Arms

Tel 057 284 633

4 Edmondthorpe Road Wymondham Leicestershire LE14 2AD   **Map 7 E3**

Nice roadside village inn, bought by a pub-loving Frenchman in
1985. *Beer Draught Bass, Greene King. Garden, children's play area.*

Wytham   White Hart

Tel 0865 244372

Wytham Oxfordshire   **Map 16 C2**

Famous stone pub in the centre of a pretty village. Very popular
summer barbecues in the rose garden. Part-panelled bar with
flagstones, an open fire and high-backed black settles. *Beer Tetley,
Wadworth 6X. Garden. Family room.*

Yarde Down   Poltimore Arms

Tel 0598 710381

Yarde Down nr South Molton Devon EX36 3HA   **Map 13 D2**

Lovely pub in a tiny hamlet which can nonetheless boast its own
cricket team – just about everybody's in it. A rustic setting and a
charmingly down at heel country interior. *Beer Cotleigh, Ruddles.
Garden, children's play area. Family room.*

Yarmouth   Bugle

Tel 0983 760272

The Square Yarmouth Isle of Wight PO41 0NS   **Map 14 C4**

Lively seaside pub whose nautically themed bar features ship's
planks, pennants and pictures aplenty. *Beer Marston, Whitbread.
Garden. Family room.*

Yattendon   Royal Oak   ★   **FOOD**

B&B

Tel 0635 201325   Fax 0635 201926

The Square Yattendon nr Newbury Berkshire RG16 0UF   **Map 16 C3**

Dating back to the days of Oliver Cromwell, the creeper-clad Royal
Oak is only ten minutes drive from junction 13 of the M4, at the
heart of a pretty Berkshire village that is a regular winner of 'best-
kept' awards. Food continues to be the main attraction in both the
busy beamed bar (where all tables are set for diners) and in the calmer
dining room (featured in our *1993 Hotels & Restaurants* Guide). A
new door now leads straight out from the tiny bar counter into a
walled garden where a few tables nestle under vine-clad trellises; in
summer this is a delightful spot for a drink – at other times of the
year almost every visitor to the pub comes for the tip-top bar food.
New owner Julie Huff and chef Dominique Orizet are continuing the
tradition and standards set by Richard and Kate Smith (now at the
Beetle and Wedge Hotel in Moulsford-on-Thames) by offering an
extensive hand-written bar menu that is changed daily and usually lists

up to 25 dishes, both small and large. The prices veer towards those of a restaurant, but one feels no compulsion to order anything more than one dish. Snack-type dishes range from melon with port or fresh fruit and champagne (£4.95), fish soup with rouille and croutons (£4.50), rough salmon paté (£5.75), and salads of warm goat's cheese with croutons and lardons (£6.75) or crispy duck with frisée salad (£5.25/£8.50) to popular favourites like asparagus hollandaise or with vinaigrette (£6.75) and fine ploughman's lunches (served with a selection of cheeses £5). The choice of more substantial dishes always includes good fish: pan-fried fillet of zander with julienne of vegetables and beurre blanc (£12.50), or ragout of monkfish, salmon, Dover sole and seafood with a saffron sauce (£10.75); John Dory, red mullet and halibut also make appearances. Grilled calf's liver and bacon (£11.95) is a regular offering, as are medallions of pork fillet, with a Meaux mustard, green peppercorn or apple and cider sauce (£10.95). Sirloin steaks are treated in a straightforward manner, usually grilled and served, perhaps, with either a béarnaise sauce or melted garlic butter (£12.75). Desserts are on a separate list: meringue or hot lemon sponge with Jersey cream (£4.25), profiteroles with hot chocolate sauce (£4.25) are typical, plus interesting and unusual farmhouse cheeses (£4.75). There's usually a good selection of quality bottles of wine open behind the bar for serving by the glass. Upstairs, three of the five bedrooms have smart en-suite bathrooms (the other two have their own private bathrooms across the hallway) and feature king-size beds; generous towelling and thoughtful extras like quality toiletries and mineral water bring the rooms up to a good hotel standard. Some rooms overlook the small garden, others the historic village square. Good, leisurely breakfasts are served in the dining room. The Royal Oak is an exceptional combination of local pub, friendly inn and smart restaurant – if only there were more around the country; it sets an example that many other inns would do well to follow. **Bar Food & Restaurant Meals** *12-2, 7-10. Vegetarian dishes. Children's portions. Free House.* **Beer** *Wadworth 6X, Adnams Best Bitter, Burton's Tanglefoot. Garden, outdoor eating.* **Accommodation** *5 rooms, 3 en-suite, £80, single £70. Children welcome overnight, cots available. Check-in all day. Access, Amex, Diners, Visa.*

lifetime™

Whatever life holds in store.

If the majority of your calls can be made outside peak business hours, Cellnet Lifetime is the service for you.

Giving you more flexibility to juggle business commitments, social responsibilities and your leisure pursuits, Cellnet's exciting new Lifetime service makes mobile communications more affordable for the less frequent user.

Ideal when there's a sudden change of plan, when you're running late – and in emergencies it really comes into its own.

With Lifetime you can always keep in touch. And what's more your friends, relatives and customers can always get in touch with you.

lifetime™ You'll wonder how you ever managed without it.

cellnet
The nearest phone.

For further details call Cellnet on
0800 21 4000

Scotland

Aberdeen   **Prince of Wales**

Tel 0224 640597

7 St Nicholas Lane Aberdeen Grampian AB1 1HF   Map 3 D4

An atmospheric, usually very busy, old tavern located down a cobbled
alley underneath the city centre, with the longest bar counter in town
winding round several distinctly styled drinking areas. No children
under 14. *Free House.* **Beer** *Bass, Caledonian 80/-, Theakston Old
Peculier, Younger's No 3.*

Almondbank   **Almondbank Inn**

Tel 0738 83242

FOOD

Main Street Almondbank Tayside PH1 3NJ   Map 3 C5

Just off the A85 to the west of Perth, on the village main street, the
whitewashed Almondbank Inn enjoys fine views over the River
Almond from its small well-kept rear garden. It's not a quiet pub: a
juke box in the bar regularly pumps out the latest hits, and there's a
pool table on the first floor. Food is taken fairly seriously, however,
and the Birdcage Bistro, despite some rather gimmicky, tacky
descriptions (a "galaxy of titbits", "salad days are here again") produces
generally pleasing food, the majority of it from fresh produce,
including some first-rate home-made chips. All the beef used is
Aberdeen Angus from the licensee's own family butcher, and even the
scampi is fresh and crumbed on the premises. The menu itself is long,
running from first courses like "name that tuna" and deep-fried
Camembert with cranberry sauce (£2.50), to main courses such as
steak and onion pie (£3.85), chicken in a creamy curry sauce (£4.65),
and a whole list of Angus minute steaks with a variety of sauces. All
come with fresh vegetables, as well as the aforementioned chips.
Puddings are largely ice-cream based and there's good cappuccino
(80p) and espresso coffee. On Friday and Saturday evenings, a slightly
different menu is heavy on steak (Bonnie Prince Charlie sirloin steak
£10.25) and chicken dishes, and prices throughout are very
reasonable. The uniformed staff are friendly and approachable and the
locals, gathered on stools at the bar, are also only too willing to chat.
Bar Food *12-2.15, 5-8.30 (6.30-10 Fri/Sat). Vegetarian dishes.
Children's menu (£1.65 per dish). Free House.* **Beer** *Greenmantle Real
Ale, Tennents 70/-. Riverside Garden (River Almond), outdoor eating.
Access, Visa.*

Anstruther   **Dreel Tavern**

Tel 0333 310727

16 High Street Anstruther Fife KY10 5DL   Map 3 D5

Attractive, traditional three-storey 16th-century stone pub with a
garden overlooking Dreel Burn. Real fires. *Free House.* **Beer** *Alloa
Beers, Tetley Bitter, Archers 80/-. Garden.*

Applecross   **Applecross Inn**

Tel 05204 262

Shore Street Applecross Highland IV54 8LR   Map 2 A3

Inspiring views of Skye are one of the rewards at the end of a lovely
scenic drive. This traditional Scottish inn is reached by way of the
highest mountain pass in Britain. *Free House.* **Beer** *McEwan Export,
80/-. Seashore garden.*

Ardentinny   Ardentinny Hotel

FOOD
B&B

Tel 036981 209   Fax 036981 345

Loch Long Ardentinny nr Dunoon Strathclyde PA23 8TR

Map 3 B5

☺

50 yards from the beach, the Ardentinny is an old west-coast droving inn by Loch Long in the Argyll Forest Park. It has a buttery, two popular public bars with stunning loch views, and a hotel dining room. Lots of local produce – particularly strong on venison, lamb and seafood. Popular dishes from the bar are Musselburgh pie (£6.25), venison sausages with onion sauce (£3.95), and crab torte (£7.90). The restaurant table d'hote menu (£19.50) offers local wild salmon tartare, tomato and red pepper tartlet, Molly Malone pie, roast spatchcock marinated in Arran mustard, venison casserole with juniper berries (steaks with a supplement) and a choice of Scottish cheeses. Good wine list. Popular with Clyde yachtsmen at weekends and fishermen. Bedrooms are good-sized, neat and bright, with white units or period furniture; some have showers only. *Bar Food 12-2.30 (12-3 Sat), 6-10. Restaurant Meals 7.30-9.30. Vegetarian dishes. Children's menu (£2 per dish). Children allowed in bar to eat. Free House. Beer Webster's Yorkshire, McEwan Export. Seaside garden, outdoor eating. Family room. Accommodation 11 bedrooms, all en suite, from £49 (single £24). Children welcome overnight, additional beds (£7), cots supplied (£3). Check-in all day. Hotel closed 1 November to 15 March. Access, Amex, Diners, Visa.*

Arduaine   Loch Melfort Hotel

Tel 08522 233

Arduaine by Oban Argyll Strathclyde PA34 4XG

Map 3 B5

Well-known, high-class hotel, secluded from the busy road by splendid grounds that provide wonderful views. The simple, brightly lit, subtly nautical non-residents' bar is popular with locals and tourists. *Free House. Beer McEwan Export. Garden.*

Ardvasar   Ardvasar Hotel

Tel 047 14 223

Ardvasar Sleat Isle of Skye Highland IV45 8RS

Map 3 A4

Handsome 18th-century inn, not far from the shore, with superb views across the Sound of Sleat to the mountains beyond. *Beer Tennent's. Patio/terrace.*

Auchencairn   Balcary Bay Hotel

Tel 055 664 217

The Shore Auchencairn Dumfries & Galloway DG7 1QZ

Map 4 B3

Distinguished white-painted 17th-century hotel, with a strikingly simple yet elegant interior. Romantic setting, almost on the beach, in glorious isolation. *Garden.*

Beauly   Priory Hotel

Tel 0463 782309

The Square Beauly Highland IV4 7BX   Map 2 B3

Bustling, friendly local hotel in the main square, close to the ancient priory ruins. *Children's play area. Family room.*

Brig o'Turk   Byre Inn

Tel 087 76 292

Brig o'Turk by Callander Central FK17 8HT   Map 3 B5

Converted 18th-century cow byre on the A821. Unusual interior, informal, airy and relaxed, clean and well run. *Beer Broughton Greenmantle Ale. Garden.*

Brodick   Ormidale Hotel

Tel 0770 2293

Brodick Isle of Arran Strathclyde KA27 8BY   Map 4 A1

An appetising menu of fine malts by the glass is just one of the attractions at this sandstone hotel overlooking the golf course. The cosy bar is popular with locals; there's also a conservatory. Real fire; no music. *Beer McEwan 70/-.*

Burrelton   Burrelton Park Hotel

Tel 082 87 207

High Street Burrelton Tayside PH13 9NX   Map 3 C5

A lot less grand than it sounds, but nonetheless a rather smart, proprietor-run roadside inn. *Beer Theakston. Children welcome overnight.*

Busta   Busta House Hotel

Tel 080 622 506

Busta Brae Shetland Islands ZE2 9QN

FOOD

B&B

Map 2 D1

Tremendously civilised hotel in a wild place. A 16th-century former laird's home overlooking the sea, simply furnished in Scottish rural style and, beyond its rather formidable exterior, open to non-residents for good home-cooked bar lunches and suppers – marinated Shetland herring and oatcakes (£2.25), Shetland lamb cutlets (£4.85), broccoli and mushroom quiche (£4.20), steak, red wine and mushroom pie (£4.95), grilled Shetland salmon with cheddar and onion sauce (£5.25). The restaurant offers a 5-course daily-changing fixed-price menu (£19.50) which could include local oysters with brown bread and roast guinea fowl with ginger and orange sauce, followed by home-grown rhubarb crumble. A roast dish (£5.25) is available on Sundays in winter. All fresh vegetables, and Raven Ale from 'nearby' Orkney. 136 malt whiskies on offer! Four acres of walled garden, small private sea harbour, and holiday packages of the fly/sail and drive kind too. *Bar Food 12-2 (12.30-2 Sun)-2, 6-9 (6-9.30 summer).* *Restaurant Meals 7-9. Vegetarian dishes. Children's portions. Children are allowed to eat in the bar. Free House. Beer Orkney Raven Ale, McEwans Export. Garden, outdoor eating. Accommodation 20 bedrooms, all en suite, £73 (single £56). Children welcome overnight, additional beds (£10), cots supplied. Pub and accommodation closed Xmas week. Check-in until 11pm. Access, Amex, Diners, Visa.*

Canonbie   Riverside Inn

Tel 03873 71512

Off A7 Canonbie Dumfries & Galloway DG14 0UX

This pristine white-painted Georgian country inn is in a quiet spot overlooking the river Esk, just over the Scottish border, some twelve miles off the top of the M6. Within, it's authentically rural rather than rustic in style, neat, clean and simple with a definite and individual charm which is, however, not the nicotine-stained creaky timbered gloom of the classic English alehouse. The carpeted bar has simple country chairs, some cushioned, some not, around sewing machine tables, and a stone fireplace and bar front; a few discreet decorations line the plain cream walls, framed fishing flies, the odd old cider jar, but there are otherwise few frills. The dining room is similar, but with proper eating height tables and chairs, and the small, cosy residents' lounge, which has the air of a private house sitting room, has a chintzy three-piece suite and a few other chairs arranged around a log-effect fire. Bedrooms are the prettiest feature of the inn, two of them with draped bedheads, another with a four-poster bed, and all individually styled with good quality fabrics and thoughtful little extras, electric blankets among them. Bathrooms are spotless, with decent toiletries. Bar food is never less than satisfactory, occasionally excellent, and takes particular care with first-rate fresh ingredients – local fish (some of it from the river only yards away), local suppliers, an increasing use of organic and farm produce, vegetables from their own garden, and a delicious range of unpasteurised British cheeses (selection £4.25). The long-standing hosts share the cooking duties, and are making good use of their new chargrill. Home-made soups are often intriguing combinations, like apricot and lentil (£1.55); terrines and patés are light but well-flavoured – especially the fishy ones, a creamy smoked mackerel with just a hint of horseradish (£3.95), a subtle herring roe mousse, or luxurious potted salmon. Main courses offer both modern dishes like calf's liver with smoked bacon and more homely country fare: a properly made quiche, a moreish chicken and mushroom pie (£5.25), proper fish and chips, and the home-made duck sausages (£7.25) are always worth a try. The bread comes from the renowned Village Bakery at Melmerby. Gorgeous and often unusual puddings too; they use their own ice cream in the profiteroles. There's also a daily changing 5-course table d'hote restaurant menu (£21) langoustines £6.95, wild salmon £7.25. Satisfying hearty breakfasts. *Bar Food* 12-2 *(except Sun)*, 7-9. *Restaurant Meals 7.30-8.30 (except Sun). Vegetarian dishes. Children's portions. Free House Beer Yates and changing guest beer. Children allowed in bar to eat. Garden, outdoor eating. **Accommodation** 6 bedrooms, all en suite, from £68 (single £50). Children welcome overnight. Check-in all day. Pub and accommodation closed February. Access, Visa.*

Carbost   Old Inn

Map 2 A3

Tel 047 842 205

Carbost Isle of Skye Highland IV47 8SR

Next to the loch, and near the Talisker distillery, a charming, chatty little island cottage, popular as a walkers' base. *Family Room. Lochside patio/terrace, children's play area. Children welcome overnight. No credit cards.*

Carnock   Old Inn
Tel 0383 850381

Main Street Carnock Fife KY12 9JQ   Map 3 C5

Carpeted dining bar with roughcast cream painted walls and copper-top tables, set with Old Inn mats. Single-storey restaurant extension. *Beer Maclay. Garden, children's play area.*

Castlecary   Castlecary House Hotel
Tel 0324 840233

Castlecary Road Castlecary Cumbernauld Strathclyde G68 0HD   Map 3 C5

Splendidly old-fashioned public bars at a popular hotel with rooms in a large cottage annexe. *Beer Belhaven 80/-, Broughton Greenmantle Ale, Jennings Bitter, Maclay 70/-.*

Clachan Seil   Tigh-an-Truish

FOOD

Tel 08523 242

B&B

Clachan Seil by Oban Isle of Seil Strathclyde PA34 4QZ   Map 3 B5

18th-century inn right on the sea by the Atlantic Bridge. Boarded nicotine yellow ceiling, old pine bar counter and twin dartboards; popular with locals. Limited winter menu (perhaps only soup and sandwiches), but recommended for high-season bar food – home-made soup (£1.50), venison in Drambuie and cream (£6), beef and mushroom pie (£5.30), locally caught prawns (£6), roast lamb and pork, followed by such home-made sweets (all £1.80) as chocolate biscuit cake and sticky toffee pudding. Bed and breakfast is available in two good sized bedrooms both equipped with hairdryers and telephones, one with bath, the other shower only, but breakfast is still a self service affair. *Bar Food 12-2.15, 6-8.30. Vegetarian dishes. Children's portions. Free House. Beer McEwan 80/-, Murphys Stout. Garden, outdoor eating. Family room. Accommodation 2 bedrooms, both en suite, £40 (single £25). Children welcome overnight, additional beds (£5), cots supplied. Check-in all day. Accommodation closed December/January. No credit cards.*

Clachan Seil   Willowburn Hotel
Tel 08523 276

Clachan Seil by Oban Isle of Seil Strathclyde PA34 4TD   Map 3 B5

Cottage hotel in two acres on the sheltered south-east shore; a peaceful haven on an island linked by bridge to the mainland.

Comrie   Royal Hotel
Tel 0764 70200

B&B

Melville Square Comrie Tayside PH6 2DN   Map 3 C5

At the heart of this L-shaped inn on the village square is the convivial cocktail bar, decorated in the owner's tartan and stocked with over 50 malt whiskies. There is also a simpler public bar and a comfortable residents' lounge. Queen Victoria once stayed here and her visit is remembered by a four-poster sporting the royal coat of arms in one of the bedrooms. All rooms have TVs, tea-makers, direct-dial telephones, and all except one have en-suite facilities. *Free House. Beer McEwan 80/-, Tartan Special, Mild. Garden, children's play area. Accommodation 9 bedrooms, 8 en suite £50 (single £30). Children welcome overnight, additional beds and cots available. Check-in by arrangement. Access, Amex, Visa.*

Coylton   Finlayson Arms Hotel

Tel 0292 570298

B&B

Coylton nr Ayr Strathclyde KA6 6JT

Map 4 A1

Easy to spot with its brilliant white exterior, the Finlayson Arms stands on the A70 six miles from the birthplace of Robbie Burns and just four from Ayr racecourse. It is also an ideal place for golfers and T-off times are arranged free of charge. The bright, well-kept look continues both in the lively bar and in the neat little bedrooms which are all en suite. Murdo Munro personally prepares a hearty breakfast guaranteed to start the day well. *Free House. Beer Broughton, guest beer. Garden, children's play area. Accommodation 9 bedrooms, all en suite, £55 (single £32). Children welcome overnight, additional beds and cots available, no charge for children under 12. Check-in all day. Access, Visa, Amex, Diners.*

Crail   Golf Hotel

Tel 0333 50206

4 High Street Crail Fife KY10 3TB

Map 3 D5

Busy inn in beautiful East Neuk fishing village; lively public bar, plain lounge. *Free House. Beer McEwan 80/-, Younger Tartan Special, PA. Family room.*

Crinan   Crinan Hotel

Tel 054 683 261

Crinan by Lochgilphead Strathclyde PA31 8SR

Map 3 B5

Very smart, large white hotel by the harbourside, with a famous seafood restaurant upstairs, but also a piney, civilised café-bar where excellent light meals can be had for a fraction of Lock 16 prices. The restaurant takes it name incidentally, from the fact that lock number 15 on the Crinan Canal, which guides boats into open sea, is right outside the hotel. You can watch them from the small paved terrace at one side of the Crinan Bar. *Beer Broughton Greenmantle Ale, Maclay 80/-, Tennent 80/-. Riverside garden, children's play area.*

Cromarty   Royal Hotel

Tel 038 17 217

Marine Terrace Cromarty Highland IV11 8YN

Map 2 C3

White harbourside hotel overlooking the Cromarty Firth and Ross-shire mountains. The bedrooms have good views. *Garden, children's play area. Family room.*

Drymen   Winnock Hotel

Tel 0360 60245

The Square Drymen Central G63 0BL

Map 3 B5

Large, attractively situated hotel. They specialise in interesting malt whiskies, the latter a 57-strong list. *Beer Broughton, Ruddles, Theakston. Garden. children's play area. Family room.*

Dundee   Mercantile Bar

Tel 0382 25500

100-108 Commercial Street Dundee Tayside

Map 3 C5

Reconstructed Victorian bar in an old warehouse setting, with reasonable Dundee prices throughout. *Beer Draught Bass, Ind Coope Burton Ale, Maclay 80/-, McEwan 80/-. Family room.*

Dysart   Old Rectory Inn

`Tel 0592 51211`

West Quality Street Dysart Fife KY1 2TA

FOOD

Map 3 C5

Just a few hundred yards off the main road from Kirkcaldy to Leven, in the pretty village of Dysart, is the imposing single-storey Rectory Inn, resplendent on its corner site perched above the fishing harbour, and with a delightful walled garden. The main bar is beamed, while a second room is served by a large hatch, and there's a third small room through the dining area. Furnishings are a mixture of old solid wood tables and chairs and more modern upholstered bench seating. Dining is very much the thing, and tables are pre-set with mats (no cloths). Fresh flowers and free-range butter are plus points. An extensive menu is supplemented by daily specials listed on a blackboard in the main bar. At lunchtime: home-made soups (£1.25), chicken liver paté (£2.40), lamb goulash with yoghurt (£4.85), salmon and fish risotto, with proper risotto rice (£5.25), tagliatelle marinara (£4.85); at suppertime poached cod steak in white wine with grapes and prawns (£6.50), roast loin of port with cherries and brandy (£6.50). Delicious home-made carrot cake (£1.85) or pineapple upside down pudding with custard (£1.85) are bar favourites for puddings. Salads are of the help-yourself sort, from around eight different selections at the serving hatch. Real coffee with accompanying cream is a bonus and of the bottomless sort. Many fellow-lunchers are evidently regulars, on first-name terms with the owner-licensees, who are, however, commendably uncliquey and friendly to strangers. It's also a popular business lunch venue in a small local way. The menu's quite different in the evening in the dining room, with lots more meat and fish dishes – chilled plum soup (£2.70), hot savoury tartlet of chicken livers in mild mustard sauce (£2.65), salmon off-the-hook (£11), hotpot Wynd – fricassee of salmon, prawns, scallops, sole and crab (£10.95). There's a variety of steaks – one dish features three medallions with three different sauces (£15). A whole Stilton is renewed each week. Vegetarians are not obviously provided for, but can have something rustled up on the spot. There are high-chairs for children. *Bar Food & Restaurant Meals 12-2.30, 6.30-9.30 (6.30-9.45 Sat). Vegetarian dishes. Children's portions. Children allowed in bar to eat. Free House. Beer McEwan's 80/-. Garden, outdoor eating. Access, Amex, Visa.*

Eaglesham   Eglinton Arms Hotel

`Tel 035 53 2631`

Gilmour Street Eaglesham Strathclyde G16 0LG

Map 3 B6

Village hotel, once a coaching inn, with a games-playing, real fire-lit snug. *Beer Younger's No.3. Children welcome overnight.*

Edinburgh   Doric Tavern Wine Bar & Bistro

`Tel 031-225 1084`

15 Market Street Edinburgh Lothian EH1 1DE

Map 3 C5

Wine bar style upstairs, particularly as the first encounter is with the little bistro-style eating area; the separate little bar is at the back, often crammed with students and other trendy types. But there's no mistaking it's a pub downstairs, in the spartan public bar, complete with dartboard by the door (watch out when entering). Tremendous atmosphere in the evenings, with deep reds and blues, and candlelight. *Beer Bass, Caledonian, Maclay 80/-, McEwan 80/-.*

Edinburgh   Fishers

Tel 031-554 5666

1 The Shore Leith Edinburgh Lothian EH6 6QW

FOOD

Map 3 C5

Fishers is a jewel cast up from the sea, an outstanding seafood –
speciality bar which serves full meals all day, noon – 10.30 pm. It's
taken root in a renovated corner building at the end of The Shore, at
the foot of what looks like an ancient bell-tower or lighthouse. The
bar area, in which you can also eat, groups high stools around higher-
still tables. Up a short flight of steps, the main eating area features
light-wood panelling with night-sky blue tables and chairs, windows
half of frosted glass, half giving a view to the harbour and beyond,
and all presided over from a great height by a bejewelled mermaid
figure. The pricing structure and the variety of food on offer are
admirably suited to most appetites and pockets, whether for serious
eating or quick snacking. It's worth going the full three rounds from
starter to pudding, and make an evening of it, when it's also wise to
book; word is spreading. In addition to the photocopied-handwritten
menu, a blackboard of daily specials offers a host of starters and main
courses which should appeal to more than fish fans alone: perhaps a
fine piece of roast beef with shallot gravy (£7.20). The creamiest,
most deeply delicious salmon soup (£2.50) competes for attention
with fish patés and oatcakes (£2.85), mussels in white wine, garlic,
tomato and herbs (£2.50), seafood platter (£9) or one of the day's
specials; a sheep's cheese and olive salad (£5.50) in a creamy sauce fills
a whole platter, with little room left for the new potatoes, garnished
with mint. Salads are crunchy, fresh and in plenty – endive, Chinese
leaves, tomatoes, radishes, mangetout and spring onions. Chose your
dressing from a piquant selection of onion, hazelnut or raspberry
vinaigrette, or mix your own combination from the bottles of Spanish
olive oil and French champagne vinegar thoughtfully provided on
each table. If any room remains, there are simple home-made fruit
flans, pies and crumbles (£2.50). Altogether excellent quality and
value for money. *Bar Food & Restaurant Meals 12-10.30 (from
12.30 Sun). Vegetarian dishes. Children's portions. Free House. Beer
Caledonian 80/-, Deucharn IPA. Riverside, outdoor eating. Family room.
Access, Amex, Visa.*

Edinburgh   Rutland Hotel

Tel 031-229 3402   Fax 031-228 5322

3 Rutland Street Edinburgh Lothian EH1 2AE

B&B

Map 3 C5

Overlooking the Castle from its convenient position on Princes Street,
the pub at No1 Rutland Place is a tremendously popular drinking
venue, with two floors of heavily Victorian bars and a cellar bar
offering live entertainment. Double-glazed bedrooms, in contrast, are
quiet and peaceful, with access at the back of the building by resident's
key only. TVs, tea-makers, and trouser presses are standard and most
have modern bathrooms, the rest share four public ones. *Beer
McEwans 80/-. Open all day. Accommodation 18 bedrooms, 10 en suite,
£70 (single £50). Children welcome overnight, additional beds and cots
available. Check-in all day. Access, Amex, Diners, Visa*

Edinburgh   Stockbridge Bar

Tel 031 220 3774	**FOOD**
44 St Stephen's Street Edinburgh Lothian EH3 5AL	Map 3 C5

A well-known pub in a trendy part of town which, on Sunday mornings, becomes a bolt-hole for morning-after blues and can usually provide a friendly opinion on the day's rugby and golfing prospects. The two-part eating area sits 18 comfortably in appropriately relaxed surroundings. Don't be put off by the numerous framed rugby pictures decorating the walls: scrumming is only necessary for the bar stools. Service is casual but prompt, and ever-respectful of the sanctity of your Sunday paper. This is a place for big, filling breakfasts (£4): the full, traditional line-up of bacon, eggs, sausages, beans, black pudding and potato scones, all remarkably low on the grease and black bits so often expected from a fry-up. Practically everything on the menu (even the toast and marmalade) could be prefixed with "mansize" and is, at £4, including tea or coffee; exceedingly good value for money. Some popular typical bar snacks and meals include Scotch broth (85p), mushrooms on toast (95p), lamb chop hotpot (£3.10) and vegetable lasagne (£3.10) *Bar Food 12-2.30 (10.30-1.30 Sun brunch). Vegetarian dishes. Children's portions. Children allowed in bar to eat. Free House. Beer Caledonian 80/- and 70/-, McEwan 80/-, Timothy Taylor's Landlord. Garden. No credit cards.*

Edinburgh   Tattler

Tel 031-554 9999	**FOOD**
23 Commercial Street Leith Edinburgh Lothian EH6 6JA	Map 3 C5

To step into the Tattler is to step several decades back into the subdued splendour of Scottish Victoriana – fringed table lamps, some of smoked glass, a bird cage in the window, green velvet bar stools, a chaise longue by the bar and, most charming of all, attentive and old-fashioned courtesy from the bar staff. The bar is popular itself – a gentlemanly local for unhurried chat – but most come to eat. The Tattler restaurant, another creature altogether, is reached through the snug and has a different menu, though there are a few overlaps. Music is speakeasy 1920s, with live piano some evenings. The walls are adorned with humorous antique prints and an intricately-carved dark wood fireplace with inset tiles completes the picture. Food is now served all day on Saturday and Sunday. From 11.30am on Sundays, a full cooked breakfast is served (£4.95). Starters include mulligatawny soup (90p) or a portion of paté (£1.95). The main course list strikes a good balance between fish and meat dishes: a Dunbar crab salad (£4.25), grilled swordfish steak (£4.25), roast beef or lamb on Sundays (£4.95) and the homely seafood haddie (£4.25) is an enduring favourite, combining smoked haddock and prawns in an egg and cheese cream sauce topped with piping-hot potato. Portions are generous. Likewise, a doorstep-thick braised pork chop à l'orange (£4.25) assumes hunger of a serious kind, and comes with huge helpings of potatoes and salad. Little room is left to indulge in the huge coupes of ice-cream (£2.95). Blackboard specials change daily. It's truly first-class value for money: an opportunity to splurge without overspending. *Bar Food 12-2.30, 6-10 (12-10 Sat & Sun). Vegetarian dishes. Children's portions. Free House. Beer Tetley Bitter, Caledonian 80/-, Alloa Special. Family Room. Access, Amex, Diners, Visa.*

Edinburgh   **Waterfront Wine Bar**

Tel 031-554 7427

FOOD

1c Dock Place Leith Edinburgh Lothian EH6 6LU

Map 3 C5

The Waterfront's plain, redbrick exterior gives little indication of what lies within – this is one of Edingburgh's favourite food and drink spots. By the entrance there are dozens of wines served by the glass, as well as unusual beers. Through the first doorway is a low-ceilinged room lit by low lamps, nautical maps and wine-crate panels doubling as wallpaper. Further back, the romantically-sited conservatory ("always fully booked") is attractively overhung by a growing vine, and looks out over the water; beyond this, a narrow pontoon seats a few summer tipplers. Service is casual but friendly, waiters often identifiable only by the speed at which they move; music is low and classical. Ashtrays are changed with unfailing regularity. There are no fixed or printed menus, and the dishes of the day are all listed on a blackboard: a rich and creamy fish soup (£1.80) served with plenty of chunky bread, chicken wings with coconut and lemon sauce (£2.90) with lots of colourful side salad and a fine vinaigrette, and Polish stuffed cabbage with caraway sauce (£3) makes a substantial starter in winter weather. There's wild salmon in tarragon sauce (£7.50), aubergine, sweet pepper and mozzarella filo bake (£5), pan-fried duck breast with cherry sauce (£7.80), and to finish, a raspberry cheesecake (£2.40), bearing little relation to the usual pub pudding of that name, somehow contrives to be both intensely fruity and light. Coffee is fresh and good (no cappuccino). Book well in advance for a weekend evening. *Bar Food 12-2.30 (12-3 Fri/Sat/Sun), 6-9 (6-10 Fri/Sat, 6-9.30 Sun). Vegetarian dishes. Children's portions. Children allowed in bar to eat (minimum age 5). Free House.* **Beer** *Caledonian 80/-, Caledonian IPA. Riverside pontoon, outdoor eating. Access, Visa.*

Elie   **Ship Inn**

Tel 0333 330246

FOOD

The Toft Elie Fife KY9 1DT

Map 3 C5

☺

Recent rebuilding of the Ship, part of a terrace of old cottages down by the harbour, has, to the relief of the locals, left the original bar very much as it was before with wooden benches around the dark-painted, boarded walls, beamed ceiling and back room with booth seating. What has been added is a pair of restaurant rooms with old dining tables, sturdy kitchen chairs and, on the first floor, a small balcony with coin-operated binoculars for scanning the harbour. There is no food served in the bar but there is no minimum charge in the restaurant where one can have just a single dish from the printed menu – soup of the day (£1.15), home-breaded scampi (£3.95), sirloin steak (£7.95) plus children's dishes – or blackboard specials which at night feature local seafood like lobster (£12.95), white Dover sole (£13.95) and monkfish with cockles, mussels and white wine sauce (£7.50). Home-made scones feature in the afternoon tea that is served daily from 3-6pm. In July and August tables on the sea wall opposite the Ship are served by an open-air barbecue. When the tide is out a vast expanse of sand is revealed where, twice a year, the Ship's own cricket team plays a match against a visiting side. *Restaurant Meals 12-2.30, 6-9 (9.30 Fri/Sat). Afternoon Tea 3-6. Vegetarian dishes. Children's menu/portions. Free House.* **Beer** *Belhaven 80/-, Courage Directors. Family room. Access, Visa.*

Eskdalemuir   Hart Manor Hotel

Tel 038 73 73217

Eskdalemuir by Langholm Dumfries & Galloway DG13 0QQ

Map 4 C2

Remote hilltop hotel in lovely countryside. *Beer Broughton.*

Falkland   Covenanter Hotel

Tel 0337 57542

High Street The Square Falkland Fife KY7 7BU

Map 3 C5

Pleasant old hotel in a pretty village, known for its splendid palace – the old hunting palace of the Stuarts.

Fettercairn   Ramsay Arms Hotel

Tel 056 14 334

Fettercairn Grampian AB30 1XX

Map 3 D4

Roadside village inn, a lot older than it looks; Queen Victoria stayed here in 1861. Cheery, homely lounge. *Beer Theakston, Youngers. Garden, children's play area. Family room.*

Fochabers   Gordon Arms

Tel 0343 820508

B&B

High Street Fochabers Grampian

Map 2 C3

Antlers decorate the exterior of a former coaching inn standing alongside the A96 and a short walk away from the River Spey, while the public bar sports a variety of fishing bric-a-brac – including stuffed prize catches. Simple overnight accommodation is provided by 12 well-equipped bedrooms (TVs, tea-makers, hairdryers and direct-dial telephones), which include both older rooms with large carpeted bathrooms and a number of smaller but quieter ones in the extension. *Free house. Beer McEwan's 80/-. Garden. Family room. **Accommodation** 13 bedrooms, all en suite, £65 (single £45). Children welcome overnight, additional beds (from £10), cots supplied. Check-in all day. Access, Visa, Amex.*

Gifford   Tweeddale Arms

Tel 062 081 240

High Street Gifford Lothian

Map 3 D6

Civilised, prettily set old white-painted inn, modernised and loungey, with a particularly splendid hotel sitting room. *Beer McEwan 80/-. Family room.*

Glasgow   Babbity Bowster

Tel 041-552 5055   Fax 041-552 5215

FOOD

B&B

16/18 Blackfriars Street Glasgow Strathclyde G1 1PE

Map 3 C5

A renovated Robert Adam town house in the city's business district is the setting for splendidly informal and convivial Babbity Bowster (named after a dance), which is not exactly a pub, rather, a light and stylish café-bar, with a restaurant and hotel attached. Euro-café style, food of all kinds, from light snacks to full meals, are available all day – smoked ham houghs (£4.45), tattie pot (£3.75) or rabbit civet in red wine (£4.65) in the bar. The Schottische Restaurant (also named after a dance) is on the first floor, and there's a charming outdoor drinking area. French chef Jean-Claude Marcocio provides a variety of Scottish dishes and guests can choose from two fixed price menus (£10.50 and

£12.50) or a la carte. The choice may include terrine de la mer
(£3.65), mignons of venison with whisky sauce (£11.50), stuffed
rosettes of Scottish lamb on Madeira sauce (£10.85) and home-made
puddings of which the soufflé du jour (£4.25) is Jean-Claude's
speciality. Bedrooms have neat fitted furniture, duvets and shower
rooms. Assured parking. *Bar Food 12-9 (12.30-9 Sun)*. *Restaurant
Meals 12-3, 6.30 till late (except Sun)*. *Vegetarian dishes. Children's
portions. Free House.* *Beer Maclay's 80/-, 70/- and Porter, three guest beers
per week. Patio/Terrace, outdoor eating.* *Accommodation 6 bedrooms, all
en suite, £56 (single £36). Children welcome overnight. Check-in all day.
No dogs. Access, Amex, Visa.*

Glasgow   Ubiquitous Chip

Tel 041-334 5007	**FOOD**
12 Ashton Lane Glasgow Strathclyde G12 8SJ	Map 3 C5

Busy bar above famous Glasgow restaurant; famously trendy and
Bohemian. Impressive bar food of a resolutely simple kind. Eating
here is largely a vehicle for some serious people-watching. Try the
oak-smoked mackerel paté with dill and yoghurt (£2.80), Ayrshire
honey roast ham (£2.75), vegetarian haggis 'n' neeps (£2.75), saddle
of Inverness venison with Cumberland sauce (£9.95), split Finnan
haddie and bacon (£4.25), bream on the bone with butter (£5.65)
and local cheeses including Mull of Kintyre Truckle cheddar and
Inverloch goats cheese. *Bar Food 12-11 (12.30-11 Sun)*. *Vegetarian
dishes. Children's portions. Free House.* *Beer Caledonian 70/-, 80/-.*
Cider Addlestones. Family room. Access, Amex, Diners, Visa.

Glencarse   Newton House

Tel 073 886 250	
Glencarse nr Perth Tayside PH2 7LX	Map 3 C5

Former dower house built circa 1840, in its own grounds, just six
miles from Perth, catering to tourist and business trade. Inside, a cross
between country house and modernised Scottish inn. *Garden, children's
play area. Family room.*

Glendevon   Tormaukin Hotel

Tel 0259 781252	**FOOD**
	B&B
Glendevon by Dollar Tayside FK14 7JY	Map 3 C5

Just south of Gleneagles, on the A823, and surrounded by glorious hill
country, this ruggedly handsome old white-painted inn sits on the
bank of the river Devon, and is remarkably peaceful, except when it's
busy, which is apparently often. The warm and welcoming interior
consists of several communicating rooms, all with lots of exposed
stone, rough whitewashed walls and ceiling beams. Old settles (one of
them beautifully carved), upholstered stools and roundback chairs
surround heavy iron-legged tables. Old black and white photographs,
colourful plates and pictures adorn the walls, and a splendid open fire
makes the Tormaukin an ideal retreat from the chill Scottish winter.
Food's a major attraction, to the extent that the bar menu makes a plea
for patience at busy times; this printed list is supplemented by a daily
specials board. Begin with perhaps potato skins, or a naturally-
flavoured smoked fish paté (£3.10), followed by venison sausages in
port wine sauce (£5.25), smoked haddock crepe (£5.75), or a home-
made pie (£5.25). Cooking is competent, if unspectacular; fresh local
produce makes all the difference. To the other side of the entrance, an

exposed stone and beam-laden restaurant features smartly laid polished tables, candle-lit in the evening. The printed menu isn't wide in its scope – half the space is taken up by various steaks – but not without interest; a duo of local venison and loin of hare cooked in whisky and wild mushrooms (£13.50) and fresh halibut on samphire with strawberry sauce (£13) stand out from the list, and prices are a good deal higher than the bar menu, with starters at around £5, main courses averaging £13. A roast is available on Sundays. Scottish cheese is featured on the board and all the puddings are home-made. Recently refurbished bedrooms are extremely comfortable and appropriately styled in keeping with the inn's age. Original features include yet more exposed stone and a generous sprinkling of beams. Floral fabrics match with pretty wallcoverings, furniture is pine and freestanding, beds are comfortable, sheets crisp. Nice local toiletries and plenty of towels compensate for slightly cramped sizes. Four of the rooms, in a converted stable block, are more contemporary in style, and all the bedrooms are named after whiskies. Service is admirably efficient and friendly from a young, mostly female staff, who take most things in their stride. *Bar Food 12-2, 5.30-9.30 (12-9.30 Sun). Restaurant Meals 6.30-9.30. Vegetarian dishes. Children's portions. Free House Beer Burton Ale, Harvistoun. Patio, outdoor eating. Accommodation 10 bedrooms, all en suite (7 with baths, 3 with showers), £60 (single £45). Children welcome overnight, additional beds (£15), cot supplied. Check-in all day. No dogs. Hotel closed 2nd and 3rd week January. Access, Amex, Visa.*

Glenelg   Glenelg Inn

Tel 059 982 273

Glenelg by Kyle of Lochalsh Highland IV40 8AG   Map 3 B4

Tucked away old beachside inn at the end of a gloriously scenic drive. Attractive old-fashioned interior and stylish restaurant. *Garden, children's play area.*

Glenfarg   Bein Inn

FOOD
B&B

Tel 0577 830216

Glenfarg Tayside PH2 9PY   Map 3 C5

By the A912 to the south of Perth, this pebble dash former drovers' inn gets a mention on many old maps. Actually just to the north-east of Glenfarg, it stands on its own just five minutes from Junction 9 of the M90 in front of the river Farg. Inside has an unfussy and homely feel. There are old, well-worn wing chairs aplenty and a grandfather clock in one corner. The small uncluttered bar has red plastic upholstered banquettes, wooden chairs and walls littered with clan coat of arms plaques, a large map of Scotland, rugby cartoons, golf prints and a few pieces of horse tacky. On the food side, evenings see a concentration on the restaurant and its à la carte menu. Typical of the choice are smoked haddock and mussel chowder (£2.95), Brie and apple pastries (£4.20), Barbary duck with honey and Glayva sauce (£12.50), poached Tayside salmon with shellfish sauce (£12.50), mushroom and courgette stroganoff (£9.25), scallops of beef fillet with port and Blue Stilton sauce (£16.50) – served in rather quaint silver service style. The lunchtime bar menu includes savoury chicken pancake (£4.50), fried herring in oatmeal (£4.30), and steak and mushroom pie with ale (£4.50), again competently handled. Good overnight accommodation is provided in thirteen bedrooms, 11 of them housed in a extension, the upper floors of which connect with the main building courtesy of a walkway. Ground floor rooms are the largest, upper rooms very compact. All are furnished in unpretentious fashion with fitted units, matching curtains and duvets, with fully-tiled bathrooms (shower over the bath). However, extractor fans are rather noisy and go on for some time. The remaining two rooms are in the main house, neither of them en suite, but sharing a well-maintained bathroom. *Bar Food 12-2, 5-9. Restaurant Meals 7-9.30. Vegetarian dishes. Children's menu (lunch only £2.30 2 courses). Free House. Beer Theakston's Best Bitter, McEwan 80/-, Tartan Special. Family Room. Accommodation 13 bedrooms, 11 en suite, £51 (single £37.50). Children welcome overnight, cot supplied. Check-in all day. Access, Visa.*

Glenfinnan   Stage House

| Tel 0397 832246 | **B&B** |

on A830 Glenfinnan Highland PH37 4LT — Map 3 B4

A prettily set late 17th-century pub alongside the main road near Loch Shiel (where it has extensive fishing rights and several boats), offering accommodation (closed Jan-Mar, no children under 5) and bar snacks. *Beer Ind Coope Burton Ale. Patio. Access, Visa.*

Glenfinnan   Stage House Inn

| Tel 0397 83246 |

Glenfinnan Highland PH37 4LT — Map 3 B4

A prettily set, late 17th-century pub alongside the main road near Loch Shiel (where it has extensive fishing rights and several boats). B&B. *Beer Burton Ale.*

Greenlaw   Castle Inn

| Tel 03616 217   Fax 03616 500 | **FOOD** / **B&B** |

Greenlaw Borders TD10 6UR — Map 3 D6

Greenlaw is a small town on a major road; though not far from Hume Castle and other attractions, there is not a lot of reason to stop at Greenlaw other than passing through to other places. Except, that is, for the handsome Georgian Castle Inn, which is the sort of place you could take a variety of people for lunch and feel confident that they would find something to their taste. It is expensive for bar meals, by local standards, and falls into the middle ground of bar meal and restaurant. The Mirror Room, where drinking and dining take place, is large and splendid; a large mirror on top of a marble fireplace transforming what would otherwise be a hall into a splendid room, with a comfortable sitting area by the fireplace, and ruffled curtains framing elegant Georgian windows, through which there's a view to well kept gardens. The octagonal room is a superb feature room to take coffee in, whilst a small library also makes an excellent coffee shop, and the bar itself is popular with the locals on Friday nights and weekend lunchtimes. The welcome is friendly but not intrusive. Children are welcome, and family facilities excellent: high chairs, baby foods, a Freddy Fox children's menu, books in the library and cheerful, tolerant staff. "Where you haste to the welcome, and prolong the goodbyes", their rather contrived catch phrase, appears with monotonous regularity in case you forget it. The printed menu, supplemented by blackboard specials, is certainly very varied, with English (grilled liver and bacon £4.20), Indian, Chinese, Italian, Spanish paella £7.00) and French elements (galette crepes – range of six from £4.90) served with french bread, or sole dieppoise £8.25), as well as steakhouse food, some seafood and a vegetarian selection. Bread is crusty and fresh (mini-baguettes are used for sandwiches), butter comes in pots, tables are laid with mats rather than cloths, and puddings are displayed in a chill cabinet. A 2-course traditional Sunday lunch is served (£6.50) with a choice of ragout or roast. The local cheese is good and always features Kelsea and Stichell (cheese platter £2.50), and house wine very drinkable. *Bar Food 12-2.30, 6.30-10. Vegetarian dishes. Children's menu (£2.25 per dish). Free House. Beer Caledonian 80/-, Greenmantle. Garden. Family room. Accommodation 6 bedrooms, 1 en suite £40 (single £20). Children welcome overnight, additional beds (from £5), cots supplied. Check-in all day. Access, Amex, Diners, Visa.*

Houston   Fox & Hounds

Tel 0505 612448

South Street Houston Strathclyde PA6 7EN   Map 3 B6

Modernised but attractive village inn with public 'Stables' bar, smarter Fox and Vixen lounge, and Huntsman restaurant. *Beer Broughton Greenmantle Ale, McEwan. Family room.*

Innerleithen   Traquair Arms

FOOD

Tel 0896 830229   Fax 0896 830260

B&B

Traquair Road Innerleithen Borders EH44 6PD   Map 4 C1

Hidden down a side street off the main road (well signposted) which runs through Innerleithen and five minutes walk from the River Tweed is the Traquair Arms Hotel, a handsome stone building on the road leading to St Mary's Loch, which is, incidentally, a delightful journey across sheep strayed roads to one of the most picturesque parts of the Borders. The bar leads off the hotel reception area; dine here, or in the more comfortable dining room, or, if weather permits, in the garden. A choice of dining areas and a wide choice of freshly prepared meals is typical of the admirable flexibility of the Traquair Arms, where children are positively welcomed, even the most boisterous. For adults, a well-stocked bar features the Traquair's own Bear Ale, with a teddy bear clad pump. The pub opens at 7.30am in order to serve a full breakfast (£6). Afternoon teas and high teas are also available. Service is genuine and informal, the atmosphere convivial. A variety of omelettes (from £2.95) and salads (from £4.60) is served in the bar and hot dishes include Finnan Savoury (smoked haddock in cheese, onion and cream sauce £4.20), Traquair steak pie (cooked in home-brewed ale – £4.35), pasta with tomato and cashew balls (£3.50). One benefit of dining in the bar is that the glass doors lead off into the garden, which is enclosed and safe for energetic children. The linen-laid dining room proper, though pleasant in the evenings, is rather too formal for lunchtime. Diners are offered 3- and 4-course table d'hote menus (£13.50, £16) with choices such as smoked pheasant with melon, goujons of sole, Poachers salmon, and Aberdeen Angus steak. The cheeseboard features Scottish cheeses only (3 are local). Bed and breakfast is recommended – particularly the handsome Scottish morning meal, complete with superb kippers. Traquair House, next door, is well worth a visit too, a romantic old house with pretty grounds and its own ancient brewhouse; the front gates of Traquair are firmly shut, and will never open again until a Stuart returns to the throne of Scotland. *Bar Food 12-9. Restaurant Meals 7-9. Vegetarian dishes (section on menu). Children's Portions. Free House. Beer Traquair Bear Ale, Broughton Greenmantle Ale, Scottish Oatmeal Stout. Garden,*

outdoor eating, children's play area. Family room. **Accommodation**
*10 bedrooms, all en suite, from £54 (single £35). Children welcome
overnight, additional beds (from £5), cots supplied. Check-in all day.
Access, Visa.*

Invermoriston   Glenmoriston Arms Hotel

Tel 0320 51206

Invermoriston nr Inverness Highland IV3 6YA   Map 3 B3

Pleasant white-painted hotel in an attractive spot on the A82 by Loch
Ness. The public bar, the 'Glenmoriston Tavern', is a rather spartan
brown room – as is the hotel dining room, though huntin', shootin'
and fishin' paraphernalia cheer up some of the public areas. A huge
selection of malts. *Beer McEwan 80/-. Garden.*

Inverness   Coach House Inn

Tel 0463 230244   **B&B**

Stoneyfield Nairn Road Inverness Highland IV1 2PA   Map 2 C3

Solid white-painted inn near Culloden Field offer accommodation in
five rooms. Modernised but attractive bars: the simple but
incongruously carpeted Ostlers (public), and hotel-like, armchair-filled
Lairdshall Lounge. Nice views from the terrace. *Patio/terrace, children's
play area.* **Accommodation** *5 bedrooms, all en suite, £40 (single £27.50).
Children welcome overnight, cots available. Check-in all day. Access, Visa.*

Inverness   Glen Mhor Hotel

Tel 0463 234308

Ness Bank Inverness Highland IV2 4SG   Map 2 C3

Modernised hotel of great contrasts. Atmospheric, unspoilt Nicky
Tams bar, and garish pizza parlour-style Nico's Bar. Comfortable
rather than stylish bedrooms. *Beer Caledonian, Burton Ale.*

Inverurie   Thainstone House Hotel

Tel 0467 21643

Inverurie Road Inverurie Grampian AB5 9NT   Map 3 D4

Country house with recent additions of bedroom block, leisure club
and conference centre. *Beer Courage, Orkney, Tetley, Whitbread.
Garden, children's play area. Family room.*

Isle of Whithorn   Steam Packet Hotel

Tel 098 85 334

Harbour Row Isle of Whithorn Dumfries & Galloway DG5 8HZ   Map 4 B3

An excellent weekend haven in a quaintly beautiful harbourside
setting. Ask for a room at the front. Lovely views, too, from picture
windows in the plush, attractively modernised bar. Boat trips from the
harbour. *Garden, children's play area.*

Jedburgh   Carters Rest

Tel 0835 63414

Abbey Place Jedburgh Borders TD8 6BE   Map 5 D2

Well-known central Borders pub-restaurant, much used for functions.
18th-century origins – built of old abbey stones – but now cheerfully
modernised; bustling and friendly. *Family room.*

Kenmore   **Kenmore Hotel**

`Tel 0887 830205`   **B&B**

Kenmore by Aberfeldy Tayside PH15 2NU   **Map 3 C5**

The Kenmore claims to be Scotland's oldest inn, dating from 1572, in a lovely Perthshire village at the eastern tip of Loch Tay. The Poet's Parlour bar, devoted to Burns, is cosy, with green tartan seats; Archie's Bar is simpler, with glorious views of the river. Excellent salmon fishing. *Riverside garden. Children's play area. Family room.*

Kilberry   **Kilberry Inn**   ★

`Tel 08803 223`   **FOOD**

Kilberry by Tarbert Strathclyde PA29 6YD   **Map 3 A6**

This single-storey white cottage in an isolated, pretty little hamlet is located half a mile from a glorious coastline, and reached by an invigorating 16-mile drive down a winding, hilly, single-track road from the north, with superb views of Jura and other islands. John and Kath Leadbeater, English chef-proprietors, are vigorously interested in good food, and justifiably proud of their achievements here, in an out of the way spot where the vegetables come via van and taxi, and fresh fish is peculiarly hard to get. It's very much a dining pub, though locals and others are equally welcome to drop in for a drink. The building was originally a crofting house, and the snugly comfortable little bar, with a peat fire at one end, a wood-burning stove at the other, still has an unpretentious rural style. Leading off at the left, the brighter, plainer dining and family room has good-sized pine dining tables and a genuine welcome for children; John's Donald Duck impression certainly breaks the ice. The daily blackboard-listed short menu (perhaps only four or five main courses at lunchtime), genuinely home-made and morning-planned, is cheerfully annotated for ditherers with lively accounts of how each was made, and what's particularly recommended that day. This is very much John's role, circulating, chatting, advising, gossiping and occasionally quacking, in between stints in the kitchen and bar; Kath is very much behind the scenes, doing the hard work at the stove! The house speciality is home-made meat dishes of an old-fashioned country sort, often with a modern reinterpretation, and delicious: perhaps a hearty sausage pie (£6.95), roast loin of pork suffed with "locally caught haggis" (£13.50), beef in Old Peculier casserole (£10.50), rumpsteak and kidney pie (£10.50); Kath has a famously light hand and the pastry is superb. She also makes the bread, and pickles, jams and chutneys on sale at the bar. Fish isn't really their interest, but the salmon fish pie (£7.95), layered with sliced potato, is creamy and satisfying. Whatever you do, make sure you leave room for one of Kath's delicious fruit pies, which are laid out on the counter as soon as they come out of the oven. Equally scrumptious are the bread and butter pudding, fresh lemon cream, grapefruit cheesecake and chocolate fudge. Though there's no real ale, the Greenmantle range from Broughton Brewery in the Borders is available by the bottle, and the wine list includes a few offered by the glass. Note that the pub is closed in winter and never opens on Sundays. *Bar Food 12.15-2, 6.30-9. Vegetarian dishes. Children's portions. Free House. Beer No real ale but large range of Scottish bottled beers. Family room (no smoking). Inn closed mid October – Easter (open at New Year for 10 days). Access, Visa.*

Kilchrenan   Taychreggan Hotel

Tel 086 63 211

Kilchrenan by Taynuilt Strathclyde PA35 1HQ

Map 3 B5

Gracious large white inn, in its own splendid grounds by lovely Loch Awe. Bedrooms offer spectacular views, and prime local produce foods into the substantial bar lunches and more formal 5-course dinners. *Children welcome overnight.*

Kilfinan   Kilfinan Hotel

Tel 070 082 205   Fax 0700 82205

Kilfinan nr Tighnabruaich Strathclyde PA21 2EP

FOOD

B&B

Map 3 B5

A delightful Swiss/Scottish couple, Rolf and Lynne Mueller, now manage this remote white-stoned coaching inn, reached down a single-track road (B8000, off the A886) between Strachur and Tighnabruaich. The Dunoon ferry is less than an exhilerating hour's hell-raising drive across the moors. Purchased about ten years ago by the Laird of Kilfinan, so that it would not fall into the hands of developers, the inn has exclusive access to beautiful Kilfinan Bay (about 20 minutes walk through the garden and the estate) as well as its own fishing, stalking and shooting. At present there are two bars, neither of them a lounge, but both cosy and characterful with log fires, and the bedrooms – some antique-furnished – offer all the usual little luxuries, including good-quality toiletries in the carpeted en-suite bathrooms. Incidentally, don't be alarmed by the brown peat-coloured water. The above-mentioned Rolf brings Swiss precision into his cooking, exemplified in the £21 fixed-price dinner menu that naturally features local produce (poached Loch Fyne oysters with a truffle cream sauce, Scottish salmon served with tarragon and mussels, fresh raspberries on a toffee sauce), and on the bar menu: estate-shot venison burger (£4.50), Otter Ferry salmon fishcake (£4.50), steak and stout pie (£4.80) and chicken pancake (£4.20). The ploughman's is prepared with Scottish cheeses and the puddings (fruit crumble, treacle tart, tarte tatin – from £2) are home made, of course. For the less hungry, if such a person exists after arriving here, soup, sandwiches and paté are also avaiaiable. *Bar Food 12-2.30, 5-8.30. Restaurant Meals 12-2.30, 7.30-8.30. Vegetarian dishes. Children's menu/portions. Beer Theakston. Garden, outdoor eating, outdoor play area, summer barbecue. Family room. Accommodation 11 bedrooms, all en suite, £68 (single £45). Children welcome overnight, cot available. Check-in all day. Access, Amex, Visa.*

Killiecrankie   Killiecrankie Hotel

Tel 0796 473220

Killiecrankie by Pitlochry Tayside PH16 5LG

Map 3 C4

A smart, traditional country hotel with mahogany-panelled bar and beech tables in the conservatory. It's a fine white-painted old property, a former dower house, in its own grounds at the northern end of the famous pass, in glorious central Scotland scenery. Well equipped pine-furnished befrooms, all with smart modern bathrooms. *Children's play area.*

Killin   Clachaig Hotel

FOOD
B&B

Tel 05672 270

Falls of Dochart Killin Central FK21 8SL

Map 3 B5

18th-century ex-smithy and coaching inn, once closely linked with the
McNab clan, and beautifully set overlooking the spectacular Falls of
Dochart with the River Tay a five-minute walk down the road; very
Richard Hannayish. Rather basic inside, though, its bar usurped by
juke box and pool table, but bar food is plain and decently cooked –
Scotch broth (95p), home-made steak pie (£3.75), haggis (£2.95),
Highland crumble (£1.50); and the dining-room seats 48 in the
evenings – Clachaig paté (£2.95), Highland venison (£8.95) and
steaks, trout Rob Roy (£8.95), Loch Tay salmon (£9.25), sweet and
sour vegetables (£4.25) and home-made puddings (£1.50). Restaurant
meals are also available during the day in the bar. The clean and
modest bedrooms are good value for the area equipped with TVs, tea
and coffee making facilities and hairdryers on request. The best of
them have dramatic views over the Falls. *Bar food 12-4, 5.30-9.30.*
Restaurant meals 6.30-9.30. Vegetarian dishes. Children's menu
*(£1.50 per dish). Free House. **Beer** McEwan 80/-, Tartan. Garden,*
*outdoor eating. Family room. **Accommodation** 9 bedrooms, 8 en suite, £36*
(single £18). Children welcome overnight, additional beds (£9), cots
supplied. Check-in all day. Access, Visa.

Kilmahog   Lade Inn

FOOD

Tel 0877 30152

Kilmahog by Callander Central FK17 8HD

Map 3 B5

Located 200 yards from the River Teith, this is a tremendously
popular stone-built single-storey pub with a two-storey addition. One
bar to the left of the entrance hall has panelling, pine tables and chairs;
there's another bar to the right. The dining area has large windows
and leads out into the garden. The walls are mainly exposed stone and
what looks like mock beams; bars are carpeted throughout, while
prints and whisky boxes adorn the walls; the whole effect is clean,
fresh and spacious. Tables are only set when food is ordered. Quiet and
relaxing at 12.30, the lunch trade in summer is such that by 1 o'clock
the Lade is usually packed with people. They come for the good,
honest home cooking, like Cullen Skink (a traditional Shetland
smoked haddock chowder £2.25), hearty steak pies (£4.95),
mushroom and nut fettuccine (£4.95), venison sausages bordelaise
(£4.75) – all main courses come with the inevitable chips (fairly
inevitable in Scotland anyway), though you can opt for a jacket potato
instead and a help-yourself salad. A separate menu caters for the
evening meals and is more substantial – smoked trout (£2.95), haggis
écosse (£2.35), innkeeper special (3-courses £11.95), Laird's mixed
grill (£9.75), Barbary duck with orange (£7.95) as well as Indian
'specials' (chicken tikka masala £6.95). Service is informal but good
and friendly. The Lade Inn is worth knowing about as a genuine,
good-value oasis in the often tourism-blighted Callander area. *Bar*
Food 12-2, 6-9.30 (all day Sun). Children's menu (£2.95 per dish). Free
*House. **Beer** Ruddles County, Yorkshire Bitter, Courage Directors. Garden,*
outdoor eating. Family Room. Access, Visa.

Kilmartin   Kilmartin Hotel

B&B

Tel 05465 250

Kilmartin By Lochgilphead Strathclyde PA31 8RQ

Map 3 B5

The first floor rooms at this delightful little inn/hotel, are perfectly decent (though perhaps a little cramped) but the second-floor attic doubles are spacious and charming, and represent great value for money in a busy tourist area. One looks out over the green at the front of the inn, the other over the less inspiring rear; they share an adjacent, spruce and attractive public bathroom, and the third room, is a gracious family room (one double bed, one single) with a nice little en-suite bathroom, free-standing furniture (including an attractive old bed) pretty fabrics, twin bedside tables and a dressing table. A cot can also be provided – but watch out on the top floor if you have toddlers or crawlers in tow – there are alarmingly wide gaps in the banister; it's very quiet up here though. Downstairs, the cosy, rambling bar, very popular with locals and buzzing with traditional pub atmosphere, has bar stools, a lovely stone fireplace (coal fire in winter) an ochre-panelled ceiling at one end, by the bar counter, and a little square sitting area with lovely old spindle-backed and carved oak settles, a piano, and lots of Burns memorabilia. There's fiddle music at weekends. Leading off, a plushly comfortable little residents' lounge can be used for non-resident family visits, and has piped music ranging from Simon and Garfunkel to invigorating Russian operas. The licensees are charming and personable, often coming through to the lounge to socialise. *Free House.* **Beer** *Tennents 80/- and 70/-, Beamish Stout. Garden. Family room.* **Accommodation** *5 bedrooms, 3 en suite, £37 (single £20). Children welcome overnight, additional beds (from £2.50), cots supplied. Check-in all day. No credit cards.*

Kincardine O'Neil   Gordon Arms Hotel

FOOD

Tel 03398 84236

B&B

38 North Deeside Road Kindcardine O'Neil Grampian AB34 5AA

Map 3 D4

An early 19th-century coaching inn of sombre grey stone, the Gordon Arms stands alongside the busy A93, almost opposite the derelict 13th-century village church. Behind a rather anonymous exterior is an inn of warm and informal atmosphere. The main bar area is spacious, sparsely furnished and utterly unpretentious, its high ceiling creating echoes on quiet days, plain-painted walls minimally dotted with pictures, and the part bare-floorboard, part modestly-carpeted floor topped with varying sizes of tables and a motley crew of cushioned chairs. A large rough-stone fireplace is decorated with old cider jars, and the wall above hung with a couple of fishing rods (this is a rich fishing area); there's a piano and splendid antique sideboard. A separate public bar has part panelled walls, old black and white photographs of the area, a television set and electronic games. There are two separate menus: a short bar choice with standard items like steak pie (£3.95), chicken curry (£3.95) and deep-fried haddock (£4.25), and a more interesting and enterprising dinner menu with an unusually wide choice of inventive vegetarian dishes (some suitable for vegans), like stir-fried tofu and peanuts (£4.50), broccoli and mushroom pie (£4.50). Carnivores aren't forgotten, though, with game pie and a choice of steaks are typical: the house special, Scotty steak, is a sirloin steak on a crouton grilled with Banchory black cheese and bacon (£11.95). Bread is baked on the premises, and there's a fair selection of organic wines. Cheeses come from a local sheep dairy and puddings are home-made (sticky toffee £1.75).They also do a very popular Scottish high tea, in which tea, toast, scones and cakes are included in the price of a main course. The seven bedrooms are comfortable and unfussy. Care has been taken to keep decor and furnishing in keeping with the building's age, and all are of useful size. Some fine pieces of antique furniture are partnered by a worn, but very comfortable armchair. Two of the en- suite rooms have compact shower rooms, the third a slightly larger bath/shower. The remaining rooms share two bathrooms located down a flight of stairs. *Bar Food 12-2.15 , 5-9 (10 in Summer)*. *Restaurant Meals 5-9*. *Vegetarian dishes. Children's portions. Children allowed in bar to eat. Free House*. *Beer Theakston Best, guest ales. Terrace, outdoor eating. Accommodation 7 bedrooms, 3 en suite, £40 (single £25). Children welcome overnight, additional beds (from £3), cots supplied. Check-in all day. Access, Amex, Visa.*

Kinnesswood   Lomond Country Inn

Tel 0592 84253

Kinnesswood Tayside KY13 7HN   Map 3 C5

Dramatically set, proprietor-run, attractive 19th-century inn close to Loch Leven. *Beer Jennings, Tetley. Children's play area. Family room.*

Kippen   Cross Keys

FOOD
B&B

Tel 0786 87293

Main Street Kippen Central FK8 3DN   Map 3 C5

A simple, welcoming Scottish pub with rooms, rather than an inn proper, set in a pleasant rural village not far from Stirling. The entire pub has recently been refurbished. The locals' public bar is large and basic, with pool table, fruit machine and television; a smaller, long and narrow lounge is where most of the food is served, and a larger family room has high-chairs primed and ready for use; there's also a small restaurant with seating for about 20. Most of the walls are of exposed stone, colour-washed white, and the furnishings a collection of old, polished tables and chairs. The restaurant is more modern. Bar food, which is well cooked rather than exciting, is chosen from a standard enough printed menu (crispy mushrooms with garlic mayonnaise (£1.80), home-made lasagne (£3.75) and steak pie (£4.50), enhanced by daily specials: poached salmon (£5.25), roast venison in raspberry and red wine sauce (£8.55)). Home-made beefburgers (£3.40), meaty and moreish, come with good crunchy buttered cabbage and chips. Soups are thick and warming. An apple pie is made daily (£1.80). The restaurant is open in the evenings and offers more elaborate dishes such as spinach and pear soup (£1.15), fillet steak in brandy sauce (£11.95), salmon in lime and ginger sauce (£8.25). Most of the produce is from local suppliers and Kippen's bakery supplies the bread. If staying the night, ask for one of the rooms under the eaves, which have sloping ceilings and fine views. Bedrooms are simple and homely, with the usual tea and coffee kits, and wash handbasins. Towels of good quality are provided, and there are extra blankets in the wardrobe. Housekeeping in the rooms is good. There is no residents' lounge, just the main bars downstairs, busy even midweek with diners and locals. Breakfasts, served on linen-laid tables in the restaurant, are hearty traditional fry-ups, but not too greasy, and service is pleasant and helpful. There's a beer garden at the rear with access from both the public and lounge bars. *Bar Food 12-2 (12.30-2 Sun), 5.30-9.30*. *Restaurant Meals 12 (12.30 Sun)-2, 5.30-9.30. Vegetarian dishes. Children's portions. Free House Beer Broughton*

Greenmantle, Younger's No.3. Garden, outdoor eating. Family room.
***Accommodation** 3 bedrooms, sharing a bathroom, £39.50 (single £19.50). Children welcome overnight, additional beds. Check-in all day. Access, Visa.*

Kippford   Anchor Hotel

Tel 055 662 205

Quayside Kippford Dumfries & Galloway DG5 4LN   Map 4 B2

Prettily set, harbourside pub, with a characterful, rambling drinking bar. Young, casual staff are friendly and tolerant of toddlers; one high chair. ***Beer** McEwan 80/-, Theakston Best & Old Peculier. Family room.*

Kirkcaldy   Hoffmans   ★

Tel 0592 204584   **FOOD**

435 High Street Kirkcaldy Fife KW1 2SG   Map 3 C5

Hoffmans is an extraordinary place. Situated to the east of the town centre (don't be confused by the High Street address), it's an unlikely looking venue for a pub serving imaginative food, but first impressions can deceive. Owned in partnership by Vince and Paul Hoffman, it opened in March 1990, after Vince returned to his home town and set up at a previous pub just down the road. The building they subsequently decided on to set up on their own was unpromisingly seedy; they smartened up the interior with subtly toned wall covering, brown upholstered bench seating, polished tables, a large central ceiling fan, angled mirrors, and fake greenery. The attractive seascape and still life oils are courtesy of Hoffman sisters, and rather fine colour photographs from a couple of regulars. But the food is the thing here, and so popular that booking is advised for lunch as well as dinner. And rightly so. Vince Hoffman is so confident in the quality of his raw ingredients that local suppliers are listed at the front of the menu, which is handwritten and changes daily. Often it's not even decided on until just before opening time, when suppliers and fishmongers have been visited and produce assessed. Fish is a particular interest of Vince's, from a traditional deep-fried haddock (£3.50) to an elaborately modern salmon and monkfish dish in lobster sauce (£10.25). The raw materials are first class (no dye in smoked fish), the handling first rate, and the prices remarkable: at lunchtime, main courses like Chicago pepperpot, poached haddock with Norwegian prawn sauce, pasta Toscana or roast stuffed lamb cost just over £3. A three-course lunch can be had for as little as £6.50! In the evening, the room is partitioned, half the space reserved for drinkers, the other run as an à la carte restaurant Wednesday to Saturday, when tables are laid and candle-lit, and there's waitress service. Expect to pay around £35 for two for smart evening food of a more complex kind: marinated kipper fillet (£2.95), noisettes of lamb (£10.25), venison with redcurrants (£10.25). Vince's wife Jan makes all the puddings, Dundee Bonnet (£2.25), ice creams (£2.25). Capable service is also genuinely friendly, thanks to the Hoffman teamwork. ***Bar Food** 12-2, 5.30-7.30. **Restaurant Meals** 7.30-9.30 (Wed/Thu/Fri/Sat). Vegetarian dishes. Children's portions. Children allowed in bar to eat. Free House. **Beer** McEwan's No. 3, 80/- and Tartan. No credit cards.*

Kirkcudbright   Selkirk Arms

Tel 0557 30402

Old High Street Kirkcudbright Dumfries & Galloway DG6 4JG   Map 4 B3

Modernised but characterful sleepy town hotel, its simple public bar
popular with locals. Go on a sunny day and have a drink under the
trees in the pretty little garden; they'll even carry out a high chair for
babies. *Free House.* **Beer** *McEwan Export, PA, Youngers Tartan,
Tennent 80/-. Garden.*

Kirkton of Glenisla   Glenisla Hotel

Tel 057 582 223

FOOD

Glenisla nr Blairgowrie Tayside PH11 8PH   Map 3 C4

☺

Set high up in Glenisla, one of the 'Angus Glens', this old coaching inn
dates back over 300 years to the days before the Jacobite rebellion. A
warm welcome avails todays travellers in the split level, beamed bar
with its real fire (even in summer on chilly days) and posies of heather
and wild flowers on the tables. At lunchtime a daily-changing menu
offers the likes of haddock and chips (£4), burgers (£3) and
ploughman's (£3.95); at night main courses such as breast of chicken
poached in garlic and cream (£6.95) and lamb cutlets grilled with
rosemary (£6.15) can be preceded by Orkney herring marinated in
dill (£1.95), salad of melon and prawns (£2.95) or home-made
chicken liver paté (£2.50), and followed by homely afters such as
bread-and-butter pudding with strawberries, plum crumble and hot
toffee pudding. Afternoons bring cream teas with scones fresh from
the oven and home-made jam. A pretty restaurant opens for both
lunch and dinner at the weekends (Friday, Saturday and Sunday) and
at other times by prior arrangement. *Bar Food 12-2.30, 6.30-9
(8.30 winter).* **Restaurant Meals** *(Fri, Sat & Sun) 12-2.30, 6.30-9.
Vegetarian dishes. Children's portions.* **Beer** *Theakston's Best, Old Peculier,
S&N 80/-.* **Cider** *Scrumpy Jack. Garden, outdoor eating, children's play
area. Family room. Access, Visa.*

Kylesku   Kylesku Hotel

Tel 0971 2231

Kylesku Highland IV27 4HW   Map 2 B2

On the south side of the old ferry crossing, close to the spectacular
new bridge, the Kylesku is more an inn than a hotel, and has
marvellous views of mountain and water. Its proximity to deserted
beaches can guarantee peace for those who require it.

Leadburn   Leadburn Inn

Tel 0968 72952

Leadburn West Linton Borders EH46 7BE   Map 3 C6

A smartly carpeted, attractively modernised 18th-century inn, its
atmosphere bordering on the genteel. **Beer** *Broughton Greenmantle Ale,
Caledonian. Family room.*

Lewiston   Lewiston Arms Hotel

Tel 04562 225

B&B

Lewiston nr Drumnadrochit Highland IV3 6UN   Map 2 B3

All bedrooms are now en suite at this homely old inn; half are in an
adjoining converted farmhouse. The spacious, relaxing interior has a
comfortable lounge bar and residents lounge. The River Coilty runs at
the end of the garden. *Free House.* **Beer** *McEwan's Export. Garden,*

outdoor eating. **Accommodation** *9 bedrooms, all en suite, £45 (single £22.50). Children welcome overnight, additional beds available. Check-in all day. Access, Visa.*

Linlithgow   Four Marys

Tel 0506 842171

65 High Street Linlithgow Lothian EH49 7ED   Map 3 C5

High-street old coaching inn near the famous palace where Mary Queen of Scots was born; the bars are full of Mary-obilia. Handsomely refurbished lounge. **Beer** *Belhaven, Fullers, Harviestoun, Mitchells. Family room.*

Loch Eck   Coylet Hotel   **FOOD**

Tel 036 984 322   **B&B**

Loch Eck nr Kilmun Strathclyde PA23 8SG   Map 3 B5

It's the setting that makes the Coylet really special: just the west coast road to Dunoon, shrouded in trees, separates the pretty white building from the glorious beauty of Loch Eck and the hills beyond. Not another house can be seen in any direction; be early for a window seat in the bar or dining room. Inside it charms in an unaffected way. The public bar, is handsome and cosy, and friendly local ghillies and others gather on bar stools to pass the time day. The beer's good too. Through the hall is an attractively simple little dining bar, where families (even tiny babies) are welcome. Through into the dining room proper are half a dozen tables (one, large group size, in the prize window spot), wheelback chairs and a piano. The food is a mix of standard bar menu stuff, from sandwiches (even in the evening) and ploughman's to vast well-cooked platefuls of haddock and chips, or sizzling steaks; the quality draws both locals and tourists. But it's worth waiting for the specials board, a daily-changing short blackboard list which applies from 7pm. It might typically feature home-made liver paté and Scotch broth, local game in season (from £6.50), grilled local salmon (from £5.75) or trout, and langoustine risotto (£8.15). If the risotto is on, you should order it and enjoy a generous pile of tender, fresh Loch Fyne langoustines in a delicious sauce with garlic, cream, wine and herbs: a true and memorable bargain. Vegetables are also exceptional: crisp mangetout, perfect new potatoes, tender carrots; all included in the main-course price. Puddings, all home-made, are also good, and come in hefty portions (all £2): chocolate roulade, pineapple cheesecake or a real apple pie are typical of the choice. Upstairs are three tiny little bedrooms which offer simple comfort. All have sash windows with views over the loch, and pretty cottagey print paper and fabrics. The twin is a bit bigger than the two doubles. The shared bathroom, a very attractive, immaculately clean, carpeted and pine-panelled room, is bigger than any of them. Breakfasts are ungreasy and commendably accommodating of personal preferences. Finally, a word about the service, which is genuine and friendly from both the resident owners and their few, able staff. **Bar Food & Restaurant Meals** *12-2 (12.30-2 Sun), 5.30-10 (7-9 Sun). Vegetarian dishes. Children's portions. Free House.* **Beer** *Younger No. 3, McEwan 80/-, Deuchars IPA. Garden, outdoor eating. Family room.* **Accommodation** *3 bedrooms, sharing facilities, £35 (single £17.50). Children welcome overnight, cots supplied with advance notice. Small dogs permitted. Check-in by arrangement. No credit cards.*

Lybster   Bayview Hotel

Tel 059 32 346	**B&B**

Russel Street Lybster Highland KW3 6AG

Map 2 C2

Conveniently placed for the A9, the Bayview is a little black-and-white painted inn standing in the town centre just above the harbour. New owners have recently taken over and there is a warm and cosy lounge bar where the local fisherman and farmers can be found in the public bar. Modest overnight accommodation is provided by three efficiently heated bedrooms with simple modern furniture, TVs and tea-makers. All have washbasins and share a functional public bathroom. *Free House.* **Beer** *Tennent's Special, Light, 80/-, Beamish. Garden.* **Accommodation** *3 bedrooms, not en suite, £30 (single £15). Children welcome overnight, cots available. Check-in all day. Access, Visa.*

Melrose   Burts Hotel

	FOOD
Tel 089 682 2285 Fax 089 682 2870	**B&B**

Market Square Melrose Borders TD6 9PN

Map 4 C1

Imposing 18th-century inn at the heart of still-fairly-sleepy, affluent Melrose, located 200 yards from the River Tweed – "Scotland's favourite salmon river". Bar food shows an appetising balance of the comfortingly traditional and modern aspirational – and this philosophy could be said to sum up the whole hotel – game broth (£1.30), roulade of trout and salmon (£3), lamb casserole with honey and grapes (£5), haddock and mushroom bake (£5). The bar is comfortable rather than quaint. Good Scottish produce is featured on two table d'hote menus in the rather smart restaurant – lunch £13.75 and dinner £18.50, in addition to à la carte dishes – local lamb, stuffed partridge with grapes and calvados, salmon and halibut with lobster sauce, fresh scallops with wild mushrooms. A choice of eight cheeses are always on offer including locals such as Bonchester, Teviotdale and Lanark Blue. The bedrooms are light, contemporary and in pristine order. Five have just shower/WC. **Bar Food** *12-2, 6-9.30 (10.30 Fri/Sat).* **Restaurant Meals** *12.30-2, 7-9 (9.30 Fri/Sat). Vegetarian dishes. Children's portions. Children allowed in bar to eat. Free House.* **Beer** *Belhaven 80/-, Courage Directors Choice. Garden, outdoor eating.* **Accommodation** *21 bedrooms, all en suite, £64 (single £40). Children welcome overnight, additional beds (£15), cots supplied. Check-in all day. Access, Amex, Diners, Visa.*

Moffat   Black Bull

Tel 0683 20206 Fax 0683 20483	**B&B**

Churchgate Moffat Dumfries & Galloway DG10 9EG

Map 4 C2

Modernised 16th-century street-side local with a beer garden outside and duckpond nearby in this curiously old-fashioned, isolated little spa town, whose life blood is coach party tourism. It has been recently refurbished, but the proper local bar survives. There are now an additional four bedrooms making a total of eight – four look on to the courtyard and four on to the churchyard opposite. Each bedroom has a different colour scheme and is fully equipped with TV, telephone, and tea & coffee making-facilities. **Beer** *Theakston's Best, McEwan's 80/-, guest ale changing weekly. Garden, outdoor eating. Family Room.* **Accommodation** *8 bedrooms, 6 en suite, £48 (single £29). Children welcome overnight, additional beds (£6), cots available. Check-in all day. No dogs. Access, Visa.*

Monymusk   **Grant Arms Hotel**

Tel 046 77 226

The Square Monymusk Inverurie Grampian AB51 7HJ   **Map 3 D4**

18th-century coaching inn in picturesque village, modernised but
attractive inside with its comfortable lounge, and fruit-machine and
space-game public bar. Excellent fishing on ten miles of the river Don.
Ghillies available at reasonable rates. *Free House.* **Beer** *McEwan.*
Children's play area. Family room.

Muir of Ord   **Ord House Hotel**

Tel 0463 870492   **B&B**

Muir of Ord Highland IV6 7UH   **Map 2 B3**

Opposite a little loch, this charming country house hotel is a listed
building dating from 1602 in grounds of 50 acres of parkland (with
woodland trails), fields, and formal garden. Pleasant bedrooms with
garden views have antique furniture, coffee & tea making facilities,
hairdryers and there is a laundry service if required. *Free House.*
Garden, children's playing area. Family room. **Accommodation**
*12 bedrooms, 10 en suite, from £54 (single £30). Children welcome
overnight, additional beds (from £10), cots available. Check-in all day.*
Access, Amex, Visa.

Netherley   **Lairhillock Inn**

Tel 0569 30001   **FOOD**

Netherley Grampian AB3 2QS   **Map 3 D4**

Standing alone surrounded by fields, the Lairhillock is easily spotted
from the B979, thanks to the large white INN daubed on its roof.
The closest major village to the inn is Peterculter, some four miles to
the north; Netherley's a mile to the south. Formerly a farmhouse, the
original building is 17th-century, with careful extensions, and the
interior is full of old rustic atmosphere. The large lounge is dominated
by a central log-burning fireplace; walls are half-panelled, and exposed
floorboards covered with numerous rugs. The public bar, in the oldest
part, is by far the most characterful room, with its exposed stone,
panelling, open fire, old settles and bench seating, every kind of horse
tack, polished brasses and numerous other bits and pieces. Bar food is
certainly taken seriously at the Lairhillock, where only fresh produce
is used, cooked to order. The lunchtime menu, more limited than in
the evening, still carries a fair choice, changing daily. Typically there
might be wild boar terrine (£3.95), scallops of venison with wild
mushroom sauce (£6.95), locally-made Swiss-style sausage with
mushroom and onion sauce (£5.25). Puddings like sticky toffee
pudding and clootie dumpling (both £2.15) are changed daily. It gets
extremely busy, especially on Friday and Saturday evenings. Across
from the main building, in the old stables, is the evening restaurant,
with its high beamed ceiling, stone walls, red-tiled flooring and solid
polished tables. There's candle-light and a pianist plays nightly. There's
a wide and interesting choice of dishes here too – langoustines
(£4.50), Royal Greenland prawns with dill sauce in a puff pastry case
(£4.50), rack of lamb (£7.50). A variety of Scottish cheeses is always
available. Service is pleasantly informal but always efficient. A
recently built conservatory with panoramic views furnished with Lloyd Loom
tables and chairs provides an ideal room for families to eat.
Bar Food *12-2, 6-9.30 (6-10 Fri/Sat).* **Restaurant Meals** *12-2 (Sun
only), 7.30-9.30 (7.30-10 Fri/Sat). Vegetarian dishes. Children's portions.*

Beer Courage Directors, McEwan's 80/- and Export, Boddingtons Best Bitter, guest ale every week. Patio/Terrace. Access, Amex, Diners, Visa.

New Abbey   Criffel Inn

FOOD

B&B

Tel 038785 305

New Abbey nr Dumfries Dumfries & Galloway DG2 8BX

Map 4 B2

Located five miles from the coast, an unassuming inn on the village square, with a small garden for summer sipping. The McCullochs are the most welcoming of hosts, and Jenny keeps the customers well fed with a good variety of wholesome home cooking using local products and vegetables from her garden. Lunchtime brings soup – perhaps a warming vegetable broth – and a daily special like roast pork with apple sauce (£4) or savoury mince pie (£4), supplementing toasted sandwiches, salads, fish (fresh Solway salmon £5) and roast beef (£4). It's worth leaving room for the day's special sweet, which could be bread and butter pudding or a tart of locally picked fruit. From 4.30pm high tea (£5-£6 – main course with cake-stand featuring home-baked bread, jam, scones – meringues feature daily) is served and early evening menus are similar but shorter. There is a 3-course roast lunch (£6) on Sunday. Spotless bedrooms (TVs but no phones) share an equally spruce tiled bathroom and residents have their own lounge. *Bar Food 12-2, 4.30-7. Vegetarian dishes. Children's menu (£1.75 per dish). Free house. Beer Belhaven Best Bitter, Broughton Bitter. Patio, outdoor eating. Family Room.* **Accommodation** *5 bedrooms, shared facilities, £39 (single £19.50). Children welcome overnight (0-5s free), additional beds. Check-in all day. No credit cards.*

Newton Stewart   Creebridge House Hotel

Tel 0671 2121

Minnigaff Newton Stewart Dumfries & Galloway DG8 6NP

Map 4 A2

Charming and pleasingly pubby bar with a delightful country house setting in its own pretty grounds, just before the bridge on the Minnigaff-approach to Newton Stewart. Tolerant and helpful towards parents with young children, too. *Beer Bellhaven, Theakston Best Bitter & XB. Garden. Family room.*

Peebles   Kingsmuir Hotel

Tel 0721 20151

Springhill Road Peebles Borders EH45 9EP

Map 4 C1

Handsome Victorian stone-built, gabled hotel on the quiet side of this attractive market town. Functional, spartan locals' bar; comfortable residents' lounge with pretty views, clean simple bedrooms. *Beer Broughton. Garden, children's play area. Family room.*

Perth   Greyfriars

Tel 0738 33036

15 South Street Perth Tayside PH2 8PG

Map 3 C5

Friendly little city pub with upstairs dining room; lots of foreign bottled beers. *Beer Caledonian, Ind Coope Burton Ale, Orkney Raven Ale. Family room.*

Pitlochry   East Haugh House

Tel 0796 473121

East Haugh Pitlochry Tayside PH16 5JS

Map 3 C4

Handsome 17th-century turreted stone house in two acres of grounds. *Garden, children's play area.*

Portpatrick   Crown Hotel

FOOD

B&B

Tel 077 681 261   Fax 077 681 551

Portpatrick Wigtownshire Dumfries & Galloway DG9 8SX

Map 4 A2

Right down by the harbour, the blue and white painted Crown is a bustling, friendly place where the several unpretentious rooms that form the bar – with a real fire even in summer on chilly days, and a motley collection of prints above dado panelling – contrast with a stylishly informal restaurant and smart, appealing bedrooms. The latter have loose rugs over polished parquet floors, a variety of good freestanding furniture and attractive floral fabrics along with pristine bathrooms and the standard modern necessities of direct-dial phone and TV. Restaurant and bar share the same menu (except for the basket meals and sandwiches that are served in the bar only), which majors on seafood. Chef Robert Campbell knows that the lobster and crabs are fresh as he's out in his boat at 6 o'clock each morning to collect them. Much of the other fish is bought direct from the Fleetwood trawlers that call in at Portpatrick to unload their catches. Grilled scallops wrapped in bacon (£4.35), moules marinière (£4.05), herring in oatmeal (£3.45), whole plaice with almonds and chips (£5.60), vegetable pancake (£5.40), beef hot-pot (£4.10) and chicken and chips (£4.05) are a few examples from a longish menu. Service is swift and efficient. ***Bar Food & Restaurant Meals*** 12-2.30, 6 (6.30 Sun)-10. *Vegetarian dishes. Children's portions. Free House. **Beer** S&N 80/-, Tartan Export. Family room. **Accommodation** 12 bedrooms, all en suite, £62 (single £33). Children welcome overnight, additional beds (ages 4-10 £10), cots supplied. Check-in all day. Access, Amex, Diners, Visa.*

Ratho   Bridge Inn

Tel 031-333 1320

27 Baird Road Ratho Lothian EH28 8RA

Map 3 C6

Part of the Edinburgh Canal Centre, which also features two canalboat restaurants. A well-run, popular, family-orientated pub; also facilities for disabled persons. Huge variety of children's play equipment includes a putting green. ***Beer** Belhaven 80/-. Children's play area. Family room.*

St Andrews   Grange Inn

Tel 0334 72670

Grange Road St Andrews Fife KY16 8LJ

Map 3 D5

Isolated pub on a quiet road, a mile and a half out of town. The pubbiest bar for miles around, particularly in winter, with its dark wood and glowing fire; unspoilt and very civilised. *Garden.*

St Boswells   Buccleuch Arms Hotel

Tel 0835 22243

The Green St Boswells Borders TD6 0EW   Map 4 C1

Large, plain, Victorian corner site hotel near the village green. Good
Border estate contacts for huntin', shootin' and fishin' enthusiasts, a
recurrent decorative theme. **Beer** *Broughton Greenmantle Ale. Garden.*

St Fillans   Achray House Hotel

Tel 0764 85231

St Fillans Loch Earn Tayside PH6 2NF   Map 3 C5

Family-run hotel by the lochside in pretty countryside. Interior
typically Scottish – pine panelling, tartan carpet in dining room;
bar rather garishly modernised. *Free House.* **Beer** *McEwan.*

St Mary's Loch   Tibbie Shiels Inn

Tel 0750 42231   **FOOD**

St Mary's Loch Borders TD7 5NE   Map 4 C1

The Tibbie Shiels Inn itself is a lovely whitewashed single storey
cottage with add-ons, on the shore of St Mary's Loch, in the glorious
Yarrow valley. Tibbie Shiels started the Inn in 1826 and it's now
famous throughout the Borders and elsewhere. It can be recommended
for three main things: first, the atmospheric bar, busy with friendly
locals and fishing and sailing types, second the quality of the meat
dishes, (Scottish lamb and Aberdeen Angus beef), and third the
situation of the Inn itself: the large dining room overlooks the
beautiful loch and surrounding hills in this utterly remote and
enchanting place. Dishes include holy mole chili (£4.25), spicy
chicken (£3.50), poacher's pouch (stuffed sirloin steak) (£9), scallops
with bacon and cream sauce (£8), venison in red wine (£7.50), and
home-made clootie dumpling (£1.75). The Tibbie is an excellent
place to stop after a sojourn on the Southern Upland Way. **Bar Food**
(except Mon in Winter) 11-11 (12.30-11 Sun), high tea 3.30-6.
Restaurant Meals *(except Mon in Winter) 6.30-8.30. Vegetarian dishes.
Children's portions. Free House.* **Beer** *Belhaven 80/-, Broughton
Greenmantle. Children allowed in bar to eat until 8pm. Patio/terrace,
outdoor eating. Pub closed on Monday in winter. Access, Visa.*

Sheildaigh   Tigh an Eilean

Tel 052 05 251

Sheildaigh by Strathcarron Highland IV54 8XN   Map 2 B3

Beautifully set at the head of the loch, with soothing views and
stunning sunsets. Spartan locals' public bar, but homely and
comfortable residents' lounges. *Free House.* **Beer** *Tennent's Export.*

Sheriffmuir   Sheriffmuir Inn

Tel 0786 823285

Sheriffmuir nr Dunblane Central FK15 0LH   Map 3 C5

A real oasis in a wild moorland location, a pub more of the English
than Scots sort, with plush upholstered banquettes and prettifying
touches. **Beer** *Arrols 80/-, Ind Coope Burton Ale. Garden, children's
play area. Family room.*

Spean Bridge   Letterfinlay Lodge

Tel 039 781 622   **B&B**

Spean Bridge Highland PH34 4DZ   Map 3 B4

Sturdy 19th-century inn, overlooking Loch Lochy, seven miles north
of Spean Bridge; run by the Forsyth family for well over 25 years.
Comfortable bar with banknote-adorned beams and good views from
the sun lounge. Modestly furnished bedrooms, some compact and
modern, others old and spacious. Public bathrooms have original
Victorian fittings. *Children's play area. Family room.*

Stirling   Birds & The Bees

Tel 0786 73663

Easter Cornton Road Causewayhead Stirling Central FK9 5PB   Map 3 C5

Converted farmhouse with a striking interior, its open-plan bar
adorned with eccentric bits of agricultural equipment. Pétanque is
keenly played in the garden. *Beer Broughton, Caledonian, Tetley.*
Children's play area. Family room.

Stonehaven   Marine Hotel

Tel 0569 62155

9 + 10 The Shorehead Stonehaven Grampian AB3 2JY   Map 3 D4

Lively, atmospheric harbourside pub-hotel, with very much a local
pub downstairs: dining room upstairs. Good views from most
bedrooms. *Beer Bass, Taylor. Children's play area. Family room.*

Strathblane   Kirkhouse Inn

Tel 0360 70621   Fax 0360 70896   **B&B**

Glasgow Road Strathblane Central G63 9AA   Map 3 B5

On the A81 Stirling to Aberfoyle road, ten miles north of Glasgow,
this roadside inn is at the foot of the Campsie Fells and thus popular
with walkers. An ideal touring centre as Loch Lomond, the Trossachs,
Glasgow and Stirling are all within 30 minutes by car. Sprucely kept
public areas include a busy public bar and quieter lounge and
restaurant. Pastel colours are used in the bedrooms, which include a
honeymoon suite with a sunken bath. Children up to 12 stay free in
parents' room. Adventure weekends are a new attraction.
Accommodation 15 rooms £72. Garden, pool table. Access, Amex, Visa,
Diners

Swinton   Wheatsheaf Hotel

                                                                     FOOD
Tel 089 086 257   **B&B**

Main Street Swinton Borders TD11 3JJ   Map 3 D6

The village of Swinton is six miles north of Coldstream, on the way
to nowhere, and is easy to miss. The Wheatsheaf, dominating this
simple Scots farming hamlet, overlooks the plain little village green
and has very limited parking; at busy periods, the main street is full
up with cars. This is very much a dining pub (drinking goes on in the
pool-tabled, fruit-machined public bar at the back, so separate from
the food operation that most visitors aren't even aware it exists) with a
very well-regarded restaurant, the Four Seasons, and it's wise to book
even for bar meals, such is the reputation of the pub in the Borders.
The emphasis is on fresh food: a menu reproduced on one blackboard,
daily specials listed on another – hot baked avocado with seafood
(£3.85), lamb's liver with onions and bacon (£5.25), home-

made duck terrine with Cumberland sauce (£4.25), supreme of wild salmon Jemma Louise (£7.95), beef in ale (£5.25), spinach pancake with cheese sauce (£4.65) and a choice of home-made puddings (the summer pudding (£2.50) is a house speciality). Tables are laid with cloths and place mats; freshly baked wheaten rolls are presented as a matter of course, and butter comes in a slab on a saucer, with no foil packets or sauce sachets in sight. Salads are imaginative and fresh. Cheeses are good, and come with a mini-bottle of Leith port. Service is assured, if a little over-attentive, with frequent bouts of "everything alright?" from the uniformed waitresses. But this is still the best bar meal in the Borders. **Bar Food** (*except Monday*) *11.45-2.15, 6.30-9.30. Vegetarian dishes. Children's portions. Free House.* **Beer** *Broughton Greenmantle Ale, Broughton Special Bitter, Tennent's 70/-. Garden, outdoor eating, children's play area. Family Room.* **Accommodation** (*closed middle two weeks Feb*) *4 bedrooms, 2 en suite, £54 (single £40). Children welcome overnight, additional beds, cots supplied. Check-in all day. Access, Visa.*

Tain   Morangie House

Tel 0862 892281

Morangie Road Tain Highland IV19 1PY   Map 2 C3

Civilised 19th-century mansion house hotel with nice bar and pretty, light dining room. **Beer** *McEwan. Family room.*

Talladale   Loch Maree Hotel

Tel 044 584 288   Fax 044 584 241   **B&B**

Achnasheen Talladale Highland IV2 2HC   Map 2 B3

A purpose-built fishing hotel beautifully situated on the banks of the loch between Gairloch and Kinlochewe. The glorious outdoors is certainly a major attraction, and inside things have changed dramatically from the former time-warp Victorian cosiness. The hotel owns eight boats (complete with mandatory ghillies) for sea trout and salmon fishing on the loch. **Accommodation** *18 rooms £66. Garden, fishing, boating, games room. Access, Visa.*

Tayvallich   Tayvallich Inn

Tel 05467 282   **FOOD**

Tayvallich by Lochgilphead Strathclyde PA31 8PR   Map 3 A5

This simple white-painted dining pub – though it's fine to pop in for a drink, most people come for the food – is in a marvellously pretty location at the centre of a strung-along-the-road, scattered village stretching around the top of Loch Sween. Sit outside, on the front terrace, at one of the five parasolled picnic tables, and enjoy the view of a dozen little boats, and low wooded hills fringing the lochside; the work Tayvallich means "the house in the pass". Inside, the Tayvallich is surprisingly modern – smartly pine-clad, with a little bar and larger adjoining dining room proper. The bar is tiled-floored, with raffia back chairs and little wood tables, the dining room similar, but spacious and relaxing, with a woodburning stove, attractive dresser, and bentwood chairs around scrubbed pine dining tables. The star of the handwritten menu is the freshest local seafood; so local that oysters (half a dozen £5.50) come from just yards away in Loch Sween itself, and clams from the Sound of Jura (£9.50) just round the coast. Langoustines are local and beautifully fresh (stir-fried £10), as are scallops (£8.75), or lobster (£15-17); mussels plump (£2.50/£5), salads imaginative and crisp. Finger bowls are provided, and clean napkins with each course. Portions are generous, and the whole atmosphere is very informal and relaxed. Holidaymakers turn up in shorts, and babies are commendably tolerantly treated, with clip-on-chairs and specially rustled up toddler food – they'll even find chips for philistine youngsters. Puddings (all £1.75), made by the landlady, are of the chocolate nut slab and banoffi pie sort; few dedicated seafood lovers, having munched through two courses already, get that far though! Non-fish choices could include Cajun chicken (£4.90), vegetable and cheese bake (£4.25) or red, yellow and orange peppers with goat's cheese (£3.75). Expect to pay about £33 for a three course lunch for two, including half a litre of house wine. *Bar Food 12-2, 6-9. Restaurant Meals 7-9. Vegetarian dishes. Children's portions. Free House. Beer Dryboroughs Heavy, Tetley Drum Bitter. Patio/grassy foreshore, outdoor eating. Inn closed 1 November to 31 March. Access, Visa.*

Troon   Clubhouse

Tel 0292 317918

22 Ayr Street Troon Strathclyde KA10 6EB   Map 4 A1

Atmospheric upstairs bar whose golfing links (so to speak) include many fascinating old photographs. *Free House. Beer McEwan.*

Turriff   Towie Tavern

Tel 08884 201   **FOOD**

Auchterless Nr Turriff Grampian AB53 8EP   Map 2 D3

A favourite for its satisfying, wholesome food, this is a roadside pebbledash pub on the A497, some four miles south of Turriff and a short distance from the National Trust's 13th-century Fyvie Castle. Seafood is featured at the Towie and a different daily menu assures very fresh produce. The 'Fisherman's choice' offers whatever is available that day: plaice, herring, mackerel or perhaps haddock (poached or deep-fried £4.95). The food is more elaborate in the restaurant with such dishes as supreme of chicken Cassandra (£9.75), rack of Scottish spring lamb (£11.25), roast beef (on Sundays – £6.25). Vegetarians are catered for (broccoli and cauliflower cheese bake £4.60) and puddings are home-made (butterscotch meringue £2.50). Smartly rustic decor and a new children's play area equipped with swings and rope ladders. Music in the non-smoking dining room. 50 whiskies. *Bar Food 12-2, 6-9 (5-8.30 Sun). Restaurant Meals 6-9. Vegetarian dishes. Children's menu (£1.95-£2.50 per dish). Children allowed in bar to eat. Free House. Beer McEwan's Export. Patio/Terrace, outdoor eating. Access, Visa.*

Tweedsmuir   Crook Inn

Tel 089 97 272   **B&B**

Tweedsmuir nr Biggar Borders ML12 6QN   Map 4 C1

Famous old drovers' inn standing on the A701 in glorious Tweed valley countryside. A strange but winning amalgam of old stone-flagged farmers' bar and 1930s ocean liner-style lounges in the airy modern extension. *Beer Broughton Greenmantle Ale. Garden. Children's play area. Family room.*

Ullapool   Ceilidh Place

FOOD

Tel 0854 612103

B&B

West Argyle Street Ullapool Highland IV26 2TY

Map 2 B3

Located 200 yards from Loch Broom, this is a celebrated northern community centre, which started as a coffee shop, and, like Topsy, just growed. Three cottages in this seaside village were knocked into one and Ceilidh Place was created. The pastry chef is kept busy all day providing scones, pancakes and cakes from 9.30am in the coffee shop and home-made puddings (trifle, pavlova, crème brulée) for lunch or supper. Extremely informal and friendly; musicians perform live music during the summer (traditional Scottish, opera, chamber); regularly changing exhibitions take place throughout the year, and the restaurant, which opens at 8am for breakfast, also offers a smart "ally carte": fried aubergine slices in garlic mayonnaise (£3), grilled whole sole with parsley butter (£10), prawns and scallops provencale (£13.50), dressed crab & salad (£7.50), beef stroganoff. The fish is from Loch Broom. The bar has a wide range of salads and stovies (£2.50) together with soup (£1.20), haggis pie (£3.25) and roulades (£4) . The pretty bedrooms are comfortable and spotless; the eight rooms that are en suite also have phones. *Bar Food 9.30-6 (7 in Summer). Restaurant Meals 6.30-9.30. Children's portions. Children allowed in bar to eat. Free House. Beer McEwan's Export. Patio, outdoor eating, children's play area. Accommodation 15 bedrooms, 8 en suite, £86 (single £46). Children welcome overnight, additional beds (from £6), cots supplied. Check-in after midday. Pub and accommodation closed two weeks mid January. Access, Amex, Diners, Visa.*

Ullapool   Morefield Motel

FOOD

Tel 0854 612161

B&B

North Road Ullapool Highland IV26 2TH

Map 2 B3

Most of the specials at the Morefield involve scallops, prawns or langoustines in some form or another; it's the week's recurrent leitmotif. They're very much dependent on what's in season and in the catch at this remote north western location on the shore of Loch Broom. There are personal reasons for the pre-eminence of shellfish here too: the co-owners, including resident licensee David Smyrl, were previously skippers of a pair of fishing and diving boats, who diversified into activity holidays and ploughed all their profits into buying the Morefield Motel. That was 10 years ago, and their expertise has built an international reputation for genuinely sea-fresh fish and seafood. A sneaky glimpse of the visitors' book reveals fan messages from all over the world, but particularly Germany, for some reason – and it's especially revealing that so many of their remarks declare (in a tone of some astonishment) that they were unable to finish their meal. Portion control is a foreign language up here; when something's in season, it's generally piled high, and the seafood extravaganza is particularly unfinishable (£32 for two in the restaurant; £13.95 each in the bar). Aside from the Steak Plaice restaurant (naff name, fab food, and booking essential in summer), you can eat in the lounge bar of beer garden, and enjoy superb bar food at value-for-money prices. The printed broadsheet menu offers meat and fish in about equal proportions – this may be the king of seafood bars, but the Scottish meat also praiseworthy; try a Highland Stalkers Pie – venison with mushrooms in red wine (£5.95), sirloin stroganoff (£5.75), chicken champignons (£5.75), or one of five sorts of steak, plain or well sauced. A roast dish is available every day (£5.50). The strong fish list ranges from simple, fresh fried haddock (£4.95) to grilled langoustines (£12.95) or a whole lobster (£14.99) or carpetbagger: Aberdeen Angus steak with scallops (£14.50), from rolled smoked salmon stuffed with prawns in Marie Rose sauce (£5.95) or a vast dish of mussels (£9.50) to a homely haddock and cheese bake (£5.95). Puddings are home-made. House wine by the carafe deeps things nicely informal. The bedrooms are equipped with tea and coffee making facilities, colour TVs and hairdryers, and irons and boards are available. *Bar Food* 12-2, 5.30-9.30 (6-9.30 Sun). *Restaurant Meals* 6-9.30. *Vegetarian dishes. Children's menu (£2.50 per dish). Free House.* *Beer* *McEwans Export and 80/-, Tennents 70/-. Garden, outdoor eating, children's play area.* *Accommodation* *11 bedrooms, all en suite, £40 (single £26). Children welcome overnight, additional beds (£10), cots supplied. Check-in all day. Accommodation closed November – March. Access, Amex, Visa.*

Ullapool   Argyll Hotel

Tel 085 461 2422	**B&B**
Argyll Street Ullapool Highland IV26 2UB	Map 2 B3

New owners have taken over this white-painted inn close to the shore of Loch Broom. There's plenty of local character in its modest, neatly kept bars. Overnight accommodation is provided by twelve bedrooms, with TVs, tea-making facilities and quilts and electric blankets for extra warmth. Six bedrooms have full en-suite facilities while the others share two bathrooms. *Free House.* *Beer* *McEwan's 80/-.* *Accommodation* *12 bedrooms, 6 en suite, £50 (single £25). Children welcome overnight, additional beds and cots available. No dogs. Check-in all day. Access, Visa.*

Weem   Ailean Chraggan Hotel

Tel 0887 820346	**FOOD**
	B&B
Weem by Aberfeldy Tayside PH15 2LD	Map 3 C4

Delightful little cottage inn, beautifully located against a steep woodland backdrop, and with two acres of gardens overlooking the Tay valley. The bright, sunny, well-kept bar has a central log-burning stove, with a dining area beside the picture windows. Simple, well-cooked food, highlighted by superb local seafood; try the Loch Etive mussels (£6.50), served in huge steaming portions with garlic bread or the Sound of Jura prawn platter (£11.95). There are special set menu seafood nights. Scottish cheeses on offer include Caboc and Tobermory. Bedrooms are also recommended: spacious and light with nice pieces of old furniture, armchairs, and, in two rooms, small dressing areas. All are equipped with TVs, hairdryers and tea/coffee making facilities. Ask for one of the front bedrooms, which have inspiring views to wake up to. *Bar Food* 12-2, 6.30-10 (8.45 winter). *Children's portions. Children allowed in bar to eat. Garden, outdoor eating.* *Accommodation* *3 bedrooms, all en suite, £52 (single £26). Children welcome overnight, additional beds (£13 from 5yrs). Check-in all day. Access, Visa.*

Yarrow   Gordon Arms

Tel 0750 82232

Mountbenger Yarrow Valley Yarrow Borders TD7 5LE   Map 4 C1

Beautifully situated old inn, close by the Southern Upland Way, and popular with walkers. **Beer** *Broughton, Jennings. Children welcome overnight.*

Wales

Aberdovey   Penhelig Arms Hotel

FOOD
B&B

Tel 0654 767215   Fax 0654 767690

Aberdovey Gwynedd LL35 0LT

Map 8 C3

"On the main road by the railway bridge" are directions which might usually strike fear into the hearts of prospective customers. But here are also unrivalled views across the Dyfi estuary to Ynyslas, making a splendid setting for Robert and Sally Hughes' smart black and white painted pub by the A493. Some disadvantages are inherent in a situation where no pavement exists 'twixt front door and double yellow lines, nor greater space, almost, between the single rail line at Penhelig halt and the hotel's gable end. Road noise and BR's occasional arrivals notwithstanding, the sea wall opposite makes a marvellous spot at any state of the tide to enjoy a leisurely al fresco lunch, while the tiny Fisherman's Bar provides a relaxing, and shady, alternative. Fan-cooled on the hottest summer days, and heated by two open fires in winter (set back-to-back beneath a central stone chimney), here's an ideal place to enjoy a pint of good beer and catch up on some local gossip. The bar's the focal point of lunches from Monday to Saturday, and, when the weather's inclement, eaters soon overflow into the restaurant next door. Bar food features terrine of chicken (£2.65), and fresh fish vol-au-vents served with salad (£4.50), besides more substantial meals served with vegetables or chips, perhaps grilled trout (£4.95) or oxtail stew (£4.75). By night, bar meals are suspended in favour of a set-price dinner (3 courses £15.95) offering diverse daily choice: cream of watercress soup; dressed crab or seafood salad; grilled Welsh lamb cutlets; steamed fillet of salmon; grilled breast of Barbary duck with redcurrant and juniper sauce. Sunday lunch, rather more economically priced (3 courses £9.50), has a more limited choice, but brings cooking of equally consistent quality: roast beef, loin of lamb, cutlets of salmon or fillets of plaice. Booking is advised. Plump for a room with a view: in fact, only two of the bedrooms lack a seascape. All have a cottagey feel and benefit from an individual approach to decor which makes the best of their higgledy-piggledy layout. Private bathroom, television and radio, and beverage trays are included throughout, but for a truly special occasion ask for one of the three superior rooms, with balconies and sea views. *Bar Food & Restaurant Meals 12-2, 7-9, 7-9. Free House. Beer Tetley Traditional, Marston's Pedigree, Felinfoel Double Dragon. Patio, outdoor eating. Accommodation 11 bedrooms, all en suite, £52 (single £36). Children welcome overnight. Additional beds and cots available. Check-in all day. Access, Visa.*

Abergavenny   Llanwenarth Arms Hotel

FOOD
B&B

Tel 0873 810550

Brecon Road Abergavenny Gwent NP8 1EP

Map 9 D5

If you think Llanwenarth is tough to pronounce, try Pantrhiwgoch, the former name of this much extended Usk-side inn with 10 acres of garden. There are two friendly bars, an attractive conservatory and a restaurant overlooking the river and valley, two stretches of good fishing are available to residents. The same menu of home-made food is available in both bar and restaurant – try the chicken and leek pie (£7.50), salmon, prawns and asparagus in cheese sauce (£7.25) followed by waffles with maple syrup (£3.80). Compact modern bedrooms in three-storey annexe, are equipped with TV, telephone, trouser press and tea/coffee making facilities, and all enjoy splendid views. *Bar Food & Restaurant Meals 12-2 (12-1.30 Sun), 6-9.45*

(7-8.30 Sun). Vegetarian dishes. Children's menu (£3 per dish). Free House. **Beer** *Bass, Wadworth 6X. Garden, outdoor eating. Family room.* **Accommodation** *18 bedrooms, all en suite, £59 (single £49). Children welcome overnight. Additional beds (£5), cots supplied. Check-in all day. No dogs. Access, Amex, Diners, Visa.*

Abergorlech   Black Lion

Tel 0558 685271

Abergorlech nr Carmarthen Dyfed SA32 7SN   Map 9 B5

High-back settles, oak furnishings, flagstones and a woodburning stove in this 16th-century timbered pub, which also has trout and salmon fishing rights on the river Cothi. Just off the B4310. *Free House.* **Beer** *Felinfoel, Double Dragon. Riverside garden, children's play area.*

Alltwen   Butchers Arms

Tel 0792 863100

Alltwen nr Pontardawe West Glamorgan SA8 3BP   Map 9 C5

Traditional pub overlooking the Swansea valley. No juke box, no games machines. Off the A474. *Free House.* **Beer** *Courage Directors, Everards Old Original, Fuller's London Pride.*

Babell   Black Lion Inn

Tel 0352 720239

FOOD

Babell nr Holywell Clwyd CH8 8PZ   Map 8 D1

Parts of the Black Lion date back to 1259. Originally a licensed farmhouse which brewed its own mead. It's a peaceful country pub and has been in the same hands for almost 30 years. Popular dishes in the bar are sauté of lamb lyonnaise (£6.25) and home-cooked ham in Madeira sauce (£6.25). In the evening, guests can choose either supper (à la carte menu) in the conservatory or dinner in the restaurant where a 4-course menu is priced according to choice of main dish – lobster (£18.25), roast duckling (£17.95) or Black Lion country pie (£16.95). The cheeseboard offers a good variety and an accompanying wine can be chosen from a list of over 100. Home-made puddings include bread-and-butter pudding or biscotten torte (both £2.25). **Bar Food & Restaurant Meals** *12.15-2 (except Lunch Sat & all Sun), 7.30-9.45. Vegetarian dishes. Free House.* **Beer** *Younger's Scotch Bitter, McEwan's Export. Amex, Visa.*

Beaumaris   Liverpool Arms Hotel

Tel 0248 810362

B&B

Castle Street Beaumaris Anglesey Gwynedd   Map 8 B1

Although a hotel since 1700, the Liverpool Arms is now completely modernised. All that remains unsullied is a listed staircase. Architectural heritage has given way to theme, in this case maritime memorabilia. There are some fine model sailing ships in glass cases downstairs and the bedrooms bear the names of famous admirals. The simple, well-kept bedrooms have en-suite bath or shower rooms, TVs, direct-dial telephones and tea-makers. **Beer** *Theakston. Family room.* **Accommodation** *10 bedrooms, all en suite, £46.50 (single £28). Children welcome overnight, additional beds and cots available. Check-in all day. Access, Amex, Visa.*

Beaumaris   Ye Olde Bull's Head   ★

FOOD
B&B

Tel 0248 810329   Fax 0248 811294

Castle Street Beaumaris Anglesey Gwynedd LL58 8AP

Map 8 B1

A stone's throw from Beaumaris Castle, the Grade II listed Bull dates back to 1472, though it was largely rebuilt in 1617. The original posting house of the borough, its courtyard arch houses the largest single-hinged gate in Britain. Within its cavernous bars is a valuable array of antique weaponry, an ancient brass water clock and the town's old ducking stool. With its newly-extended family room to the rear, this makes an ideal spot for lunch. Daily menus offer the best local produce splendidly scaled down for pubby enjoyment: alongside a smoked chicken and lentil broth (£1.85) and Welsh cheese ploughman's (£3.25) may be hake fillets with cream and mushrooms (£4.95), daube of beef with red wine and vegetables (£5.95). A grilled hamburger comes with rosemary and onion gravy (£4.95), amply garnished sandwiches include rare beef, cottage cheese and tuna (£1.50-£3.50): sweets may be lemon tart or dark and white chocolate terrine (£1.90). Toby jugs and tun dishes adorn the hammer beams and roof struts of a first floor restaurant which overlooks the courtyard. Keith Rothwell's dinners put a particular accent on local fish, though Anglesey venison, Welsh lamb and seasonal game are not overlooked. The Bull's popularity as a dinner venue necessitates booking, and menus start at £16.50 per head. The smartly refurbished bedrooms are named after characters from the novels of Charles Dickens, a frequent visitor to the inn. Each room is individually decorated and contains its own special features: exposed rafters and beams, oddly-shaped doors and ingeniously fitted bathrooms, all remain sympathetic to the Bull's unbroken history, while the phones, TVs and bedside radios satisfy today's requirements whilst remaining generally unintrusive. *Bar Food* 12-2.30 (*not Sun*). *Restaurant Meals* 12-1.30 (*Sun only*), 7.30-9.30. *Children's portions. Free House. Beer* Draught Bass, Felinfoel Double Dragon, Tetley Best Bitter. *Family room.* *Accommodation* 11 bedrooms, all en-suite, £68 (single £40). *Children welcome overnight, additional beds (£15), cots supplied (£5). Check-in all day. No dogs. Access, Visa.*

Betws-Yn-Rhos   Ffarm Hotel

FOOD

Tel 049260 287

Betws-Yn-Rhos nr Aberglei Clwyd LL22 8AR

Map 8 C1

Eating is the main event at this discreet venue, hiding signless behind an impressive crenellated stone facade. The 18th-century granite manor house has been comfortably modernised and the daily changing blackboard menu offers specials such as chicken with tarragon sauce (£7.95), duck with orange (£8.50) or rack of lamb (£7.95). Smiling service. *Bar Food* 7-10. *Vegetarian dishes. Free House. Beer* Tetley. *Access, Visa.*

Bodfari   Dinorben Arms

Tel 074575 309

Bodfari nr Denbigh Clwyd LL16 4DA

Map 8 C2

Heavily timbered 17th-century inn transformed into a diverse and shipshape dining pub. Amazing gardens too, with terraces, a verandah, fountains, a covered terrace, pretty flowers, and a children's play area beyond the huge tiered car park. *Free House. Beer* Thwaites. *Garden, children's play area. Family room.*

Brecon   Wellington Hotel

FOOD
B&B

Tel 0874 625225   Fax 0874 623223

The Bulwark Brecon Powys LD3 7AD

Map 9 C5

Converted from a well-heeled merchant's town house, a Georgian-fronted hotel standing opposite the Iron Duke's statue in the market square. Recent modernisation has brought up-to-date hotel facilities but kept the informality of a popular local; the former courtyard and stables are now a shopping arcade, with a coffee shop and pub access. Diverse food choices: chicken and ham pie (£4.20), steak and kidney pie (£4.55), spinach and cheese crunch (£3.15), and 'house-special' jumbo-sized vol-au-vents (£4.05). The residents' breakfast room is coffee-shop by day, candle-lit restaurant by night, with strong showings for both traditional Welsh and modern vegetarian cooking. Guests can choose from a weekly-changing table d'hote menu (3 courses £15.95) or à la carte. The former offers five choices at each course – start with kidneys turbigo or whitebait, followed by Welsh lamb hotpot or oated mackerel and finish with a selection of Welsh cheeses. There's also Bacchus, an intimate wine bar, which offers charcoal grills (steaks £6.20, kebabs £4.95, spare ribs £4.75) and self-served salads. Neatly-kept, plainly-furnished bedrooms; first-floor residents' lounge. *Bar food 11-11 (12-10 Sun).* **Restaurant meals** *6.30-10. Vegetarian dishes. Children's menu (£4.99). Children allowed in bar to eat. Free House.* **Beer** *Bass.* **Accommodation** *21 bedrooms, all en suite, £59 (single £39). Children welcome overnight, additional beds (£12 over 12 years), cots supplied. Check-in all day. Access, Amex, Visa.*

Burton Rossett   Golden Grove

Tel 0244 570445

Llyndir Lane Burton Green Burton Rossett Clwyd LL12 0AS

Map 8 D2

Remote black-and-white old Border inn, without even a pub sign (the scattered array of timbered buildings and big car park are a clue), but traditionally pubby within: low ceilings, a mix of old furniture and open fires. Excellent family facilities. *Free House.* **Beer** *Marston. Garden. Family room.*

Caerleon   Bell

Tel 0633 420613

Bullmoor Road Caerleon Gwent NP6 1QQ

Map 9 D6

450 years old, a former coaching inn, in the famous Roman settlement of Caerleon: baths, amphitheatre, and many finds in the local museum. **Beer** *Whitbread.*

Capel Curig   Cobden's Hotel

Tel 06904 243   Fax 06904 354

Capel Curig Gwynedd LL24 0EE

Map 8 C2

Smart country hotel with plush lounge and muddy-boots public bar, in the Snowdonia National Park. *Free House.* **Beer** *Courage, Directors, Webster's, John Smith.*

Cardiff   Fox & Hounds

Tel 0222 777046

Chapel Row St Mellons Cardiff South Glamorgan CF3 9UB

Map 9 D6

On the eastern outskirts of the city, off the B4487 Newport road. **Beer** *Brains. Garden, children's play area.*

Cardigan   Black Lion Hotel

Tel 0239 612532
B&B

High Street Cardigan Dyfed SA43 1HJ
Map 9 B4

The Black Lion claims to be the oldest coaching inn in Wales, having established itself in 1105 as a "one room grog shop". Much enlarged, but originally medieval town-centre inn, with a characterful beamed interior, complete with linenfold panelling in one of the bars. Pine-furnished bedrooms, and a comfortable upstairs television lounge, as well as a quaint little writing room. Bedrooms are equipped with tea/coffee making facilities, TV and telephone. *Free House. Beer Bass, Hancocks Bitter. Accommodation 15 bedrooms, all en suite, £45 (single £28.50). Children welcome overnight. Additional beds (no charge under 10 years), cots supplied. Check-in all day. No dogs. Access, Visa.*

Cenarth   White Hart

Tel 0239 710305
FOOD

Cenarth nr Newcastle Emlyn Dyfed SA38 9JP
Map 9 B5

Unpretentious, homely but recommendable food – Anglesey eggs (£2), steak and kidney pie (£4.25), home-cooked ham (£4.25) at a characterful old village pub with low, beamed ceilings, carved wooden pews and a wood-burning stove. *Bar Food 12-2.30, 6.30-9.30. Vegetarian dishes. Children's menu (£2.50 per dish). Free House. Beer Bass, Buckleys Bitter, Worthington. Garden, outdoor eating, children's play area. Family room. No credit cards.*

Chepstow   Castle View Hotel

FOOD

Tel 0291 620349
B&B

16 Bridge Street Chepstow Gwent NP6 5EZ
Map 13 F1

Attractive white-painted 18th-century former private house with old art works and wooden winding staircase. Examples of bar food: tagliatelle (£4.95), chicken jamboree (£5.95), steak sandwich (£5.95), ploughman's (£3.20). Simple but more substantial dishes served in the restaurant include rack of Welsh lamb (£9.95), poached local salmon (£8.95) and tenderloin of pork (£9.95). A Sunday roast 3-course set menu is £9.95 served with a complimentary glass of house wine. Two bedrooms are in a modern annexe. Lovely garden. *Bar Food & Restaurant Meals 12-2, 6.30-9.30. Vegetarian dishes. Free House. Beer Tetley. Garden, outdoor eating. Family room. Accommodation 11 bedrooms, all en suite, £65 (single £44.50). Children welcome overnight. Additional beds and cots available. Check-in all day. Access, Amex, Diners, Visa.*

Cilcain   White Horse

Tel 0352 740142

Cilcain nr Mold Clwyd CH7 5NN
Map 8 D2

Classic Welsh village pub, partly 14th-century, popular with walkers (Moel Fammau is nearby). Delightful lounge with original beams, brasses, an inglenook and very low seating: other intimate drinking areas leading off, plus old-fashioned quarry-tiled public bar. Acts as local newsagent on Sundays. Four real fires in winter. No children. *Free House. Beer Ansells, Bass, Burton Ale, Marston Pedigree, Sam Powells Bitter.*

Criccieth   Prince of Wales

Tel 0766 522556

High Street Criccieth Gwynedd LL52 0HB

Map 8 B2

Busy pub, right on the square, and a lively local: live music on
Tuesday nights, and a piano in the bar (impromptu performances
encouraged). Family-orientated: children are positively welcomed, not
just tolerated. *Beer Whitbread. Family room.*

Crickhowell   Bear Hotel

Tel 0873 810408   Fax 0873 811696

Brecon Road (A40) Crickhowell Powys NP8 1BW

FOOD

B&B

Map 9 D5

As late as the year 1852 there were a dozen daily coach departures
from the Bear, the London coach heading for Gloucester at 4.50pm
and the North Mail leaving for Brecon at midnight. Vehicular access
today is through the same cobbled archway, and the probably former
waiting rooms. The bars of today are still evocative of those romantic
days, with open fires, blackened oak beams, ponderous Welsh dressers
and Victorian farmhouse furniture. Further inside in a maze of rooms
and recesses, the original layout, with its various levels, has been
mercifully preserved in three tiers of restaurant and function rooms
which share the tranquillity of rear views across the garden. Where
the old now meets the new is virtually impossible to detect. Eating
arrangements are similarly two-tiered. Aged-looking bar menus offer
starters and light snacks like soups, Welsh filo of Pencarreg cheese
with redcurrants (£2.75), roll of smoked salmon with cream of
salmon filling (£3.50), and wild local rabbit and hazelnut terrine
(£3.95). More substantial dishes include home-made salmon fish cakes
(£5.75). Typical of the pudding list are raspberry sablé (£2.95),
bread-and-butter pudding with rum-soaked raisins (£2.50), and the
cautionary "chocoholics anonymous" (£2.50). A la carte dishes include
braised quail (£3.25), potato basket of wild mushrooms (£3.95),
Cornish scallops (£3.95), loin of Welsh venison (£13.95) and parsnip
and cashew nut bake (£9.50). Attractive main-house bedrooms are
approached overlooking the Bear's wondrous interior on stairs with
antique gnarled oak balustrades; the curve of the main road, less
enchantingly, brings modern traffic within inches of the windows, a
disadvantage of the front rooms. The inn's extension successfully
echoes the balconied theme, with access to the neatly appointed new
bedrooms looking inwards over the brick paving and flower beds of
the courtyard. There is also a splendid honeymoon suite with four-
poster bed and whirlpool bath. *Bar Food 12-2, 6-10 (7-9.30 Sun).
Restaurant Meals 7-9.30 (except Sun). Vegetarian dishes. Children's
portions. Free House. Beer Bass, Ruddles, Webster. Garden, outdoor eating.
Family room. Accommodation 29 bedrooms, all en suite, £48 (single
£34). Children welcome overnight, additional beds (from £5), cots
supplied. Check-in all day. Access, Amex, Visa.*

Crickhowell   Nantyffin Cider Mill

Tel 0873 810775

Brecon Road Crickhowell Powys NP8 1SG

FOOD

Map 9 D5

Owned by the Tretower estates whose lands border the north-west
bank of the river Usk, the pink-painted former cider mill is once
again in the hands of tenants whose abiding interest lies in a quality
food operation. This is evidenced by a comprehensive menu
(supplemented by daily blackboard specials) that is served in the newly

carpeted lounge, the stylish dining room – whose centrepiece is a reconstruction of the original cider press – and out in the picturesque garden that overlooks both road and river. Breadcrumbed sardines with garlic and parsley butter (£2.95) and deep-fried Brie with blueberry and apple purée (£3.25) are typical starters, followed by skate wings with samphire and lemon butter (£8.25), dressed crab salad (£8.70), rack of lamb with sweet red cabbage (£9.85) or grilled gammon and fried egg (£5.95). For vegetarians, Stilton and walnut filo parcels (£3.95) and spring rolls filled with Oriental vegetables (£6.95); for the sweet-toothed white and dark chocolate mousse (£2.85) and crème brulée with orange biscuits (£2.85). Though most of the lighter fare is available for a bar snack, the menu carries a weight with it that suggests that mere casual trade is being somewhat overlooked. Nantyffin remains nonetheless a pub at heart, whose bars retain much of their original Welsh slate and serve a good selection of real ales and cider; what it lacks, perhaps, is the ability to take itself a little less seriously. *Bar Food 12-2, 6-10 (Sun from 7). Vegetarian dishes. Free House. Beer Marston Pedigree, Felinfoel Double Dragon, Burcombe Bitter, Stedmans SB. Cider Stonehouse, Weston's West Country. Garden, outdoor eating. Access, Visa.*

Dulas   Pilot Boat Inn

Tel 0248 88205

Dulas Amlwch Anglesey Gwynedd LL70 9EX   **Map 8 B1**

A smithy in the 19th century, and now a popular pub within view of the sea. *Beer Robinsons. Garden, children's play area. Family room.*

East Aberthaw   Blue Anchor   ★

Tel 0446 750329

FOOD

East Aberthaw nr Barry South Glamorgan CF6 9DD   **Map 9 C6**

There's a full six centuries of history to the splendid Blue Anchor, and the old cliché about stepping back in time is truer here than is usual. Entering this quaint thatched cottage through the black oak door, under hanging ivy that appears to be holding the old stone walls together, visitors are taken by way of tiny nooks and crannies into a smugglers' den which includes an internal doorway little more than four feet high. Fifty years now in ownership of the Coleman family, and administered day-to-day by the urbane Jeremy, the pub has gone from strength to strength since the opening last year of its new restaurant. A nearly hidden, almost cavernous stairway leads to a dining room of surprising spaciousness, presided over by brilliant young chef, Andrew Lawrence. The output of his young team producing bar lunches daily (except Sunday), a six-night restaurant menu (not Sunday), and comprehensive Sunday lunch (3-courses £8.95), is little short of prodigious. The Coleman vegetable garden weighs in with onions and fresh vegetables, garden fruits and herbs, and local suppliers add the fresh, free-range meats and eggs, as well as a commendable list of Welsh cheeses. From a regularly changing restaurant menu choose the smoked Wye salmon, asparagus and mango salad (£5.25) or leek, laverbread and crab cocottes (£3.95); followed perhaps by roast Aylesbury duck (£11.20), fillets of Welsh beef (£11.95) or Wye salmon (£10.35) and a home-made pudding (£2.50), while the blackboard serves as a market place for predominantly fishy specials. Full of interest and atmosphere, the Blue Anchor is also a draw for history buffs and real ale aficionados, its regular beer list supplemented by often interesting guest names.

Bar Food 12-2 (*not Sun*). *Restaurant Meals* 12-2 (*Sun only*), 7.30-9.30 (*except Sun*) (7-9.30 *Sat*). *Vegetarian dishes. Children's menu (lunch in bar – £1.50 per dish). Free House.* **Beer** *Buckley, Marston, Theakston, Wadworth. Patio, outdoor eating. Family room. Access, Visa.*

Felindre Farchog   Salutation Inn

Tel 0239 820564	**B&B**
on A487 Felindre Farchog Dyfed SA41 3UY	Map 9 C5

Modernised, well-kept old inn (original building goes back to 16th century) at the centre of the Preseli National Park. 'Olde worlde' lounge, games room-cum-public bar, and overflow Garden Room leading off, with patio doors to riverside garden. Good bedrooms in modern wing are well-equipped and maintained; bright, good-sized residents' lounge. *Free House.* **Beer** *Ind Coope Burton Ale. Riverside garden, outdoor eating, children's play area. Family room.* **Accommodation** *9 bedrooms, all en suite, £52 (single £32). Children welcome overnight, additional beds (from £5), cots supplied. Check-in all day. Access, Visa.*

Glanwydden   Queen's Head

Tel 0492 546570	**FOOD**
Glanwydden Llandudno Junction Gwynedd LL31 9JP	Map 8 C1

Hidden down a maze of country lanes, Glanwydden is best found by following the Llanrhos road from Penrhyn Bay (B5115). Motivator of the Queen's Head's admirable food operation is chef/landlord Robert Cureton, who sets great store by careful shopping for his daily-updated menus. Fresh fish thus plays a major part: there are local plaice fillets with hazelnut butter (£5.50), the "house speciality" seafood platter (£8.50) and a prize-winning dish of Conwy mussels topped with smoked Caerphilly (£4.95). Meat-based signature dishes carry more weight in winter, as in spicy lamb's kidneys with peppercorn and brandy sauce (£6.25), braised oxtail with pickled walnuts in Guinness sauce (£6.50) and the ever-popular steak and mushroom pie (£5.50). Start, perhaps, with potted local seafood (£4.75) or a creamy tomato and orange soup (£1.75) and finish with a wide choice of nursery puddings – including spotted dick or treacle tart (£2.20) – or creamy chocolate brandy trifle (£2.20). From a lighter snack menu there's even more choice from smoked chicken salad with curried mayonnaise (£5.75) or a country lentil crumble (£5.50) at lunchtime, through to deep-fried Pencalf Brie (£4.25) and chicken chasseur (£6.75) by night. Hand-pulled beers are suitably well kept and house wines by the glass sensibly supplemented by special offer bin ends; an above-average wine list comes from Rodney Densen of Nantwich. Embarking on a second decade here, the Curetons' ever-expanding business, serving up to 80 meals per session, cries out for more space. Meanwhile, parties of six or more may only book for the early evenings or Sunday lunch, while children under 7 remain excluded. *Bar Food* 12-2, 6.30-9 (*Sun from 7*). *Vegetarian dishes.* **Beer** *Ansells, Tetley, Burton, guest ale. Access, Visa.*

Glyn Garth   Gazelle Hotel

Tel 0248 713364	
Menai Bridge Glyn Garth Anglesey Gwynedd LL59 5PD	Map 8 B1

Attractive white-painted country hotel on the edge of the Menai Straits, directly opposite Bangor Pier. **Beer** *Robinsons. Riverside garden. Family room.*

Hanmer   Hanmer Arms

`Tel 094874 532`

Hanmer nr Whitchurch Clwyd SY13 3DE   Map 6 A3

Popular pub near the church in a pretty village off the A539, six miles
west of Whitchurch. *Free House.* **Beer** *Tetley, Burton. Garden, children's
play area.*

Hay-on-Wye   Kilvert Country Hotel

`Tel 0497 821042   Fax 0497 821004`   **B&B**

Bull Ring Hay-on-Wye Powys HR3 5AG   Map 9 D5

A town-centre inn dating from the late 17th century, named after the
diarist Reverend Francis Kilvert. The characterful single bar also
doubles as reception, and behind a stained-glass partition is the
intimate residents' lounge. Splendid brass bedsteads are a feature of the
bedrooms, many of which are beamed. All have en-suite shower
rooms as well as modern hotel conveniences. *Garden. Free House.* **Beer**
Bass, Flowers. **Accommodation** *11 bedrooms, all en suite, £57.50 (single
£32.50). Children welcome overnight, additional beds and cots available.
Check-in by arrangement. Access, Amex, Visa.*

Hay-on-Wye   Old Black Lion   **FOOD**

`Tel 0497 820841`   **B&B**

26 Lion Street Hay-on-Wye Powys HR3 5AD   Map 9 D5

Tucked away from the bustling centre of this Welsh Marches town
(renowned for its book shops), the Lion has established an enviable
reputation for its food: what it lacks is room. Residents have priority
in the restaurant (open evenings only) where booking is essential: as
diners study their menus in the single bar there can be a scramble for
seats and bar menus, and thus a log-jam of orders. From a very long
menu choices range from a simple ploughman's (£3.20) through to
seafood pancakes with spicy tomato sauce (£5.25) and aubergines in
chili and garlic sauce (£4.75) and there's a "simply steaks" menu in the
£8-£12 range. Choose from the restaurant menu from soup, paté and
pan-fried escargots to precede cider-baked Barbary duck or rainbow
trout with hazelnut butter, and perhaps a coffee and Tia Maria
meringue to follow. The pub's blackened beams and bowers, though
not all original, are nonetheless full of character, and the restaurant has
been smartened up with table linen, candles and fresh flowers.
Accommodation is divided between the main house and a purpose-
built extension adjoining the car park. All rooms except one are en-
suite and all are neatly kept: what the older rooms may lack in space
and modern-day comforts is now compensated by some smart new
fabrics and carpets alongside the evocative character of little-changed
17th-century inn. **Bar Food** *12-2, 7-9.* **Restaurant Meals** *12-2, 7-9
(Sun only). Vegetarian dishes. Children's portions. Free House.* **Beer**
Draught Bass, Flowers Original. Outdoor eating. **Accommodation**
*10 bedrooms, 9 en suite, £40 (single £25). Children welcome overnight,
additional beds (£10), cots supplied. Check-in by arrangement. Access,
Visa.*

Howey   Drovers Arms

Tel 0597 822508

Howey nr Llandrindod Wells Powys LD1 5PT   Map 9 C4

Characterful Victorian pub; piano in the public bar; woodcarving in the lounge. **Beer** *Whitbread, Marston Pedigree.*

Landshipping   Stanley Arms

Tel 0834 891227

Landshipping nr Narberth Dyfed SA67 8BE   Map 9 A5

Just 200 yards from the estuary, and moorings are available there for customers' use. Nice interior includes 18th-century public bar with original slate floor; live music Fridays in summer, Saturdays in winter. **Beer** *Worthington Best, Crown SBB. Garden. Family room.*

Llanarmon Dyffryn Ceiriog   West Arms Hotel   **FOOD**

Tel 069176 665   Fax 069176 622   **B&B**

Llanarmon Dyffryn Ceiriog nr Llangollen Clwyd LL20 7LD   Map 8 D2

In a picturesque hamlet at the head of the Ceiriog Valley, this 16th-century former farmhouse stands to the front of well-manicured gardens which run down to the river bridge. Black and white painted outside and bedecked with creeper and summer flowers, it's a haven of cosy comfort within, the tone set by open log fires, flagstone floors, blackened beams and rustic furniture. Tucked around the back, the Wayfarers' Bar serves a modest selection of well-prepared snacks in chintzy surroundings with an adjacent family lounge and patio. Following soup (£2.40), smoked mackerel paté (£3) and Stilton mushrooms (£3.50), local Ceiriog trout (£5.75) heads a list of main meals that might include turkey, ham and mushroom pie (£4.75), tagliatelle with peppers, mushrooms and cream (£4.50) or a cauliflower, peanut and cream cheese bake (£2.50). Apple pie (£2.25) and chocolate mousse (£2.50) are typical puddings. Bedrooms retain the period comfort afforded by handsome antique furnishings alongside modern fitted bathrooms; homely extras include pot pourri and quality toiletries. Five rooms are reserved for non-smokers and the two suites have plenty of space for family use. Table d'hote dinner is available to residents and others priced around £20 per head. **Bar Food** *12-2.30, 6.30-9.30 (Sun from 7).* **Restaurant Meals** *12-2.30 (Sun only), 7.30-9.30. Free House.* **Beer** *Boddingtons. Garden, outdoor eating, children's play area. Family room.* **Accommodation** *14 rooms, all en suite, £78, single £49.50. Children welcome overnight, additional beds £21.50. Cots supplied £10. Access, Amex, Diners, Visa.*

Llanbedr Dyffryn Clwyd   Griffin Inn

Tel 0824 702792

Llanbedr Dyffryn Clwyd nr Ruthin Clwyd LL15 1UP   Map 8 D2

A popular old inn, once an important coaching stage on the old turnpike road from Mold to Ruthin. Rambling interior, with a public bar, restaurant, and smallish lounge warmed by an open fire, but beyond the lounge a larger, plain extension, and then a cosy little sitting area complete with piano. Good views from the terrace. **Beer** *Robinson's, Hartleys XB, Fellrunners.*

Llanbedrog   Glyn-y-Weddw Arms

Tel 0758 740212

Abersoch Road Llanbedrog Gwynedd LL53 7TH   Map 8 B2

Attractive, popular pub close to a delightful beach; the garden can get very hectic in summer, when the whole village is a sheltered sun-trap. *Garden, children's play area. Family room.*

Llanbedrog   Ship Inn

Tel 0758 740270

Bryn-y-Gro Llanbedrog Gwynedd LL53 7PE   Map 8 B2

Cosy and traditional inn with a popular outside sitting area. **Beer** *Burtonwood. Family room.*

Llanddarog   Butchers Arms

Tel 0267 275330   **FOOD**

Llanddarog nr Carmarthen Dyfed SE32 8NS   Map 9 B5

This tiny pub stands by the 19th-century stone-built St Tarog's church, and the old village street runs down to where the old A40 once thundered by. We say hooray today for the new by-pass which makes this such a sleepy spot, and say another as the low, flower-bedecked exterior of the pub gives way to a splendidly atmospheric interior. Felinfoel ales take their rightful place at the bar, as Welsh is widely spoken here, though this in no way detracts from the warm welcome and friendly service. A word to the wise: if you have decided to eat, then book ahead and side-step the queue. Take time, however, to admire the Toby jug collection hanging in the bar, and the shining collection of miniature brass lamps and candleholders on the mantel, under which the dog-grate glows in winter and flower vases add a blaze of summer colour. In addition to the regular menu, on which the prime steaks offer particularly good value, look for the specials board, which is strong on fresh fish and seafood: king prawns (£3.60), fillets of river salmon in strawberry sauce, and a herby stuffed trout (£6) are typical examples. Otherwise, you might start with smoked venison, or avocado and bacon salad, followed by mixed grill (£11), pork fillet with garlic and mushroom sauce (£8.30), or Hungarian chicken (£5.50). Garlic potatoes are so good as to be obligatory. Equally desirable for drivers and lunchtime generally are the 25cl bottles of Bordeaux; the white version cools neatly in a pint mug of iced water. **Bar Food & Restaurant Meals** *11-2.45 (except Sun), 6-10. Vegetarian dishes. Children's menu (from £1.20). Free House.* **Beer** *Felinfoel, guest beers. Children allowed in bar to eat. Patio, outdoor eating. Family room. Access, Visa.*

Llandissilio   Bush Inn

Tel 0437 563626   **FOOD**

Llandissilio nr Clynderwen Dyfed SA66 7TS   Map 9 B5

Tiny, characterful little bar in cosy old pub. Open fires, polished tables, plants and dressers crammed with plates and ornaments provide a cosy background in the bright dining room, where help-yourself salads are laid out for choosing; try them with home-cooked local turkey (£4.95), home-made cheese and onion tart (£3.95), or go for a simple hot dish like lasagne (£3.95), followed by good local cheese and apple crumble or treacle tart (£1.60). **Bar Food & Restaurant Meals** *12-2.30, 6.30-9.30. Vegetarian dishes. Free House.* **Beer** *Bass, Worthington. Garden, outdoor eating. No credit cards.*

Llandogo   Sloop Inn

| Tel 0594 530291 | **B&B** |
| Llandogo nr Monmouth Gwent NP5 4TW | Map 9 D5 |

18th-century inn, a mix of ancient and modern. Bedrooms include a
suite with a French window leading out on to a private balcony.
Free House. **Beer** *Hook Norton, Smiles, Bass. Garden, children's play area.*
Accommodation *4 bedrooms, all en suite, £39 (single £25.50).*
Check-in all day. Access, Amex, Visa.

Llandovery   King's Head Inn

| Tel 0550 20393 | **B&B** |
| Market Square Llandovery Dyfed SA20 0AB | Map 9 C5 |

The Madeira-Coles have been welcoming visitors for over 20 years to
their historic inn of medieval origins, strikingly painted in black with
white woodwork. It's projecting cornerstone (designed to protect the
building from cartwheels) was used as a pulpit by the first Welsh
Methodist. Inside, medieval stonework and massive low timbers (mind
your head!) add to the charms of the neat bedrooms with tea-makers,
radio-alarms and bathrooms. There is also a residents' TV lounge.
Free House. **Beer** *Hancock's.* **Accommodation** *4 bedrooms, all en suite,
£44 (single £26). Children welcome overnight. Check-in all day.
No credit cards.*

Llandrindod Wells   Llanerch Inn

| Tel 0597 822086 | |
| Llanerch Lane off Waterloo Road Llandrindod Wells Powys LD1 5BG | Map 9 C4 |

Welcoming and attractive 16th-century inn; good summer garden,
where boules is keenly played. *Free House.* **Beer** *Bass, Hancock HB,
Robinson Best. Garden, children's play area. Family room.*

Llandudno   Cottage Loaf

| Tel 0492 870762 | |
| Market Street Llandudno Gwynedd LL30 2SR | Map 8 C1 |

Smartly styled newish conversion from the old bakery. **Beer** *Ruddles,
Webster's. Garden.*

Llandudno   King's Head

| Tel 0492 877993 | |
| Old Road Tram Station Llandudno Gwynedd LL30 2NB | Map 8 C1 |

Three family areas; dogs welcome in quarry-tiled ares; log fires all
winter. **Beer** *Ruddles, Webster's. Garden. Family room.*

Llandybie   Red Lion

| Tel 0269 851202 | |
| Llandybie nr Ammanford Dyfed SA18 3JA | Map 9 C5 |

A Grade II listed 18th-century pub run by a brother and sister team.
Comfortable series of individual rooms, old mirrors and local pictures.
Beer *Whitbread, Marston Pedigree. Garden, children's play area. Family
room.*

Llanengan   Sun Inn

Tel 0758 712660

Llanengan Abersoch Gwynedd LL53 7LG   **Map 8 B3**

Traditional pub by Hells Mouth beach on the edge of the Lyn. *Free House.* **Beer** *Tetley Bitter, Burton Ale. Garden, children's play area.*

Llanferres   Druid Inn

Tel 035285 225

Ruthin Road Llanferres nr Mold Clwyd CH7 5SQ   **Map 8 D2**

Family-owned and run, attractive white-painted roadside inn with charming views and mountain walks, overlooking the Alyn river. Plain, modernised interior decor. *Free House.* **Beer** *Burtonwood.*

Llanfrynach   White Swan

Tel 0874 86276

Llanfrynach Powys LD3 7BZ

FOOD

Map 9 C5

Flagstone floors, rough stone walls, beams and a vast inglenook create a simple rustic setting for the Bells' hearty, carefully prepared food at this pretty village pub. French onion soup (£2.15), smoked mackerel paté (£3.90) and tasty meat (beef and mushroom £7.20) and fish pies are popular dishes. Vegetarians are catered for (macaroni and broccoli cheese £4.30) and a children's menu is available in the bar. *Bar Food (except Mon) 12-2 (12-1.30 Sun), 5-10 (7-9 Sun). Vegetarian dishes. Children's menu (£3.50). Children allowed to eat in bar. Free House.* **Beer** *Brains, Whitbread. Garden. Family room. No credit cards.*

Llangollen   Britannia Inn

Tel 0978 860144

Horseshoe Pass Llangollen Clwyd LL20 8DW

B&B

Map 8 D2

In the 11th century a group of monks lived here. Their burial ground is at the rear of the inn and one of the bedrooms' fireplaces dates back to this period. Local craftsmen have brought traditional Welsh furnishings in local elm to both the characterful old bars. All bedrooms have four-poster beds. *Free House.* **Beer** *Flowers, Boddingtons. Garden, outdoor eating.* **Accommodation** *6 bedrooms, all en suite, £40 (single £25). Children welcome overnight. Additional beds (from £2). Check-in all day. Access, Amex, Diners, Visa.*

Llangorse   Castle Inn

Tel 0874 84225

Llangorse nr Brecon Powys LD3 7UB   **Map 9 D5**

17th-century cottage pub with flagstoned bar and open fireplace. **Beer** *Whitbread, Hancocks HB, Brains SA. Family room.*

Llangorse   Red Lion

Tel 0874 84238

Llangorse nr Brecon Powys LD3 7TY

B&B

Map 9 D5

Nestling in a lovely valley between the Brecon Beacons and the Black Mountains is a pleasant 180-year-old village pub offering accommodation in ten homely, comfortable bedrooms. All rooms are equipped with tea-makers, TVs and radio-alarms. Half have simple but immaculately kept en-suite bathrooms, the remainder showers and washbasins only. There is a tiny residents' lounge, and downstairs two cosy, stone-walled bars. *Free House.* **Beer** *Flowers Original, Marston's Pedigree, Brains SA and Boddingtons. Riverside terrace/patio. Family room.* **Accommodation** *10 bedrooms, 5 en suite, £48 (single £24). Children welcome overnight. Additional beds (no charge under 12 yrs) and cots supplied. Check-in all day. No credit cards.*

Llangrannog   The Ship Inn

FOOD

Tel 0239 654423	**B&B**
Llangrannog Dyfed SA44 6SL	**Map 9 B4**

A narrow winding road (watch out for a very steep hairpin bend) leads down to the delightful little seaside village of Llangrannog and the white-painted Ship Inn, just 50 yards from the beach. It's run by two couples, the Boxes and the Browns: Lynne and De are responsible for the bar menu which, in addition to standard items like steak and kidney pie (£4.75), steaks (well hung by the local butcher – from £7.45), ploughman's (from £2.90), jacket potatoes and sandwiches, roams far and wide with pizza (from £2.95), doner kebabs (£2.35), Madras curry (£4.75) and, from the blackboard 'Specials' menu, snails in garlic butter (£2.75) and tandoori chicken masala (£4.95). Local seafood features strongly in summer with dressed crab (£4.65), baked mackerel (£2.95) and, given 24 hours notice, a special seafood platter (£9.65) that includes lobster, scallops, cockles, mussels, whelks, crab and prawns. Eat in one of the two bars (which feature in the TV production of Kingsley Amis's *The Old Devils*) or outside under colourful awnings that keep the showers at bay while you watch the world go by. Three bedrooms (available in summer only) are let either together as a self-catering apartment or separately on a bed and breakfast basis with guests sharing the lounge and bathroom.
Bar Food *12-3, 6-10. Vegetarian dishes. Children's menu/portions. Free House.* **Beer** *Burton, Worthington. Family room, Outdoor eating.* **Accommodation** *3 bedrooms, sharing bathroom, £30 (single £15). Children welcome overnight. Check-in all day. No credit cards.*

Llangurig   Blue Bell Inn

Tel 05515 254	**B&B**
Llangurig nr Llanidloes Powys SY18 6SG	**Map 9 C4**

A welcome in the hillside – courtesy of Diana and Bill Mills – awaits you in their charming 16th-century fishing inn in Wales' highest village. An old black iron range stands on the slate floor of the simple, friendly bar. Enjoy a game of darts or dip into a book in the homely residents' lounge. Compact, rustic bedrooms have modern units and co-ordinated decor. One has en-suite facilities; the others share two modern public bathrooms. *Free House.* **Beer** *Whitbread Best, Flowers Original.* **Accommodation** *10 bedrooms, 1 en suite, £33 (single £26.50). Children welcome overnight. Additional beds and cots available. Check-in by arrangement. Access, Visa.*

Llannefydd   Hawk & Buckle Inn

Tel 074579 249 Fax 074579 316	**B&B**
Llannefydd nr Denbigh Clwyd LL16 5ED	**Map 8 C1**

Standing opposite the Saxon church, the Hawk & Buckle dates from the 17th century. A splendid mural of the village adorns the residents' entrance and a couple of original beams lend character to the main bar. Bedrooms, mainly in an extension at the back, have built-in wardrobes with curtains for doors, direct-dial phones, TVs and tea-makers, as well as modern bathrooms with showers over the tubs. No real ales. *Free House. **Accommodation** 10 bedrooms, all en suite, £48 (single £36). No children under 8. No dogs. Check-in all day. Access, Visa.*

Llanvetherine   King's Arms

Tel 0873 821221

Llanvetherine nr Abergavenny Gwent NP7 8RG   Map 9 D5

17th-century coaching inn on the B4521, within 400 yards of the Offa's Dyke footpath. *Free House. **Beer** Morland Best, Felinfoel, Double Dragon, Taylor. Garden, children's play area. Family room.*

Llanwnda   Goat Inn

Tel 0286 830256

Llanwnda Gwynedd LL54 5SD   Map 8 B2

In the Griffith family for over 150 years; Ann's father and grandfather were here before her. *Free House. **Beer** Draught Bass, Boddingtons. Garden, children's play area. Family room.*

Llanwrtyd Wells   Neaudd Arms Hotel

Tel 05913 236

The Square Llanwrtyd Wells Powys LD5 4RB   Map 9 C4

Imposing riverside hotel at the centre of Britain's smallest town. The landlord is a great organiser of walks, cycling (hire) and the mid-Wales Beer Festival (November). Traditional Welsh back bar with traditional Welsh singing at weekends; more sedate lounge. Very friendly. *Free House. **Beer** Draught Bass, Felinfoel Double Dragon, Hancock's HB, Worthington Dark Mild, guest beer.*

Llowes   Radnor Arms

Tel 0497 847460   **FOOD**

Llowes Powys HR3 5JA   Map 9 D5

Developed over the years from its original identity as the old village school to its current state of culinary refinement, the Radnor Arms nevertheless still remains more a pub for eating in than a restaurant-with-bar. With only a dozen tables and no more than forty seats, it's surprising to encounter 99 starters, snacks and main dishes from which to choose! Despite the useful summer overflow to several picnic tables in the garden, still the pub's so tiny that both gents' and ladies' toilets are relegated to the outhouse. Inside, the Radnor Arms divides by means of heavy pine panels into the bar area proper, popular by day, and a more spacious, lofty-beamed garden side for more leisurely evening enjoyment, and for which you ought to book. Either way, there's good beer from the bar – with Marston's Pedigree and Felinfoel Double Dragon on handpump – and a modest selection of house wines. Now to the menu, where the soup choice might include French onion (£2.20); lamb's liver and bacon (£6.75), cottage pie (£4.70), stuffed quail in brandy sauce (£6.50), tournedos Rossini (£12.95); tiger prawns with garlic bread (£6.50), haddock mornay (£6.95), or monkfish kebab (£11.75). Puddings include gateau Véronique (£2.90) and sticky toffee pudding (£2.85). Some homely touches help to extend a warm Welsh welcome. Cruets and coffee sets are of hand-made Black Mountain pottery, and there are woolly dolls and framed three-dimensional paper cut-outs for sale. ***Bar Food** (except Sun eve & all day Mon) 11-2.30 (12.-2.30 Sun), 6.30-11 (except Sun). Vegetarian dishes. Free House. **Beer** Felinfoel Black Dragon, Marston's Pedigree. Garden, outdoor eating. No credit cards.*

Llwyndafydd   Crown Inn

| Tel 0545 560396 |
| Llwyndafydd nr New Quay Dyfed SA44 6FU | Map 9 B4 |

Comfortably modernised 18th-century inn, in a wooded valley a mile and a half from the sea; a side lane by the pub leads down to a little cove. Huge patio seats 90 people, prettily landscaped garden and extensive play area. *Free House.* **Beer** *Bass, Flowers IPA, Original. Garden. Family room.*

Llyswen   Griffin Inn   ★

FOOD
B&B

| Tel 0874 754241   Fax 0874 754592 |
| Llyswen Brecon Powys LD3 0OU | Map 9 D5 |

Mythically speaking, the griffin is a creature of vast proportions, half lion, half dragon, its whole being considerably less awesome than its constituent parts. No such problems exist for Richard and Di Stockton, for their Griffin is nothing short of splendid in all departments and so conspicuously well-run as to have been voted the most welcoming pub in Britain. That locally-caught salmon and brook trout feature so regularly on the menu is scarcely surprising as the Griffin employs its own ghillie, and fishing stories abound in the bar, which is the centre of village life. It's hung with framed displays of fishing flies and maps of the upper and lower reaches of the Wye valley, and dominated by a splendid inglenook fire. Beer is also taken seriously and kept in tip-top condition, summer Boddingtons and Flowers IPA giving way to sturdier guest beers in winter. In the adjacent lounge, low tables, high-backed Windsor chairs and window seats make a comfy setting for either a light snack or one of the daily-changing hot dishes, perhaps home-made soup (£2.50), hot chicken liver and bacon salad (£3.35), ratatouille pasta (£5.95) or jugged venison (£7.50). Evening meals provide a wider choice of more substantial fare, either in the no-smoking restaurant or the bars, as space allows. Here you might order Stilton, celery and port terrine (£3.75) then ragout of wild rabbit (£8.50) or fresh poached salmon in (£9.50), followed by treacle tart or wimberry crumble (both £2.55). Bedrooms, recently increased to eight and all but one with en-suite facilities, revert to the fishing theme: Alexander Durham Ranger and Green Highlander, for instance, being named after fishing flies. To say that they are cottagey is not to decry the pretty floral curtains and bed-covers; they are also wonderfully tranquil, and though there are telephones, television is considered superfluous. The splendid new residents' lounge on the upper floor of the inn's oldest part is dramatically set under original rafters dating, it is thought, from 1467. *Bar Food 12-2, 7-9. Restaurant Meals 1-3 (Sun only), 7-9. Vegetarian dishes. Children's portions. Children allowed in bar to eat. Free House. Beer Whitbread, Boddingtons Bitter, Flowers IPA. Patio, outdoor eating. Accommodation 8 bedrooms, 7 en suite, £50 (single from £30). Children welcome overnight. Additional beds and cots available. Check-in all day. Access, Amex, Diners, Visa.*

Lydart   Gockett Inn

Tel 0600 860486

Lydart nr Monmouth Gwent NP5 4AD

This former staging post on the St David's to London route stands atop an escarpment (now the B4293) three miles outside Monmouth; "Gockett" was the local name for the black grouse which inhabited these heathlands until their extinction a century or so ago. Central to the inn's modern attractions are Hazel Short's daily selected menus, wherein brevity is made a virtue by careful buying of top-quality foodstuffs, and by her innovative approach to traditional recipes. Thus the beef pie today may be cooked with Guinness and mushrooms; tomorrow's chock full of smoked oysters. Equally popular pies are rabbit with mustard and rosemary, or chicken and asparagus (£4.95). Home-made soups (£2.25) are thick, flavourful, and popular, along with the likes of garlic mushrooms, duck liver paté, local salmon mayonnaise (£3.95) or tagliatelle Alfredo. Though all are officially starters, a light lunch of two of them is equally acceptable, except on Sundays, when bookings should be made for the fixed-price lunch (3 courses £8.95). Alongside the hefty pies other main courses are equally substantial: fillet of beef en croute stuffed with Stilton (£11.50), pan-fried lemon sole (£10.95), and vegetarian alternatives like a vegetable stroganoff with green noodles. To accompany, expect a generous side plate of assorted fresh vegetables and potatoes. A variety of cheeses is always available and the pudding list which follows is simple but commendable in scope (all £2.25). Leather banquettes, silk flowers and gathered drapes lend a bright, cottagey feel to the original dining room, where tables are neatly spaced in front of a smoky, stone fireplace hung with horse brasses and copper bed-warmers. A more recent extension to the bar has increased the space – though not perhaps enhanced the character – and leads to an enclosed rear patio, and a neat garden for al fresco eating in fine weather. *Bar Food & Restaurant Meals 12-2, 7-10 (7-9 Sun). Vegetarian dishes. Children's portions (£2.25 per dish). Children allowed in bar to eat. Free House. Beer Bass, Felinfoel. Cider Westons. Garden, outdoor eating, children's play area. Access, Visa.*

Maentwrog   Grapes Hotel

Tel 0766 85208

Maentwrog nr Bleinau Ffestiniog Gwynedd LL41 4HN

Map 8 C2

Most attractive, stone-built 19th-century inn, with a lovely old bar, unspoilt by progress. Children are allowed on the verandah. *Free House. Beer Bass, Theakston XB.*

Mold   We Three Loggerheads

Tel 035 285 337

Ruthin Road Loggerheads nr Mold Clwyd CH7 5PG

Map 8 D2

Well-run, busy old pub, with a characterful original little bar, bigger, pool-table dominated locals' bar and modern, attractive high-raftered upper lounge. Nature trails and good walks in the surrounding country park. *Beer Bass. Riverside patio/terrace.*

Monmouth   Punch House

Tel 0600 713855

Agincourt Square Monmouth Gwent NP5 3BT   Map 9 D5

Historic, pristine old inn dominating the market square; pretty
cobbled drinking area. **Beer** *Bass, Wadworth 6X.*

Montgomery   Dragon Inn

Tel 0686 668359

Montgomery Powys SY15 6AA   Map 8 D3

Timbered 17th-century coaching inn, modernised and with an indoor
heated pool. **Beer** *Woods, Sam Powell, Felinfoel Bitter. Garden. Family
room.*

Newport   Golden Lion

Tel 0239 820321

East Street Newport Dyfed SA42 0SY   Map 9 D6

A pleasant rambling pub on the east side of the town. **Beer** *Whitbread,
Boddingtons, Crown, Buckley Bitter. Garden, children's play area.*

Nottage   Rose & Crown

Tel 0656 784850   **B&B**

Nottage Heol-y-Capel nr Porthcawl Mid Glamorgan CF36 3ST   Map 9 C6

Very popular as an overnight stop, this old whitewashed pub offers
accommodation in eight pretty, pine-furnished bedrooms. All the
rooms have neat, fully tiled bathrooms with good showers over the
tub, as well as trouser presses, TVs and direct-dial telephones.
Downstairs, potted plants and polished brass counters add to the
homely charms of the comfortable, beamed bars with their rustic
stone walls and wooden settles. **Beer** *Ruddles Best & County, Webster's
Yorkshire.* **Cider** *Scrumpy Jack. Garden, children's play area.*
Accommodation *8 bedrooms, all en suite, £56 (single £43). Children
welcome overnight, cots available. No dogs. Check-in by arrangement.
Access, Amex, Diners, Visa.*

Old Radnor   Harp Inn

Tel 054421 655

Old Radnor nr Presteigne Powys LD8 2RH   Map 9 D4

Friendly, welcoming and comfortable – a good place to take a break;
traditional bars of real character, and chatty hosts. Delightfully
peaceful, with seats on the large common overlooking the valley. *Free
House.* **Beer** *Boddingtons, Woods Special & Wonderful, Wyr Valley
Hereford Bitter. Garden, children's play area. Family room.*

Old Walls   Greyhound Inn

Tel 0792 390146

Old Walls North Gower nr Swansea West Glamorgan SA3 1HA   Map 9 B6

Attractive, well-run free house in the middle of the unspoilt Gower
peninsula. Go down to the astonishingly dramatic Rhossili beach for a
walk. **Beer** *Hancocks HB, Fuller's London Pride. Garden, children's play
area. Family room.*

Pant Mawr   Glansevern Arms

| Tel 05515 240 | **B&B** |

Pant Mawr nr Llangurig Powys SY18 6SY   Map 9 C4

Polished brass candlesticks and antimacassars give a pleasingly dated air
to the charming little pub where Mr Edwards has held sway for 26
years. The neat, cheerful bedrooms are just large enough for the TV
and tea/coffee-making equipment, all have bathrooms, one with
shower only. Ask for one of the front rooms, which have beautiful
views down the upper reaches of the Wye valley. *Free House.* **Beer**
Bass. **Accommodation** *8 bedrooms, all en suite, £52.50 (single £35).
Children welcome overnight, additional beds available, children over
8 charged half price. Check-in by arrangement. Closed 10 days at
Christmas. No credit cards.*

Pembroke   Old King's Arms Hotel

| Tel 0646 683611 | **B&B** |

Main Street Pembroke Dyfed SA71 4JS   Map 9 A5

Wall lamps cast soft shadows in the cosy, stone-walled bars of this
ancient coaching inn on the main street. Run for over 30 yaers by the
same family. Homely bedrooms, including some with beamed ceilings
in the main building, others in an extension, vary in size but all have
good desk space and TVs, tea-makers and direct-dial phones, cheerful
floral bedspreads and bathrooms supplied with ample towels. *Free
House.* **Beer** *Bass. Open all day.* **Accommodation** *20 bedrooms, all en
suite, £45 (single £30). Children welcome overnight, additional beds
£2 and cots available. Check-in all day. Access, Amex, Visa.*

Penallt   Boat Inn

| Tel 0600 712615 |

Lone Lane Penallt Gwent NP5 4AJ   Map 14 A2

Live folk music on Tuesday evenings, and jazz on Thursdays are a
popular local attraction at this classic riverside pub. There's usually a
wide selection of real ales. *Free House.* **Beer** *Theakston Best, XB, Old
Peculier, Old Hookey, Morlands Speckled Hen, Oakhill, Wadworth 6X.
Riverside garden. Family room.*

Penmaenpool   George III Hotel

| Tel 0341 422525   Fax 0341 423565 | **B&B** |

Penmaenpool nr Dolgellau Gwynedd LL40 1YD   Map 8 C3

In a memorable location hedged between the road (A493) and former
railway line, the George III, which hugs the bank of the tidal
Mawddach estuary, was once an integral part of Penmaenpool railway
station. Today's inn was created in the 1890s from two 17th-century
buildings, one the original pub and the other a ship chandler's which
serviced the adjacent boat-builder's yards. As an alternative to sharing
with locals and visitors the stone-flagged cellar bar where there's some
passable Felinfoel in cask, residents might prefer the rather dated air of
the Welsh Dresser bar and its cosy lounge with striking copper-
hooded inglenook. Main-house bedrooms, two without private
bathrooms, echo the period feel with creaky floors and some fine
exposed roof timbers. The Victorian Lodge, which, prior to the
railway's closure by Dr Beeching in 1964, housed the station waiting
room and ticket office, was converted latterly into six quite stylish
bedrooms, all en suite, which enjoy the pick of the views. We learned,

just prior to publication, that the pub was due to change ownership in late 1992: hopefully some of the more obvious signs of neglect will speedily be rectified. *Free House. Beer Marston's Pedigree, Felinfoel Bitter & Double Dragon. **Accommodation** 12 rooms, 10 en suite, £63, single £44. Children welcome overnight, additional beds £5. Cots supplied. Check-in all day.*

Penybont   Severn Arms Hotel

Tel 0597 851224 Fax 0597 851693	**B&B**
Penybont nr Llandrindod Wells Powys LD1 5UA	Map 9 C4

The A44 is the old coaching route from west Wales to the English Midlands, and this black-and-white pub was once a staging post. The hotel overlooks the River Ithon and two roomy bars cope well with the summer rush; a large garden invites outside drinking. Ten bright, welcoming bedrooms include some that enjoy lovely views from a top-floor position. Private bathrooms with showers, TVs, dial-out phones and clock radios are standard. *Garden. Free house. Beer Bass. **Accommodation** 10 bedrooms, all en suite, £48 (single £27). Children welcome overnight, additional beds £10 for children over 10, cots available £5. Check-in all day. Access, Visa, Amex. Accommodation closed one week Christmas. Access, Amex, Visa.*

Pisgah   Halfway Inn

Tel 097084 631	
Devil's Bridge Road Pisgah Aberystwyth Dyfed SY23 4NE	Map 9 C4

A marvellous country pub in a lovely setting, 650 feet up, with magnificent views; well known as a beer-lovers' favourite, with its choice of six beers, three of which are self-served. *Free House. Beer Whitbread, Wadworth 6X, Felinfoel Double Dragon. Garden, children's play area. Family room.*

Pont ar Gothi   Cresselly Arms

Tel 0267 290221	
Pont ar Gothi nr Nantgaredig Dyfed	Map 9 B5

A good pub for family expeditions; fun play equipment for children in the garden. *Beer Whitbread, Marston Pedigree. Riverside garden, children's play area. Family room.*

Pontblyddyn   New Inn

Tel 0352 771459	
Pontblyddyn nr Mold Clwyd CH7 4HR	Map 8 D2

A useful stop-off and a typical country pub, with its own working cooperage. *Beer Ruddles Best & County. Riverside garden, children's play area. Family room.*

Raglan   Beaufort Arms Hotel

Tel and Fax 0291 690412	**FOOD**
	B&B
High Street Raglan Gwent NP5 2DY	Map 9 D5

Spotlessly maintained both inside and out, a whitewashed village inn, built in the 15th century: exposed stonework and Tudor timbers survive in the Castle Country Bar. Bar food is wholesome and home-made: soup (£1.50), mussels provençale (£2.95), fresh sardines (£2.50). A 3-course £12.50 table d'hote menu is available in the restaurant – sirloin of beef in red wine and peppercorns, lamb cutlets in cider and redcurrant sauce. Bedrooms are bright, comfortable and attractively decorated. *Bar Food 12-2, 6-10. Restaurant Meals 7-9.30. Vegetarian dishes. Children's menu (£3.99). Children allowed in bar to eat. Free House Beer Courage. Patio, outdoor eating. Accommodation 15 bedrooms, all en suite, £45 (single £35). Children welcome overnight. Additional beds and cots available. Check-in all day. Access, Amex, Diners, Visa.*

Red Wharf Bay   Ship Inn

Tel 0248 852568   **FOOD**

Red Wharf Bay Anglesey LO75 4RJ   Map 8 B1

Right on the shore at Traeth Coch and overlooking the sweep of the bay, the low white-painted limestone Ship Inn is fronted by hanging baskets and sports a fine pair of Lloyd and Trouncer cast-iron street lamps at its entrance. A depiction of SS Royal Charter is inlaid in the upper wall, and a Silver Jubilee replica of the royal yacht Britannia's wheel is mounted in the bar. Customers come early at mealtimes, so at busy summer peak times delays are unavoidable, yet the menu remains sensibly short and with it comes a guarantee of freshness. Stick around a while and see the local fishermen delivering their catch. The menu includes a selection of light meals, described as snacks: paté and toast (£3.50), smoked salmon trout, stuffed mushrooms (£3.90) and Stilton and apple in filo pastry (£3.95), all of which come with salad. Main meals, accompanied by chips or baked potato, start with beef and garlic sausage in burgundy wine sauce (£5.30), spicy monkfish casserole (£5.20), chicken stuffed with Stilton and wrapped in bacon (£5.40) or the grilled catch of the day in the £7-£9 range. The board may change at a moment's notice, the likes of lasagne and chili con carne regularly moving in to fill the gaps. Desserts include apricot tarte tatin (£2.45) or chocolate and orange roulade (£2.45). Quarry-tiled floors, genuine exposed beams and stonework, plus a mish-mash of maritime memorabilia and chiming clocks all make for an interesting interior; look too for the Tom Browne snooker cartoons and the fine Toby jug collection, whose rarest specimens are glass-encased. Beer-drinkers fare well on well-kept Tetley and Marston, and wine-drinkers are offered a fair selection. Children can enjoy their own menu (£2.25-2.65 per dish) in the little back family room, or, while parents keep a constant eye on the treacherous tide, they can romp in the garden on the shore line. *Bar Food 12-2.15 (Jul-Sep 12-9.15), 7-9.15. Restaurant Meals 12-2.15 (only Sun in winter), 7-9.15 (only Fri/Sat in winter). Vegetarian dishes. Children's menu (£2.25-£2.65). Free House. Beer Marston, Tetley. Garden, outdoor eating, children's playing area. Family room. Access, Visa.*

Rhewl   Drovers Arms

Tel 0824 703163

Rhewl nr Ruthin Clwyd LL15 2UD   Map 8 C2

18th-century cottage pub; guest beers always on offer. *Beer Ruddles Best & County. Garden, children's play area.*

St Dogmaels   Ferry Inn

Tel 0239 615172

St Dogmaels nr Poppit Sands Dyfed SA43 3LF   Map 9 B4

Riverside inn with a nautical theme; 'quarterdeck' and 'lower deck'
bars, waterside gardens and views; welcoming to young families, very
much geared to dining. Pétanque and quoits in garden. **Beer** *Brains
Bitter & S.A., Felinfoel Double Dragon, Burton Ale, Wadworth 6X.
Riverside garden, children's play area. Family room.*

Shirenewton   Carpenters Arms

Tel 02917 231   **FOOD**

Shirenewton nr Chepstow Gwent NP6 6BU   Map 9 D6

Arguably one of Gwent's most characterful pubs, the Carpenters stands
hard by the B4235, a row of low, white-painted 17th-century cottages
which once housed a smithy and wheelwright's, as well as the local
carpenter's workshop. There are many unique reminders within,
among them the original foot-operated bellows, suspended from the
ceiling of the Smithy Bar, itself framed in several places by aged
wagon wheels set into the stone. Echoing the seven phases of the
moon and seven ages of man (not to mention the seven deadly sins),
landlord James Bennett promotes his business as offering seven rooms,
seven real ales and seven-day opening, in a location exactly seven miles
from the Severn Bridge. A high-backed settle partitions an entrance
lobby area in which hang the blackboard menus, while to one side, a
central three-legged brazier warms two of the rooms from beneath its
copper-hooded open chimney. On any one day, Courage,
Boddingtons, Wadworth, and Smiles breweries together with a choice
of guest beers might be represented on the handpumps here. More
suitable for quiet snacking is a carpeted lounge with gas fire and
central heating, and with direct access to half-a-dozen roadside picnic
tables in a setting embellished by flowerpots and hanging baskets. In
this context, the menu is largely popular by design, led by a profusion
of filled baguettes and baked potatoes, and quite a lot from the fryer.
Nonetheless, Japanese prawns (£2.75) to start, followed by steak and
mushroom pie (£4.95), rabbit casserole (£3.75) or lasagne (£3.95),
and bread and butter pudding (£1.75) or fresh strawberries to finish
won't upset more discerning diners, nor offend their pockets. **Bar
Food** *12-2, 7-9.30. Vegetarian dishes. Children's menu (£1.75 per dish).
Free House* **Beer** *Wadworth, Boddingtons, Smiles Exhibition, changing
guest beers. Patio, outdoor eating. No credit cards.*

Siginstone   Victoria Inn

Tel 0446 773943

Siginstone nr Cowbridge South Glamorgan CF7 7LT   Map 9 C6

A delightfully atmospheric old pub, always busy despite its fairly
remote location. **Beer** *Bass, Worthington Best.*

Swansea   Langland Court Hotel

Tel 0792 361545   **B&B**

31 Langland Court Road Langland Swansea West Glamorgan SA3 4TD   Map 9 C6

Take the A4067 from Swansea to Mumbles, head for Caswell, turn
left at Newton Church, and follow the sign to this old clifftop Tudor
pub and hotel. Beyond the impressive entrance hall are two bars, the
cocktail bar and 'Polly Garters', which commemorates Dylan Thomas.

Accommodation ranges from bow-windowed Tudor-style rooms with four-posters to attic rooms with third-bed alcoves and convertible couches. Rooms in a coach house across the road are smaller but equally bright, clean and well-equipped. *Free House.* **Beer** *Webster, Ruddles. Garden.* **Accommodation** *21 bedrooms, all en suite, £70 (single £50). Children welcome overnight, additional beds (£3-12), cots supplied. Check-in by arrangement. Access, Amex, Visa.*

Trecastle   Castle Hotel

Tel 0874 636354 Fax 0874 638000	**B&B**
Trecastle Powys LD3 8UH	Map 9 C5

Imposing Georgian hotel, a former coaching halt, with lots of character surviving. Bar meals in the cosy hotel bar – open fire, long wooden tables, benches and window seats; also elegantly proportioned restaurant. Individually decorated bedrooms vary in size from small to spacious. *Free House.* **Beer** *Courage. Patio/terrace, outdoor eating.* **Accommodation** *9 bedrooms, 5 en suite, £48 (single £38). Children welcome overnight. Additional beds and cots available. Check-in all day. Access, Visa.*

Trellech   The Village Green

Tel 0600 860119	**FOOD**
	B&B
Trellech nr Monmouth Gwent NP5 4PA	Map 9 D5

Saved from dereliction five years ago by Bob and Jane Evans, the 450-year-old, creeper-clad Village Green comprises restaurant (recommended in our 1993 *Hotels and Restaurants Guide*) and bistro as well as pub, and there are even a couple of small bedroom suites with kitchenette-cum-lounge and bedroom with en-suite shower room (they are let either on a self-catering or a bed and breakfast basis). The two small, carpeted bars display rugby paintings by Richard Wills, one of Wales's best-known artists, who lives locally, and the stone-walled bars is festooned with bunches of dried flowers hanging from the rafters. In the bistro, a long, wide-ranging blackboard menu changes frequently and might include whole grilled lobster (£11.50), beef teriyaki (£7.75), loin of pork in cider (£7.75), a tender, winey beef bourguignon (£8), chicken niçoise (£7.50) and deep-fried potato skins. A separate bar menu offers more traditional pub fare with sandwiches (from £1.50), jacket potatoes and various ploughman's lunches (from £3.50) that come with their own delicious home-made bread. **Bar Food** *11.45-2, 6.30-9.45. Vegetarian dishes. Children's portions. Free House.* **Beer** *Bass, Worthing. Outdoor eating. Family room.* **Accommodation** *2 bedrooms, both en suite, £45 inc. Continental breakfast only (single £30). Children welcome overnight. Check-in by arrangement. Access, Visa.*

Tremeirchion   Salusbury Arms

Tel 0745 75262	
St Asaph Tremeirchion Clwyd LL17 0UN	Map 8 C1

No juke box, no pool table, no fruit machine or similar, at this staunchly traditional, attractively modernised old pub. *Free House.* **Beer** *John Smith, Ruddles County. Garden.*

Tyn-y-Groes   Groes Inn

Tel 0492 650545

Tyn-y-Groes nr Conwy Gwynedd LL32 8TN   Map 8 C2

14th-century Free House with old beams, log fires, and a collection of
antique tins, as well as jugs, hats, carnival glassware and portraits.
Lovely river Conwy views from the pretty summer garden. *Free
House.* **Beer** *Ind Coope, Tetley Bitter. Garden, children's play area.*

Usk   Royal Hotel

Tel 0291 672931

New Market Street Usk Gwent NP5 1AT   Map 9 D5

Grade II listed Georgian market town inn, with pleasingly traditional
atmosphere. **Beer** *Bass, Hancocks HB, Felinfoel Double Dragon.*

Whitebrook   Crown at Whitebrook

FOOD
B&B

Tel 0600 860254   Fax 0600 860607

Whitebrook Monmouth Gwent NP5 4TX   Map 14 A2

Scarcely the archetypal Welsh pub, hardly, in fact, a pub at all, the
Crown's uniqueness lies in the successful re-creation of a French-style
auberge deep in the Wye valley. Don't be deterred by the road:
Whitebrook may be signposted as a mile from the A466 at the river
bridge, but the inn is at least two, through a doubt-inducing farmyard
crossing; keep going. Once safely within, a welcoming lounge, mixing
deep sofas and coffee tables leads to an almost rustic dining room and a
gingham-clothed extension which serves as a breakfast room. For
lunch or dinner (the latter menu also optional at lunchtime), the
accent of Sandra Bates's menu is set firmly in France, yet remains in
harmony with the rural Welsh setting. Dinner is *prix fixe* (£24.50):
tagliatelle with monkfish, or *tartelette alsacienne* (with cheese, smoked
ham and onions) preceding *medallions de veau grillés*, or *poulet aux
échalottes et lentiles*, with perhaps *feuilles de chocolat et biscuits* or *ananas
et oranges au kirsch*. The £14 lunch menu is a little simpler: perhaps a
salad of warm goat's cheese, fillet of salmon baked with Cajun
seasoning, and a baked spiced banana in filo pastry served with
caramel sauce. Bar meals are somewhat secondary by comparison,
though equal in quality and imagination. Pancakes filled with melted
Gruyère, mushroom and ham (£4.95), home-made venison sausage
rolls with chutney (£4.95), salad of freshly cut smoked sewin (£5.25)
and *ficelles de mer* stuffed with crab and prawns (£4.95), are typical of
the light main courses, with a *tartelette Normande* (£4.25) or *glace au
Grand Marnier* (£3.75) to finish. Splendid accompaniments include a
100-bottle wine list with, in addition, 30 half bottles; and a fine
selection of mostly Welsh cheeses. Residents are particularly rewarded
by their journey up the valley; this is a delightful refuge from the
world. A dozen pastel-coloured bedrooms feature up-to-date fittings,
cosy, carpeted bathrooms, and peace undisturbed by anything other
than whispering trees and the dawn chorus. Morning brings a
commendably un-Gallic tradition: full English (or is it Welsh?)
breakfast in bed. **Bar Food** *12-2 (except Mon).* **Restaurant meals** *12-2,
7-9.30. Vegetarian dishes. Children's portions. Free House* **Beer** *Samuel
Smith, Whitbread Best. Patio, outdoor eating. Family room.*
Accommodation *(closed first 2 weeks Jan), 12 bedrooms, all en suite, £80
(single £50). Children welcome overnight. Additional beds and cots
available. Check-in all day. Access, Amex, Diners, Visa.*

**Owning a mobile phone
is now more affordable
than you think. More useful
than you can imagine.**

**Isn't there room in your life
for Cellnet?**

0800

lifetime™
primetime™

Now you have the choice.

For further details call:

21 4000

Channel Islands
& Isle of Man

Alderney

St Anne   Georgian House

Tel 0481 822471	**FOOD**

Victoria Street St Anne Alderney

Map 13 F4

Attractive whitewashed Georgian house on a picturesque, cobbled
street. Convivial hosts and a characterful bar. Popular also with the
locals for consistently good food. Fresh fish is a speciality: Alderney
sea bass (£7), plateau de fruits de mer including oysters and crab
(£38.50 for two) and seafood risotto (£4.50). The restaurant provides
à la carte lunch and dinner. Recent renovations include a smartly
decorated dining area and the Walpole Suite function room which
seats up to 24 people. Refurbishment of bedrooms has been shelved, so
no overnight accommodation. *Bar Meals 12-2.30 bar snacks lunchtime
only.* *Restaurant 12-3, 7.30-12. Vegetarian dishes. Children's
menus/portions.* *Beer Guernsey Brewery Bitter. Garden, outdoor eating.
Summer barbecue. Access, Visa, Amex.*

Guernsey

Le Bourg Forest   Deerhound Inn

Tel 0481 38585	

Le Bourg Forest Guernsey

Map 13 E4

Cosy, friendly country inn. *Beer Guernsey Brewery Bitter. Garden,
children's play area. Family room.*

Pleinmont   Imperial Hotel

Tel 0481 64044 Fax 0481 66139	**B&B**

Pleinmont Torteval Guernsey

Map 13 E4

A turn-of-the-century inn situated on the beach overlooking
Rocquaine Bay and Portelet Harbour and boasting fine sea views. The
new owners, Patrick and Diana Lindley, have renovated extensively
including up-grading all bedrooms as en suite. Sepia-tinted
photographs of the original dining room (circa 1900) adorn the walls
downstairs. Children are especially welcome. *Beer Triple X, Randalls,
Worthington. Garden.* *Accommodation 17 bedrooms, all en suite, £52
(single £26). Children welcome overnight, additional beds and cots
available, children under 2 (£5), over 2-11 50% reduction. Check-in all
day. Access, Visa.*

St Peter Port   Ship & Crown

Tel 0481 721368	

Pier Steps St Peter Port Guernsey

Map 13 E4

Usually-buzzing yachting pub opposite marina. Lots of maritime
pictures and memorabilia, in simply furnished busy main bar and
quieter back drinking area. This was the Germans' naval HQ during
the World War II island occupation. No children. *Beers Guernsey
Brewery Bitter.*

Jersey

St Aubin	Old Court House Inn	FOOD
Tel 0534 46433 Fax 0534 45103		**B&B**
St Aubin Jersey		Map 13 F4

Modern comforts and old-world charm in a tall, handsome house
dating back to 1450 and overlooking the harbour. It's a family-run
hotel/restaurant/inn with a young outlook and a popular alfresco
eating trade – bar snacks on the front patio and à la carte in the rear
courtyard. Bar snacks include lasagne (£4.25), moules marinière
(£4.45), grilled prawns (£5.40), sausage and mash with onion gravy
(£3.95) and ploughman's lunches (from £2.45). The carte extends to
battered gambas with a chili dip (£5.40), potato skins with crispy
bacon bits and avocado and blue cheese dip (£3.90), dressed shanker
crabs (sold by weight) and spicy baked chicken (£6.95); seafood is the
real speciality with goof fisherman's platters, oysters and more
involved dishes like sea bass with a white wine, herb and lemon juice
sauce (£12.50). Vegetarians are offered vegetable terrine with a
tomato dressing (£4.25); children offered their own short menu or
smaller portions, charged accordingly. The beamed cellar bars and
upstairs Mizzen Bar (well-known to *Bergerac* fans as the *Royal Barge*
pub) are favourite rendezvous. Sunday lunch is served downstairs
from 12.30 to 4pm. Bedrooms, the best with harbour views, are
furnished with old pine; the penthouse is top of the range. No dogs.
Bar Food *12.30-2.30, 7.30-9.30* **Restaurant Meals** *12-2.30, 7.30-10.30.*
Free House. **Beer** *Marston's Pedigree, John Smith's.* **Accommodation**
*9 rooms, all en suite, £80, single £40 (plus supp.). Family room. Children
welcome overnight, extra beds and cot provided. Check-in all day. Closed 25
& 26 Dec. Access, Visa.*

St Brelade	La Pulente Hotel	
Tel 0534 41760		
Quaisne Bay St Brelade Jersey		Map 13 F4

Dramatically set above a rocky cove; cleanly modernised inside, pretty
terrace. **Beer** *Bass. Family room.*

St Brelade	Smugglers Inn	
Tel 0534 41510		
Quaisne Bay St Brelade Jersey		Map 13 F4

A good traditional atmosphere in the stone and timber bars, close to
beach. **Beer** *Bass. Family room.*

Isle of Man

Peel   **Creek Inn**

| Tel 0624 842216 | **FOOD** |

The Quayside Peel Isle of Man   Map 4 B4

A bustling pub right by the quayside of Peel harbour, out of which working boats ply their trade. The industrious and friendly landlords Robert and Jean McAleer offer seafood specialities from the fish yard in their large, bright and unpretentious bar: fresh seafood platter with home-made patés (£4.95), fresh crab salad (£4.40), Manx scallops (known as Queenies) served on the shell in a mornay sauce (£4.95). Other offering srange from open sandwiches (£1.95-£3.95) to curries, home-made pizzas and steak and kidney pie (£3.95). Several fruit tarts (£1.40) or home-made gateaux to follow. Junior diners pay £1.50 or £1.75 for their portions. Full selection of Irish spirits. Easy parking. *Bar Food 11-10.45 (Sun 12-1.30, 8-10). Vegetarian dishes. Children's menu (£1.50-2.00 per dish). Beer Bass, Okells. Outdoor eating on the quayside. Children welcome in bar 12-1.30 if eating. No credit cards.*

Pubs In Waterside Locations

London

Chiswick, W4 **Bell & Crown**
Chiswick, W4 **Bull's Head**
Hammersmith, W6 **Dove**
London Bridge, SE1 **Horniman's**
Wandsworth, SW18 **The Ship**

England

Avon, Combe Hay **Wheatsheaf**
Avon, Oldbury-on-Severn **Anchor Inn**
Bedfordshire, Bedford **Embankment Hotel**
Berkshire, Kintbury **Dundas Arms**
Cambridgeshire, Sutton Gault **Anchor Inn**
Cornwall, Helford **Shipwrights Arms**
Cornwall, Port Isaac **Port Gaverne Hotel**
Cornwall, Sennen Cove **Old Success Inn**
Cumbria, Armathwaite **Duke's Head Hotel**
Cumbria, Eskdale Green **Bower House Inn**
Cumbria, Little Langdale **Three Shires Inn**
Cumbria, Loweswater **Kirkstile Inn**
Cumbria, Metal Bridge **Metal Bridge Inn**
Cumbria, Wasdale Head **Wasdale Head Inn**
Devon, Beer **Anchor Inn**
Devon, Brendon **Stag Hunters Hotel**
Devon, Cockwood **Anchor Inn**
Devon, Cockwood **Ship**
Devon, Dartmouth **Royal Castle Hotel**
Devon, Milton Combe **Who'd Have Thought It**
Devon, Southpool **Millbrook Inn**
Devon, Tuckenhay **Maltsters Arms**
Dorset, Corscombe **Fox Inn**
Dorset, Sutton Poyntz **Springhead**
Dorset, West Bexington **Manor Hotel**
Dorset, Winkton **Fisherman's Haunt Inn**
East Sussex, Chiddingly **Six Bells**
Essex, Burnham-on-Crouch **Olde White Harte Hotel**
Gloucestershire, Bibury **Catherine Wheel**
Gloucestershire, Bledington **King's Head**
Gloucestershire, Chedworth **Seven Tuns**
Gloucestershire, Fossebridge **Fossebridge Inn**
Gloucestershire, North Cerney **Bathurst Arms**
Hampshire, Bursledon **Jolly Sailor**
Hampshire, Faccombe **Jack Russell Inn**
Hampshire, Testcombe **Mayfly**
Hereford & Worcester, Carey **Cottage of Content**
Hereford & Worcester, Ruckhall **Ancient Camp Inn**
Hereford & Worcester, Whitney-on-Wye **Rhydspence Inn**
Hereford & Worcester, Woolhope **Butchers Arms**
Humberside, North Dalton **Star Inn**
Isle of Wight, Ventnor **Spyglass Inn**
Kent, Fordwich **Fordwich Arms**
Kent, Marshside **Gate Inn**
Kent, Smarden **Chequers Inn**
Lancashire, Slaidburn **Hark to Bounty Inn**
Lancashire, Whitewell **Inn at Whitewell**
Leicestershire, Hallaton **Bewicke Arms**
Middlesex, Shepperton **Anchor Hotel**
North Yorkshire, Castleton **Moorlands Hotel**
North Yorkshire, Wath-in-Nidderdale **Sportsman's Arms**
Oxfordshire, Chislehampton **Coach and Horses**

Oxfordshire, Church Enstone **Crown Inn**
Oxfordshire, Godstow **Trout**
Oxfordshire, Oxford **Queen's Arms**
Shropshire, Bridgnorth **Falcon Hotel**
Somerset, Exford **The Crown**
Suffolk, Chelsworth **Peacock Inn**
Suffolk, Orford **King's Head Inn**
West Sussex, Fulking **Shepherd & Dog**
West Sussex, Stopham Bridge **White Hart**
Wiltshire, Bradford-on-Avon **Bunch of Grapes**
Wiltshire, Nunton **Radnor Arms**

Scotland

Borders, Greenlaw **Castle Inn**
Borders, St Mary's Loch **Tibbie Shiels Inn**
Dumfries & Galloway, Portpatrick **The Crown**
Fife, Dysart **Old Rectory Inn**
Fife, Elie **Ship Inn**
Highland, Lewiston **Lewiston Arms Hotel**
Highland, Lybster **Bayview Hotel**
Highland, Muir of Ord **Ord House Hotel**
Highland, Ullapool **Argyll Hotel**
Highland, Ullapool **Morefield Motel & Steakplace**
Lothian, Edinburgh **Fishers**
Lothian, Edinburgh **Waterfront Wine Bar**
Strathclyde, Ardentinny **Ardentinny Hotel**
Strathclyde, Tayvallich **Tayvallich Inn**
Tayside, Almondbank **Almondbank Inn**
Tayside, Glendevon **Tormaukin Hotel**
Tayside, Glenfarg **Bein Inn**

Wales

Clwyd, Llanarmon Dyffryn Ceiriog **West Arms Hotel**
Clwyd, Llangollen **Britannia Inn**
Dyfed, Felindre Farchog **Salutation Inn**
Dyfed, Llangranog **Ship Inn**
Gwent, Abergavenny **Llanwenarth Arms Hotel**
Gwent, Whitebrook **Crown at Whitebrook**
Gwynedd, Penmaenpool **George III Hotel**
Gwynedd, Red Wharf Bay **Ship Inn**
Powys, Crickhowell **Nantyffin Cider Mill**
Powys, Llangorse **Red Lion**

Islands

Isle of Man, Peel **Creek Inn**

Pubs for Families

England

Avon, Bathampton **George Inn**
Avon, Paulton **Somerset Inn**
Bedfordshire, Broom **Cock Inn**
Berkshire, Chaddleworth **Ibex**
Cheshire, Bickley Moss **Cholmondeley Arms**
Cheshire, Higher Burwardsley **The Pheasant**
Cleveland, Guisborough **Moorcock Hotel**
Cornwall, St Austell **White Hart**
Cumbria, Askham **Queen's Head**
Cumbria, Cartmel Fell **Masons Arms**
Cumbria, Talkin Village **Hare & Hounds Inn**
Derbyshire, Castleton **Castle Hotel**
Derbyshire, Woolley Moor **White Horse**
Devon, Dartmouth **Royal Castle Hotel**
Devon, Exeter **Double Locks**
Devon, Kingsteignton **Old Rydon Inn**
Dorset, Ansty **The Fox**
Dorset, Sutton Poyntz **Springhead**
Dorset, Winfrith Newburgh **Red Lion**
East Sussex, Old Heathfield **Star Inn**
Essex, Dedham **Marlborough Head Hotel**
Gloucestershire, Bibury **Catherine Wheel**
Gloucestershire, Bledington **King's Head**
Gloucestershire, Colesbourne **Colesbourne Inn**
Gloucestershire, Gretton **Royal Oak**
Gloucestershire, North Cerney **Bathurst Arms**
Gloucestershire, Upper Oddington **Horse & Groom**
Hampshire, Beauworth **Milbury's**
Hampshire, Linwood **High Corner Inn**
Hampshire, Priors Dean **White Horse**
Hereford & Worcester, Fownhope **Green Man**
Hereford & Worcester, Ledbury **Ye Olde Talbot Hotel**
Humberside, Bishop Wilton **Fleece Inn**
Humberside, Broughton **Red Lion**
Humberside, Skidby **Half Moon Inn**
Humberside, South Dalton **Pipe & Glass Inn**
Isle of Wight, Chale **Clarendon Hotel & Wight Mouse Inn**
Isle of Wight, Seaview **Seaview Hotel**
Isle of Wight, Ventnor **Spyglass Inn**
Kent, Biddenden **Three Chimneys**
Kent, St Margaret's-at-Cliffe **Cliffe Tavern**
Kent, Warren Street **Harrow Inn**
Lancashire, Slaidburn **Hark to Bounty Inn**
Leicestershire, Empingham **White Horse**
Leicestershire, Hallaton **Bewicke Arms**
Norfolk, Stow Bardolph **Hare Arms**
Norfolk, Winterton-on-Sea **Fisherman's Return**
North Yorkshire, Coxwold **Fauconberg Arms**
North Yorkshire, Harome **Star Inn**
North Yorkshire, Horton-in-Ribblesdale **Crown Hotel**
North Yorkshire, Sleights **Salmon Leap**
North Yorkshire, Snainton **Coachman Inn**
North Yorkshire, Wass **Wombwell Arms**
North Yorkshire, Wykeham **Downe Arms**
Northamptonshire, Ashby St Ledgers **Olde Coach House Inn**
Northamptonshire, East Haddon **Red Lion Hotel**
Northumberland, Haydon Bridge **General Havelock Inn**
Norwich, Scole **Crossways Inn**
Oxfordshire, Burford **Bull Hotel**
Oxfordshire, Freeland **Shepherd Hall Inn**
Oxfordshire, Frilford Heath **Dog House Hotel**

Oxfordshire, Kidmore End **New Inn**
Oxfordshire, Shiplake **Baskerville Arms**
Oxfordshire, South Leigh **Masons Arms**
Oxfordshire, Stanton St John **Star Inn**
Shropshire, Bridgnorth **Down Inn**
Shropshire, Bridgnorth **Falcon Hotel**
Shropshire, Norton **Hundred House Hotel**
Somerset, North Wootton **Crossways Inn**
Somerset, Over Stratton **Royal Oak**
Somerset, West Pennard **Lion at Pennard**
South Yorkshire, Sutton **Anne Arms**
Surrey, Bramley **Jolly Farmer**
Surrey, Elstead **Woolpack**
Warwickshire, Broom **Broom Tavern**
Warwickshire, Ilmington **Howard Arms**
West Sussex, Elsted **Three Horseshoes**
West Sussex, Elsted Marsh **Elsted Inn**
West Sussex, South Harting **White Hart**
Wiltshire, Aldbourne **Crown at Aldbourne**
Wiltshire, Salisbury **Coach & Horses**

Scotland

Borders, Greenlaw **Castle Inn**
Borders, Innerleithen **Traquair Arms**
Dumfries & Galloway, New Abbey **Criffel Inn**
Dumfries & Galloway, Portpatrick **The Crown**
Fife, Elie **Ship Inn**
Fife, Kirkcaldy **Hoffmans**
Grampian, Stonehaven **Lairhillock Inn & Restaurant**
Grampian, Turriff **Towie Tavern**
Lothian, Ratho **Bridge Inn**
Strathclyde, Ardentinny **Ardentinny Hotel**
Strathclyde, Kilberry **Kilberry Inn**
Strathclyde, Kilfinan **Kilfinan Hotel**
Strathclyde, Loch Eck **Coylet Inn**
Strathclyde, Tayvallich **Tayvallich Inn**
Tayside, Almondbank **Almondbank Inn**
Tayside, Kirktown of Glenisla **Glenisla Hotel**

Wales

Gwent, Trellech **Village Green**
Gwynedd, Red Wharf Bay **Ship Inn**
Powys, Llanfrynach **White Swan**

Other guides available

Egon Ronay's Hotel & Restaurant Guide 1993

The best in food and accommodation
throughout the British Isles
Sponsored by Cellnet
£13·99

★★★

Egon Ronay's Just a Bite Guide 1993

The best places for eating on a budget
Published March 1993 £8·99

★★★

Egon Ronay's Guide 1993
...and Baby Comes Too

Food and accommodation for families
with babies and young children
Published March 1993 £8·99

Index

READERS' COMMENTS

Please use this sheet, and the continuation overleaf, to recommend pubs of **really outstanding quality.**

Complaints about any of the Guide's entries will be treated seriously and passed on to our inspectorate, but we would like to remind you always to take up your complaint with the management at the time.

We regret that owing to the volume of readers' communications received each year we will be unable to acknowledge these forms, but your comments will certainly be seriously considered.

Please post to: **Egon Ronay's Guides, 73 Uverdale Road, London SW10 0SW**

Please use an up-to-date Guide. We publish annually. (Pubs 1993)

Name and address of establishment	Your recommendation or complaint

Readers' Comments continued

Name and address of establishment	Your recommendation or complaint

Your Name (BLOCK LETTERS PLEASE)

Address

READERS' COMMENTS

Please use this sheet, and the continuation overleaf, to recommend pubs of **really outstanding quality.**

   Complaints about any of the Guide's entries will be treated seriously and passed on to our inspectorate, but we would like to remind you always to take up your complaint with the management at the time.

   We regret that owing to the volume of readers' communications received each year we will be unable to acknowledge these forms, but your comments will certainly be seriously considered.

Please post to: **Egon Ronay's Guides, 73 Uverdale Road, London SW10 0SW**

Please use an up-to-date Guide. We publish annually. (Pubs 1993)

Name and address of establishment	Your recommendation or complaint

Name and address of establishment   **Your recommendation or complaint**

_____   _____

_____   _____

_____   _____

_____   _____

_____   _____

_____   _____

_____   _____

_____   _____

_____   _____

_____   _____

_____   _____

_____   _____

_____   _____

_____   _____

Your Name (BLOCK LETTERS PLEASE)

_____

Address

_____

_____

_____

_____

READERS' COMMENTS

Please use this sheet, and the continuation overleaf, to recommend pubs of **really outstanding quality.**

   Complaints about any of the Guide's entries will be treated seriously and passed on to our inspectorate, but we would like to remind you always to take up your complaint with the management at the time.

   We regret that owing to the volume of readers' communications received each year we will be unable to acknowledge these forms, but your comments will certainly be seriously considered.

Please post to: **Egon Ronay's Guides, 73 Uverdale Road, London SW10 0SW**

Please use an up-to-date Guide. We publish annually. (Pubs 1993)

Name and address of establishment	Your recommendation or complaint

Readers' Comments continued

Name and address of establishment

Your recommendation or complaint

Your Name (BLOCK LETTERS PLEASE)

Address